D1261197

GARDEN FRESH
GARDEN FRESH
31
33

Everyday Foods

FIFTH EDITION

JESSIE W. HARRIS

ELISABETH LACEY SPEER

Edited by ALICE F. BLOOD

HOUGHTON MIFFLIN COMPANY

Boston · New York · Chicago · Dallas · Atlanta · San Francisco The Riverside Press

❧ The Authors

JESSIE W. HARRIS is dean of the College of Home Economics of the University of Tennessee, Knoxville, Tennessee. Formerly she was supervisor of home economics education in the state of Texas.

ELISABETH LACEY SPEER is professor of home management in the University of Tennessee. She has taught home economics in Alabama College, Montevallo, Alabama, and in Cornell University, Ithaca, New York.

ALICE F. BLOOD was formerly director of the School of Household Economics of Simmons College, Boston, Massachusetts.

 The Riverside Press, CAMBRIDGE, MASS.
PRINTED IN THE U.S.A.

❧ Preface

EVERYDAY FOODS IS WRITTEN for youth of high-school age to whom a knowledge of the science of nutrition and the application of this knowledge in their everyday lives offers a promise of vigorous health and an abundant life. Nutrition in relation to health is a major concern of the nation. A study of foods and nutrition therefore merits an important place in the secondary school curriculum.

Everyday Foods is written with the idea of making food study a science comparable to other sciences. It is a practical food and nutrition text. This book is equally usable at home and at school. The home work is as carefully suggested as the class work.

The material used comes within the experience of young people and is selected in accordance with their problems, interests, and responsibilities both at school and at home in matters pertaining to food: the wise selection of food for themselves and others; good manners and courtesy; marketing; preparing and serving meals; planning for special occasions; and food preservation.

The book is divided into seven units. A glance at the Contents will show, as a distinctive feature, that Unit Three is a general section for reference and that Unit Seven is the Cook Book. Attention is also called to the chapter organization, where the subject matter is reinforced by a few pertinent references and by Class Problems, which serve as a summary. The Home Problems are an important part of *Everyday Foods*. Home work is recognized in *Everyday Foods* as practical and necessary for the successful acquisition of knowledge about foods and of skill in food selection, preparation, and in serving meals.

Everyday Foods is flexible. The chapters may be used in any sequence to fit the program in use in any school.

Acknowledgments

THE AUTHORS WISH to express their appreciation to the following for help in the preparation of the fifth edition of *Everyday Foods:*

The many students, teachers, and supervisors who have used earlier editions of *Everyday Foods* and have shared their experience with the authors.

Miss Ida Adelaide Anders, Dr. Florence L. MacLeod, and Miss Florence Langford, of the faculty of the University of Tennessee; and Mrs. Ula Dow Keezer, formerly of the faculty of Simmons College, for their interest and assistance.

Barbara Witham, Mary Hahn, Helen Gilpin, Sam Maloney, and Noreen Stollberg for posing for some of the illustrations.

Howard Knaus and Robert Stollberg for taking the color photograph used as a frontispiece, and the Piggly Wiggly Store No. 6 in West Lafayette, Indiana.

The Agricultural Extension Service, U.S. Department of Agriculture, for the use of Figures 122 and 124.

Aluminum Cooking Utensil Company for Figure 167 (top).

Aluminum Goods Manufacturing Company for Figure 168.

The Bureau of Human Nutrition and Home Economics, U.S. Department of Agriculture, for the use of Figures 22, 53, 54, 56, 63, 64, 67–71, 81–85, 87–89, 92, 97, 104, 110–112, 115, 116, 123, 125–128, 136–142, and 157–162; also for their generous provision of text materials, information, and recipes. Special thanks are due Dr. Hazel Stiebeling, Dr. Louise Stanley, Miss Catherine Cronister, Miss Katherine Schultz, Dr. Louise Phipard, and Mrs. Bernice Watt.

Consumers' Guide, U.S. Department of Agriculture, for Figures 52 and 121.

Farm Journal and Farmer's Wife for Figure 44.

Philip Gendreau for Figures 57 (top) and 73.

General Electric Company for the color picture facing page 386 and for the picture facing page 1.

General Foods Corporation for Figure 62.

General Motors for Figure 55.

Good Housekeeping Magazine for Figure 107.

H. J. Heinz Company for Figure 93.

Harold M. Lambert for Figures 3, 4, 6, 19, and 57 (bottom).

Libby, McNeill, and Libby for Figure 58.

The Manual Arts Press, Peoria, Illinois, for Figures 31–33 from *Meal Planning and Table Service*, by N. Beth Bailey.

National Pressure Cooker Company for Figure 167 (center).

The Production and Marketing Administration, U.S. Department of Agriculture, for the use of Figures 2, 59, 61, and 94; and for supplying and checking certain facts.

H. Armstrong Roberts for Figures 114 and 117.

Sears Roebuck and Company, for the use of Figures 163–166.

The Spry Kitchen, Cambridge, Massachusetts, for the use of Figures 24, 25, 65, 66, 74, 76–80, 86, 90, 95, 96, 108, 109, 118, 131, 133, and 151–156; also for their generous co-operation in allowing many photographs to be taken in the Spry Kitchen.

Territorial Information Department — Commonwealth Edison Company and Associated Companies, Chicago, Illinois, for Figure 5.

Upjohn Company for Figure 119.

West Bend Aluminum Company for Figure 167 (bottom).

CONTENTS

Unit One · INTRODUCTION

Unit Two · BREAKFAST

Unit Three · GENERAL

Unit Four · LUNCHEON OR SUPPER

Unit Five · DINNER

Unit Six · NOW AND THEN

Unit Seven · THE COOK BOOK

Appendix

To the Student

Wouldn't you feel the joy of achievement if all by yourself you could create a tangy salad, tasty muffins, a delicious baked dish, and other delicacies that melt in one's mouth? Everyone likes to create something, and the study of *Everyday Foods* gives you the opportunity to learn how to create flavorful, attractive, and satisfying meals, and treats for special occasions such as parties and picnics.

In studying *Everyday Foods* you will also have an opportunity to learn other important and helpful information about the art of cookery:

How to purchase food to get your money's worth
How to plan nutritious meals
How to store or preserve food to keep its quality
How to plan and furnish the kitchen and the dining room
How to feel self-confident and at ease with others at mealtime or refreshment time
How to plan the food for festive occasions
How to entertain with graciousness and charm

UNIT ONE · INTRODUCTION

CHAPTER ONE

Our Daily Food

ONE OF THE MOST IMPORTANT THINGS you do every day is to eat. What you eat has a lot to do with how you feel. Do you feel "like a million dollars," ready for fun and new adventures? Or do you feel listless and bored? If you want to be strong, wide-awake, full of pep and good cheer, observe the rules of good health, including those that tell what to eat.

The health rules that deal with food are based on the facts that have been learned about how the body uses food and about the values of different kinds of food. There are two reasons why you should know some of these facts. (1) When you know the facts, you can apply your knowledge in your daily living. Thus you can maintain the buoyant health that is so desirable. (2) As a future homemaker, you can use your knowledge to help build a happy home. Thus you can serve, not only yourself and your family, but your country as well.

There are many hungry people in the world. Sometimes you are hungry because you have not had enough to eat and you feel empty. You might be said to be temporarily suffering from "hollow hunger." Many people are hungry because they do not eat the right kinds of food. They do not realize that they are hungry, for they are suffering from "hidden hunger." Usually these people do not even know that they are hungry. They do not have that familiar empty feeling. But their color may be poor and their lips pale; they may slump when standing and slouch when sitting; their skin may be scaly and their eyes dull; their hair may look lifeless or their teeth may decay easily; they may tire quickly and be unable to do a full day's job of work, study, or play. Certainly hidden hunger is a condition to avoid!

A nation is as strong as its citizens. America has an abundance of food, but abundance is not enough. Americans must choose to eat the kinds of food that make and keep them strong.

The Basic Seven Food Groups

To help Americans choose their food wisely, the government has published a National Food Guide. The guide lists different kinds of foods in seven groups. If a person eats food from each group every day, he will get the nourishment he needs to avoid hidden hunger and maintain buoyant health. The groups are as follows:

1. Leafy, green, and yellow vegetables
2. Citrus fruit, tomatoes, raw cabbage
3. Potatoes and other vegetables and fruits
4. Milk, cheese, and ice cream
5. Meat, poultry, fish, eggs, dried peas and beans
6. Bread and cereals
7. Butter and fortified margarine

These seven groups of food are called the *Basic Seven*, because they are basic — that is, absolutely necessary — to good health. The results that come from habitually eating food from every group every day are so good that some people call the groups the Magic Seven! But this magic is a kind that you can understand.

Of course, there are some persons who have special food problems. Perhaps they cannot eat certain foods without becoming ill (that is, they have "food allergies"). Perhaps they have other difficulties that call for special medical attention. These people must seek and follow the advice of a physician in selecting foods from the Basic Seven groups. Most people, however, have it within their own power to eat wisely and well. They can use the Basic Seven to help themselves maintain good health.

On this page and on pages 4 and 5 are lists of the foods in each of the seven groups. As you read the lists, look for the following points.

1. What foods are in each group. Notice the variety. You can plan interesting and palatable meals by using the Basic Seven.
2. How much you should eat from each group every day. The number of servings given is the smallest number you should have. And teen-agers and active adults need especially large servings.

Group 1. LEAFY, GREEN, AND YELLOW VEGETABLES

Raw, cooked, frozen, canned

One or more servings daily

Asparagus, green
Beans, snap, green
Beans, Lima
Broccoli
Brussels sprouts
Cabbage, green
Chard
Collards
Endive, green
Escarole
Kale
Lettuce, leaf
Mustard greens
Okra
Peas, green
Peppers, green and red
Spinach
Turnip greens
Wild greens
Other greens, including salad greens

Carrots
Pumpkins
Squash, winter, yellow
Sweet potatoes

Group 2. CITRUS FRUIT, TOMATOES, RAW CABBAGE

Other high Vitamin C foods

One or more servings daily

Grapefruit
Grapefruit juice
Kumquats
Lemons
Limes
Oranges
Orange juice
Tangerines

Tomatoes
Tomato juice

Cantaloupes (muskmelons)
Pineapples, raw
Strawberries, raw

Cabbage, raw
Greens, salad
Peppers, green, raw
Turnips, raw

A large serving of the above vegetables can be substituted for the fruits listed in this group

If foods in Group 2 are hard to get, use more, especially raw, from Groups 1 and 3.

Group 3. POTATOES AND OTHER VEGETABLES AND FRUIT

Raw, cooked, frozen, canned, dried

Two or more servings daily

Potatoes
Sweet potatoes

Artichokes
Beets
Cabbage, white
Cauliflower
Celery
Corn, sweet
Cucumbers
Eggplant
Leeks
Lettuce, head
Mushrooms
Onions
Parsnips
Radishes
Rutabagas
Salsify, or oysterplant
Sauerkraut
Squash, summer
Turnips

Apples
Apricots
Avocados
Bananas
Berries
Cherries
Cranberries
Currants
Dates
Figs
Grapes
Peaches
Pears
Persimmons
Pineapple, canned
Pineapple juice, canned
Plums
Prunes
Raisins
Rhubarb
Watermelons

Also, vegetables and fruits not listed elsewhere.

Group 4. MILK, CHEESE, ICE CREAM

Children through teen age: 3 to 4 cups milk daily
Adults: 3 or more cups milk daily

Milk may be whole, skim, evaporated, condensed, dried, or buttermilk. On the basis of calcium content, the following may be used as alternates for 1 cup of milk: Cheddar-type cheese, 1 oz.; cream-type cheese, 4 oz.; cottage cheese, 12 oz.; ice cream, 2 to 3 large dips.

Group 5. MEAT, POULTRY, FISH, EGGS, DRIED BEANS AND PEAS, NUTS

Meat, poultry, fish — fresh, canned, or cured

One serving daily, if possible

Beef
Veal
Lamb
Mutton
Pork (except bacon and fat back)
Lunch meats, such as bologna

Variety meats, such as liver, heart, kidney, brains, tongue, sweetbreads
Game

Poultry, such as chicken, duck, goose, turkey

Fish and shellfish

Eggs . . . *Four or more a week*

Dried beans and peas; nuts and peanut butter

Two or more servings a week

Dried beans	Soybeans	Peanuts
Dried peas	Soya flour and grits	Peanut butter
Lentils		Nuts of all kinds

Group 6. BREAD, FLOUR, AND CEREALS

Whole-grain or enriched or restored

Every day

Breads:
- Whole-wheat
- Dark rye
- Enriched
- Rolls or biscuit made with whole-wheat or enriched flour
- Oatmeal bread

Crackers, enriched, whole-grain, soya

Flour, enriched, whole-wheat, other whole-grain

Corn Meal, whole-grain or enriched

Grits enriched

Cereals:
- Whole-wheat
- Rolled oats
- Brown rice

Converted rice

Other cereals, if whole-grain or restored

Group 7. BUTTER AND FORTIFIED MARGARINE

Some daily

FOODS NOT IN THE BASIC SEVEN — ENERGY FOODS

Basic Seven foods give energy and protect health. The foods listed below chiefly give energy. They may be eaten in addition to the Basic Seven foods but not in place of them. Hence the rule to eat first what you need, and then eat other foods you want.

Bacon
Drippings
Lard, other shortenings
Mutton fat
Poultry fat
Salad dressings
Salad oils
Salt pork, fat back
Suet

Honey
Jams
Jellies
Molasses
Preserves
Sirup
Sorghum
Cakes
Candy
Chocolate
Cocoa
Cookies
Pastries
Sugar
Other sweets

Corn meal, degerminated
Cornstarch
Hominy grits
Macaroni
Noodles
Rice, white
Spaghetti

Unenriched:
- Crackers
- White bread, rolls
- White flour

How Good Are Your Food Habits?

What you eat is largely a matter of habit. If you have the habit of eating food which gives the nourishment you need, you are lucky. If you habitually fail to eat the kinds of food you need, you should change your eating habits.

It is a good plan for everyone to check his food habits occasionally. Make a list of all the food you eat in a day, both at meals and between meals. Next to each food on the list, write the number of the group to which it belongs. Then check to see whether you have had all seven groups and at least as many servings as you should have. A skimpy serving doesn't count as a full serving; remember that at your age you need large servings. It does not matter if all the groups do not appear in every meal; it is the total for the day that counts.

A look into your food habits should be a signal for action if your food habits need improving. Your signal might be compared to a traffic light. After you have checked your daily food habits for one week, use your record to decide whether your signal is "Go Ahead," "Caution," or "Stop."

This check of your food habits will be most worth while if you act on what you learn from it. If your eating habits are good, keep them good. If your food signal indicates that you must learn to eat new foods, then set out to do so in earnest.

Fig. 1. WHAT IS YOUR SIGNAL ON FOOD HABITS?

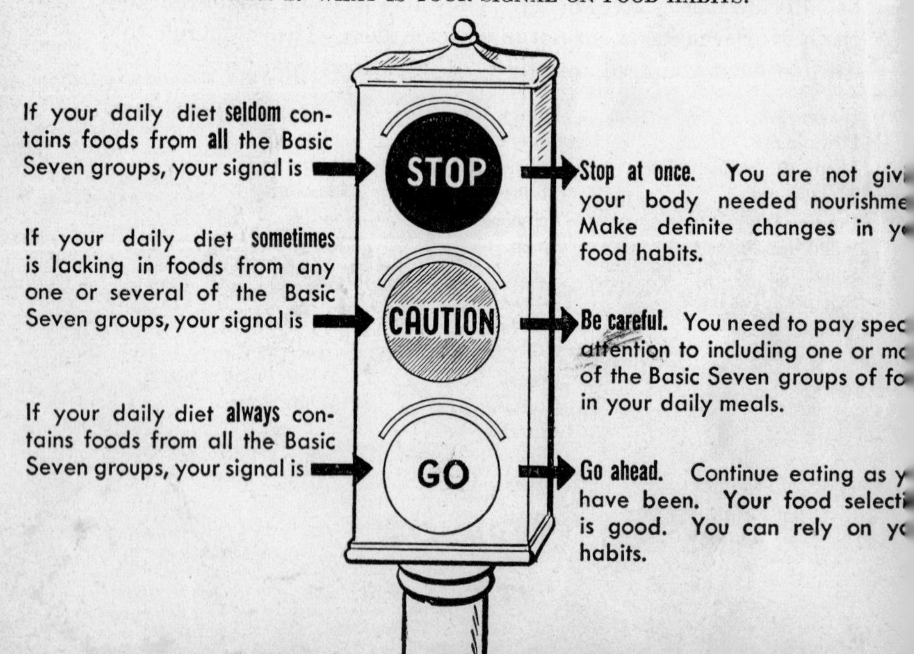
If your daily diet seldom contains foods from all the Basic Seven groups, your signal is
STOP
Stop at once. You are not giv
your body needed nourishme
Make definite changes in y
food habits.
If your daily diet sometimes is lacking in foods from any one or several of the Basic Seven groups, your signal is
CAUTION
Be careful. You need to pay spec
attention to including one or mc
of the Basic Seven groups of fo
in your daily meals.
If your daily diet always contains foods from all the Basic Seven groups, your signal is
GO
Go ahead. Continue eating as y
have been. Your food selecti
is good. You can rely on yc
habits.

THE BASIC SEVEN

leafy, green, and yellow vegetables
1 or more servings

TWO
citrus fruit, tomatoes, raw cabbage
1 or more servings

THREE
potatoes and other vegetables and fruits
2 or more servings

FOUR
milk, cheese, and ice cream
3 or more cups of milk

FIVE
meat, poultry, fish, eggs, dried peas, beans
1 to 2 servings

SIX
bread, flour, cereals, whole grain or enriched
every day

SEVEN
butter, fortified margarine
some daily

FROZEN SPINACH
VEGETABLES
CITRUS JUICE
FROZEN FRUIT
DRY MILK
EVAPORAT
BUTTER
OLEO
CEREAL

FIG. 2. THE BOYS IN THIS CAFETERIA LINE SHOW THEIR GOOD FOOD HABITS BY CHOOSING MILK AND SALAD AS PART OF THEIR SCHOOL LUNCH

WILL YOU CHOOSE A WELL-BALANCED DIET?

The human body is made of many materials, and the food you eat must supply the materials. Food materials are called *nutrients*. Almost every food contains several nutrients. Nutrients are of three kinds.

1. Some nutrients are needed for growth. Your body is changing constantly. Even after you stop growing your body will continue to change during the rest of your life. Tissues are continually wearing out, and your body must rebuild them. The nutrients for building and repairing body tissues are particularly needed for your bones, muscles, teeth, and all the organs of your body.

2. Other nutrients are needed to supply energy; that is, they are used as fuel. You need energy for running or walking, for working or playing. You need energy even when you are sitting still, because the beating of your heart, the movement of the respiratory muscles, and many other body processes require a certain amount of energy.

3. Still other nutrients are needed to keep the body in good running condition. These food materials regulate the way in which

the various parts of the body act and protect the body from disease.

When the food you eat during a day contains all the materials the body needs — that is, all the nutrients — you have a well-balanced diet. The reason for grouping foods into the Basic Seven groups is to make it easy for everyone to be sure he is getting all the necessary materials. If you use the Basic Seven as your guide, your diet will be well-balanced. Follow the Basic Seven for more than just the meals you eat at home. If you take your lunch to school, prepare lunches that will add something to each day's Basic Seven. If you buy your lunch in the school cafeteria, choose foods that will help in filling out the day's Basic Seven requirement. Even when you plant a garden or choose foods to store or can, consider the Basic Seven.

Growth and Repair of the Body

Have you ever heard the human body compared to a machine? In some ways it is similar to a machine, but it is much more remarkable than any machine ever invented. No machine can do its own repair work as the body can. The tissues of the body are constantly undergoing change; so they constantly need repair. The materials with which they are repaired come from food.

Proteins. The chief nutrients used in building and repairing body tissues are called *proteins.* (Such foods as meat, eggs, and milk products are the most important sources of proteins.) Muscles are made up largely of proteins, and the blood also contains proteins. In fact, all the cells in the body are made of proteins and must have a constant supply of proteins to replenish themselves.

The proteins in food are not all equally efficient for building and repairing tissues. Some food proteins are *complete;* that is, they furnish all the material needed to produce body proteins. Other food proteins are *incomplete;* they lack some essentials necessary for body proteins. Nevertheless, they are valuable.

Minerals. Other nutrients important as body-building materials are the *minerals.* Iron is one mineral you already know. It is needed by the red cells in your blood. These cells also need copper, another mineral with which you are familiar. The body needs calcium, which you may know as lime. It also needs phosphorus, in order to build strong teeth and bones. All these minerals, and others, are supplied by the food you eat. All body tissues contain minerals.

FIG. 3. FOODS FOR GROWTH HELPED THESE STURDY CHILDREN BECOME HEALTHY AND ATTRACTIVE YOUNG PEOPLE

Vitamins. Without the aid of vitamins, the body cannot properly use proteins and minerals for growth and repair. Minerals, water, and vitamins all are body regulators, as well as building materials. They are discussed further on pages 11–13.

ENERGY FOR THE BODY

You know that there are several kinds of fuel on the market — gasoline, kerosene, coal, Diesel fuel, wood, and so on. There are also several kinds of fuel that can be used to give energy to the human body. You probably get most of your energy from the nutrients called *carbohydrates* (starches and sugars). The *fats* in the food you eat are "high-powered" nutrients that supply you with much energy. If you should fail to get carbohydrates and fats in your food (which is extremely unlikely), your body could use proteins as fuel; but it could not use minerals or vitamins as fuel.

The fuel foods, fats, carbohydrates, and proteins, are measured by calories. Just as we cannot measure cloth by quarts, so we cannot measure water, vitamins, and minerals by calories, for these are not fuel foods. All measures are limited in their application. In the same way that we have inches, feet, yards, miles, to measure length; pints, quarts, gallons, to measure volume; so we have calories to measure heat and energy value. For example, the amount of energy obtained from one pound of white sugar is about 1700 calories, and the amount resulting from one pound of butter is about 3500 calories. (Other calories values are given in Table VI in the Appendix.)

How Much Fuel Food Do You Need? You are always using energy — in growing, in moving about, and even in staying alive. During the periods of your life when you are growing rapidly, you need more fuel food than you will need when you are fully grown. Boys and girls — and adults — who are very active and take part in a great deal of outdoor work and play need more fuel food than those who spend their time quietly indoors. In general, an athletic high school boy uses as much energy every day as he can get from food which gives 3200 or more calories; and an average high school girl uses as much energy every day as she can obtain by eating food which gives approximately 2400 to 2600 calories.

Suppose you don't eat food that gives that many calories. Then your body has to use up its own tissues, and you get thin and underweight. Suppose you eat food that gives, say, 4500 calories when you need only 3000 calories. Then your body stores that food as fat, unless you exercise more than usual.

Adults do not ordinarily need so much fuel food as young people. People who take little exercise need less fuel food than those who exercise a great deal. A person who is naturally short may need less fuel food than a person who is naturally tall. You can obtain more information about the amount of fuel

FIG. 4. ENERGY FOR SUCCESSFUL COMPETITION COMES FROM FUEL FOODS

food different people need by consulting Table V in the Appendix.

Whenever you hear anyone speak of calories, remember that calories indicate the energy value of a food. They tell nothing at all about its other values: whether it is a good body-builder, whether it can supply vitamins, or what minerals it contains.

Regulation and Protection of the Body

A person may eat all the fuel food he needs and still suffer from hidden hunger. He may actually become ill because his body does not get the vitamins and minerals needed. Because vitamins and minerals protect the body from certain diseases, they are called body *protectors*. As you know, they also help the various parts of the body to work together properly; therefore they are called body *regulators* as well. But minerals and vitamins are not the only body regulators. Water and the cellulose or fiber of fruit and vegetables also serve as body regulators.

Water and Roughage. Water serves as a body regulator by doing part of the job of getting rid of waste materials. Another part of this job is done by the fiber or cellulose of fruits and vegetables — the parts that are not digested. Cellulose supplies the bulk, or *roughage*, needed to keep the digestive tract in good condition. You have probably heard that eating vegetables and fruits helps a person avoid constipation. It does so because the cellulose in these foods helps regulate the movements of the intestines.

Minerals. You have already learned that minerals are important as body builders. They are equally necessary as body regulators. Do you remember that calcium is necessary for building firm teeth and strong bones? It is equally necessary for keeping muscles acting normally. One very important muscle is the heart. Calcium is necessary to maintain the steady working of the heart.

Some minerals are needed by the body only in very small amounts. However, if these tiny quantities are not supplied in the diet, serious illness may result. For example, only a very little iodine is necessary, but if this small amount is not present, the disease called goiter results. Fortunately, foods that contain iron, calcium, and phosphorus usually contain the other necessary minerals as well.

Vitamins. The word *vitamin* is familiar to everyone nowadays, but many people can remember the time when it was completely unknown. In those days, even the scientists who knew most about food thought that proteins, carbohydrates, fats, water, cellulose, and minerals were all that the body needed. Then doctors began to notice that some people whose diets contained all these substances were not in good health. In searching for the cause of this poor health, they learned that there were other necessary nutrients. These nutrients are now called vitamins. Many vitamins have been discovered; probably others are still unknown. At least six vitamins are now known to be so important that everyone should be supplied with them every day. These six vitamins are listed here.

1. VITAMIN A. Vitamin A is a nutrient that is essential for growth. This vitamin helps to keep the membranes of the eyes, digestive tract, and all the vital organs of the body in good health. Vitamin A helps the eyes to adjust more readily to light and dark.

2. THIAMIN, ALSO CALLED VITAMIN B_1. Thiamin is a nutrient that promotes growth, stimulates the appetite, and aids digestion. Thiamin also helps keep the nerves healthy.

3. VITAMIN C, ALSO CALLED ASCORBIC ACID. This nutrient is also necessary for growth. It helps develop good teeth and healthy gums, and helps keep the soft tissues of the body healthy. Vitamin C is essential for keeping blood vessels in good condition.

4. VITAMIN D. Vitamin D aids the body in its use of phosphorus and calcium for developing strong bones and teeth. Consequently it is especially important during the growing period. If a growing person does not get enough Vitamin D, his legs may be bowed or his spine may be curved. Lack of Vitamin D causes the disease known as rickets.

5. RIBOFLAVIN, ALSO CALLED VITAMIN G. Riboflavin helps protect the health of the digestive system, and also helps protect the body against infectious diseases.

6. NIACIN, ALSO CALLED NICOTINIC ACID. Niacin is necessary for general good health. It is especially important for the health of the skin and of the digestive tract. Niacin prevents most of the symptoms of a disease known as pellagra. Although the other name, nicotinic acid, sounds like the word "nicotine," niacin is *not* the same as nicotine; it is an entirely different substance.

These six vitamins, and others, are found in fresh, natural food. When food is improperly cooked or stored, vitamins are destroyed, especially Vitamin C. You should learn to cook food so that its

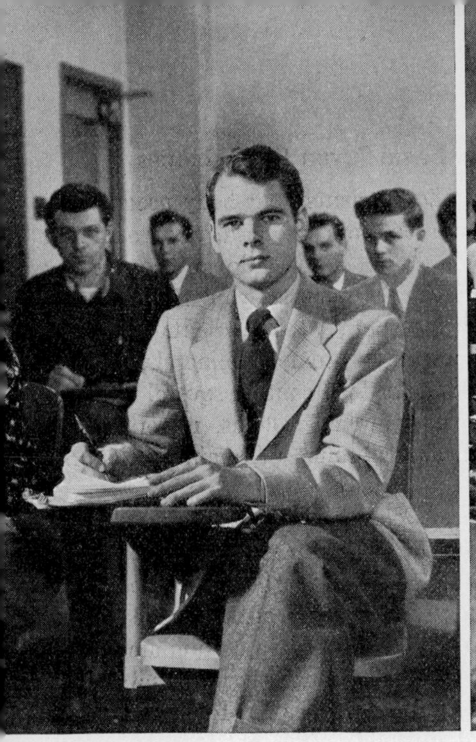

Fig. 5. AT SCHOOL OR ON THE JOB, YOU PROFIT FROM A WELL-BALANCED DIET

vitamin value is kept. But it is important to eat some uncooked food daily.

One of the vitamins, Vitamin D, can be made in the body. When the sun shines directly on the skin, it causes the body to manufacture the vitamin. For this reason, Vitamin D is sometimes called the "sunshine vitamin." Vitamin D is found in fewer foods than other vitamins; so it is important to spend some time in the sunshine every day that you can do so.

Plan to get your vitamins from the food you eat and from sunshine. The market basket and the garden are better sources of vitamins than pills and capsules. Do you see why? Fresh, natural food contains all the known vitamins. If there are still unknown vitamins (as there probably are), fresh, natural food contains them, too. But vitamin pills contain only the known vitamins. The vitamins in pills have been taken out of foods, or manufactured to be like the known vitamins in foods. Let your doctor decide when you need to supplement your diet with vitamin pills.

Nutrients and the Basic Seven Food Groups

If you had to think about the nutrients your body needs every time you plan a meal or choose food in a cafeteria, you would find the job rather hard. But you do not need to do so, because you have the help of the Basic Seven. Of course, you want to know how using the Basic Seven helps you get the nutrients you need. Some kinds of food are rich in protein, some in minerals, some in vitamins, and so on. Most kinds of food contain several different nutrients. Milk, for example, contains proteins, minerals (calcium, phosphorus, and iron), and vitamins (Vitamin A, thiamin, and niacin).

Foods that Contain Proteins. Foods such as milk, cheese, eggs, and meat, fish, and poultry are the best sources of proteins. These foods are listed in Groups 4 and 5 of the Basic Seven. Dried beans and peas, which are also listed in Group 5, are also valuable sources of proteins. The foods of Group 6 contribute a certain amount of proteins, but they should not be relied upon as the principal source.

Sources of Minerals. It is important to plan for an adequate supply of minerals in your daily food. It is not easy to supply your needs of these essential nutrients. Here again the Basic Seven food groups are a safe guide. To insure an adequate supply of minerals, one must include in the daily diet a liberal amount of one or two foods rich in each of these three minerals: calcium, iron, and phosphorus. Full information on the occurrence of minerals in foods is given in Table X in the Appendix.

For *calcium*, milk and cheese are most important; that is, Group 4 of the Basic Seven. You also get some calcium from the vegetables in Groups 1, 2, and 3, and from eggs (Group 5).

For *iron*, eat leafy, green vegetables, meat and eggs, and whole-grain cereals. These foods are from Groups 1, 5, and 6 of the Basic Seven.

Foods in Groups 4, 5, and 6 of the Basic Seven supply *phosphorus*. Milk, meat and eggs, and whole-grain cereals are the important sources of this mineral.

Sources of Vitamins. The Basic Seven food groups are a good guide to follow to make sure the daily diet contains all the important vitamins.

Foods providing *Vitamin A* are found in Group 1 (green and yellow vegetables), Group 4 (cream and cheese), Group 5 (eggs), and Group 7 (butter and fortified margarine).

For *thiamin*, or Vitamin B_1, the vegetables and fruits in Groups 1 and 3, and pork and soybeans in Group 5 are good sources. The whole-grain or enriched cereals and breads of Group 6 also supply thiamin.

The surest sources of *Vitamin C* are certain fresh raw foods taken daily. Vitamin C may be lost during such household processes as storing or cooking. Also, not much Vitamin C can be stored in the body. Therefore, the fresh raw fruits and vegetables of Group 2 are the chief source of Vitamin C.

As you know, sunshine helps your body build *Vitamin D.* But some Vitamin D comes from foods. Certain foods in Group 5, such as fish, Vitamin D milk, and liver, are the chief source of Vitamin D in the Basic Seven food groups. Rapidly growing children, especially infants, need cod-liver oil as a regular supplement to the Basic Seven provision of Vitamin D, particularly if sunshine is lacking.

The vitamin known as *riboflavin* is found in such foods as milk and cheese, meat and eggs, and whole- or enriched-grain products. These foods are listed in Groups 4, 5, and 6 of the Basic Seven food groups.

The important sources of *niacin* are lean meat and fish in Group 5, and whole- or enriched-grain products in Group 6. The fruits and vegetables of Groups 1 and 2 also supply some niacin.

For full information on the distribution of vitamins in foods, see Table IX in the Appendix.

Fuel Foods — Fats and Carbohydrates. Bread, flour, and cereals, butter and margarine are the foods in the Basic Seven food-selection plan that insure a supply of fuel in the diet. These foods are to be found in Groups 6 and 7. You also receive energy from the sweets that you eat. See the list of energy foods on page 5. Remember, however, that it is important to eat all the foods required from the Basic Seven food groups before eating these extra energy foods.

Good Food and Good Health

It is not enough to know what food should be included in each day's meals. It is also necessary to know how to select that food in the garden or the market, how to prepare it so that it will be tasty, and how to serve it so that it will be tempting. Remember, though, that the tastiest, most tempting meals are poor unless they

FIG. 6. IT'S MORE FUN TO PLAY WHEN YOU ARE WELL-FED

are part of a well-balanced diet. As you study home economics, you will learn more about the science and art of providing the family meals.

A well-balanced diet always does something *for* you. It gives springiness to the step, erectness to the bearing. It imparts a glow to the skin and a sparkle to the eye. It puts you "on top of the world," with that "million-dollar" feeling we all want.

You must eat to live; you must eat well to live well. The challenge is to you. The reward is buoyant health and the greater achievement that buoyant health makes possible.

CLASS PROBLEMS

1. Keep a record of what you eat for several typical days that represent what you usually eat. Evaluate what you ate in terms of the Basic Seven groups. Is your signal on food totals as rated by what you ate on those days go, caution, or stop? What would you need to do to improve your choice of foods?
2. Did you ever try to establish a new habit or break an old one?

Discuss ways of establishing a good food habit that you or someone you know needs to establish.

3. Most people limit their food to too small a variety. This is especially true of vegetables.

Make a list of the vegetables that are available in your market, or that might be grown in gardens in your locality. How many of these are included frequently in what you eat?

From this list select one or two vegetables that would add valuable food nutrients to your family's diet. Tell what the inclusion of these vegetables could add to your body's supply of food nutrients. Suggest a plan to your family for learning to use these vegetables.

4. Write to the Agricultural Extension Service at your State Agricultural College and find out whether they have available any bulletins, films, or movies on the subject of good nutrition. Procure and examine any of these and discuss them in class.

5. Discuss the meaning of abundant health in terms of what high-school boys and girls like to do. Ask the football coach, or someone who has been in the Army or Navy, or a college athlete if there is any acknowledged relationship between what we can do and what we eat.

6. What would you like to learn about food? List some of the subjects and activities involving food that you would like to have included in your study of foods. Discuss these topics in your foods class and help plan the course to include what is most important.

CHAPTER TWO

❧ Preparing and Serving a Meal

YOU CAN WATCH or read about an experienced homemaker in order to see how she does the work of preparing a meal, but until you have tried to do the job yourself and can do it well, you have not really learned how it should be done.

What a good manager does:

Plans meals that meet the nutrition requirements of her family.

Buys food that fits the family pocketbook.

Cooks food in delectable dishes so that the family enjoys eating a balanced diet.

Uses time, materials, and equipment economically.

Serves meals artistically.

Enjoys her work and has time to do many other things.

The difference between people who get things done and those who don't is that those who accomplish things have learned management.

This chapter will serve as a slow-motion picture to point the way to good management in the kitchen. Let us select a light breakfast as the subject, and see how a good manager plans her work. Later you will want to try planning menus of your own, but for the present we shall take one that has been planned for us.

The Importance of Efficient Work. Have you ever thought about, or discussed, why people like to work efficiently? It is a good subject to discuss because it concerns all of us, whatever our work may be. Many hours are saved by those who work with ease and dispatch, or are lost by those who work in a hit-or-miss way. Some of the reasons for working efficiently are the following:

Efficient workers get a great deal done in a short time.

Working efficiently saves more time for other things, such as recreation.

Self-confidence is developed by those who learn to work well.

There is pleasure in work well done.

Ready for Work in the Kitchen

The efficient worker includes getting ready for her job as part of her work. Handling food requires absolute cleanliness. Everyone who is to prepare food must, therefore, meet the exacting requirements of cleanliness.

What one wears in the kitchen — inexpensive house dress, or smock, or apron — should be washable, attractive, and of course spick-and-span.

Shoes should be comfortable and neat.

Hair should be out of the way so that it will not be falling in the eyes or into the food. Such an arrangement can and should be becoming.

Handkerchief should be placed safely in a pocket.

Hands, especially the nails, should be thoroughly clean before handling food, and of course hands are never clean unless they have just been washed.

A hand towel should be conveniently placed so that hands may be washed frequently. Never fail to wash your hands after using a handkerchief, going to the toilet, or soiling the hands in any way.

The Route to Good Management in the Kitchen

There is a way to manage work instead of letting it manage you. It may seem easier in some ways just to start getting a meal, because it takes some time to make a plan. A good manager, however, always lets her head save her hands and her heels by planning her work before she starts. The results make the effort worth while, especially when she becomes such an experienced planner that she can carry the plan in her head; beginners, however, should always make written plans.

A good manager can do many things at the same time; in fact, that is the test of good management. A person who has not learned to manage may be able to cook one food at a time, but she has trouble in getting a whole meal together. Good management is based on good work habits. The sooner you form good habits the better, because habits can either save or make work, thus adding to your joy or sorrow in the kitchen. If you have ever tried breaking a bad habit, you know the significance of the old adage that "an ounce of prevention is worth a pound of cure." Then, too, habits not only save or waste time, but in cooking they also have a part in making what we cook good or poor.

On with the Breakfast

Let us suppose, for this slow-motion word picture of getting breakfast, that the family has just returned from a holiday. There are no food supplies on hand except such staples as sugar and salt. Plans are to be made for breakfast next morning. The meal we have chosen for our word picture is just a sample. We might have selected some other fruit, or another beverage, or a hot bread, or a breakfast cereal, but a simple breakfast will demonstrate the principles of good management just as well as a more complicated one. Our menu is very simple:

Apple Sauce
Cocoa Hot buttered toast

What Supplies Are Needed? To answer this question we must know not only the menu but also the recipes. To find the recipes we need, let us consult the index which is a tool for using a book. The index is planned to help you as much as possible, so almost everything is listed under more than one heading. You wish to locate the recipe for apple sauce so you look first for "Apple Sauce"; in this case you will find it.

If you did not find it, but are resourceful, the thought might occur to you to look under "Sauces," or "Apples," or "Fruits." Here you would find page references which would locate the group of recipes in which you would find Apple Sauce. Consult the index to see if this method would locate Apple Sauce in *Everyday Foods*. Next locate the recipe for cocoa by means of the index.

Buying Supplies. In this case there is nothing in the house except sugar and salt and such staples as would not spoil while the family was away on vacation. A list of the supplies to be bought must first be made. We consult the recipes and then make our list. It includes:

Apples	Bread
Cocoa	Butter
Milk	Soap flakes

Of course an experienced home manager would not shop for one meal, but would make her plans for three meals.

To Market, to Market. If you ever shop with an experienced homemaker, you are no doubt impressed that she knows exactly what she wants and why she wants it.

Apples are bought by the pound, and buying them in quantity

is often economical if they can be used advantageously before they spoil. In some stores apples are sold by Government grades. A good manager selects a store that sells by grades. She asks for U.S. No. I, or U.S. No. I Early, or U.S. Utility for her apple sauce. Perhaps the store does not sell graded fruit. Our experienced marketer would, however, be able to buy apples for apple sauce that are not graded, for she would recognize the small tart apples, moderately priced, which would be suitable for her purpose.

Although five or six small apples will make enough apple sauce for this meal, a thrifty manager will decide to buy enough for several meals, because apple sauce will keep, and it is not much more trouble to make a large amount than a small amount.

COCOA is available in large or small packages, but is less expensive if bought by the half pound or pound rather than in smaller packages. A half pound is purchased. A tin container is chosen because the cocoa keeps well in an airtight package.

MILK calls for a real decision. It may be bought raw, pasteurized, canned, or dried. Bottled pasteurized milk is chosen, with a cap that covers the bottle top, since the family has been using canned and dried milk at the vacation camp and will enjoy the variety of fresh milk even at a higher cost.

BUTTER our housewife buys by the pound, in convenient quarter-pound sticks. We note that she asks for pasteurized butter from a dairy that she knows is clean and furnishes butter of good quality.

If our shopper lives where butter is marketed by grades, she can buy her butter by the grades plainly shown on the label. This is an advantage over buying by brand.

BREAD offers a wide variety for her choice. For convenience she selects a one-pound loaf of sliced whole wheat bread. The unsliced bread will keep better, but with the appetite of this family there will be no loss in the sliced bread, and convenience is an item.

HOME AGAIN AND INTO THE KITCHEN

Our experienced homemaker decides to let her daughter prepare the apple sauce immediately and place it in the refrigerator to be ready for breakfast the next day. Let us suppose we are watching the inexperienced daughter, perhaps your age, prepare the apple sauce under her mother's directions. She proceeds in this manner:

1. Our worker locates the recipe quickly through the use of the index and reads it carefully.

Fig. 7. LOOKING UP RECIPE

Fig. 8. WASHING HANDS

Fig. 9. ASSEMBLING MATERIALS

Fig. 10. PARING APPLES ON A PAPER

Fig. 11. REMOVING WASTE

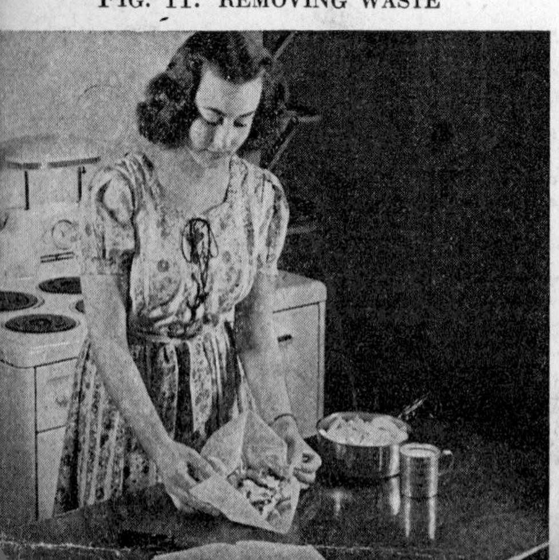

Fig. 12. STIRRING SAUCE WHILE COOKING

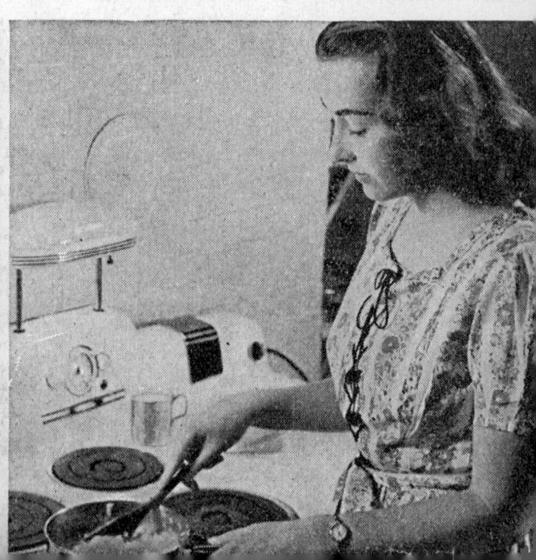

2. She plans the jobs to be done, taking into consideration:
   The time each will take
   Equipment needed
   Supplies and measurements.
3. She carries out the plans in the kitchen without any hurry. In orderly fashion she gets out exactly what she needs in supplies and equipment — no more, no less.

FIG. 13. ADDING SUGAR

A Slow-Motion Word Picture of Action in the Kitchen

Our efficient manager:

1. Thinks over her recipe and plans her time.
2. Washes her hands, gets ready for work.
3. Gets out her equipment:
   - Measuring cup
   - Spoons
   - Paring knife
   - Utility pan for spoons, etc., while in use (to keep from soiling surfaces of stove or table).
   - Container for waste: Several thicknesses of paper spread out on the worktable to serve as a quick way of cleaning up. When the work is finished, she rolls up the paper, puts it in the garbage pail (if local ordinances permit), and all is in order.
   - Container for finished product: A covered dish

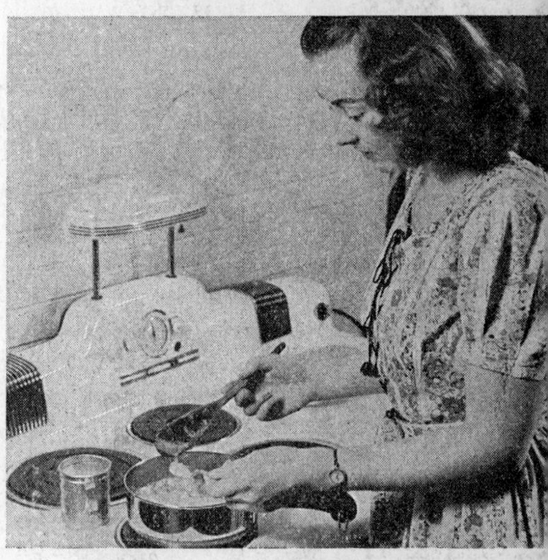

FIG. 14. TASTING SAUCE WITH TASTING SPOON

FIG. 15. PUTTING IN REFRIGERATOR WHEN COOL

in which the apple sauce may be put in the refrigerator when cool.

4. Measures her supplies
   Accurately (as the recipe calls for); using level measurements (see Directions for Measuring, page 28)
5. Proceeds to cook
   Avoids spilling and splashing. Controls the heat so that there is not too much or too little. Watches the cooking. Stirs occasionally. Avoids boiling over or burning.
6. Works neatly
   Confines her work to as small area as possible.
   Uses as few utensils as possible.
   Keeps soiled utensils stacked — cleaning up as she goes.
   Gets rid of the garbage and starts cleaning up the working surface while the sauce is cooking.
7. Evaluates the finished product
   Inspects and judges it by standards for good apple sauce:
   Appearance
   Consistency
   Taste (Clean spoon is used for tasting. When once used, it is not put back in the apple sauce, but is placed with soiled utensils or washed.)
8. Stores the apple sauce in a clean uncovered dish until cool. When it is cool, covers it and places it in a cool place, preferably in the refrigerator.

Principles of Good Management

This slow-motion word picture of food preparation shows the principles of good management. A principle is a rule that can be used over and over again in new situations. What are the principles of good management illustrated by this preparation of apple sauce?

I. *Have a Definite Goal or Objective.* This is the first principle of all good management. The goal in cookery, of course, is to make the best products we can, so we must know not only what we want to cook, but how we want it to appear, to taste, and to be served. In other words, what are the acceptable standards for the product to be prepared?

II. *Have a Plan of Work.* This includes securing recipes, getting the supplies, and making a work schedule. Making a plan is an important step in good management, whether one is building a house, taking a trip, making a dress, or cooking a meal.

III. *Carry Out the Plan Effectively.* Every good manager is a good manager because she is able both to make and carry out good plans. The test of good plans is whether or not they are workable. A really good manager makes plans and then works by them, modifying the plans as the need arises. No good manager is a slave to her plan; on the contrary, in carrying it out, she is quick to see changes that make for improvement. You will understand this better when you make a plan for preparing a meal and try it out in your home kitchen or in the school laboratory. Don't forget, however, that cookery is a creative job. When you make apple sauce, or a cake, or cook a whole dinner, you follow a plan, but you also create something.

IV. *Judge the Results.* Everybody knows that "the proof of the pudding is in the eating." When the pudding is not so good as it might be, you think through what you have done and try to find out what you did wrong. Or if it is unusually good, you also try to discover the reasons. Almost instinctively you say, "When I do this again I will do thus and so." In other words, you are evaluating your experience and will profit by it.

Good Management in Meal Preparation

Let us see how our four principles of management apply to the preparation of the single breakfast the next morning.

I. *Objective.* What would be the goal or objective of this breakfast? To have all of the food good, and all of it ready at the right time, attractively served. This means hot, smooth cocoa just right in flavor; crisp hot toast ready at the right moment with butter at hand; apple sauce cold; an attractive breakfast table and a family ready on time, including the cook.

II. *The Plan.* Think through the jobs to be done. Analyze the recipes separately. See that you understand clearly what is to be done. Make a schedule of:

Things that may be done first
Things that must be done at the last minute
Things that will take longest to do, so they can be in progress while other tasks are being carried out.

In this breakfast these tasks line up as follows:

The apple sauce is all ready.

The table can be set first.

The cocoa will take the longest time.

Last-minute jobs are pouring the water and finishing the toast.

III. *On With the Cooking.* We carry out the plan in the following order:

If a coal or wood stove is to be used, build the fire first.

Set the table.

Get the supplies and utensils.

Turn on electric stove, or light gas, or oil stove.

Measure ingredients for cocoa and begin the preparation.

Put water on in double boiler for making the cocoa. Put cocoa in top of double boiler and add other ingredients.

Get bread ready for toasting.

Get apple sauce, butter, and cold water from refrigerator and serve.

Start the toast.

Announce breakfast.

Serve toast and cocoa after family are seated (or toast may be made at the table with an electric toaster).

IV. *Evaluation.* Did you and the others enjoy the breakfast? Clues to watch for are: "May I have another cup of cocoa?" "This toast is so good, I will take another piece." If the breakfast is not eaten with relish, it has still been a valuable experience if you find out what the trouble is and profit by your experience.

General Rules of Work in Preparation of Meals

When the experience of many people points out a really good way to do a job, this experience is summed up in a group of rules or general principles. When such general rules are available, the inexperienced person should profit by this summarized experience of others. General rules, based on the experience of efficient homemakers, are available on measuring; on systematic methods of work; on cleaning and dishwashing. These rules are listed here with the suggestion that "a hint to the wise is sufficient" whether at home or at school.

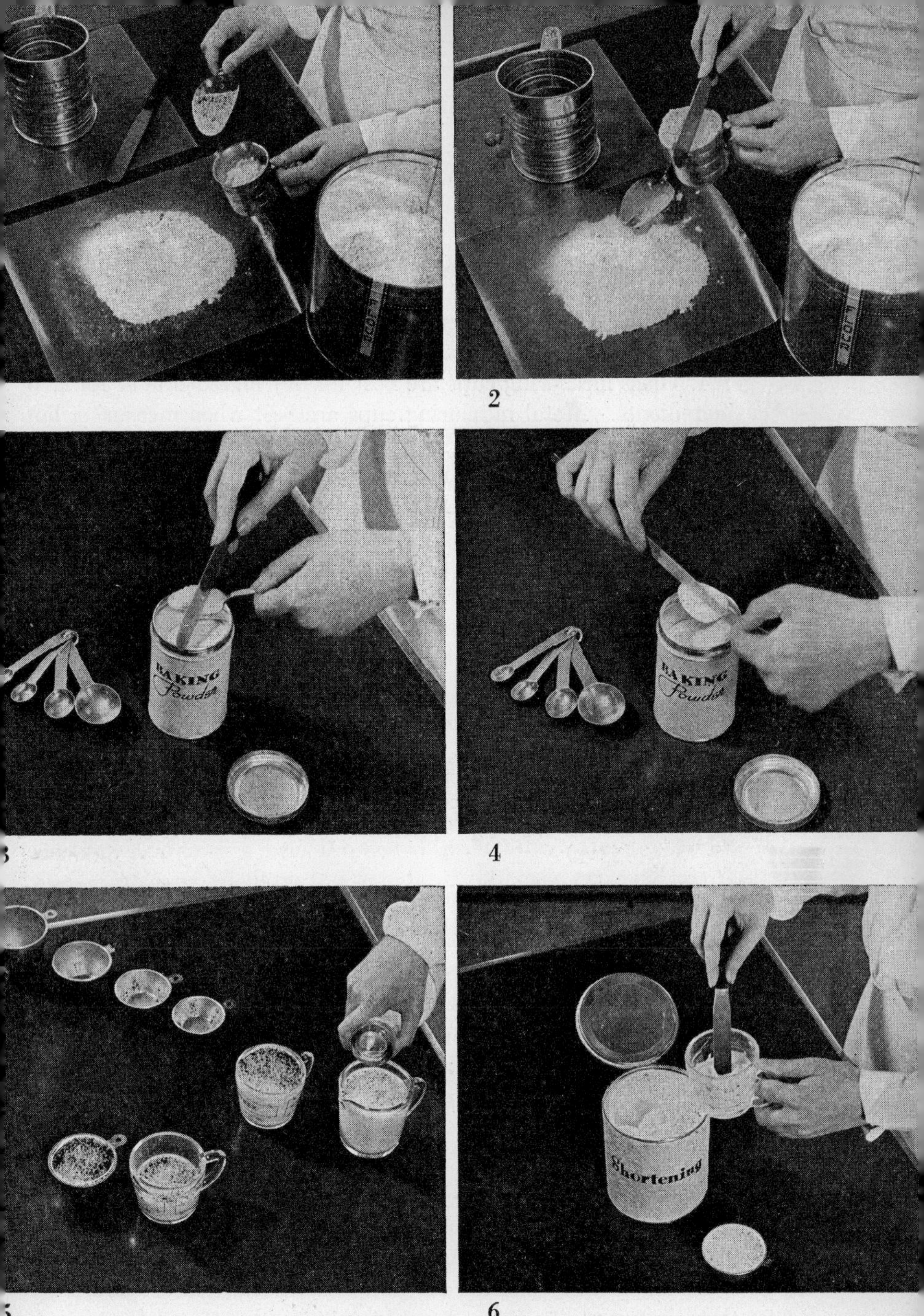

FIG. 16. MEASURE ACCURATELY

1. Pile flour lightly. 2 and 3. Level with a spatula. 4. Dividing a teaspoon. 5. Measuring a liquid. 6. Packing shortening carefully.

Directions for Measuring

1. Make it a rule to be accurate in measuring.

2. Level all measures, preferably with the back of a knife. Liquids are correctly measured when the measure is level full. Do not fill to overflowing.

3. If half a spoonful is called for, fill the spoon, level it off, and divide lengthwise. See illustration, page 27.

4. Glass measuring cups are best for dry ingredients or for cold ingredients. Metal measuring cups are best when measuring hot ingredients. Flour should be sifted once before it is measured, because after one sifting the measurement will be more accurate. It should then be handled so that it will not pack down in the measure. Pile it lightly into a cup with a spoon and level it off with the straight edge of a knife. If it is dipped with a cup, it will pack, with the result that a cup will sometimes hold an extra amount of flour packed down. Solid fat is measured in a cup, or in special measures that hold parts of a cup.

Table of Measures

(Used in the recipes in this book)

3 teaspoons = 1 tablespoon

16 tablespoons = 1 cup (4 tablespoons = ¼ cup; 8 tablespoons = ½ cup)

2 cups = 1 pint

2 pints = 1 quart

4 quarts = 1 gallon

Table of Abbreviations

t. — teaspoon

T. — tablespoon

c. — cup

pt. — pint

qt. — quart

lb. — pound

General Rules for Orderliness in the Kitchen

1. A place for everything and everything in its place.

2. Use equipment for what it is intended. Have special dishes for use in the kitchen and in the refrigerator. Do not use dining room dishes for kitchen work.

3. Dish towels should be used for dishes and utensils, never for hands. Paper towels are convenient for hand towels.

4. Pot holders, conveniently placed, are needed in every kitchen.

5. Use a utility pan for small utensils that are in use and keep them in the utility pan. A spoon that has been used for tasting should not be returned to the cooking mixture unless it is washed.

6. Avoid spilling and splashing. Just turning on the kitchen faucet too much can make such a splash and such a mess! A little forethought can save much cleaning up.

7. Put away surplus food immediately after using.

8. Use only necessary equipment to save dishwashing and extra steps.

9. If equipment is not to be used again soon, wash and dry it and return it to its place. For example, the meat chopper and egg beater should be washed and put away instead of waiting until the end of the meal, because they will be hard to wash after the food has dried on them. Also they clutter up space unnecessarily.

10. Keep your mind on your work in the kitchen, and avoid burning and boiling over of food.

11. Control the heat in the stove. It saves money and avoids disaster.

12. Be careful how you use equipment. For example, your enamel pans will last longer if you avoid putting cold things in hot pans or hot things in cold pans. Do not put them when empty on the fire or in the oven. Because enamel is a glass-like coating it will pop off or crack. A nicked edge on an enamel pan usually means that a thoughtless person has knocked a spoon or a knife on the edge.

13. Keep the sink free of pots and pans. It is a work space and you cannot work at a cluttered sink.

14. Prepare for cleaning as you go. Soak pans when you empty them.

15. Leave the kitchen clean: stove, sink, garbage pail, table, breadboard, and floor.

General Rules for Cleaning Up and Dishwashing

Clearing the Kitchen. Before bringing the dishes into the kitchen some people prefer to clean up all the pots and pans. Others find it preferable to stack the pots and pans, or put them to soak. Of course if the pots and pans are washed first, we need a fresh supply of hot water for washing the dishes.

Good rules for tidying the kitchen are:

1. Store all left-over foods, usually covered. Food that spoils quickly should be put in a cool place, preferably in the refrigerator. Oil paper held in place with rubber bands, or oil silk covers with elastic bands, make good covers for foods.

2. Wipe greasy pans with absorbent paper before washing. Soak with a little washing soda if necessary.

3. Soak in cold water pans in which starchy material (cereals), or eggs have been cooked. It is a good practice to fill up such a pot with water as soon as it is emptied, and put it at the back of the stove where it will not be in the way.

4. Soak sticky pans (sugar) with hot water.

5. Pans (except those made of aluminum) in which food is scorched should be filled with hot water to which a little washing soda has been added. Heat until the scorched material is loosened; it can then easily be removed. Being careful not to scorch food in the first place beats cleaning it out of pans, but if food is scorched, the pans should not be scraped in cleaning them.

6. Clean aluminum pans containing scorched food by soaking them with plain hot water. Aluminum pans may then be scoured with a fine steel wool or with a scouring powder. Avoid using soda or alkalis with aluminum ware. Soda will darken the aluminum.

Rules for Dishwashing

Getting Ready. When clearing the table, use a tray or movable table to hold soiled dishes.

Remove all the food from the dishes and stack them in the order in which they are to be washed with those that are to be washed first nearest the sink or dishpan. If you are right-handed, place the soiled dishes at your right. If you are left-handed, place them at the left.

Plenty of hot water and soap will take the drudgery out of dishwashing. Chemists have come to the aid of homemakers who must use hard water by creating water softeners. The amount needed depends partly on the hardness of the water, but the amount used is always small. Do not use more than necessary.

Quick Method of Washing Dishes. Who wishes to be found guilty of using a slow method of dishwashing? Nobody. This is the way to do it quickly.

Materials needed:

Hot soapy water for washing dishes
Clear boiling water for rinsing dishes
Racks for draining dishes and drying china
Clean dish towel
A tray for stacking the clean dishes

FIG. 17. WASHING DISHES: READY TO BEGIN

In washing dishes, place a few in the pan at a time. A good order for washing dishes is glassware first, silver next, china next. A fresh supply of hot soapy water should be used as needed. Glassware should be washed in the first hot soapy water and dried immediately without rinsing. Silver should be rinsed in scalding hot water and dried immediately.

After washing china, stack it in the drainer and rinse thoroughly with scalding water. China scalded with hot water will dry in a dish rack in one to three minutes, and does not need to be dried with a towel. This method takes less time than hand drying and leaves the dishes cleaner. If it is allowed to drain in this way, the china will also be dry and ready to put away when you have finished putting away the glassware and silver.

Dish towels should be washed in hot soapy water and rinsed in hot clear water. Occasionally add a few drops of vinegar to the rinse water and rinse again in clear water. An occasional final rinse in cold water helps to keep dish towels white. At intervals dish towels should be boiled in soapy water and then thoroughly rinsed. Sunshine, if available, is an excellent aid in keeping dish towels in good condition.

Keeping the Kitchen and Its Equipment Clean

Cleaning the Sink. The sink should not be used for the disposal of garbage. To avoid trouble in the sink drain, use a strainer for removing all food particles from dishwater and other refuse. The newer types of sinks are provided with a sink strainer in the drain, which may be easily removed and washed.

Occasionally the sink drain should be cleaned with a strong alkali. Special preparations are available and directions are usually given on the can. Plenty of hot soapy water and daily care in keeping food out of the sink will make little special care of the drain necessary.

The sink should be kept clean. A porcelain sink will last longer if the surface is not scratched; therefore, if a cleaning powder is used, be sure that it is a very fine one. Enamel surfaces are also injured by chipping. Do not crack ice in the sink.

Cleaning the Stove. A careful worker seldom needs to clean a stove except by wiping the surface with clean paper or cloth. Different types of stoves call for different types of cleaning, but all stoves must be kept clean. Iron surfaces can be cleaned with steel wool and then washed with soapy water and dried at once. An occasional treatment with stove polish may be desirable to keep an iron stove in good condition. Enamel surfaces can be cleaned with soap and water, and the newer types of stoves have removable parts which can be washed. For cleaning a new stove consult the manufacturer's instructions.

It is well in the beginning to learn good habits in using the stove so that difficult cleaning is avoided.

1. Cook in a pan or a dish that is big enough so that food will not boil over on top of the stove or in the oven.
2. Control the heat to prevent boiling over in the oven.
3. Take the precaution of putting a pan under anything likely to boil over in the oven, as, for example, a berry pie.
4. Do not fill pans too full. In baking a batter that will rise, allow space for the increase. A good rule is to fill pans from one half to two thirds full.

Refrigerator. The first rule in the care of the refrigerator is to keep it clean. Never put into a refrigerator a dish or bottle on the outer surface of which there is any food. If anything is spilled in the refrigerator, wipe it up immediately. When cleaning a refrigerator, which should be done once a week, wash the interior with cool water in which one or two tablespoons of washing soda have been dissolved.

A refrigerator can do its work best when the door is closed. Open it as little as possible, and keep the door open as short a time as possible. Cool hot foods to room temperature before placing them in the refrigerator.

Defrosting a Mechanical Refrigerator. The mechanical refrigerator should be defrosted at regular intervals. When the freezing compartment is covered with one-quarter inch of frost the refrigerator needs defrosting, because this coating interferes with refrigeration. Defrost by turning off the motor, and allowing the frost to melt from the cooling unit. Wipe off unit and wipe out the interior with soda water each time the refrigerator is defrosted.

Placement of Food in the Refrigerator. The temperature is different in different parts of the refrigerator. Use a thermometer to study your refrigerator. Cold air falls and warm air rises. The coldest place, therefore, is usually just under the ice or cooling unit. In a mechanical refrigerator any area near the freezing compartment is cold.

1. The most perishable food should go in the coldest part of the refrigerator: milk and cream, raw meat, fish, poultry.

2. Cooked meats, eggs, butter, and cooked foods which contain eggs, milk, and meat should be placed in the next coldest place.

3. Raw vegetables and fruits need the next coldest part of the refrigerator.

4. Frozen foods should be kept in the freezing compartment. This compartment may also be used for frozen desserts. Frozen foods which are kept frozen can be safely held for a long period.

In some mechanical refrigerators food will dry unless it is kept covered. Special containers are provided to avoid this difficulty.

The Kitchen Itself. Cupboards, floors, and all surfaces must be spotlessly clean. Any food material left in cracks and crevices is an invitation to insects to take up their abode in the kitchen.

The garbage can needs daily treatment with hot soapy water and, if possible, sunshine. If sunshine is not available, use extra precaution in cleaning the garbage can by the use of washing soda in the rinse water. Here again an ounce of prevention is worth a pound of cure. Careful kitchen workers line their garbage cans with paper. They also wrap their garbage in paper, if local ordinances permit.

Learning to Cook Is Worth While

Cooking is invariably associated with satisfying home life. A high compliment to a public eating place is to describe the food served there as "home cooking."

There is a tradition about the home kitchen that associates it with delicious foods and good times. To uphold that tradition you want to become both a good cook and a good manager. In order to enjoy cooking one must learn to manage. Only by skilled management of time, money, materials, and equipment can a busy person enjoy creating economical meals to the "queen's taste." This is our objective.

Activities in Good Management

You want, of course, to learn to work efficiently in a kitchen. This ability can be developed only by practice.

Using the principles of good management as set forth in this chapter, plan all of the steps in getting the following meals:

Breakfast A
Stewed dried apricots
Cracked wheat cereal with dried milk
Hot muffins Tea or Milk

Breakfast B
Orange or tomato juice
Poached egg on rye bread toast
Milk, or coffee (for adults)

Breakfast C
Cream of Wheat with dates
Waffles Bacon
Cocoa

Breakfast D
Strawberries and cornflakes
Omelet Biscuit
Chocolate

Compare plans with several of your classmates and discuss the relative merits of the various plans. Revise your plan.

Try one of the plans at home at the beginning of your study of breakfasts. Save this plan. Later, when the unit on Breakfasts is completed, revise your plan and try preparing the same breakfast a second time at home.

Evaluate your experiences in terms of the progress you have made in learning to manage in preparing a meal.

UNIT TWO · BREAKFAST

CHAPTER THREE

What Shall We Have For Breakfast?

WHAT A PERSON eats for breakfast depends largely on who he is. Grandmothers do not eat the same breakfasts as growing boys and girls. A man who works all day in his office does not eat or need the same breakfast as a soldier who is on the march all day. You do not have the same breakfast now that you had when you were a two-year-old. Sick people eat different breakfasts from those that well people eat. We leave it to you to say whether boys and girls eat the same breakfasts.

When large numbers of people have the same habit, it is called a custom. The division of the day's food into meals is largely a matter of custom and varies in different parts of the world.

From the following typical breakfast menus you can compare the customs of different countries with your own in regard to the first meal of the day.

French

Coffee or cocoa or tea
Cold Rolls
Jam (occasionally)

English

Tea with cream and sugar, or cocoa
Porridge with cream and sugar
Bacon and eggs, or kippers (dried fish)
Deviled kidneys or sausage
Tomatoes
Muffins or cold rolls or buns
Toast and marmalade (always)

Mexican

Early breakfast before 8:00 A.M.
Coffee or spiced Chocolate

Breakfast 11:00 A.M. to 1:00 P.M.
(Comparable to our luncheon)
Eggs (always) Cold rolls
Sapa de pan (a piece of toast moistened with highly seasoned meat stock or gravy)
Frijoles (brown beans) Cakes
Spanish rice
Fresh fruit (always)

American Breakfast Menus. Any American breakfast menu will contain some of these foods: fruits, cereals, beverages (usually hot), breads, eggs and bacon, or perhaps a meat. A breakfast

FIG. 18. SUGGESTIONS FOR BREAKFAST SERVICE

consisting of all these items is termed a heavy breakfast. A breakfast consisting of a goodly number of these items, but not all, is considered a medium breakfast.

Heavy Breakfast

Fruit
Oatmeal, cream, sugar
Bacon and eggs
Muffins
Hot cakes and sirup

Medium Breakfast

Fruit
Shredded wheat, cream
Coffee or milk or cocoa
Soft cooked egg
Toast

Light Breakfast

Fruit
Toast
Coffee or milk or cocoa

The Importance of Eating Breakfast. The word breakfast means exactly what it says. *We break our fast.* For twelve hours or more we have eaten nothing. In fact, for at least eight hours of that time we have been relaxed in sleep, or should have been. To start our bodies out for the day with no breakfast would be like trying to ride a train without buying a ticket. Just as tramps ride without tickets, so some people force themselves to face the day's labors without breakfast. They are food tramps. There are dangers and a lack of comfort in both cases.

What Are the Reasons for Eating Breakfast? Three meals each day is the first step in good nutrition. Because they are building their bodies, growing boys and girls need proportionally more food than adults. The fact is, that three meals a day are not sufficient for young children, and at times even older children need more than three meals daily.

More people under twenty years of age are underweight than overweight. Thus if they omit breakfast they miss one of the three chances to get building materials and fuel supplies. The person who goes without breakfast runs a great risk of being undernourished. Three well-balanced meals constitute a full ticket for a ride in comfort on the "healthland" railway.

One of the recognized ills of modern life is constipation. The omission of breakfast, or the eating of a hasty breakfast and rushing away immediately to school, to work, or to play, are often causes of constipation.

Breakfast and the Day's Food. The deficiencies in the diets of American families is headline news.

Nutrition Experts Analyze Diets of Nation's Families

Diets Show General Improvement

Vitamins and Calcium Most Striking Deficiencies

The Bureau of Human Nutrition and Home Economics, U.S. Department of Agriculture, has completed a follow-up study of the diets of typical American families. Its nutrition experts have translated the meat and potatoes, carrots and beans, caramel cake and cinnamon rolls, bacon and eggs, eaten by these families, into energy values, vitamin values, protein values, mineral values. They have found that considerable improvement

Diet News — continued

has been made since the famous study of 1936 which showed that one third of the nation was ill-fed.

In the former study it was found that three quarters of the population did not get adequate amounts of riboflavin. Now only half the population does not get enough of this vitamin. Formerly half the families in the nation had diets low in calcium, thiamin, and Vitamin C. Now one third do not get enough calcium; one fourth do not get enough thiamin; and one tenth do not get enough Vitamin C.

Nutrition experts pointed out that the American diet is still found wanting when weighed in the balances. They stated that most families who do not get adequate food fail to do so because they do not know how to plan balanced meals. The most widespread dietary deficiencies are lacks of calcium and vitamins.

What is the significance of this newspaper story? It means that while you are learning to cook breakfast dishes, you have the responsibility for planning meals that will avoid or correct such common deficiencies in the diet. What can we do about the deficiencies of calcium and vitamins? Is breakfast a meal in which these major nutritional needs could be partially met? What foods are good sources of calcium and vitamins? Are any of these foods suitable for breakfast menus? What penalty will families pay if their diets are continuously lacking in needed calcium?

The health of American families is of national concern. That is why the federal government has many scientists studying the nutritive values of food materials, the dietary habits, and the income and spending habits of families in the United States.

Our everyday food habits and our spending habits will determine in an important measure what kind of people future Americans are to be.

CALCIUM — ITS BREAKFAST SOURCES AND ITS EFFECT ON PEOPLE

Breakfast Dishes as Sources *		*What Adequate Calcium Helps Do for Us*	*What a Lack of Calcium Can Do to Us*
Excellent Source	*Good Source*		
Eggs Milk Cream Cheese	Bran Dates Figs Oatmeal	Builds strong bones, well-shaped body, hard teeth that can resist decay	Poor teeth Stunted bones
	Oranges Prunes Raisins Raspberries	Helps the heart, nerves, and muscles to be in trim for their work	Brittle bones Misshapen bones and joints (rickets)
(Vegetables are our other chief source of calcium)	Rhubarb Strawberries	Essential for the complex chemical work of the body fluids	Excessive bleeding when accidents occur
		Necessary for coagulation of blood	Poor dispositions (irritable and nervous)
			Weakened heart and muscles

* For other sources of Calcium see Table X in the Appendix.

The body contains more calcium than any other mineral element. An examination of the above foods shows that they lend themselves to breakfast menus. This meal may go far toward supplying enough calcium to balance body needs.

What of Vitamin A? An examination of the ways of meeting

the need for Vitamin A in the diet shows that we can "kill two birds with one stone."

VITAMIN A: ITS BREAKFAST SOURCES AND ITS EFFECT ON PEOPLE

Breakfast Food Materials as Sources of Vitamin A		*What Vitamin A Helps Do for Us*	*What a Lack of Vitamin A can Do to Us*
Excellent Source	*Good Source*		
Apricots	Bananas	Promotes normal growth	Stunts growth
Butter	Cantaloupe		
Cheese	Kidney		Produce intestinal disorder
Cod liver oil	Milk (whole)	Keeps the membranes of the eyes, mouth, air passages, digestive tract in good health	Causes poor appetite
Cream	Oranges		
Eggs	Peaches		
Liver	Prunes		Lowers resistance to disease
	Tomato juice		
(Yellow and green vegetables are other important sources.)		Makes possible good vision at night	Reduces energy
			Causes poor vision at night, making motoring hazardous — night blindness
		Helps us live longer and healthier lives	

Vitamin B_1 — Whole-Grain Cereals the Best Source. See Tables in Appendix for source and functions of this and other minerals and vitamins.

In the next chapter we shall see that fruit for breakfast offers a major opportunity for meeting the Vitamin C requirement of the body. A person who does not eat a good breakfast has missed a major chance for meeting the body need for nutrients most lacking in American diets — Vitamins A, B_1, C, and calcium.

Note that eggs, milk, cream, cheese, oranges, and prunes supply both calcium and vitamins in substantial amounts. Custom has made all of these, with the possible exception of cheese, staple articles for good breakfasts. Whole-grain cereals, such as oatmeal, would still further fortify the supply of bone and teeth material so much needed by boys and girls who have not yet completed their growth.

CLASS PROBLEMS

1. Check your breakfast habits to see if you are in the large group of Americans who do not get enough calcium and Vitamins

A, B, and C. How should you change your habits at breakfast to include a more adequate supply of these essentials?

2. Have boys and girls in a class write down what they ate for breakfast. Compare the two lists as to the type and quantity of the food. Which group uses breakfast to better advantage?

3. Make out a list of health habits that fit into the day from arising until school time. Score the class accordingly. Encourage the establishment of these habits by all the class.

4. Bring to class a breakfast menu from a hotel. There are usually two kinds of menus: club breakfasts, and breakfasts à la carte. Choose from each of these menus a light, a medium, and a heavy breakfast which will make an excellent contribution to your food needs.

HOME PROBLEMS

1. List the members of your family and for three days record what each one eats for breakfast. Keep the list as a basis for study of balanced meals throughout the breakfast series.
2. Find out what your height and weight should be for your age.
3. Begin now to eat a good breakfast, each day, regularly and leisurely, and have a little spare time before leaving for school.

REFERENCES

Lanman, Faith R., McKay, Hughina, Zuill, Francis. *The Family's Food.* J. B. Lippincott Company. Chapter I.

Rose, Mary Swartz. *Feeding the Family.* The Macmillan Company.

Rose, Mary Swartz. *Foundations of Nutrition.* The Macmillan Company.

Wood, Mildred W., Lindquist, Ruth, and Studley, Lucy A. *Managing the Home.* Houghton Mifflin Company. Pages 221–222.

Bulletins. Bureau of Human Nutrition and Home Economics, United States Department of Agriculture.

CHAPTER FOUR

Fruit For Breakfast

Cook Book References

Table of Measurements	*Page* 388
Directions for Measuring	*Page* 28
Fruits — Ways of Preparing	*Page* 389

Food Value

Nutritive Value of Foods	*Table* VI,	*Appendix*
Food Value in Shares	*Table* VIII,	*Appendix*

FOLLOW NATURE'S SEASONS and not only is variety yours but economy also; for fruits are cheapest when in season, and best of all they are then superior in quality and in food value. In the late spring, or summer, what a variety Nature offers us in berries: strawberries, blackberries, raspberries, and others. In the summer, the list of melons is long. Dried fruits are available throughout the year. From distant places come prunes, figs, dates, raisins, apricots. These lend further variety to our menus when they are cooked with cereals.

How Shall We Have Our Fruit? Fruit is most acceptable when it is clean, fresh, ripe, sound, cold, and, last but not least, attractively served. If we use fruit in season it needs no additional sugar. Nature includes the sugar when the fruit ripens on the trees.

Variety can also be secured by differences in the preparation and serving of fruit. Apples may be used uncooked, baked, or prepared as apple sauce. Oranges may be served in halves, peeled and sliced, in sections with all skin removed, or as juice.

One breakfast table that was greeted with "Ohs" and "Ahs" was set with plain soft blue dishes, a centerpiece of pansies, and, you guessed it, bowls of luscious ripe strawberries at each place. Colorful fruit is prettiest when it appears, as in this case, on simple plain dishes. When fruits are plentiful, a tray of mixed fruits used as an attractive centerpiece for the breakfast table permits each individual to make his own choice.

Many fruit juices, such as peaches or plums, stain linen. Finger bowls and paper napkins should be provided if the fruit is served whole and is to be pared, cut, or sliced at the table.

How Fruits Help to Keep Us Well

Fruits as Appetizers. By their attractive appearance and fragrance and by their appealing flavor, fruits tempt the appetite. Food eaten with relish is digested quickly; the mouth's watering for a food means that the digestive juices are being stimulated. Thus the stomach is ready for food as it is swallowed, and digestion begins at once. The fact that fruit is relished makes it doubly desirable for breakfast, because many appetites need stimulating for the morning meal and there are fewer foods with rich flavors available for breakfast than for other meals. Fresh fruits are more stimulating in flavor than are cooked or dried fruits.

Fruits as Sources of Vitamins. Fruits for breakfast provide an excellent way of including in the diet the much-needed fresh raw food and Vitamin C which must be supplied daily because the body does not store much of it and it is needed constantly. It is necessary for the health of the gums and many other soft tissues in the body. It helps wounds to heal easily and protects against a disease called scurvy. It is especially important in the diet of children because it promotes growth, helps build teeth, and aids resistance to disease. Because it is easily destroyed by the heating, drying, or aging of foods, it is called unstable. For this reason fresh, uncooked fruits or vegetables must be included in the diet daily. A small glass of orange juice, grapefruit juice, tomato juice, or fresh berries in season served at breakfast is a good start toward supplying the daily need for Vitamin C. Grapefruit juice and lemon juice have about the same Vitamin C content as orange juice; tomato juice contains about half as much as orange juice, and pineapple juice contains a fourth to a third as much.

Fruits, in general, are good sources of Vitamins A, B, and C.

Fruits are Laxative. One of the fundamental health rules is a regular bowel movement. Fruit has a most wholesome effect on the intestines. Both the fiber and the acids which fruits contain produce a laxative effect. The fiber in fruits and vegetables is called cellulose. The body does not digest and assimilate cellulose, but it is beneficial because it furnishes needed bulk (sometimes called roughage) which helps in elimination of waste.

Energy Value of Fruits. Fruits vary greatly in the number of calories which they contain, a fact shown by the table below. Dried fruits are no more expensive as a source of energy than butter, milk, or cheap cuts of meat; and fresh fruits, judged on energy alone, are as economical as good cuts of meat.

ONE-HUNDRED-CALORIE PORTIONS OF FRUITS [1]

Apple, fresh, 1 large
Apricots, canned, 3 large halves and 2 tablespoons of juice
Bananas, 1 medium
Blackberries, fresh, 1 cup (50 berries), stewed ¼ cup
Cantaloupe, 1 melon, 5″ diameter
Cherries, stoned, 1 cup
Dates, 3 to 4
Figs, dried, 1½ large
Grapes (Concord), 1 large bunch
Grape juice, ⅔ cup
Lemon juice, 1⅛ cups
Oranges, 1 large
Orange juice, ¾ cup
Peaches, fresh, 2 medium
Peaches, canned or stewed, 2 large halves and 3 tablespoons of juice
Pears, canned, 3 halves and 3 tablespoons of juice
Pears, fresh, 2 medium
Pineapple, canned, 1 slice and 3 tablespoons of juice. Shredded, ¼ cup
Pineapple, fresh (4 half-inch slices)
Plums, fresh, 3 or 4 large
Prunes, 4 medium
Raisins, ¼ cup (seeded)
Raspberries, 1⅛ cups
Strawberries, 1⅓ cups

Mineral Content of Fruits. All fruits contain some minerals. The mineral content of fruits vies in importance with their Vitamin C content. In fact, milk, fruits, vegetables, and meat are our chief sources of these substances.

A diet sufficient in calories may not be adequate in minerals. There are at least three minerals needed by the body that must be consciously included in our daily meals. These are iron, calcium, and phosphorus. Extremely small amounts of copper, iodine, and a few other elements are also essential. Most fruits contain some iron. Peaches, apricots, strawberries, pineapple, oranges, and grapefruit are regarded as fair sources of iron. The pulp as well as the juice of fruits should be eaten because it contains a large part of the iron. Oranges, grapefruit, and figs are sources of fair amounts of calcium. Phosphorus also is well distributed in fruits. Small amounts of copper, which is important in helping the body to make use of the iron in food, occur in many fruits.

Dried Fruits. At first, fruit was dried in order to save the sur-

[1] M. S. Rose. *Laboratory Handbook for Dietetics.* The Macmillan Company.

plus crop, but now drying fruit is an industry by itself. In California large orchards are planted for the sole purpose of procuring fruit for drying. Fruit may be either sun-dried or artificially dried.

Because dried fruit contains much sugar, it has good fuel or energy value. It contains the good qualities of fresh fruit, except for Vitamin C, which may be wholly or partially destroyed in drying. Because of their concentration, dried fruits are particularly good sources of iron, calcium, and phosphorus. However, care should be taken in the preparation of dried fruit to prevent the loss of minerals, which are soluble in water. The water in which the fruit is soaked should be mostly absorbed by the fruit in cooking. The remaining juice should be served with the fruit.

Canned Fruits. The canning of fruits is also an important industry. Peach canning in California and pineapple canning in the Hawaiian Islands are two of the principal industries of this kind. Apricots, pears, cherries, and berries are also canned on a large scale. Acid fruits retain their Vitamin C very well in the canning process. If a fruit was a good source when raw, it is likely to be a good source when canned.

Canned fruit is also often less expensive than fresh fruit, especially when fresh fruit is not at the height of its season. If you have the choice, buy fruit that has been canned without added sugar, because the flavor is sometimes hidden by the excessive amounts of sugar used in some canning. It is easy to add sugar if it is needed when the canned fruit is served.

Is Fruit a Luxury? As sources of fuel, fresh fruits cannot be considered so economical as some other foods, such as grain products, but when fresh fruits are in season they are not so expensive as is often supposed. Dried fruits are cheap sources of fuel. As sources of protective and regulatory substances fresh fruits are necessities rather than luxuries.

Buying and Caring for Fruit

There are many kinds of fruit buyers. As consumers we should be polite and co-operative. It is not co-operative to pinch and poke fruit, because fruit is easily bruised and when bruised it spoils quickly, resulting in a loss to the retailer, or to another customer who may unknowingly buy it.

Selecting and Buying Fresh Fruit. Buy fruit in season. Buy and use fresh fruit as freely as your purse will allow. The purse will allow more when fruit is bought in season. It is usually cheaper at this time and the quality is usually superior, especially in the early part of the season when the supply just reaches its height. Notice in the Fresh Fruit Calendar when this occurs in the United States as a whole and compare this general condition with conditions in your locality.

FRESH FRUIT CALENDAR

Showing months in which, in United States generally, quality of fresh fruits is usually excellent and price is low. The italic type indicates usual time of largest supply.

	Jan.	*Feb.*	*Mar.*	*Apr.*	*May*	*June*	*July*	*Aug.*	*Sept.*	*Oct.*	*Nov.*	*Dec.*
Apples.........	*X*	*X*	*X*	X	X		X	X	X	*X*	*X*	X
Bananas........	X	X	X	*X*	*X*	*X*	X	X	X	X	X	X
Blackberries.....						*X*	*X*					
Cantaloupes.....						X	X	*X*	X	X		
Cherries........					X	*X*	*X*					
Cranberries.....										X	*X*	X
Currants........						X	*X*					
Gooseberries....						*X*	*X*					
Grapefruit......	*X*	*X*	*X*	*X*	*X*					X	X	X
Figs...........						X	X	*X*	X	X		
Grapes.........									X	*X*	X	
Lemons.........	X	X	X	*X*	*X*	*X*	X	X			X	X
Oranges........	*X*	*X*	*X*	*X*	*X*	X	X	X	X	X	*X*	*X*
Peaches.........					X	*X*	X	X				
Pears...........							X	*X*	*X*	X	X	
Pineapples......				X	*X*	X	X					
Plums..........							*X*					
Raspberries.....					X	X	*X*	X				
Rhubarb........				X	*X*	*X*	X					
Strawberries.....					*X*	*X*						
Tomatoes *.....						X	X	*X*	X			
Watermelon.....						X	*X*	X				

* Tomatoes are included in this fruit calendar and also in the vegetable calendar, page 295, because they have a similar nutritive value to citrus fruits, and are often served as a fruit. Farm families may well preserve tomato juice to use instead of citrus fruit for breakfast.

Select sound, ripe fruit, but if it is to be kept for a while, buy it slightly underripe. Brightness of color, fragrance, and plumpness are usual characteristics of ripe fruit. Avoid fruit at or near the overripe stage.

Buy in Quantity for Lower Prices. Because there is often a great variation in the price per pound of fresh fruit bought in small and in large quantities, buy in large quantity, that is, by the box or bushel, when there is sufficient difference in price and when storage space at a satisfactory temperature is available. Weight is a more reliable measure than size of container because sizes and shapes are deceptive. Those who buy in quantity should know the approximate weight of a bushel of the fruit in order to judge its cost per pound. Legal requirements vary in different states; write your state department of agriculture for the legal weights in your state.

Citrus fruits are sold by sizes according to the number that are packed in a box. Orange sizes range from very large or 80's to very small or 324's; medium sizes are from 150's to 216's, about 2¾ inches in diameter. Grapefruit sizes range from 28's to 80's, a medium size being 64's or about 4½ inches in diameter. Lemon sizes range from 240's to 490's, medium sizes being 360's to 420's.

Buying by Grades. Buy by grade when you have the opportunity. Grades, if used, are stamped on boxes, barrels, or bushel baskets, but not on smaller containers or on the fruit itself. More definite information about the exact grades may be obtained by writing the Agricultural Marketing Service, United States Department of Agriculture, Washington, D.C., and asking for a copy of the definitions of grades of each fruit in which you are interested.

Buying Individual Fruits. Apples should, when fully mature, have rather firm flesh and bright skin. Different varieties have distinctive flavors. Apples may be bought by grades. When buying apples in quantity, sample one or two to get flavor and quality you desire. Juicy apples are to be preferred to mealy ones for eating apples. A tart, firm apple is to be preferred for baking.

Bananas when fully mature are firm and have small brown flecks. Avoid thin, withered, or very soft bananas.

Berries should be bright and firm, plump, and of good color for the variety. Avoid any that are dull or soft, or that are leaking or have stained the containers, or show any mold. Buy as near the time of use as possible.

Cantaloupes when ripe have a soft blossom end. If veined, whitish veins indicate ripeness. If the stem scar is smooth, clean, and cup-shaped, with no stem adhering to the melon, the fruit was pulled when fully ripe. A fragrant odor indicates ripeness; if too pronounced, it indicates overripeness.

Citrus fruits should in general seem heavy for their size, have fine-textured and thin skins. Firmness is a desirable quality, except that grapefruit should also be springy to the touch. Most varieties should have smooth skins. Grapefruit pointed at one end is usually thick-skinned. Russet or brown-skinned grapefruit is good in flavor and often low in price.

Grapes should have a fresh appearance, be plump, have high color for the variety, and be firmly attached to stems. Avoid a dull, sticky look, a milky appearance, shriveled, wet, or moldy grapes. Avoid those that have stained their containers.

Peaches when fully ripe have very good color and are firm. Be suspicious of softness, avoid fruit with "pin-sized" dark spots as indication of worm infestation, and fruit with small spots.

Pears should not be judged by color, but should be firm, not hard, and free from blemish. Storage-ripened pears have finer-textured skins than tree-ripened pears. Avoid wilted or shriveled pears. When soft to the touch at the base of stem, pears are ready to eat and will not keep.

Caring for Fruit at Home. All fully ripe fruits (except bananas, citrus fruit, and apples) keep best in a very cold place, such as a refrigerator. Apples, citrus fruit, and bananas should be kept in a cool place in a vegetable rack or similar place where air will circulate well around them. Inspect them frequently to remove any that are beginning to spoil. Place in the refrigerator long enough to chill for serving. Keep underripe fruit as apples and oranges are kept.

Guard against spray residue on fresh fruits by discarding the parts on which the residue is most likely to have collected. The stem and blossom ends should be carefully cut out and discarded. You can easily see the gray or possibly light-green deposit that indicates a residue of the poisonous spray that has been used to keep the fruit free from insects. As a matter of fact, it is desirable to discard the entire skin as well as the stem and blossom ends of fruits that may have been treated with poisonous sprays.

See Chapter 26 for Buying Canned Fruits.

Preparing and Serving Fruit for Breakfast. The first rule in preparing fruit for the table is to wash it thoroughly and remove all spray residue. Care must be taken not to bruise it, because if cut or bruised it will spoil quickly. Only fruit which is sound, ripe, and fresh should be served uncooked. Sugar is not needed with thoroughly ripe fruit. One of the most common faults of American diets is too much sugar. Learn to eat fruits without adding sugar.

If fruit knives, paper napkins, and finger bowls are used, fresh fruit may be prepared at the table. Usually it is prepared in the kitchen and is on the table in individual servings when breakfast begins. Fruit was formerly eaten as a first course, but now it is often placed on the table with the breakfast and eaten at the time which each individual prefers.

Care must be taken in preparing and serving fresh fruits to make available the maximum Vitamin C content. Vitamin C in fresh fruits is destroyed by storage, by exposure to air, as when cut, and upon thawing of frozen foods. Based on these facts the following precautions in the preparation of fresh fruit will save Vitamin C:

1. Serve fruits raw when possible.
2. Prepare cut or chopped fruit for breakfast, or for salads, just before serving.
3. Serve frozen fruit immediately after thawing or before it is entirely thawed.
4. Prepare orange and grapefruit juice just before serving.

Oranges are served sliced, in the half skin with the sections loosened, in sections, and as orange juice. Grapefruit is served in the half skin with the pulp cut loose from the bitter, white part of the skin and from the tough sectional divisions. Grapefruit is also served in sections. Sometimes the juice is used for a drink.

Apples served raw may be peeled at the table. Baked apples, stewed apples, and apple sauce, are also served for breakfast. Pears are served either raw, baked, or stewed.

Bananas are often sliced and eaten with milk or cream and with sugar. They should not be prepared until it is time to serve them, because they darken if allowed to stand, and they lose some Vitamin C. Bananas are served with dry prepared cereals.

Berries should be washed thoroughly immediately before serving and care taken to avoid mashing them. They are served with milk or cream (and sugar), or they may be combined with dry prepared cereals and served with milk or cream (and sugar).

Cantaloupes and similar melons such as casaba and honeydew are chilled and served sliced or in half, according to the size of the melon. They may be eaten with salt and pepper; often a little lemon juice is squeezed over them.

Peaches and apricots are usually served raw and sliced, with milk or cream. They should be prepared immediately before serving. Peaches may also be served with dry cereals.

Cherries, plums, and grapes are usually chilled, thoroughly washed, and served on individual plates.

Fresh pineapple is peeled and sliced or diced. In countries where the pineapple is a native fruit, it is luscious, sweet, and juicy. Ripe pineapple does not ship well. The pineapple in our markets is improved when prepared with a little sugar.

Fresh figs, a delicious fruit grown in the southern part of the United States, keep so poorly that they are not shipped long distances. They do not resemble dried figs any more than grapes resemble raisins. For breakfast, they are peeled and served with milk or cream. Little or no sugar is added, because the fruit is very sweet when ripe. They are also served with dry cereals.

Canned fruits are not so popular as fresh fruit for breakfast, but they may be used at that meal.

Prunes are the most popular dried fruit used for breakfast. They are usually cooked in the water in which they have been soaked, slightly sweetened, and served either with the resulting sirup, or with milk or cream.

Dried peaches, apricots, and apples are usually stewed. Although they may be served for breakfast, they are more frequently used for luncheon and supper as a simple sweet. Dried figs, raisins, and dates are often steamed and served with cooked cereals.

Cooking of Fresh Fruit. Fruit should always be washed before it is cooked. In preparing apples or pears for cooking, peel to remove the spray residue. If the peel is used, wash the fruit thoroughly; then remove and discard the stem and blossom ends.

Fruit is cooked to soften the cellulose. Cooking is sometimes necessary when fruits are prepared for children, invalids, or convalescents. For very young children cooking does not soften the fiber enough, therefore the cooked fruit is pressed through a strainer or cheesecloth. Straining should be done when cold.

If fruit is overripe, cooking it will stop fermentation.

Cooking increases the ways in which fruit may be served.

It is especially important to save as much of the vitamins and minerals as possible when cooking fruits. Desirable practices are:

1. Because Vitamin C is destroyed by exposure to air, especially when hot, do not strain fruit pulp, such as apple sauce, until cold.

2. Because long slow cooking destroys Vitamin C, cook fresh fruits quickly rather than "stewing" them slowly.

3. Because most of the vitamins and minerals are soluble in water, use as little water as possible and use the "juice."

4. Because frying is most destructive of Vitamins A, B, and C, avoid this method of cooking fruit.

5. After fruit is pared or sliced, it should be cooked at once.

Cooking of Dried Fruit:

1. Carefully inspect dried fruit for insects.
2. Wash it well through several waters.
3. Soak in water until plump. It may be heated slightly to decrease time needed for cooking. The soaking time varies with the kind and quality of fruit from 30 minutes to several hours.
4. Cook it in a covered vessel until it is tender, using the water in which the fruit was soaked. Some dried fruits (raisins, prunes, figs, dates, currants) are steamed in a double boiler.

The Addition of Sugar to Cooked Fruit. In cooking fruit the use of sugar retards the softening of the fiber; hence sugar may be used, with care, to prevent fruit from cooking to pieces. In such cases sugar may be added to the fruit, or it may be cooked in a sugar sirup. In baking and preserving fruits, especially watery varieties, sugar is used to help keep the shape of the fruit.

When sugar is used merely for sweetening, as in the case of prunes, it is added last in order not to delay the cooking process.

Finding Other Information About Fruits

This book and many other books contain much more information on fruits. How would you locate this information?

Three of the most serviceable portions of this or any other book are: Table of Contents, Appendix, and Index. Turn to the front of the book and examine the Table of Contents so that you may be familiar with the organization of the book.

How to Use the Appendix. The Appendix is supplementary material included as a handy reference. Consult the Table of Contents to see the useful collection of tables included in the Appendix of *Everyday Foods.*

This is a good time to learn to use the Appendix. Suppose you wish to know the food value of an average serving of fruits. The Table of Contents lists Table VI, Nutritive Value of Foods, pages 589–599. When you turn to the table, you see that it is alphabetically arranged. Because it is, your first step is to make an alphabetical list of the fruits in which you are interested. Then find those fruits in the table.

You can often use a table such as Table VI to help you solve a very practical problem. You might want to know, for instance, whether putting sliced bananas on your breakfast cereal furnished you with the same amounts of Vitamins A and C as drinking orange juice. Table VI gives the values for three fourths of a cup of sliced bananas and one half cup of orange juice. If these amounts are similar to the quantities you ordinarily take, you can compare the figures given; if the amounts differ, you must make an adjustment. For the same weight (100 grams), you find that bananas supply more Vitamin A than orange juice, and that orange juice supplies more Vitamin C than bananas.

How to Use the Index. The Index is a guide to all the material in a book organized by topics. The most useful part of this or any other text or reference book is the Index. Now is a good time to learn to use the Index. Suppose you wish to locate all other information about fruits in *Everyday Foods.* You look up the word "Fruit" in the Index, which is alphabetically arranged. If you wish to locate recipes or information concerning a particular fruit, you look in the Index for page references listed under that special fruit — say, pineapple, peach, cranberry, and so on.

Or suppose that you want to learn about frozen fruits. You may want to know how to buy them, how to thaw them, and how to use them. You may want to know how you yourself can proceed to freeze fresh fruits. What equipment do you need? Where can you store the results of your labors? You may be interested in finding out whether frozen fruits have the same nutritive value as fresh fruits. You can find all the discussions of frozen fruits in *Everyday Foods* by using the Index. You will save time and frayed nerves if you learn to use an Index efficiently.

CLASS PROBLEMS

1. What fruits are available in your local market now? (*a*) Fresh; (*b*) Dried; (*c*) Frozen?
2. Study one fresh fruit, one dried fruit, and one frozen fruit (if available) as to price variations based on (*a*) quality, (*b*) quantity, (*c*) kind of store, (*d*) packaging, (*e*) season, (*f*) transportation.
3. On the basis of the price and commodity study in Problem 2, formulate some general rules for purchasing fruit for your family.
4. Compile a fresh fruit calendar for your locality, showing the fruits in season each month in the year. During the year revise this list and put in new prices as the seasons change.
5. List the dried fruits available in your market. Compare the prices and discuss the relative merits of dried fruit in bulk and in packages.
6. Make a class excursion to the market to study buying fruits.
7. Each member of the class may keep a record for a week of the fruit eaten. Check the occurrence of vitamins, and iron, phosphorus, and calcium. (See Tables IX and X in the Appendix.)
8. For a family of six, compute the cost of fruit for a week under the following conditions:
   (1) A fresh fruit that is in season locally.
   (2) A fresh fruit out of season locally but in the local market.
   (3) A dried fruit.
9. Exhibit one-hundred-calorie portions of all available fruits, both fresh and dried. Make a comparison of the cost of each.
10. Plan a series of breakfasts in which the only thing varied is the fruit.

Prepare three breakfast menus: (1) using a fresh fruit, (2) using a dried fruit, (3) using a cooked fresh fruit.

Make a work plan that will insure the maximum of Vitamin C, and minerals in each case.

HOME PROBLEMS

1. Do you live in a town? Purchase for a week the fruit used by your family.
2. If you live on a farm, plan ways in which your family could have fruit the year round from the farm.
3. Procure from your grocer the prices of fresh and dried fruits.

4. Plan for a week the breakfast fruit for your family. Compare the costs of fresh and dried fruits for these breakfasts.
5. Keep an account of the fruit that the various members of your family eat in a week. Should your family spend more for fruit? Why?
6. Prepare the fruit for your family's breakfast for a week.

REFERENCES

Chaney, Margaret S., and Ahlborn, Margaret. *Nutrition.* Houghton Mifflin Company.

Consumers' Guide. A publication dealing with current food problems. Consumers' Council Division, Agricultural Adjustment Administration, Washington, D.C.

Council on Foods of the American Medical Association. *Accepted Foods and Their Nutritional Significance.* American Medical Association, Chicago, 1939. Sections III and IV.

Food and Life. United States Department of Agriculture, *Yearbook*, 1939.

Heseltine, Marjorie, and Dow, Ula M. *The Basic Cook Book.* Houghton Mifflin Company.

Justin, Margaret M., Rust, Lucile O., and Vail, Gladys E. *Foods.* Houghton Mifflin Company.

Proximate Composition of Fresh Fruits. United States Department of Agriculture, Circular 50.

Rose, Mary Swartz. *Feeding the Family.* The Macmillan Company.

Sherman, Henry C. *Food Products.* The Macmillan Company. Chapters I and X.

Stanley, Louise, and Cline, Jessie Alice. *Foods.* Ginn and Company. Pages 73, 77, and 85–91.

Stewart, Jean J. *Foods: Production, Marketing, Consumption.* Prentice-Hall. Chapter IV, pages 197–215.

Todoroff, A. *The Handbook of Food Selling.* The Grocery Trade Publishing House, Chicago, 1936. Sections 1, 7, 9, and 16.

CHAPTER FIVE

❧ Milk

Cook Book References

Chocolate and Cocoa	*Page* 393
Milk Toast	*Page* 402
White Sauce	*Page* 436

Food Value

Nutritive Value of Foods	*Table* VI, *Appendix*
Food Value in Shares	*Table* VIII, *Appendix*

MILK IS FOOD number one for balancing the diet because it contributes more to good nutrition than does any other food. There is no one food, however, that contains everything the body needs and in the right proportions. This fact is a wise provision of Nature, for human beings thrive on variety and are bored by monotony. It is also a wise provision of Nature that milk and a few other foods supply abundantly much of the food materials needed daily. Therefore if we are careful to provide the regular amount of milk and of these several other foods needed for maintaining good health, we may enjoy variety by choosing the rest of our foods with a good deal of liberty. The abundant use of milk is one way in which a housewife can save work and worry in planning well-balanced meals. Milk will cover a multitude of sins of omission in the dietary. So important is it in the diet that nutritionists advise a quart daily until we are grown and after that a pint. It is not necessary to drink a quart per day; there are many ways of adding it to the day's food.

Ways of Using Milk and Milk Products for Breakfast. Breakfast is an excellent opportunity for all members of the family to make a good beginning on the day's quota of milk. All the growing members of the family should drink a glass of whole milk for breakfast in order to start the day right. Grownups may prefer coffee, but they will surely want cream, a good way to include part of the day's quota of Vitamin A. Of course cream is not all fat; it contains some milk. Since adults do not need as much milk as growing people do, this distribution of breakfast beverages is satisfactory for all.

In cold weather the entire family, except the infant member, may like a hot beverage; then cocoa made with whole milk would suit the taste of the most exacting and would fill the nutritional bill too.

SUGGESTED WAYS OF USING MILK AND MILK PRODUCTS FOR BREAKFAST

Beverage	*Cereals*	*Breads*	*Other Dishes*
Whole milk Cocoa Coffee with cream or hot milk (for adults)	Top milk or whole milk served with: Cooked cereals Prepared cereals Cereal cooked in milk	Milk toast Breads made with milk: Bread for toast Muffins Popovers Griddle cakes Biscuit	On fruit Baked apple Bananas Creamed dishes: Eggs Dried beef Fish flakes

Since time is a factor in preparing breakfast in most homes, the simpler the preparation of breakfast the better. For this reason the best way of using milk for breakfast is as a beverage or with cereals, leaving the uses that require cooking for the occasional breakfast.

Composition of Milk

Milk varies in composition according to the cow, the season, and the feeding. Most of us do not use the milk of one cow, but are supplied from the mixed milk of a herd. The average composition of such milk is:

Water	Protein	Carbohydrates
87%	3.3%	5%
Fat	**Minerals**	**Vitamins**
4%	.7%	A, B, G

Is Milk Fattening? Look at the average proportion of water in the composition given above;

FIG. 19. MILK IS A FIRST STEP TO HEALTH

87 per cent is almost nine tenths, isn't it? Do you think such a watery food could rightly be called fattening? Milk is included even in reducing diets. Percentage of fat and carbohydrate does not tell the whole story of the food value of milk or any other food; it bears further inspection. Why is it accorded such an all-important place in the diet of young and old?

Protein in Milk (3.3 per cent). Protein is needed by the body, both for repair and for growth. Milk is a cheap and important source of protein. The term protein designates a class of substances that differ somewhat in their properties. We may think of protein as the family or surname of these substances; "given names" of some of the protein family are: albumin in egg; legumin in beans; myosin in meat; gliadin and glutenin in wheat; lactalbumin and casein in milk.

That milk proteins are complete proteins is not surprising when it is remembered that Nature has provided milk as the sole food for young animals during the period of their most rapid growth. Milk proteins are those most readily made use of by the body at all ages.

Fat in Milk (4 per cent). The fat of milk is a very easily digested fat, because it is very finely divided and has a low melting point. The fat of milk also contains Vitamin A in solution.

Carbohydrates (5 per cent). Lactose, or milk sugar, is the carbohydrate in milk. It is not very sweet. When lactose ferments it changes to lactic acid, which may be beneficial in checking the growth of certain putrefactive bacteria; that is, bacteria that produce decay. These bacteria often cause intestinal disorders.

Minerals (.7 per cent). Milk is rich in two of the three minerals most needed by the body. It is the cheapest and most abundant source of calcium, which is much needed by the blood, bones, and teeth. The calcium content alone entitles milk to an important place in the diet, especially the diet of children and growing boys and girls. The fact that American diets are dangerously short of calcium means that the addition of more milk to the diet is usually the wisest first step in balancing the diet.

Milk contains less phosphorus than calcium, but in a daily quart of milk there is a sufficient supply of this important mineral for a high-school girl or boy.

Iron is not abundant in milk. Although there is already stored in the bodies of babies at birth a large supply of iron, it is necessary before the end of the first year to supplement the iron supplied by milk with some such foods as egg yolk and green-leaf vegetables, which are foods rich in iron.

Vitamins in Milk. Whole milk is one of the most important protective foods. Of the six vitamins known to be needed by human beings five occur in milk in important quantities. No food is an excellent source of all six of these vitamins (A, B, C, D, E, and G). Milk is unique among foods in vitamin content. It is an excellent source of Vitamins A and G, and a good source of Vitamin B_1.

Vitamin A. Milk is one of our best sources of Vitamin A. This vitamin is found in the fat of milk. Butter, cream, and cheese, made from whole milk, are therefore also excellent sources for Vitamin A. The amount of Vitamin A varies somewhat with the diet of the cow. When fresh green grass or a well-balanced ration is available for dairy cows, the Vitamin A content of the milk is increased. Vitamin A can be stored by the body to tide it over a shortage, but it is safest to provide this important growth-promoting, regulatory, and protective substance constantly and generously by drinking milk regularly.

Vitamin G (Riboflavin). Milk is one of the valuable sources of Vitamin G which promotes health and well-being at all ages. Because this vitamin is not destroyed by heat or storage, skim milk, dried milk, buttermilk, cooked milk, canned milk, and cheese are as good sources of Vitamin G as fresh milk.

Vitamin B_1 (Thiamin). Milk is a fair, though not a rich source of Vitamin B_1. If milk is taken in generous amounts, it makes a significant contribution of Vitamin B_1. We leave to other foods the chief responsibility of supplying Vitamin B_1; whole grain cereals are an excellent source.

Vitamin C. Raw milk contains only a small amount of this very necessary vitamin and even this small amount is destroyed during pasteurization. It is not safe to count on milk as a source of Vitamin C.

Vitamin D. Milk is not an adequate source of Vitamin D, but it is possible to add Vitamin D to milk. This addition is important in infant and child feeding. Three kinds of Vitamin D milk are now on the market in many places: fortified milk which has cod liver oil or other forms of Vitamin D added; irradiated milk which is produced by submitting milk to the effects of ultraviolet light; and metabolized milk which is produced by feeding cows irradiated yeast. Irradiated evaporated milk is also valuable.

If Vitamin D milk is not available during infancy and early childhood, milk needs to be supplemented with foods rich in Vitamin D, such as cod liver (also halibut liver) oil. Because the body can make its own Vitamin D if it is exposed to sunlight, the need for using Vitamin D milk is greater in winter and in localities where sunlight is scarce.

Fuel or Energy Value. A quart of milk contains 675 calories and is equal in energy value to a pound of steak, or eight or nine eggs.

ONE-HUNDRED-CALORIE PORTIONS OF MILK AND ITS PRODUCTS

Whole milk, 5/8 cup	Butter, 1 tablespoon
Skim milk, 1 1/8 cups	Thin cream, 1/4 cup
Buttermilk, 1 1/8 cups	Thick cream, 1 1/3 tablespoons
	Whipped cream, 2 tablespoons

Buying and Using Milk Products

Skim Milk and Buttermilk. Both these forms of milk have all the food value of milk except that which occurs in the fat. Vitamins A and D are dissolved in the fat. Whey contains some of the food value of milk. The fat and some of the protein have been removed from it, leaving water, carbohydrate, whey protein, minerals, and water soluble vitamins (B_1 and G).

Cream. Cream contains from twenty per cent fat (in coffee cream) to forty per cent (in whipping cream) and is rich in Vitamin A. It also contains a small amount of the other constituents of milk.

Cheese. When cheese is made from whole milk it contains the fat and protein of milk and has all the food value of these. (See Chapter 17.)

Canned Milk. Unsweetened and sweetened milk can both be obtained in cans.

Evaporated milk,[1] also called "unsweetened evaporated milk," is whole milk, twice as concentrated as ordinary milk. Nothing has been added to the natural cow's milk from which it is prepared and nothing taken away except water, approximately 60 per cent of which has been removed by evaporation. It has been sterilized so that it is free from any bacteria.

Sweetened condensed milk,[1] also sometimes called "condensed milk," is just as concentrated as is evaporated milk, but it differs

[1] *Some Facts About Evaporated Milk and Other Dairy Products.* Evaporated Milk Association.

from evaporated milk in that it contains cane sugar which is added to preserve it.

Dried Milk. Made from either skim milk or whole milk, dried milk is a convenient form in which to buy milk. Dried whole milk is an important food. It retains all of the food value of milk with the possible exception of Vitamin C. Dried whole milk is now available in sealed containers. It should be kept tightly covered. Because the fat after a time becomes rancid, dried skim milk keeps better. Dried skim milk is recommended if good fresh milk or refrigeration is not available. It makes all the contributions to nutrition that fresh skim milk does except for fat and Vitamin A.

To use dried skim milk as a liquid, add 1/4 cup powdered milk to 1 cup of water. For dried whole milk, use 1/3 cup of milk powder to 7/8 cup of water (1 cup with 2 tablespoons dipped out).

Dried milk is usually the most economical form in which to buy milk, and evaporated usually is next. Compare the prices in your locality. Dried milk may usually be obtained at grocery stores and at bakeries, and evaporated milk is sold in both of these and in many other shops as well. Evaporated milk diluted with an equal volume of water can be used in any recipe in place of ordinary milk. Some recipes, especially for candy and cookies, written especially for evaporated milk, are planned to use the evaporated milk just as it comes from the can. It is important to read a recipe carefully to see which was intended. Dried milk may be used as a substitute for part of the flour in many mixtures by taking out up to one fourth of the flour and substituting an equal quantity of dried milk. When it is used as part of the dry ingredients, one extra tablespoon of water should be used for each one-fourth cup of powdered milk used.

Malted Milk. Malted barley wheat flour as well as milk in the dry form are contained in malted milk.

Butter. High fuel value and rich Vitamin A content make butter an important food. Butter is valuable also for its flavor. It is sold both by brands and by grades. The United States Department of Agriculture has set up standards for grading butter. The four table grades are AA, A, B, and C. Look for these grades on the butter you use.

Comparative Food Values. Equivalents in food value to one quart of fluid milk, are: 17 oz. (or about one pint) evaporated milk; one qt. skim milk with 1 1/2 oz. butter; 5 oz. yellow American cheese;

4½ oz. dried whole milk; 3½ oz. dried skim milk with 1½ oz. butter.

Milk Cookery. The most obvious effect of cooking on milk is the formation of a skim on the top. This is largely fat and protein. It should not be discarded because it contains valuable nutrients. Since milk scorches easily, it is usually cooked in a double boiler. The taste of milk is altered by cooking.

Boiling makes milk safer and more digestible by producing a flocculent curd during digestion rather than a hard mass.

The best way for the consumer to buy milk is in bottles with tight-fitting caps. The type of cap that fits down around the sides of the rim is especially sanitary. Bottled milk can be kept both clean and cool during delivery more easily than loose or bulk milk which is transported in large cans and dipped out into another container when purchased. Dipped milk is a hazard to health because of the numerous chances for contamination during handling. Also, it may be deficient in cream.[1]

Rules for Care of Milk in the Home. Milk should be kept clean, covered, and cool. Store milk produced at home in sterilized bottles.

As soon as milk is delivered, put it in the coldest part of the refrigerator. Milk, butter, cream, and milk dishes should be kept at a temperature of 45 degrees Farenheit or below.

Wash the mouth of the milk bottle before pouring the milk. Keep milk in the bottle until it is used.

Do not mix new and old milk. Why?

The refrigerator should always be kept scrupulously clean.

Milk and butter absorb odors readily. Do not put them in contact with foods of strong odor. Always keep them covered.

Safeguarding Milk

Importance of Clean Milk. Only clean milk is safe to use. If carefully handled, milk is a safe food, but if carelessly handled it may be dangerous to health. Bacteria multiply very rapidly in warm milk. In order to avoid the presence of an undesirable number and undesirable kinds of bacteria, the following precautions must be taken:

Bacteria and dirt which carries bacteria must be kept out of milk. This means that the cows should be healthy and clean when milked,

[1] *Milk for the Family.* United States Department of Agriculture, Farmers' Bulletin 1705.

workers should be healthy and clean in person and in clothes, utensils should be sterilized just before using.

Disease bacteria should be destroyed. Cows, even if they seem healthy, could be the source of germs of tuberculosis and undulant fever in milk. It has been found that a temperature of 143.5 degrees F. will destroy these germs and other disease germs if the temperature is continued for 30 minutes. When this is done, it is called *pasteurization* in honor of Louis Pasteur, a French scientist who was the first to discover that disease could be prevented by destroying bacteria with heat. This pasteurization method destroys disease bacteria, but does not destroy others that are found in milk. It does not prevent the souring of milk, which is produced by useful bacteria normally occurring in milk.

Growth of bacteria in milk should be retarded. For this reason it is important to cool milk below 50 degrees F. as rapidly as possible, and to keep it cold.

Milk Regulations. Milk supplies must be carefully regulated. Cities and states regulate both the quality and cleanliness of the milk sold within their borders. Over 800 cities and over 30 states have adopted the Standard Milk Ordinance. This is a set of regulations worked out by many doctors, public health workers, sanitary engineers, and other experts, and is sponsored by the United States Public Health Service in the Federal Security Administration. Regulations cover quality of the milk, the care of cows, health and cleanliness of the workers, rooms, and equipment for handling milk, method of pasteurizing, and other handling of milk. They also define grades of milk. You should be able to obtain a copy of this ordinance and of your state's regulations concerning milk from the State Board of Health or the Board of Health in the nearest city.

Regulations concerning quality usually specify 3 or 3.25 per cent of milk fat and about 8.5 per cent of other solids-not-fat. This requirement makes it possible for milk to have a little more than 87 per cent of water, but both skimming and watering of milk sold as whole milk are prohibited.

Ratings of Cities on the Basis of Milk Sanitation. An effective method of encouraging excellence of milk supplies is the rating of cities according to the type of control they exercise on milk. Those having excellent control work are listed in *Milk Sanitation Ratings of Cities*, published semiannually by the United States Public

Health Service and obtainable from the Government Printing Office, Washington, D.C.

Home Production of Milk. Milk is an important item which the farm home can and should have from the farm. Although about 70 per cent of the farms have one or more milk cows, many farm families would have improved diets if in the farm plans, more milk for the farm family could be provided. A farm family without an adequate supply of milk is like the proverbial shoemaker's children without shoes. Milk produced at home for home use should be just as carefully handled as milk that is sold to others. Since diseases, such as tuberculosis or undulant fever, may come from the cow, the farm animals should be tested. The cow's stall should be clean. All cleaning of the stable should be done with a stream of water rather than a dry brush or broom to avoid scattering dust in the air. The cow's udder should be washed before milking; the milker should be healthy, clean, wear clean clothes, and wash his hands carefully just before milking. The utensils should be sterilized with boiling water before use. The milk should be pasteurized, cooled quickly to a temperature below 50 degrees F. and kept in clean covered containers in a cool dark place until used, because sunlight produces undesirable changes in the flavor of milk. After use, the utensils should be washed thoroughly and sterilized.

Some doctors recommend boiling any milk for infant feeding. If the milk is of uncertain purity for any reason, it should be heated as soon as possible after it is received, then cooled quickly and refrigerated at 45 degrees F.

Home Methods for Reducing Bacteria in Milk. Three methods are suggested:

1. *Boiling.* Put the milk into a large kettle directly over the heat. Bring quickly to the boiling point (stirring occasionally), and boil for one minute. Boiled milk tastes slightly different, and contains some coagulated material which should be used, since it contains some of the nutrients of the milk.

2. Heat in a double boiler which has twice the capacity of the milk to be heated. The water should touch the bottom of the top part of the double boiler. Cook with the water boiling for eight minutes. This is not as safe a method as boiling, but there is less change in the flavor of the milk.

3. *Home and Commercial Pasteurization of Milk.* In milk-processing plants the milk should be heated in a closed vat to 143.5

degrees F. and held at this point for 30 minutes, then cooled quickly. For the home the recommended pasteurization temperature is 155 degrees F. The milk is stirred constantly as it is heated, then after it reaches 155 degrees this pan is set immediately in cold water and stirring continued until the milk is cool. An aluminum vessel is recommended because it can be cooled quickly. Glass and enamelware, but not tin, may be used.

CLASS PROBLEMS

1. Find out your city and state regulations concerning the production and handling of milk.
2. Procure bulletins on the value of milk in the diet. Suggested sources: (1) State Health Department; (2) State Agricultural College; (3) Children's Bureau, United States Department of Labor, Washington, D.C.; (4) Bureau of Human Nutrition and Home Economics, United States Department of Agriculture, Washington, D.C.; (5) National Dairy Council.
3. Visit several stores to see how milk is handled; also, find out what kinds of milk are available and at what price.
4. Visit a dairy or a creamery.
5. Plan seven breakfasts rich in Vitamin C, Vitamin A, and calcium.
6. Get acquainted with evaporated and dried milk. Examine these products. Compare in price and in flavor. Make cocoa of each and compare.
7. Can you plan several ways to include needed milk in the diet for a person who will not drink milk?
8. How much milk will be needed for a week for a family consisting of mother, father, and three growing children?
9. What will this milk cost if it is fresh whole milk? If dried whole milk? If evaporated milk?

HOME PROBLEMS

1. List all of the dishes containing milk prepared at your house for three days.
2. Make a list of ways in which the use of milk might be increased by your family through breakfasts.
3. How much milk does each member of your family obtain daily? If you do not use your daily quart, make an effort to acquire this habit.

4. If you have a younger sister or brother who does not like milk, try to plan the menus in such a way that the child will get a quart of milk daily. Try to teach the child to like milk.
5. Make milk toast several times for breakfast.
6. Prepare white sauce to use with creamed eggs for breakfast.
7. Prepare cocoa or chocolate several times for breakfast.

REFERENCES

Care of Food in the Home. United States Department of Agriculture, Farmers' Bulletin 1374.

Chaney, Margaret S., and Ahlborn, Margaret. *Nutrition.* Houghton Mifflin Company.

Food and Life. The *Yearbook of Agriculture,* 1939. United States Department of Agriculture.

Food for Children. United States Department of Agriculture, Farmers' Bulletin 1674.

Good Food Habits for Children. United States Department of Agriculture, Leaflet 42.

Lanman, Faith R., McKay, Hughina, and Zuill, Frances. *The Family's Food.* J. B. Lippincott Company. Chapter VII.

Milk and Our School Children. Health Education 11, Department of the Interior, Bureau of Education, Washington, D.C.

Milk for the Family. United States Department of Agriculture, Farmers' Bulletin 1705.

Production of Clean Milk. United States Department of Agriculture, Farmers' Bulletin 602.

Rose, Mary Swartz. *Feeding the Family.* The Macmillan Company.

Rose, Mary Swartz. *Foundations of Nutrition.* The Macmillan Company.

Sherman, H. C. *Food Products.* The Macmillan Company. Chapter III on Milk and Chapter IV on Milk Products.

Stewart, Jean J. *Foods: Production, Marketing, Consumption.* Prentice Hall.

See also:

Bulletins and materials from your own State Agricultural College.

Material published by the National Dairy Council, 221 North LaSalle Street, Chicago, Illinois: posters, suggestions for plays, pamphlets, bulletins.

CHAPTER SIX

❧ Cereal Breakfast Foods

Cook Book References

Table for Cooking Cereals	*Page* 398
Methods of Cooking Cereals	*Page* 398

Food Value

Nutritive Value of Foods	*Table* VI, *Appendix*
Food Value in Shares	*Table* VIII, *Appendix*

CEREALS ARE FOODS which the whole family can and should eat, for they are nutritious, economical, and easily prepared. In some form cereals are within reach of every pocketbook. Cereals have been used for many centuries, but some prepared breakfast foods of today look very different from the earlier cereals which were merely coarsely cracked, parched grains, cooked in water for a long time. The Indians taught the early settlers in this country to use corn, an entirely new cereal to our ancestors. The porridge which they made they called "Indian pudding" or "hasty pudding." It was nothing more than a cornmeal mush.

A modern grocery store presents a bewildering array of breakfast foods. Advertisements would lead us to believe that these packages contain magic food values. Cereals are good foods, but no matter how attractive the claims advanced for these manufactured cereals, they cannot contain any greater food values than the materials from which they are made.

Cereal Grains. Some kind of cereal grain grows in every part of the world except the Arctic regions. In all countries cereal products are staple food. Although the cereals vary a little in details of composition, they are remarkably alike in the structure of the grain, in general composition, and in use.

The most common cereals are wheat, corn, oats, and rice. Other grains used for food are barley, millet, rye, buckwheat, and kaffir corn. These various grains are used principally as breadstuffs and as cereal breakfast foods.

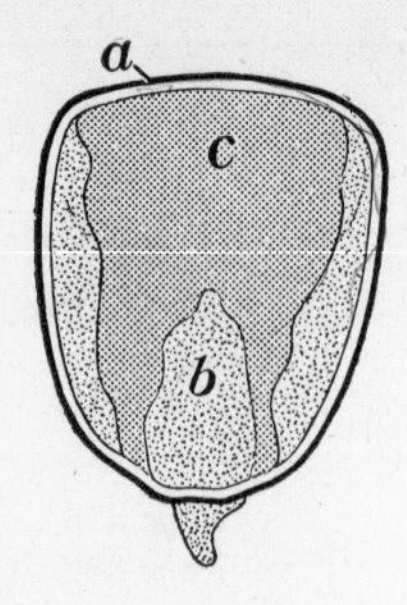

FIG. 20. DIAGRAMMATIC SECTION OF A GRAIN OF CORN
a, skin; *b*, germ; *c*, endosperm.

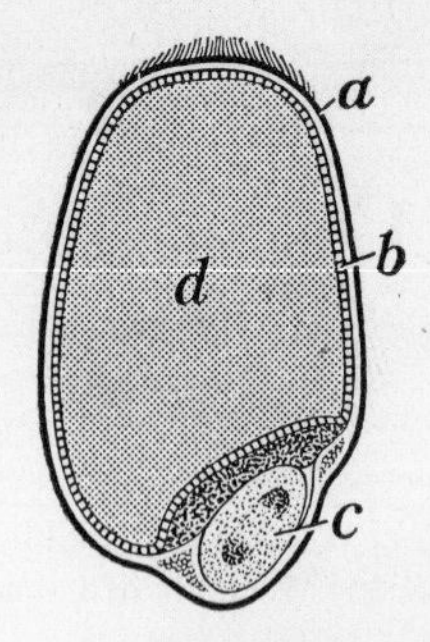

FIG. 21. DIAGRAMMATIC SECTION OF A GRAIN OF WHEAT
a, bran; *b*, aleurone layer; *c*, germ or embryo; *d*, endosperm.

Cereals are extensively used because they are inexpensive, nutritious, palatable, digestible, dry, compact, easy to keep, and easily prepared.

Structure of a Cereal Grain. All cereals are the seeds of grains. Each kernel is made up of three parts, exclusive of the outer husk:

1. The bran consists of several layers of fiber or cellulose. It contains calcium, phosphorus, iron, Vitamins B_1 and G, and some protein.
2. The endosperm, or starchy part of the grain, is the largest portion and contains chiefly starch and protein.
3. The germ, or embryo, from which the grain sprouts, contains fat, some carbohydrate, protein, mineral matter, and Vitamins B_1 and niacin.

Milled products consist chiefly of the endosperm. Thus in milling most of the cellulose, mineral matter, vitamins, fat, and some of the protein, is removed. Whole-grain cereals obviously have a greater value than highly refined cereals.

COMPOSITION OF BREAKFAST CEREALS

Water %	*Protein* %	*Fat* %	*Carbohydrate inc. fiber* %	*Fiber* %	*Minerals* %	*Calories per lb.* %
8 to 12	8 to 12 except oatmeal — 16	.3 to 2 except oatmeal — 7	66 to 80	.2 to 1.8	.3 to 2	about 1600 or 100 per oz.

CEREALS RICH IN VITAMINS A, B_1, AND G

Vitamin B_1

Wheat germ	Wheat bran
Corn germ	Rye
Rye germ	Oats
Rice polishings	Barley
Whole grain wheat	Brown rice

Vitamin G (Riboflavin)

Wheat germ
Rice polishings
Whole grain wheat

Vitamin A

Yellow corn meal

A COMPARISON OF WHEAT PRODUCTS

	Part of Grain	As Sources of Minerals and Vitamins				
		Calcium	*Phosphorus*	*Iron*	*Vitamin B_1*	*Vitamin G*
Whole Grain	Endosperm Bran Germ	Fair	Very good	Good	Good	Good
Highly processed as patented flour or white cereals made from wheat	Usually endosperm only	Poor	Poor	Poor	Poor	Poor

Scientists tell us that one reason our diets are poor is because we have drifted away from using foods as Nature gave them to us, and have substituted for them foods from which man has removed important nutrients by the process of preparing these foods for market. Cereals illustrate how we have short-changed our diets in this way. It is wise in choosing cereals to give preference to those which contain all the food that Nature has stored in the whole grain: bran, endosperm, and germ as the foregoing table shows.

By a new milling process it is now possible to include the germ in milled cereal products. In fact, there are some breakfast cereals on the market to which the wheat germ has been added. Such cereals are valuable for their Vitamin B_1 content. The wheat germ also contains some of the anti-pellagra vitamin, niacin.

Since oatmeal is not so highly refined as some cereals, it contains the fat of the germ and some of the fiber and minerals and vitamins of the bran. It is the cereal richest in iron and contains a good amount of vitamin B_1.

Fuel Value of Cereals. Approximately one ounce of dry cereals is a one-hundred-calorie portion.

ONE-HUNDRED-CALORIE PORTIONS IN READY-TO-EAT CEREALS[1]

Corn flakes, 1¼ cups
Cornmeal mush, ⅔ cup
Farina (cooked) ¾ cup
Grapenuts, 3 tablespoons
Hominy grits (cooked), ⅗ cup
Oatmeal (cooked), ¾ cup
Popcorn (popped), 1½ cups
Puffed corn, 1¼ cups
Puffed rice, 1⅓ cups
Puffed wheat, 1⅔ cups
Rice (steamed), ¾ cup
Wheat flakes (cooked), ⅔ cup
Shredded wheat, 1 biscuit
Bran flakes, ¾ cup

[1] All of this table, except bran flakes, is taken from M. S. Rose, *Feeding the Family.* Reprinted by permission of The Macmillan Company, publishers.

Food Value and Place in the Diet of Breakfast Cereals

Cereals are very easily digested and are excellent sources of energy. Cooked cereals are one of our cheapest sources of energy. A thoroughly cooked cereal is strongly recommended for the family breakfast. Children may begin eating strained cereals when four months of age. Cooked cereal (of suitable texture) made from whole grains, such as oatmeal, is the most desirable cereal for children.

Minerals in Cereals. Minerals in grains occur chiefly in the bran. Whole-grain cereals, especially oatmeal, are a fair source of calcium, and a good source of phosphorus, and iron. The bran is also responsible for the laxative property of whole-grain cereals. Since they help prevent constipation, this is another good reason for giving preference to whole-grain products in the menu.

The protein in cereals is not so complete as the protein in milk; hence it is desirable to supplement cereals with milk. Because cereal products are eaten in rather large quantities daily, the amount of protein they contribute to the family food is important. Cooked in milk, cereals form an excellent food.

Vitamin B_1 occurs in liberal amounts in whole grain, but not in the refined cereal products. Cereals are poor sources of Vitamins A, C, and D. Yellow corn, however, is a source of Vitamin A. Whole-grain cereals contain small amounts of niacin and riboflavin, if the germ is included in the food.

None of the cereals used alone will make a balanced dietary. Each should be supplemented by milk, green vegetables, and fruits, which will supply the lacking protein, minerals, and vitamins. If vegetables or fruits are hard to procure, or if the money to be expended for food must go as far as possible, whole-grain cereals should by all means be used instead of refined cereals, because the whole-grain cereals will give more iron, phosphorus, calcium, and a good supply of Vitamin B_1.

Prepared cereals are expensive, but they are convenient to use and are palatable. They add a welcome variety to the menu, especially in warm weather when a hot cereal may not be acceptable. Some of the prepared cereals are whole-grain products. Prepared cereals should be used with the knowledge that one may be paying approximately three fourths of the price for a method of preparation and one fourth for food.

Carbohydrates. Cereals are chiefly a carbohydrate food, as is shown by the table, Composition of Breakfast Cereals, on page 66. The carbohydrate group is one of the five principal foods needed by our bodies. Carbohydrates serve the body as fuel, and, as such, are important sources of energy and heat. The carbohydrates include starches and sugars. Because of their close chemical relationship, starches and sugars are classed together in the carbohydrate family.

Cooking and Serving Cereals

There are three reasons for cooking: 1. To improve the flavor. 2. To improve the digestibility. 3. To soften the cellulose, thus improving the texture. Lumpy, half-cooked, burned, or unsalted cereal is not palatable; this reason alone should bar the poorly cooked product from our tables.

Principles of Cereal Cookery. Since cereals are chiefly starch, the methods of cooking cereals are based on the principles of starch cookery.

Starch occurs in plants in granular form. This fact can easily be discerned by examining starch from various plants under the microscope. There are many starch granules in one plant cell. The cell wall and the covering of the starch granule are cellulose. Three distinct changes take place as starch cooks:

1. The starch grains absorb water. You have noticed the increase in bulk as cereals cook. This increase was due to the absorption of water.

2. The heat of cooking converts into steam the water absorbed by the starch granules. The steam bursts the granules, and the starch fills the cells. It is this bursting of the granules and the forming of soluble starch paste that causes starch to thicken as it cooks. We can imagine that each of these little microscopic starch granules explodes from the steam pressure just as a grain of popcorn does when it pops. Cooking thus changes the texture of cereals.

3. Cooking also develops the flavor of cereals, making them more palatable. Cereals need to be cooked only long enough to develop flavor. Long, slow cooking is not necessary.

Method of Cooking Breakfast Cereals. Cereals are usually cooked in boiling salted water or in hot milk. Cereals may also be cooked in the pressure cooker with cold water. The quantity of water depends upon the kind and age of the cereal. The amount of salt will

FIG. 22. FRIED MUSH WITH BACON

vary somewhat with individual taste, but one to two teaspoons of salt to each quart of liquid is a safe general proportion. If milk is used rather than water, the nutritive value of the cooked cereal is obviously increased. Dried or evaporated milk properly diluted may be used in cooking cereals.

For the first few minutes all cereals are cooked directly over the fire in boiling water or milk. In adding cereal to boiling liquid precautions must be taken to prevent lumping. Lumps are not only unsightly and unpalatable, but they contain uncooked starch.

Ways of Preventing Lumping:

1. Coarse cereals, such as rice or oatmeal, may be sprinkled slowly into rapidly boiling water. Stir constantly.

2. Fine cereals may be mixed with cold water and poured into boiling water. Stir constantly. After the first few minutes of cooking directly over the fire, the cereal may finish cooking in a double boiler, a fireless cooker, or a pressure cooker.

3. Left-over cereal may be used by re-heating. When cold cereal is re-heated it should not be stirred until it is well heated. This procedure will prevent lumping. A double boiler or a smaller pan set in water is the best way to re-heat cereals.

Serving Cereals. Cereals are usually served with milk or cream. Whole milk is preferable for children and invalids who often find the fat of cream hard to digest. Some persons prefer butter on hot cereals.

The use of sugar with cereals should be discouraged. Sugar blunts the appetite for the milder flavors of cereals, and, in quantities, is irritating to the digestive tract. It may be pointed out that when children eat cereal for the sugar rather than for the cereal, the sugar habit is established instead of the oatmeal habit.

Dried fruits (dates, figs, raisins) make a palatable addition to cooked cereal. They may be chopped and added to the cereal after the first ten minutes of cooking or served on the cooked cereal. This is a way to combine fruit and cereal in one dish for breakfast. Fresh fruits, such as berries or sliced bananas or peaches, are often served in this way also.

Prepared cereals are improved by toasting in the oven just before serving.

Buying Breakfast Cereals

Packaged Cereals. Because breakfast cereals contain about the same energy value per ounce, but differ in the amount of minerals and vitamins they contain, economical buying is concerned with getting those products that cost little per pound or per ounce and that at the same time have important amounts of growth-promoting substances. Recently four packages of breakfast cereals were found on a grocer's shelves. Their weight and prices and a general estimate of their relative vitamin and mineral value are as follows:

	Weight	*Price*	*Mineral and Vitamins*	*Require cooking*
Cereal A	3 lb.	21 cents	Very good	Yes
Cereal B	28 oz.	25 cents	Very low	Yes
Cereal C	7 oz.	15 cents	Very low	Ready to eat
Cereal D	3½ oz.	10 cents	Good	Ready to eat

Which was the best buy of the four? In order to determine this, compare the price per pound. The first one is easy. Divide the price of three pounds, twenty-one cents, by three and the cost per pound is seven cents. The others look a little more difficult. You can figure them out yourself, or use the Cost-Weight Table, pages 172–73. To use this table, look down the weight column at the left, which runs up and down the page, until you come to twenty-eight ounces, the amount of cereal package B contained. Across the top of the table the prices are listed from left to right. Find twenty-five cents and then look down the twenty-five cents column until you come to the figure in the same line with twenty-eight ounces; you find here that the Cereal B cost fourteen cents a pound. You find in the same way that Cereal C cost thirty-two cents a pound and that Cereal D cost somewhere between forty cents and fifty-two cents, or about forty-six cents a pound. When price per pound is added to the foregoing table, it looks like this:

	Weight	*Price*	*Minerals and Vitamins*	*Require cooking*	*Cost per lb. of cereal*
Cereal A	3 lb.	.21	Very good	Uncooked	.07
Cereal B	28 oz.	.25	Very low	Uncooked	.14
Cereal C	7 oz.	.15	Very low	Ready to eat	.32
Cereal D	3½ oz.	.10	Good	Ready to eat	.46

Cereal D costs more than six times as much as Cereal A and isn't quite as good in food value! A lot to pay for cooking!

All things considered, which gave the best value for the money? Do you think that in this case the cost of cooking would overcome the saving in using uncooked cereal?

Cereals in Bulk. Bulk cereals cost a little less, as a rule, than the same kind in package form. If you buy grain that is unground, you get the best bargain of all, for it costs still less per pound, and if cooked in the pressure canner it isn't much trouble, and it is delicious. See recipe in the Cook Book.

CLASS PROBLEMS

1. Study cost of cooked and uncooked cereals in your market by calculating the cost per pound using the convenient Cost-Weight Table, pages 172–73. From the one-hundred-calorie portions of cereals, estimate the calories in one serving of each of the common cereals.
2. Obtain ten or twelve different breakfast cereals, part in packages and part in bulk. Try to guess the weight of the packaged cereals before looking on the packages for weights. Then look for the weight. Is it the gross weight or net weight? Using the Cost-Weight Table, find the cost per pound. Which do you consider economical buys?
3. Examine various grains and seeds to find the three parts — bran, endosperm, germ. You can easily locate these in peanuts, for instance.
4. Read the labels on package cereals. What kinds of information do you find?
5. Collect colored pictures of cereals to show attractive ways of serving cereals.
6. Bring to class some advertisements of cereals. Also, record radio statements in advertisement of some cereals. Discuss the claims made for these products. Are they justifiable?
7. Cook different cereals in various ways, combining each with one other food to make a breakfast combination. See recipes, pages 398–401.

HOME PROBLEMS

1. Prepare the cereal for your family breakfasts for a week. Plan to have some variety.

2. Learn to eat cereal with little or no sugar and whole milk.
3. Buy the cereal for your family for the next month. Notice the sanitary conditions in the store. Does your observation bear out the statement that package cereals may be cleaner than bulk goods?
4. Estimate each morning for a week how many calories you eat in the form of breakfast cereal plus the milk or sugar you eat with it.

REFERENCES

Cooking American Varieties of Rice. United States Department of Agriculture, Leaflet 112.

Corn and Its Uses as Food. United States Department of Agriculture, Farmers' Bulletin 1236. Government Printing Office, Washington, D.C.

Council on Foods of the American Medical Association. *Accepted Foods and Their Nutritional Significance.* American Medical Association, Chicago, 1939. Unit V, especially pages 125–34.

Food and Life. Yearbook of Agriculture, 1939. United States Department of Agriculture.

Justin, Margaret M., Rust, Lucile O., and Vail, Gladys E. *Foods.* Houghton Mifflin Company. Unit Two, pages 118–132, and Unit Three, pages 420–424.

Rose, Mary Swartz. *Feeding the Family.* 4th edition. The Macmillan Company.

Sherman, Henry C. *Food Products.* 3d edition. The Macmillan Company.

CHAPTER SEVEN

Breakfast Breads and Beverages

Cook Book References

Toast	*Page* 401
Table for Flour Mixtures	*Page* 404
Popovers	*Page* 404
Waffles	*Page* 405
Griddle Cakes	*Page* 406
Muffins	*Page* 407
Biscuits	*Page* 410
Fruit Beverages	*Page* 396
Coffee	*Page* 394
Tea	*Page* 395
Chocolate and Cocoa	*Page* 393
Milk	*Chapter* 5

Food Value

Nutritive Value of Foods	*Table* VI, *Appendix*
Food Value in Shares	*Table* VIII, *Appendix*

THE MOST UNIVERSAL breakfast combination is a bread and a beverage. Whatever the menu, these two items are almost sure to be included. In fact, for adults toast-and-coffee is almost one word at breakfast time. Since you are learning to cook meals instead of single dishes, it is appropriate to consider breakfast breads and beverages together.

BEVERAGES

How Much Water Should We Drink? Water is a part of all body tissue, and is essential to the performance and regulation of body processes. Have you "done your daily half dozen"? Half dozen glasses of water, of course! The best beverage on earth! Everyone should drink at least six glasses a day, and eight glasses might be better. Many of us do not drink enough water. Do you?

The human body is fifty-eight per cent water. If you weigh one hundred pounds, the water contained in your body tissues and fluids weighs about fifty-eight pounds. Your body is constantly losing water through the lungs, skin, intestines, and kidneys. One cannot live if the amount of water is materially reduced. In thirst, Nature has provided us with a powerful reminder of our need for water. Thirst may drive us to drink the minimum amount essential to support life; we must rely on habit to supply generously our needs for water.

How the Body Uses Water. Every part of the body uses water. Four important uses are:

1. Water, the blood and lymph fluid, is the food carrier for cells of the body.

2. Many impurities and poisons formed in the body are soluble in water. Thus it assists in eliminating waste products from the body. It is a cleanser for the inside of the body as well as for the outer surface.

3. Water is a regulator of body temperature. To break out in perspiration when the weather is hot is a familiar experience. You realize how important a constant body temperature is when you recall how instantly we are alarmed by fever.

4. In the alimentary canal, water aids digestion, and absorption, and helps to prevent constipation.

Shall We Drink Water at Mealtime? The drinking of water at meals has been much discussed in the past. Some authorities formerly thought that this practice was harmful. Experiments have proved that water when taken at meals is an aid to digestion. One caution is necessary. Water must not be used to wash down food. Then it is harmful for two reasons: (1) the food is not properly masticated, but is swallowed in "hunks," unmixed with saliva, a digestive juice; (2) washing down food leads to eating too rapidly and often to overeating.

Cold water should be swallowed slowly — sipped. Drinking very cold water in large quantities should be avoided.

You can establish no better habit than that of drinking a glass or more of water a short time before each meal and especially before breakfast.

Safe Drinking Water. Is your water supply safe? Before people learned to safeguard their water supplies from contamination, typhoid was a very prevalent disease. So universal is the vigilance of health departments nowadays that the water supply of a large city is usually safe. There is, however, much typhoid in small towns and rural districts, and at times cases occur in cities.

Care must be taken that the water supply of a rural home or school is free from all surface drainage. Why?

Water that is of doubtful source should be boiled. When you go on picnics or on cross-country automobile trips, the safe thing to do is to take your own water supply, or to boil the water for ten minutes.

Water in Cookery. Without water the cook would be helpless. She depends on water for all boiling, stewing, steaming, freezing, for preparing foods for cooking, for many delectable beverages, and for cleaning the kitchen and kitchen utensils.

Water that contains much lime in solution is hard water. Hardness affects its use for cooking and washing, but does not affect its usefulness for drinking. Water that does not contain lime or other minerals is soft water. What differences have you noticed in the use of soap in hard and soft water?

Water from the hot-water faucet should not be used in cooked food, because it contains some of the metallic substance dissolved from pipes.

Milk [1]

A glass of milk for breakfast is the surest way to include one fourth of the daily requirement of a quart of milk for all who have not entirely completed their growing up, or half the supply needed by adults. Since adults need daily only half as much milk (1 pint) as children and youth (1 quart), they may omit milk as a breakfast beverage in favor of coffee, which most of them seem to prefer, without impairing their health, if they are sure to get their quota of milk in other foods during the day. They may get some of their quota in other ways than as a beverage at breakfast. How?

Milk is more than a beverage. It is the best food we have available. Serving milk as a beverage is only one of the many ways it may be used.

Cocoa and Chocolate

One of the most acceptable forms in which milk appears in the family breakfast menu is as cocoa or chocolate.

Food Value. The chief food value of cocoa and chocolate as breakfast beverages is due to milk, but these substances are also foods in themselves. In this respect they differ from tea and coffee.

[1] See Chapter 5.

Cocoa and chocolate contain theobromine, a stimulant similar to the stimulant in tea and coffee.

Composition of Cocoa and Chocolate. Fat is the chief food constituent of cocoa and chocolate. Chocolate (plain) contains about fifty per cent fat. Cocoa contains about twenty-two per cent fat.

One square of bitter chocolate yields one hundred and seventy calories; one tablespoon of grated chocolate yields thirty calories.

One tablespoon of cocoa (pulverized) yields thirty-five calories.

Both cocoa and chocolate are rich, but chocolate is the richer.

Though both are made from the cocoa bean, some of the fat is removed in cocoa. For this reason it is used for breakfast and is more satisfactory for children and for persons with weak digestion.

Tea and Coffee

Effect of Tea and Coffee. Tea and coffee may be discussed together, for they are similar in use, in composition, and in their effects on the body. Neither of these substances is a food. They are liked for their flavor and their stimulating property. Tea has the more delicate flavor. Coffee has a delightful odor, or aroma, owing to the presence of a volatile oil called caffeol.

Both tea and coffee contain a stimulant called caffein, which is a drug that stimulates the kidneys, the heart, and the nervous system. Not all people are equally susceptible to the stimulating effect of caffein. Some people do not sleep well after drinking these beverages, but others seem not to be inconvenienced. It is principally for this stimulating quality that tea and coffee are often used by adults as breakfast beverages. Young people do not need stimulants; nerves, heart, and kidneys can develop more normally without them. For this reason, and for the further reasons that tea and coffee are not foods and that they take up valuable room needed for food, growing boys and girls should avoid these beverages. High flavors serve to dull the appetite, and boys and girls need to keep their appetites keen for simple, nourishing foods without high flavor. The stimulating property is treasured by grown-ups and is especially helpful to old people, but it is not always good, even for adults.

Tannin, a substance in tea and coffee, is undesirable because it interferes with digestion and spoils the flavor of the beverage. The bitter flavor sometimes noticed in strong tea is due to tannin. Tannin is undesirable in coffee and tea even for adults, but these beverages rightly made contain little tannin.

Principle Involved in Making Tea and Coffee. Tea and coffee, properly made, we have said, contain little tannin. The method of making these beverages is based on the difference in solubility of caffein and tannin. Caffein is readily soluble in water just below the boiling point; tannin is soluble on boiling even for a few minutes, but is more soluble in tea than in coffee. Tea is made by steeping the leaves in water just below the boiling point from one to three minutes. Coffee is also best made by using a temperature just below the boiling point because more of the flavorful caffeol and less of the bitter tannin are dissolved from the ground coffee and held in the liquid at this temperature.

Kinds of Tea. Tea consists of the dried leaves of the tea bush. There are three general kinds of tea: green, black, and Oolong. These kinds differ in the methods by which they are dried and cured and not in the variety of the tea plant. Green tea is unfermented and is steam dried. Black tea is fermented and is kiln dried. Oolong tea is partly fermented. The beverage made from black tea is darker in color and contains less tannin.

Quality. The quality of tea varies: (*a*) with the country or even the district in which it is grown; (*b*) with the tenderness of the leaf; (*c*) with the degree of fermentation and other details of preparation; (*d*) with the length of time it has been kept. Many people who like tea are very particular about the kind that they drink, and it is polite to consider this preference when you are serving tea.

Source. Most of our tea comes from Japan, Ceylon, India, and Formosa. We also import tea from China and the East Indies.

Teapots. You will remember that teapots you have seen were usually of earthenware, china, porcelain, or enamel, and sometimes of glass. Even the small amount of tannic acid in well-made tea attacks some metals producing an undesirable metallic taste.

Serving Tea. Tea is not generally used for breakfast in this country, but it is almost universally so used in England. Tea is usually served with cream and sugar for breakfast, but at other times lemon is preferred by many people, especially in iced tea. The English use cream in tea; the Russians use lemon.

Source and Production of Coffee. Brazil furnishes more than half the world's supply of coffee. It is also grown in Central America, Mexico, the East and West Indies, Java, and Arabia.

The coffee tree produces a red berry, the seed of which is in two flattened halves called coffee beans. These seeds, or beans, are dried and exported as green coffee.

Buying Coffee. Coffee is roasted to develop the flavor imparted by caffeol. Coffee as purchased is usually roasted and ground. Ground coffee should be sold in tin containers or paraffin bags and should be purchased in small quantities because it deteriorates rapidly. Some people — the French in New Orleans, for example — prefer to roast their own coffee, because it has a better flavor when freshly roasted. The New Orleans French are noted for their coffee, which is a very black beverage. The intense blackness of French coffee is partly owing to chicory, and partly to a dark roast.

Coffeepots. Coffeepots should not be of tin or some other metals for the same reason that metal teapots are not satisfactory. If coffee is made by boiling, enamelware is used. Drip coffee makers are often made of glass and earthenware. Aluminum coffeepots or chromium or nickel-plated percolators are also used. For convenience and for more uniformly good coffee, the newer glass percolator or dripolator is most popular. The old-fashioned coffeepot still holds sway at picnics and in many homes. The kind of coffeepot is of less importance than its cleanliness. After each use the utensils should be washed, scalded, and dried.

Coffee substitutes: (1) Cereal coffee. A beverage similar to coffee

FIG. 23. UTENSILS FOR COFFEE-MAKING

in appearance and taste is prepared from parched cereals. This substitute coffee does not contain caffein. People who are very fond of coffee may not care for cereal coffee. It is neither a food nor a stimulant. Although the product is made from cereal, the food value is largely destroyed in the parching. (2) Decaffeinated coffee. These products are coffee from which part of the caffein has been removed. Tests have shown that the proportion removed varies considerably. A more consistent method of limiting the caffein intake might be to make weak coffee. A good way of making weak coffee palatable for those who use cream in it, is to make it of half milk, combining hot milk with the coffee after it is made.

Instant Coffee. Coffee in pulverized form instantly soluble in boiling water is on the market in several brands. It is especially useful when time, equipment, or space is short.

Hot Breakfast Breads

Bread for breakfast offers many tempting variations. Piping hot, crisp toast is a prime favorite, and there is no denying the appeal of a muffin or a biscuit that is delicately browned and "melts in your mouth." Bread has been called the staff of life, but the hot breakfast breads served with butter are better termed "a gold-headed walking cane." It may be only semi-occasionally that we serve waffles, griddle or "batter" cakes, muffins, popovers, or biscuit for breakfast, but when we serve them they must be good.

Types of Breads. There are many kinds of bread, but all of these many varieties divide into a relatively simple classification on the basis of types of bread.

CLASSIFICATION OF BREADS

Type	*Kind of Mixture*	*Products*
I. Quick Breads baking powder soda and sour milk	A. Batters	A. Popovers Waffles Griddle cakes Muffins
	B. Doughs	B. Biscuit drop rolled Loaf breads, brown bread, etc.

II. Yeast Breads	A. Sponge for first rising, then made into dough for second rising	Rolls of all kinds Plain Parker House Clover leaf Finger Bread sticks Cinnamon Nut Coffee cake
	B. Dough for first rising, called offhand doughs	
	Note: Either method may be used, but the sponge method is preferred for fancy breads and rolls	Bread of all kinds Plain Whole wheat Rye Salt rising Raisin Nut or fruit

In this chapter, with the exception of toast, the discussion is on quick breads. Yeast breads are discussed later, since they are more widely used for luncheon.

Toast. Toast is the most typical bread in an American breakfast. Some people like toast daily for breakfast. Variations are acceptable. We may have, for example (see Cook Book):

Dry toast	French toast
Buttered toast	Toast from special breads, such as:
Milk toast	Raisin bread
Cream toast	Nut bread
Cheese toast	Whole-wheat or graham bread
Cinnamon toast	Melba toast

Suggestions for Making Toast:

1. The bread used for toast should be a day or more old.
2. Thin slices are daintier and are usually better liked than thick slices. They are also more crisp.
3. A hot oven is usually required for toast. If the bread is fresh, a slow oven is best, because it will dry out the bread.
4. Brown the bread first, then butter it, if butter is to be used. Buttered toast may be placed in a warm oven for a few minutes.
5. Toast should be served hot. If it is stacked it becomes soggy.
6. Electric toasters are very satisfactory for making toast at the table. Automatic toasters almost seem to do your thinking for you; for if regulated to suit your taste, they need little watching.
7. Melba toast is thin, dry toast, prepared in a moderate or slow oven in order to dry the bread thoroughly and toast it to a very light brown.

Quick Breads. From the cook's standpoint, quick breads are spoken of as batters and doughs, or as flour mixtures. Below are given the ingredients of quick breads:

Common to all:	Additional:
Flour	Fat (shortening)
Liquid	Eggs
Salt	Substitutes for some of the flour
Leavening agent	Sweetening
	Flavoring

Pastry flour, which is a soft wheat flour and makes a tender product, is best for quick breads, but an all-purpose flour may be used for both quick and yeast breads.

The liquid in quick breads is usually water, milk, buttermilk, sour milk, or clabber. Milk may be fresh, dried, or canned.

Fat is added to improve the texture and the flavor. If much fat is used, it adds crispness to flour mixtures. Examples are pastry and cookies. Too much fat makes a product heavy.

Eggs contribute flavor, richness, and a light texture.

The leavening agent is used to produce a light texture.

Sugar is added to help the flavor and the texture.

Too much flour makes mixtures dry and tough. An excess of flour is often indicated by a cracking of the surface as the bread cooks. Sometimes a mixture contains too much flour because it was measured before sifting. The measures in recipes in this book (usually in all cook books) are based on flour after sifting and without packing.

Leavens and Leavening Agents. Air, steam, and carbon dioxide are the leavens that lighten quick breads. Each of these is a gas that expands when heated. Air is incorporated into a mixture by beating, and by beating eggs, especially egg whites, until they are light before adding them to the mixture. To some degree all quick breads are leavened by air, but in most instances we do not depend entirely on air.

When water is converted rapidly into steam, the force of expansion is great. Have you ever noticed the miniature explosion that takes place when water boils over on a hot stove? Steam expands wherever it is produced. When steam is produced in a batter it leavens the mixture. We depend upon steam to leaven popovers. They are hollow shells that look as though something had exploded inside them. When steam is the leavening agent, a hot oven is required, and the door of the oven must not be opened until the mixture has puffed and cooked. When the oven door is opened before the popovers are done, they may fall, if the steam inside condenses before the batter has cooked sufficiently to hold its shape.

Carbon Dioxide Gas is Produced by the Action of Any Acid on Soda. All baking powders contain soda (sodium bicarbonate), but the acid may vary. Examine the labels of common baking powders to discover the acids commonly used. Leavening by soda and sour milk is exactly the same chemical process as leavening by baking powder.

Self-rising flour is ordinary flour to which have been added soda and a substance that acts as an acid when wet. Thus no leavening agent need be used.

General Proportions for Quick Breads. Flour:[1] Recipes for quick breads usually call for sifted soft wheat or pastry flour. Substitutions for one cup of pastry flour may be made as follows:

- 7/8 cup of bread flour.
- 3/4 cup of coarse graham flour (unsifted. Why?)
- 7/8 cup of fine graham flour (unsifted. Why?)

These substitutions are based on equal weights as equivalents.

[1] United States Department of Agriculture, *Home Baking*, Farmers' Bulletin 1450.

FIG. 24. MAKING BAKING POWDER BISCUIT
1. Kneading the dough
2. Ready for the oven
3. Will you please have a biscuit?

Liquid.[1] Milk is usually preferred for flour mixtures. Whole milk, skim milk, or properly diluted dried or evaporated milk may be used. Sour milk may be substituted for sweet milk (cup for cup) except in popovers, which require sweet milk, since steam and not soda is the leavening agent.

Water may be used in quick breads with little change in the texture or flavor of the product, but the food value will be lessened. If cream is used the quantity of shortening may be reduced.

Proportions of Leavening Agents

If no eggs are used, 1½ to 2 t. baking powder to 1 c. flour

With well-beaten eggs, 1 t. to 1½ t. baking powder to 1 c. flour

Changing a Sweet-Milk Recipe to Sour Milk and Soda. Proportions: Use ½ t. soda to 1 c. sour milk or molasses; ¼ t. soda to 1 c. slightly sour milk or clabber; 2 t. of quick-acting baking powder = ½ t. soda in leavening power. All changes made on this basis.

Example A:

Recipe calls for:	Equivalent if sour milk and soda used:
1 c. (sweet) milk	1 c. very sour milk
2 t. baking powder	½ t. soda
1 c. flour	1 c. flour

Example B: (A recipe may use both baking powder and soda.)

Recipe calls for:	When changed to sour milk:
1 c. (sweet) milk	1 c. very sour milk
4 t. baking powder	½ t. soda
1 c. flour	2 t. baking powder
	1 c. flour

Here the maximum soda that can be used is ½ t. (milk 1 c.).

½ t. soda = 2 t. baking powder. Since the recipe calls for 4 t. baking powder we have 2 t. baking powder left over which remains in the recipe.

Example C. When slightly sour milk is used some baking powder will also be retained in the recipe.

1 c. (sweet) milk	1 c. fresh buttermilk (slightly sour)
2 t. baking powder	¼ t. soda (replaces 1 t. baking powder)
1 c. flour	1 t. baking powder

Changing a Soda and Sour-Milk Recipe to a Baking-Powder and Sweet-Milk Recipe. Since one half teaspoon of soda equals two

[1] United States Department of Agriculture, *Home Baking*, Farmers' Bulletin 1450.

teaspoons of baking powder, it is evident that a sour-milk recipe may be changed to a sweet-milk recipe by substituting four times as much baking powder for all the soda specified and replacing the sour milk with the same amount of sweet milk.

Shortening. Lard and similar fats and oils contain no water, but oleomargarine and butter contain some; a recipe, therefore, calls for slightly more butter or oleomargarine.

Seven tablespoons of butter or oleomargarine equal six tablespoons of lard and similar fats. One to two tablespoons of shortening is used with one cup of flour for quick breads. Cakes and pastry are richer in fat.

Salt. One fourth to one half teaspoon of salt is used ordinarily with one cup of flour or meal.

Method of Mixing Flour Mixtures. (See page 409, Fig. 130.) Neatness and tidiness are necessary in working with flour mixtures. It is a good plan to work with a paper spread under all utensils. This makes cleaning up easy. Accuracy in measurements is essential. Useful utensils for making flour mixtures are a measuring cup, a bowl, a wooden spoon, and above all, a spatula for doughs.

Oven Temperatures. We often hear people say that they have had good luck or bad luck with cooking. The guesswork is usually in the baking rather than in the mixing. The time consumed in baking, and the temperature are the important factors in successful baking. The oven position of the mixture during baking determines in some measure the quality of the final product.

Modern gas and electric stoves are now equipped with a device for controlling the temperature of the oven. All types of stoves, including oil stoves, are available with oven temperature control. Use an oven thermometer if the oven lacks an oven control.

If you are patient and observant you can learn by practice how to judge an oven as slow,

FIG. 25. WAFFLES, A UNIVERSAL FAVORITE

medium, hot, or very hot. Perhaps you have seen an experienced cook do this by thrusting her hand into the oven. You can learn to tell in this way, but at first you may have to use other tests.

The food should be placed in the part of the oven where the heat is even. The best results are obtained when one knows exactly how hot the oven is and how long a food should be cooked at a given temperature. See the Cook Book for time and temperature for cooking various recipes.

OVEN TEMPERATURES

	Slow Oven 250° *to* 350° *F.*	*Moderate Oven* 350° *to* 400° *F.*	*Hot Oven* 400° *to* 450° *F.*
Flour mixture	Sponge cake Angel food cake Egg leavened mixtures: soufflés Fruit cake Brownies	Bread Butter cakes: layer and loaf Cookies Cream puffs Gingerbread Spoon bread Cinnamon toast	Biscuit Muffins Pastry Corn sticks Popovers Rolls Toast
Test: Use dry flour spread thinly.	Dry flour browns in 60 seconds	Dry flour browns in 30 seconds	Dry flour browns in 10 seconds

Food Value of Quick Breads. The food value of a quick bread depends, of course, on the food value of its ingredients. The chief ingredient in any bread is flour. White flour is chiefly starch and protein. Bread is therefore a fuel food to begin with, but if whole wheat or graham flour is used, and if it is made with milk and eggs, the food value of bread is materially increased.

ONE-HUNDRED-CALORIE PORTIONS OF BREAKFAST BREADS

Toast (½ inch thick)		Muffins	One small
White bread	2 slices	Waffles	⅖ of a waffle
Whole wheat	1½ slices	Popovers	One
Biscuit	2 (small)	Rolls (plain)	One
Griddle cakes	1 (4 inches)		

ONE-HUNDRED-CALORIE PORTION ACCOMPANIMENTS FOR QUICK BREADS

Butter	1 T.	Sirup	1¾ T.
Honey	1 T.	Molasses	1½ T.
Jelly or marmalade	1¾ T.		

Judging Quick Bread. Quick breads are judged by the following standards:

Appearance: Size, shape, brownness, crust — quality.
Texture: Grain, lightness, tenderness, moisture.
Taste.

Since any score is more or less arbitrary, the class can make out a score card for judging their own products. See Cook Book, pages 407 and 410, for scores.

Serving Quick Breads. Quick breads must be served freshly baked and piping hot. In the South, where they are most used, they are invariably served with butter, and are buttered while hot.

Marmalade, jelly, and preserves are often served with toast. With waffles or griddle cakes, maple or cane sirup and honey are preferred. If these are used it should be only occasionally and in small quantities in order that they shall not replace better foods. Sweets dull the appetite for other foods. Sweets furnish chiefly calories. They should be used sparingly in order not to crowd out of one's diet the needed building and regulating foods.

CLASS PROBLEMS

1. Make a trip as a class to study the city water supply. If this is impracticable, invite a representative of the city or county health department to come to school and explain how the city safeguards its water supply.

2. Study the water supply on some farm or rural school ground. Does it seem safe? How can you make sure? If yours is a rural school, find out what kind of water you are drinking. Learn to make a paper drinking cup.

3. Write to your State Health Department for bulletins on water supplies and sewage disposal. Give class reports on these bulletins.

4. An experiment to determine how to make tea:
   (*a*) Put 1 teaspoon of tea in 1 cup of cold water. Steep 2 minutes. Strain.
   (*b*) Pour 1 cup of boiling water over 1 teaspoon of tea. Steep 2 minutes. Strain.
   (*c*) Boil 1 teaspoon of tea in 1 cup of water for 2 minutes. Strain.
   (*d*) Pour 1 cup of boiling water over 1 teaspoon of tea. Steep 12 minutes. Strain.

Make comparisons as to color, taste, and so on, and draw conclusions as to factors causing the differences.

Give rules for making good tea, and state your reasons.

Note: This experiment may be tried with green, black, and Oolong tea, and comparisons made:

Unroll wet tea leaves until an unbroken one is found. Note the shape. Is it the same for the various kinds of tea?

5. Measurements. Measure one cup of flour before and after sifting. Is there any difference in the measurements?

6. Kinds of baking powder:

Assemble various kinds of baking powder. Read the labels and tabulate the ingredients. How do baking powders differ in respect to ingredients? What three types of baking powder are there?

There has been much discussion of the relative merits of different baking powders. One kind seems to be as little harmful as another. Some powders give up their gas much more rapidly than others, and hence deteriorate more readily.

Compare the time of action of the three types of baking powders by adding a teaspoon of each kind to the same quantity of water (one half cup). Stir the three mixtures and note the gas escaping from each. Which type of powder reacts for the longest time?

The baking powder that reacts slowly has two advantages: (1) the leavening power is not lost readily if the bread mixture has to stand before being baked; (2) The powder does not so readily lose its strength in the can.

7. Examine the labels on the tea and coffee used at home and commonly sold in local stores. What information do you find? What is the price of each product per pound? Compare these findings.

8. Plan a working schedule to prepare several combinations of breakfast breads and beverages, having both ready to serve at the same time. Follow the principles of good management in Chapter 2.

Suggested combinations:

1. Toast, marmalade, and coffee
2. Cinnamon toast and tea
3. Muffins and cocoa, jelly, butter
4. Waffles, cream, coffee, butter, sirup
5. Biscuits, marmalade, chocolate

HOME PROBLEMS

Home practice is more essential for making quick breads than for making any of the products that you have studied up to this time.

1. Note how much water you drink in a day. If you do not drink a half dozen glasses, try to establish this habit.
2. Try to establish the habit of drinking a glass of water when you get up each morning.
3. If you drink tea or coffee, learn to do without it. Why?
4. Prepare plain toast and the breakfast beverage for your family until you are skillful at producing excellent products.
5. From the list of quick breads, page 401, and beverages, page 393, in the Cook Book, plan and prepare several combinations of breads and beverages for your family. See suggested combinations in the Class Problem number 8. Make your own combinations.

REFERENCES

Send to your own State College of Agriculture or State University for bulletins or circulars (of recent date) on quick breads and leavening agents.

Halliday, Evelyn G., and Noble, I. *Hows and Whys of Cookery.* The University of Chicago Press, Chicago. Chapters II, III, VI.

Hart, R. N. *Leavening Agents.* The Chemical Publishing Company, Easton, Pa.

Heseltine, Marjorie, and Dow, Ula M. *The Basic Cook Book.* Houghton Mifflin Company.

Homemade Bread, Cake and Pastry. Farmers' Bulletin 1775, United States Department of Agriculture.

Justin, Margaret M., Rust, Lucile O., and Vail, Gladys E. *Foods.* Houghton Mifflin Company.

Lanman, Faith R., McKay, Hughina, and Zuill, Frances. *The Family's Food.* J. B. Lippincott Company. Chapter IX.

Rose, Mary Swartz. *Foundations of Nutrition.* 3d edition. The Macmillan Company.

Stewart, Jean J. *Foods: Production, Marketing, Consumption.* Prentice-Hall, Inc.

Todoroff, A. *Handbook of Food Selling.* The Grocery Trade Publishing Company.

Todoroff, A. *What's What in Groceries?* The Grocery Trade Publishing Company.

CHAPTER EIGHT

❧ Eggs and Bacon

Cook Book References

Bacon, broiled	*Page* 474
Eggs	*Page* 415
Omelets	*Page* 418

Food Value

Nutritive Value of Foods	*Table* VI, *Appendix*
Food Value in Shares	*Table* VIII, *Appendix*

EGGS — HOW WILL YOU HAVE THEM?

EGGS ARE ALMOST universally a favorite main breakfast dish. People in the United States eat an average of four eggs per person per week. Nature has given us conclusive evidence that eggs are useful for building such body tissue as bone, muscle, and blood. With no other food than that contained in an egg, the baby chick is developed, and so well developed that as soon as it is hatched it has sufficient strength to run about and scratch for its food.

Why are Eggs Important as Food? Eggs are rich in complete proteins, minerals, and vitamins; all these substances are needed in the growth and repair of muscle, bone, and blood. Because of their value in the building and repairing of tissue, eggs should be included in dietaries, particularly those of growing boys and girls.

PERCENTAGE COMPOSITION OF EGGS

	Water	*Protein*	*Fat*	*Carbo-hydrates*	*100 Calories*
Whole egg..........	72–75%	12–14%	10–12%	....	1⅓ eggs
Egg white............	86.2 %	12.3 %	.2 %	....	6 or 7 egg whites
Egg yolks............	49.5 %	15.7 %	33.3 %	....	Less than 2 yolks

EGGS AS SOURCES OF VITAMINS[1]

A	Excellent	occurs in yolk only
B_1 (Thiamin)	Good	
C (Ascorbic acid)	None	
D (Anti-rachitic)	Good	occurs in yolk only one of the few foods important for D amount varies with diet of the hen
G (Riboflavin)	Excellent	
Niacin (anti-pellagra)	Good	

MINERALS

	Iron	*Calcium*	*Phosphorus*
Whole egg.......	Excellent	Good	Excellent
Egg white........	....	Fair	....
Egg yolk.........	Excellent	Good	Excellent

Composition of Egg White and Egg Yolk. An examination of the preceding tables will show that the greater part of the nutrients for which the egg is prized are in the yolk. All of the fat, and most of the vitamins, phosphorus, calcium, and iron, are in the yolk. The yolk is therefore the most valuable part of the egg for tissue building or for repair. The white of the egg is approximately one eighth protein and seven eighths water. The yolk of the egg is approximately one third fat, one sixth protein, and one half water.

Nutritive Value of Eggs

Comparative Values of Milk and Eggs as Food. Eggs resemble milk more nearly than does any other food. Like milk the protein and fat of eggs are easily digested. Egg proteins are like milk proteins in that they are complete, and the fat in each is emulsified. Compared with milk, an equal weight of egg yolk contains ten times as much Vitamin A and twice as much Vitamin B_1. Because we take much more milk than eggs, milk is just as important for these vitamins as are eggs. Neither is a good source of Vitamin C. Eggs are superior to milk as a source of Vitamin D.

Milk is a richer source of calcium than are eggs, but eggs are a

[1] Consult Chapter 1 for the functions of these vitamins in human nutrition.

richer source of iron. The presence of iron and the anti-rachitic Vitamin D makes egg yolk one of the first foods to be added to milk in a child's diet. Unlike milk, eggs contain no carbohydrates. Eggs are more economical than meat, but on the average throughout the year are not so economical as milk. Three or four eggs a week are considered a minimum allowance for good nutrition for both children and adults.

Digestibility of Eggs. Eggs are easily digested. The method of cooking them does not influence the completeness of digestibility, but it materially alters the length of time required. Soft-cooked eggs are digested in a shorter time than hard-cooked eggs. Hard-cooked eggs should be thoroughly masticated. Some people take a longer time to digest raw eggs than cooked eggs.

Tests for the Freshness of Eggs.

1. The shell of a fresh egg is chalky and rough in appearance. Old eggs have smooth and shiny shells.

2. The white of a fresh egg is thick and viscous and the membrane surrounding the yolk is tough. Both of these become thinner with time, but the change does not affect the food properties of the egg.

3. Candling is the commercial test for determining the freshness of eggs. When you hold your fingers before a lighted electric bulb you note that they appear transparent except for the bone, which appears as a shadow. Candling eggs is a similar process. The egg is placed at one end of a tube, at the other end of the tube a strong light is placed. Under the test fresh eggs appear transparent and have little or no air space; a stale egg is cloudy and has a large air space at the larger end.

Care of Eggs. Buy clean eggs. As soon as purchased, put them in the refrigerator or some other cool place. Experts say that a fresh egg kept at a warm temperature for one day may deteriorate more than one kept in cold storage for six months. They will absorb odors; therefore they should not be placed near strong foods, such as onions. Egg yolks, if unbroken, may be covered with water and kept several days in the refrigerator. Freezing in an ice tray of the refrigerator is best. Egg whites will keep for several days in a covered glass if no water is added. Never wash eggs, unless they are very dirty, until you are ready to use them, as there is a natural coating that protects the pores to some degree.

Commercial Storage of Eggs. All protein food spoils easily unless it is kept cool, or is preserved in some other way. Cold storage facilities have made eggs available in quantity throughout the year. They can be kept in cold storage in good condition if they are in good condition when placed there. The change in flavor is very slight.

Home Storage of Eggs. Home storage of eggs is practical if clean, fresh, preferably infertile, eggs are available. Eggs may be kept by preventing bacteria from entering the porous shell, or by keeping them from growing after they enter. Cold storage prevents the growth of bacteria, as we learned in the study of milk. Sealing the pores of the shells of perfectly clean, fresh eggs will prevent the entrance of bacteria.

We can seal the pores of the shell by submerging the eggs in a solution of water glass, a sirup-like liquid which can be bought at a drug store. Mix one part of the water glass with nine parts of water which has been boiled and cooled. Put the solution in a stone crock and keep it covered to prevent evaporation. Place clean, freshly laid eggs in this solution. See that the eggs are well below the surface of the liquid. Keep them in a cool place. Eggs kept in this way for several months show little or no change in flavor.

Other ways of preserving eggs are not so satisfactory as the use of water glass because the flavor of the egg is altered by the preservative. Packing in sawdust, however, is recommended if water glass is not available.

Season for Eggs. Eggs are very plentiful and low in price as a rule, from March to August. Their quality is best from March through June. These are good months in which to use eggs more generously than usual.

Egg Cookery. Heat coagulates the protein of eggs. The point at which albumen coagulates is below the boiling point of water. This property of eggs makes them useful, in cookery, as thickening agents. High temperatures toughen the coagulated protein of egg. Cook eggs and egg mixtures, therefore, at a low temperature.

Because eggs have the property of holding air when beaten, they are used to lighten mixtures. For such mixtures low cooking temperature is necessary.

Uses of Eggs in Cookery. In the household eggs are used:

1. As an important food.
2. As a thickening agent in such foods as custards, sauces, and fillings for pies.

3. As a leavening agent in omelets, soufflés, and sponge cakes.
4. To improve flavor and texture in muffins, cakes, cookies, etc.
5. As a coating agent — as in preparing food for deep-fat frying.

Eggs for Breakfast. You may have your eggs cooked in many ways; for example:

soft-cooked	shirred	combination dishes:
hard-cooked	baked	creamed eggs
poached	coddled	scalloped eggs
scrambled	omelet (a real delicacy)	eggs à la goldenrod
fried (occasionally)		

Bacon

Bacon is regarded as a meat but it is principally fat. Four small slices of crisp, broiled bacon equal one hundred calories. Bacon adds zest to breakfast which is made up of simple foods. How much is added to the cost of a breakfast for six when two slices of bacon per person are added? There are usually between twenty and twenty-five slices of bacon in a pound.

People who work long hours out-of-doors sometimes like meat for breakfast. To give variety to the breakfast menu, ham, sausage, codfish balls, and some other meats may be substituted in small servings for bacon. They may be prepared in a number of ways, such as broiled, panbroiled, creamed, or served in an omelet.

EXPERIMENTS AND CLASS PROBLEMS

1. In some places eggs are sold by weight instead of by the dozen. Is it more accurate to measure eggs by pounds or by dozens? How many eggs in a pound?

2. Test unbroken eggs for freshness. Break open and let stand on a plate. Are they fresh? How can you tell?

3. Demonstrate the method used commercially for testing eggs by making a pasteboard roll and using an electric light or a flashlight. Note the appearance of the white and the yolk, and the air space in various eggs.

4. Examine a piece of eggshell under a lens. Dip it in a solution of water glass and examine it again. What has happened?

5. Consult your State Food Department at the State Capitol to find the law concerning grading of eggs. If they are graded in your state, study the grading and determine the best use of each grade.

6. Try your skill in management by planning the preparation of breakfasts in which the only variable is the method of cooking eggs.

BASIC MENU

A half grapefruit
Eggs Whole wheat toast
Cocoa

Breakfast Number 1	*Breakfast Number 3*
Soft-cooked eggs	Eggs à la goldenrod
Breakfast Number 2	*Breakfast Number 4*
Baked eggs	Omelet (plain)

Use your experience to carry out plans and evaluate your results.

HOME PROBLEMS

1. If you are not already expert at separating egg whites and yolks, practice whenever this is to be done at home.
2. Prepare eggs several times, in each of three ways that your family likes best.
3. Prepare eggs in four unusual ways for your family, as, for example, eggs à la goldenrod, scalloped eggs, French omelet, puffy omelet.

   Do not try too large an omelet at first. One of two or three eggs is large enough to attempt, if you are unskilled.
4. Prepare several breakfasts in which eggs are included.

REFERENCES

Consumers Look at Eggs. Prepared by Consumers' Counsel Division, Agricultural Adjustment Administration, Government Printing Office, Washington, D.C.

Eggs at Any Meal. United States Department of Agriculture, Leaflet 39.

Heseltine, Marjorie, and Dow, Ula M. *The Basic Cook Book*. Houghton Mifflin Company. Chapter XIV.

How to Candle Eggs. United States Department of Agriculture, Bulletin 565.

Justin, Margaret M., Rust, Lucile O., Vail, Gladys E. *Foods*. Houghton Mifflin Company.

Sherman, Henry C. *Food Products*. 3d edition. The Macmillan Company.

Wilmot, Jennie S., and Batjer, Margaret. *Food for the Family*. J. B. Lippincott Company.

CHAPTER NINE

❧ Breakfast Is Served—By You

For Table Customs see Chapter 10.
For Table Service see Chapter 11.
For Discussion of the Dining Room see Chapter 12.

EVEN THOUGH BREAKFAST is the simplest meal of the day, the first time that you assume the full responsibility for preparing and serving the family breakfast you will discover that it takes both thought and skill to have everything ready within a reasonable time, done to a turn, and served to a queen's taste, with the cook a smiling, gracious, and unflurried hostess.

How can it be done? The job requires both skill and managerial ability, which can be acquired only through practice. If you have been following the home-problems suggestions at the end of each chapter, you have already acquired skill in the preparation of various breakfast dishes and in simple breakfast combinations. Let us review the procedure in planning, preparing, and serving breakfasts as suggested in Chapter 2. You should now have the immense advantage of much knowledge and experience. Good management, we repeat here, necessitates:

1. A clear and definite goal which includes the standards to be considered acceptable.
2. Plans for every detail.
3. Skillful execution of plans.
4. A constructive criticism (evaluation) of the results.

Though we shall here consider breakfast as a separate meal, we must remember that it should be fitted into the day's plan for meals. The foods that are needed by everyone each day have been discussed in Chapter 1. How the three meals fit together will develop as the other meals are studied.

What Is Your Standard for Breakfast? You are aiming high; you wish to have breakfasts that will mark you as one who knows how to do interesting things with food, and how to have a breakfast that will furnish a gratifying beginning for any day. What are the qualities of a satisfying breakfast?

A number of people with a reputation for good taste in food were asked what distinguishes breakfasts they like from breakfasts they don't like. They did not all say the same thing, of course, but there was one point that everyone mentioned. Perhaps you can guess what many of them said and what this one point was. A few said they like to be comfortable when they eat, and the majority said they like to eat in pleasant surroundings and with others who are in a good humor. Over three fourths said they do not like to eat breakfast in an atmosphere of hustle and bustle. A majority said, too, that they like as much daylight as possible at breakfast time. Over half said that an expensive breakfast does not necessarily mean a good breakfast; that inexpensive food can be highly satisfying.

FIG. 26. A SURPRISE FOR MOTHER

Almost half mentioned the appearance of the food and of the table. Attractiveness and cleanliness seemed to be the essentials along this line. When they were pressed to say exactly what difference appearance makes to them, personal preferences differed; for example, some liked toast to be a light brown, others preferred a dark brown; some liked their eggs hard, others liked them soft.

When asked about variety in breakfast, almost all said they like it to a limited extent for breakfast. One man explained that he is very fond of eggs scrambled with cheese, but added: "I'd certainly get tired of them if I had them very often." In general they liked what they were used to. People have more definite habits in regard to breakfast than any other meal.

The point on which all were agreed was that "*the food must be good.*" By good food they said they had in mind that it should "taste good" — and should be satisfying to the appetite. What would your family consider "good food"? Would they agree with these qualifications? Would they add any ideas? Of course, all of us are interested in pleasing the people who are to eat the meals we prepare, hence what your family likes for breakfast is important in your plan when you are responsible for breakfast.

Since good food is perhaps the most important objective in planning breakfast, what steps must we take to achieve this standard? The answer is: To achieve success we must (*a*) plan good menus; (*b*) select each food to be used on a basis of quality, and (*c*) prepare and serve it "to a queen's taste."

What Plans Will You Make for Breakfast? The most important questions to consider in planning the breakfast menu are: Who is to eat the meal? What do they like? How do they like it? While it is comparatively easy to plan balanced meals, the difficult problem is to supply them within the range of the pocketbook, and at the same time suit the tastes of the family. If the food is not eaten, both time and money are wasted.

In order to make this chapter worth while, each of you should have in mind a definite menu for a definite group of people. What does your family like for breakfast?

Planning the Breakfast Menu to Meet the Food Needs. The menus for the entire day should be taken into consideration when planning the breakfast. One meal may be poorly balanced, yet it may fit into a well-balanced dietary for the whole day. Since we have not yet covered certain important foods, a fuller discussion of menu planning will be found later in the book. (See luncheons and dinners, Chapters 15 and 23.) Breakfast should ordinarily include the following:

1. Fruit, for good health, to stimulate the appetite, and to provide Vitamin C.
2. Whole-grain cereal to furnish regulatory foods (Vitamin B_1 and also calories and minerals).
3. Milk and eggs, tissue-building foods: complete proteins, calcium, phosphorus, and iron.
4. Bread to furnish part of the calories and, if whole wheat, some of the Vitamin B_1 and minerals.
5. A beverage.

Planning the Working Schedule. Even the most skillful cook needs to plan her working schedule. She may, however, plan it in her mind rather than on paper, if convenient. The inexperienced cook needs a brief written plan. Each dish cannot be finished before another is begun. The preparation of a meal is made up of separate jobs. Just as one instrument out of tune or off key may spoil an orchestra selection, so burned biscuit, or cold, fallen omelet is disastrous to the pleasing effect of the whole breakfast.

Decide upon the menu and assemble the supplies first, then make out your working schedule.

Carry Out the Plan by Preparing the Breakfast. After having made an outline of the jobs you will do in preparing your breakfast menu, carefully schedule your time and try out your plan. The actual practice must take place in your own home or possibly in the school laboratory.

How is Breakfast to be Served? If breakfast is arranged in courses, fruit is usually served first, because it stimulates the appetite. The cereal is served next, because a mildly flavored cereal is better relished before the stronger flavored foods. Eggs, bacon, or other meats, breads, coffee, and sweets, if any, come last. Foods served for breakfast should be simple and rather quickly digested.

A note of warning is appropriate here against sugar-laden cereal and the over-rich combination of hot cakes, waffles, butter, sirup and other sweets. Simple combinations of a few well-cooked foods are satisfactory and sensible.

Judging Results. How can you judge your results? By the relish with which the meal is eaten! By the timing; that is, whether the foods were ready on time and as needed.

You can evaluate your own work by answering these questions:

In what ways were you satisfied with your results?

In what ways could you improve on this experience?

CLASS PROBLEMS

1. Plan four breakfast menus that illustrate seasonal variations.

2. Score these breakfast menus for energy factors, tissue-building factors, regulatory factors, growth and health factors. Use plus and minus signs: a triple plus sign to indicate a great abundance of a factor, a double plus for a significant amount, a single plus for an average amount, and a minus sign to indicate its absence.

3. Plan a market list, working schedule, and the utensils for the preparation of the following breakfast menus:

No. 1
Grapefruit
Oatmeal and Cream
Poached Egg on Toast
Coffee and Milk

No. 2
Prunes
Shredded Wheat Biscuit, Top Milk
Omelet Popovers
Cocoa

4. Singly, and in groups, prepare and serve simple breakfasts as class projects. Evaluate results.
5. Arrange a breakfast tray for serving a breakfast in bed.

HOME PROBLEMS

1. Plan, prepare, serve (and clean up after) breakfast for a week or two at home. One breakfast will not be enough, because the object of your problem work is to acquire skill and managerial ability. This requires a series of breakfasts. In each case try to shorten the process of meal preparation and to improve the quality of the cooking and the suitability of the menu.
2. Do the family marketing and keep accounts for a month.
3. Improve family breakfast menus both in nutritive value and in economy.
4. Plan, prepare, and serve a breakfast party or picnic.

REFERENCES

Adequate Diets for Families with Limited Incomes. United States Department of Agriculture, Circular 113.

A Guide to Good Meals for the Junior Homemaker. United States Department of Agriculture, Miscellaneous Circular 49.

Bailey, N. Beth (McLean). *Meal Planning and Table Service.* Manual Arts Press.

Bogert, L. Jean. *Nutrition and Physical Fitness.* W. B. Saunders Company.

Diets to Fit the Family Income. United States Department of Agriculture, Bulletin 1757.

Harris, Jessie W. *Home Economics Project Record Book.* Houghton Mifflin Company.

Lanman, Faith R., McKay, Hughina, and Zuill, Frances. *The Family's Food.* J. B. Lippincott Company. Chapters XII, XIII, XIV.

Lutes, Della T. *The Gracious Hostess.* The Bobbs-Merrill Company.

Rose, Mary Swartz. *Feeding the Family.* The Macmillan Company. Chapter XII.

CHAPTER TEN

❧ Etiquette

"ETIQUETTE IS THE NAME given to the rules of society and society is the game that all men play. If you play it well, you win; if you play it ill, you lose. The prize is a certain sort of satisfaction without which no human being is ever quite satisfied." [1]

The Advantages of Good Manners. Good manners are not just an ornament, they are useful in everyday living. In business life, as well as in the social world, good manners play an important part. To be at ease and free from embarrassment under all circumstances, one must be free from all self-consciousness and considerate of others. One must not only know what is good form, but must make good form a habit through daily use. Confusion results when we stop to consider what we should do. The only sure way to be well mannered away from home and school is to be well mannered at home and at school. "Company" manners are as troublesome as a sore thumb and equally as evident. Awkwardness is due to self-consciousness or to ignorance. Ease comes with habitual good manners.

TABLE CUSTOMS

Appearance at the Table. Every self-respecting person comes to the table neatly attired and clean. Hands are never clean unless they have just been washed. Fingernails must be clean. Even at the family breakfast table slovenly attire is not permissible.

The A B C's of Good Table Manners. Promptness, a virtue at all times, is a necessity at mealtime. It is inconsiderate to keep others waiting; moreover the food is at its best when first served.

At an informal meal women and girls enter the dining room first;

[1] From *Etiquette of the Table.* Courtesy, Kansas State Agricultural College.

at some formal meals each man is requested to escort his dinner partner.

Stand by your chair until mother or the hostess makes the move to be seated. Sit or rise from the left side of the chair unless this is obstructed. It is a mark of good breeding for a man to assist in seating a woman by pulling her chair out a little from the table and pushing it up a little as she sits. It is also courteous for him to assist her in rising from the table by pulling the chair out. This is not necessary, however, and if the chairs are properly placed one should be able to sit down at the table and also rise from the table without moving the chair.

Many American families observe the custom of saying grace, or returning thanks, at the table. If you do not know the custom of the family, it is best to pause a moment just before or just after all are seated in order that, if grace is to be said, you will not interrupt it with conversation.

Do not begin to eat until all are served. It is customary for the hostess to give all signals, so to speak; she is the first to sit, the first to begin to eat, the first, at the end of the meal, to place her napkin on the table and rise. It is not good form at the table to attempt to arrange hair, or to toy with the silver or dishes, thump on the table, or pick at the tablecloth or at crumbs. Sometimes it is necessary to use a handkerchief at the table, but it must be done unobtrusively. In cases where this is not possible, as in continued coughing, it is best to leave the table temporarily.

Eat in a leisurely way. Chew with the lips closed; take small bites and thus save embarrassment in conversation. If you are called upon for a remark when you have food in your mouth, do not make the mistake of trying to reply immediately. All well-bred people eat noiselessly. Do not smack your lips or gulp down water, or make any sound in eating soup. It is rude to blow on food to cool it. If even with leisurely eating and small bites, hot food cannot be eaten in comfort, wait for it to cool. When it is necessary to remove a fish bone, a fruit seed, or some other substance from the mouth, do so as unobtrusively as possible, with the thumb and finger, or with the side of the fork or the spoon, and lay it on the side of the plate.

Posture at the Table. Good posture has much to do with good looks and also with good digestion. Sit erect. It is not good form to sit so close to the table that you touch the cloth. Feet belong on the floor. There is no tasteful way to drape them about the rungs of a chair. Be comfortable, but do not use more than your share of the space under the table. Do not bend over your food. It requires some care to be able to eat without soiling the tablecloth, but only occasional accidents are pardonable.

Conversation at Table. Bid your family a cheerful "good morning" at the breakfast table. Mealtime is a time for social intercourse. Be cheerful and agreeable. Table talk must avoid disagreeable subjects and those that are likely to cause hot disputes. Good humor is an aid to good digestion. Take part in the talk by contributing news or incidents of interest to the others, but do not monopolize the conversation. Do not interrupt others. A good listener is even more appreciated than a good talker. Be respectfully attentive to older people and include them in the conversation.

At a large or formal dinner it is your responsibility to converse with the person on either side of you. At the family table general conversation is best. Never converse exclusively with one person — and certainly there should be no secrets at the table. Never read at the table unless you are alone. If an accident happens at the table, regret should be expressed and the incident considered closed. The food that is served is not discussed at formal meals; but in the family circle or with friends, where mother or sister or a friend has done the cooking, it is a mark of thoughtfulness for you to show appreciation of good food.

The Telephone at Mealtime. Interruptions at mealtime are disturbing because they disrupt the serving and the conversation. It is equally poor taste to call on someone at mealtime, or to telephone at that time.

Serving and Being Served. When you are asked your preference in food, state it, otherwise accept what is served without comment. You are expected to pass any article of food which is near you, unless there is a maid. The serving silver will be near the dish. Place the silver in the dish conveniently and offer it to your neighbor first, unless he is occupied, in which case serve yourself first. Never reach across the table or in front of anyone. Ask courteously for what you want by addressing — by name — the person nearest the article, as "Jack, please pass me the salt."

Anticipate the needs of others at the table. You should observe when anyone wants the butter or the cream and sugar near

FIG. 27. THE KNIFE AND FORK IN USE

FIG. 28. THE FORK IN USE — KNIFE ON PLATE

you. Do not overdo the passing of food, however. Never serve yourself with your own silver. Sugar spoons, butter knives, and other serving silver are provided for this purpose. Be careful not to remove from the mouth a spoon or fork with a partially eaten mouthful still on it. It is an ugly habit to take food out of the mouth. Some people acquire this habit in eating ice cream without realizing that they have it or that it is disagreeable to others. Keep your plate as neat as possible. Do not mix food in it. Do not "sop" food with bread. Dishes should stay firmly on the table; do not tip your soup bowl, or lift a dish from the table in eating from it. Conserves or jelly may be placed either on the bread and butter plate or on the dinner plate. In the former case this sweet may be used as butter is used on bread, a little at a time, spread with the butter spreader. In the latter case it is eaten as a relish, with a fork.

At home second helpings are permissible. In passing the plate for a second helping, let the silver remain on the plate laid across the middle in such a position that it will not readily slip. Good form does not demand that some food be left on the plate. This custom has been abandoned as a rather foolish formality. It is also now good form to eat the lettuce on your salad plate instead of leaving it uneaten. When you finish eating, the dishes should be left in position.

The Use of Flat Silver. The silver is usually laid from the outside in the order of use. If you are puzzled at any point as to which piece to use, watch the hostess. The silver should be left in place until needed and should be in the hand only while cutting or conveying food to the mouth. Cut only one bite at a time. Never hold a fork or spoon in mid-air with a morsel of food in it. Never place food on a fork or in a spoon and leave it on the plate.

FIG. 29. POSITION OF KNIFE AND FORK WHEN EATING IS FINISHED

During the course of a meal a knife, fork, or spoon that has been used should not be placed on the tablecloth, nor should it be placed gangplank fashion from the edge of the plate to the table. A spoon is held by the handle with the thumb and forefinger, resting on the second finger very much as a pen does. (Figure 30.) Eat from the side of the spoon. In eating soup, dip the spoon from you in order to avoid dripping the soup upon the tablecloth.

FIG. 30. EATING SOUP

For coffee a spoon is used only to stir and to sample the beverage. It should never be left in the cup. When not in use it should be placed in the saucer. In other cases, when not in use it should be placed on the service plate, saucer, or coaster. If a flat soup plate is used, the spoon should be left in the soup plate instead of on the service plate.

A knife should be used only for cutting, or for buttering bread if an individual butter spreader is not provided. The knife is held in the right hand (unless one is left-handed). You should hold the handle of the knife just as you would hold a screw driver. (Figure 27.) When the knife is not in use it should be placed across the rim of the plate with the handle and blade resting on the rim of the plate, the cutting edge of the blade toward the user.

When knife and fork are used together, the fork is held in the left hand exactly as the knife is held in the right hand. (Figure 27). The tines are turned down. When a mouthful of food has been cut, the knife should be placed on the plate and the fork changed to the right hand. In carrying food to the mouth, hold the fork in the right hand with the tines up. (Figure 28.) Tender food, such as lettuce, should be cut with the fork. In such cases use the fork in the right hand. When the fork is not in use, it is placed, tines up, with the handle toward the right hand. When the course is finished, the knife and fork are placed parallel with the handles resting on the edge of the plate, the knife on the far side. The cutting edge of the knife should be toward the fork; the tines of the fork should be turned up. (Figure 29.)

One eats with a spoon or with a fork. When in doubt as to whether to choose a fork or a spoon, it is usually safe to choose the fork. Vegetables, salads, pie, watermelon, and soft cake call for a fork. A spoon may be used for creamed vegetables if they are served in small side dishes. Most desserts are eaten with a spoon, but often a fork or a spoon may be used according to preference.

Bread. Bread, crackers, and cookies are eaten with the fingers. Do not spread a whole slice of bread or a whole cracker with butter or cheese. Break a small piece of bread, and butter it as eaten. (Figure 39.) In the South, where much hot bread is eaten, it is customary to open a biscuit or muffin with the fingers (or with a fork if it is very hot), and with the knife or butter spreader put butter into it to melt. This bread is broken into smaller pieces to eat. If a bread and butter plate is provided, all bread and all spreads for the bread should be placed on it. Otherwise the bread should be placed on the edge of the dinner plate.

Finger Foods. Other foods than bread for which one uses the fingers are olives, celery, radishes, small pickles, potato chips, corn on the cob, nuts, crystallized fruit, cookies, some kinds of cake, and fresh fruit. If the fingers become slightly soiled, they should be wiped on the napkin. When fresh fruit is served, finger bowls and paper napkins may be used. To use a finger bowl, dip the ends of your fingers into the small bowl of water that is set before you. Then withdraw your fingers and gently wipe them with your napkin.

Napkins. The napkin should be placed, partially unfolded, in the lap, and kept there, for the most part. It is permissible to lift it to wipe the lips. The napkin should never be used as a bib.

After a meal, if one is a member of the family, or a house guest, or a frequent guest, one folds the napkin, if the other members of the group fold theirs. It is folded in the lap. If one is a guest for only that meal, the unfolded napkin is placed on the table; this rule applies also when the meal is eaten in a hotel, restaurant, or some other public place. The hostess is the first to place her napkin on the table; this gesture indicates that the meal is over.

Important Don'ts. Do not criticize the table manners of other people, especially elderly people. A toothpick is an emblem of rudeness and ignorance. If it is necessary to remove particles of food from the teeth, use dental floss in the privacy of your own room. Do not allow pets in the dining room, particularly during meals.

Hints for Hostess, Host, and Guest

The Hostess. When you plan a dinner party, choose congenial guests. Be ready to greet your guests when they arrive. There should be no flurry and no evidence of last-minute preparation. Chat with the guests awhile. It is permissible to leave them for a few minutes before serving the meal, but not for long.

Plan simple menus. Guests do not wish you to go to the trouble and expense of arranging elaborate menus for them. The hostess should, if possible, remain seated at the table during the meal. Guests would rather she did not make any troublesome effort to wait on them. A tea wagon may be used as a substitute for a maid. If there is a schoolgirl daughter, or a son, in the household, she or he may leave the table to serve. It is manly for a boy to help his mother with the meal service.

At the table the hostess is responsible for the conversation. No apologies should be made. The host and hostess eat until the guests finish.

The Host. The host may finish the carving before serving any of the plates. In serving the plates he should not touch them. The carving silver should be placed on the platter in the position of the knife and fork when they are not in use. The host may consult the preferences of the guests in the food. The plates should be served attractively. Small servings and a bit of garnish for each are effective. When the host passes a plate he should designate for whom it is served.

The Guest. Punctuality is appreciated in a guest; lateness, in fact, is almost unpardonable. A dinner guest should arrive not more than five or ten minutes before the hour set for dinner. It is the responsibility of the guest to be suitably attired for the occasion. A formal invitation indicates a formal affair. A telephoned invitation is usually informal.

Enter into the spirit of things. It is better to send regrets than to cast gloom over a group, if for any reason you cannot enter into the festivities. Take no notice of irregularities. Your hostess can make adjustments without the help of an outsider.

A dinner invitation is not an invitation for the evening unless so stated. Leave shortly after dinner. The woman guest of honor leaves first, but if she tarries, one of the other women present should leave. All the guests should leave at the same time. If an important engagement prevents your staying throughout the dinner, ask your hostess's permission to leave.

A courtesy is usually returned with a similar courtesy.

Calling is not so much in vogue as formerly, but it is courteous to make a dinner call. Follow local custom in this matter.

Courtesy in the School Lunchroom

Hands should be washed before eating lunch at school. Do not push or rush to get ahead of others in the line. Watch your step to avoid running into other people. It is not polite to reserve seats for friends. Books should not be placed on the tables.

A school lunchroom is noisy at best. Do your part to keep the noise at a minimum by not scraping the floor with the chairs and by not talking loudly. Be sociable and have a good time, but do not be boisterous. When you finish eating, clear the table for the next person. Take your tray to the proper place.

The lunchroom is not a dressing room; do not use it as such. Attend to matters of personal appearance before you enter.

CLASS PROBLEMS

Every day should be a practice day for proper habits of eating. Bad manners are incompatible with home economics.

1. It is most important that every meal be a lesson in table manners. Demonstrating the correct forms and usages is not enough; practice at home and at school is necessary in order to acquire pleasing table habits.

2. Have a question box at school for receiving unsigned questions on etiquette.

3. Make a list of "don'ts" for table conversation.

4. Plan a play on the subject of table manners. An effective demonstration may be given by means of shadows on a sheet.

HOME PROBLEMS

1. Everyone is interested in acquiring personal charm. Take as your home project the improving of your manners in general and of your table manners in particular.

   Observe others and study yourself to see what improvements are needed. Ask your family, your friends, and your teacher to point out your shortcomings in this particular.
2. Teach table manners to a small child.

REFERENCES

Bailey, N. Beth (MacLean). *Meal Planning and Table Service.* Manual Arts Press. Chapter I.

Faculty of South Philadelphia High School for Girls. *Everyday Manners.* The Macmillan Company.

Gunn, Lillian M. *Table Service and Decoration.* J. B. Lippincott Company.

Hadida, Sophie C. *Manners for Millions.* Doubleday, Doran and Company.

Kansas State Agricultural College. *Table Service and the Etiquette of the Table*, pp. 355–410. Manhattan, Kansas.

Lanman, Faith R., McKay, Hughina, and Zuill, Frances. *The Family's Food.* J. B. Lippincott Company.

Lutes, Della Thompson. *The Gracious Hostess.* The Bobbs-Merrill Company.

Niles, Kathryn B. *Family Table Service.* Burgess Publishing Company, Minneapolis, Minnesota.

CHAPTER ELEVEN

❧ Table Service

See also:

Courtesy at the Table	*Chapter* 10
Preparation and Serving of the Breakfast	*Chapter* 9
Preparing and Serving the Luncheon or Supper	*Chapter* 22
Preparation and Serving of Dinner	*Chapter* 28
Entertaining	*Chapters* 29, 30

MEALTIME IS THE FAMILY social hour, and it should be an enjoyable occasion. Everyone enjoys well-prepared and well-served meals when eaten with good company. Are you good company for your family and friends at mealtime?

Planning, preparing, and serving meals require effort, and the best way of showing appreciation of this effort is to make your contribution to the pleasure of others at mealtime.

Each person can contribute much to the pleasure of the family group by being on time, properly attired, in good spirits, interested in others, and by being well mannered.

Mealtime cannot be enjoyable unless there is some leisure. Even the busiest people find it wise to relax at mealtime, and enjoy eating as a social occasion. The meal hour should, by all means, be free from interruptions. Friends will co-operate if you make known your wishes.

Well-ordered meals should be the goal of every family.

The Importance of Good Usage. If the table service for family meals is not customarily well ordered, the occasional meal for which guests are invited is less likely to be pleasing. The family are much more important than guests. No rôle in the home can be more becomingly assumed by the older son or daughter than that of assistant in serving the meals.

The standard rules given here for setting the table and serving meals are founded on good taste, good sense, and simplicity. Everyone should know and practice these accepted usages. It must be remembered, however, that since customs may vary in different localities, these are not the only correct usages. Some variances also may be necessary, of course, in adjusting to the mode of living, to the home, and even to one's personal taste. For convenience in explaining table service the terms host, hostess, and guest are used instead of designating family members.

Types of Table Service

The type of table service varies with the formality of the meal, the amount of maid service available, and the preference of the family. There are three general types in use.

Family Style of Table Service. Family style of table service is also termed English style. It is suited to the usual family meals because it requires no maid service. All of the food is served at the table by the host, the hostess, or some other member of the family. It is possible to serve the entire meal without anyone's rising from the table, though usually it is necessary for someone to leave to bring in hot or cold food or to take out soiled dishes.

This type of table service is the most hospitable, the most informal, and the most universally used. In England it is a favorite style of table service, hence its name.

Formal Style of Table Service. Formal style of table service is also termed Russian style, and is used for formal occasions rather than for family meals. All of the food is served in the kitchen. The hostess and host take no more part in the serving of the meal than do the guests. This method of serving requires one expert waiter or waitress for each four or six persons served. Special meals calling for formal service are usually served in hotels and clubs, but they are sometimes carried out in the home with the employment of extra help. When you dine at an excellent hotel the service will be formal. This is one of the charms of hotel dining.

Compromise Service. Compromise style of table service is, as the name implies, a compromise between the informal and the formal styles. It has some of the hospitality of the family service but is more formal. The first course is usually served when the meal is announced. The soup, salad, or dessert may be served in individual servings from the kitchen (formal style), while the main course, the coffee, and sometimes the salad or the dessert, are served by the host or hostess. This type of service is used, as a rule, in homes where there is a maid to assist with the meals.

Since many of us do not have maids in our homes, and since informal service is used at times even in homes where there is a maid, the family type of service is the method that each of us should know best and is therefore emphasized in this chapter. The occasional use made of the other types of service justifies their brief consideration.

Setting the Table

General Considerations:

1. To be attractively set, a table should have clean linen, polished silver, glass, china, and flowers. A very charming table can be set with inexpensive furnishings if they are in good taste and are well arranged. Simplicity is always in good taste.

2. Avoid crowding the table. Space the "covers" equal distances apart. If the table is small, do not arrange to have too many dishes served from it at one time. A tea wagon or serving table will solve the difficulty.

3. The table must be well balanced.

4. The lines on the table should be as few in number as possible, and lengthwise or crosswise, never diagonal. Lines on tables are made by the creases or the weave in the table linen, and they are also formed by the manner of placing silver, dishes, glasses, and other articles.

Table Linen. For selection and types of linen appropriate for various meals, see Chapter 12.

If a tablecloth is used, it is usually laid over a soft pad. Luncheon cloths, breakfast cloths, place mats, and runner sets are laid on the bare table. If runners and place mats are used, the runner may be long enough to take the place of the two end covers. If no table pad is used, individual pads for hot dishes may be substituted for the protection of the table. These may be asbestos pads covered with mats, or they may be thick, washable mats.

Napkins should be simply folded. The style in napkins varies, but a conservative style is always safe. Large ones should be folded in squares with four foldings. Smaller ones may be folded in squares with two foldings, or in rectangles with three.

The Individual Cover. (See Figures 31, 32, 33.) All of the silver, linen, china, and glass used by one person is called a "cover." Allow twenty to twenty-four inches for each cover. The cover should not be crowded, but should be grouped compactly in order that it may look well and that each individual may know which articles are his. The outer edge of the cover must be straight. If the table edge is straight, place the cover one inch from it. If it is rounded, the cover edge does not parallel it but is a straight line, with the outer articles in the cover one inch from the edge of the table. Note this in the diagrams.

The plate is the center of the cover and must be directly in front of the chair. The silver is placed from the outside of the cover in the order used. Thus the silver for the first course is farthest from the plate and that for the last course is nearest the plate. Knives, spoons, and glasses are placed on the right hand; forks, bread and butter plates, napkins, and salad plates are placed at the left. The following exceptions are made:

1. If no knife is used, forks are placed at the right.

2. Individual butter spreaders are placed on the bread and butter plates, parallel to the edge of the table. (See diagrams.)

3. The oyster fork may be placed at the extreme right or on the plate.

4. The spoon for orange or grapefruit may be placed on the plate on which the fruit is served. It should parallel the other silver.

5. The dessert silver is often placed with the dessert.

Knife blades are turned toward the plate; forks and spoons are placed with tines and bowls turned up. The glass is placed at the tip of the knife; the bread and butter plate at the tip of the fork; the napkin to the left of the fork, with the lower right-hand corner the open corner. Individual salt and pepper shakers may be placed above the plate in line with the glass for each cover, or between two covers.

Dishes Additional to Individual Covers. For family meals, it is customary to lay the serving silver and extra dishes on the table or on a tea wagon or small serving table convenient to the hostess in order to avoid getting up from the table. Serving silver for any dish may be placed to the right of the space for the dish, or it may be laid with the dish. It should be placed parallel to other lines of the table. The dishes needed vary with each meal, but in general the following articles will be used and placed as follows:

1. FOR BREAKFAST. (See Figure 31.) The coffee percolator or other container may be put at the hostess's right, with the handle parallel to her silver. The cups and saucers may be placed above her cover. It is best not to stack these, but if that is necessary,

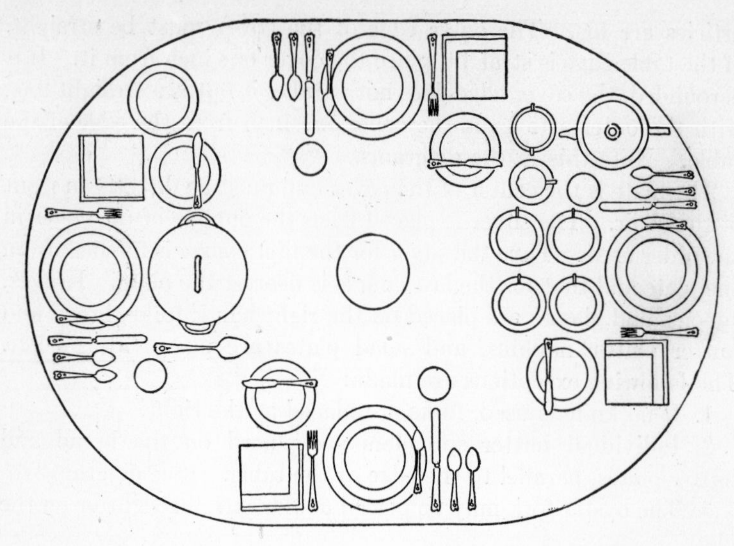

FIG. 31. DIAGRAM OF TABLE SET FOR BREAKFAST

not more than two should be stacked together. The cream and sugar should be placed to the right of the cups, above the percolator.

Prepared cereal may be served in individual bowls placed on the tea wagon or stacked at place for serving. Cooked cereal may be placed in a covered dish above the plate of one of the covers other than the cover of host or hostess. The cereal bowls should be at the left of the dish that holds the cereal.

2. FOR LUNCHEON OR DINNER. (See Figures 32, 33.) The salad on salad plates may be placed at the left of the covers, just beyond the napkin. The carving fork should be at the left of the space for the platter, the carving knife and a tablespoon at the right. The water pitcher may be placed in a plate or on a tile at the right of one cover (other than that of the host or the hostess).

Modifications if Maid Service is Available. To obviate crowding the table, the serving table or buffet may be used for extra dishes and silver. The serving table is convenient for:

1. The water pitcher, placed on a tray. A folded napkin may be placed near for use in pouring water to keep drops off the tablecloth.

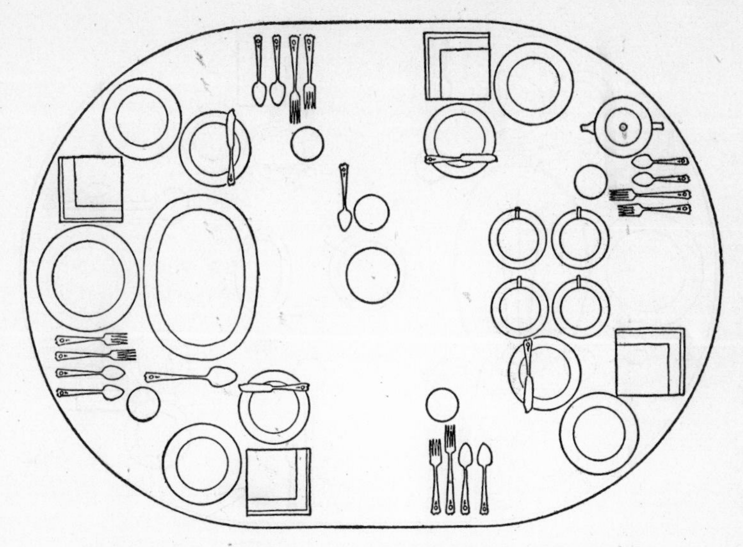

FIG. 32. DIAGRAM OF TABLE SET FOR LUNCHEON

2. A small tray, needed in serving the meal.
3. Extra china, such as cups and saucers, bowls, and plates.
4. Serving silver.
5. Cream and sugar.
6. One complete extra cover if space permits.
7. Extra butter balls.

The serving table must never be crowded. There should be space left where soiled dishes can be placed temporarily while the table is being cleared.

Table Decorations. Table decorations should be simple. A well-set table needs little ornamentation. A few fresh flowers, well arranged, or an attractive potted plant may be used on the table. Low bowls are best. Fruit may furnish the centerpiece for breakfast. For a party or a formal meal, the flowers are usually chosen to carry out a color scheme. Flower arrangements for special occasions may be more or less elaborate. Candles make a very effective table decoration. Four candlesticks are commonly used. The candles carry out the color scheme. The prevailing mode in length of candles and height of candle holders should be followed.

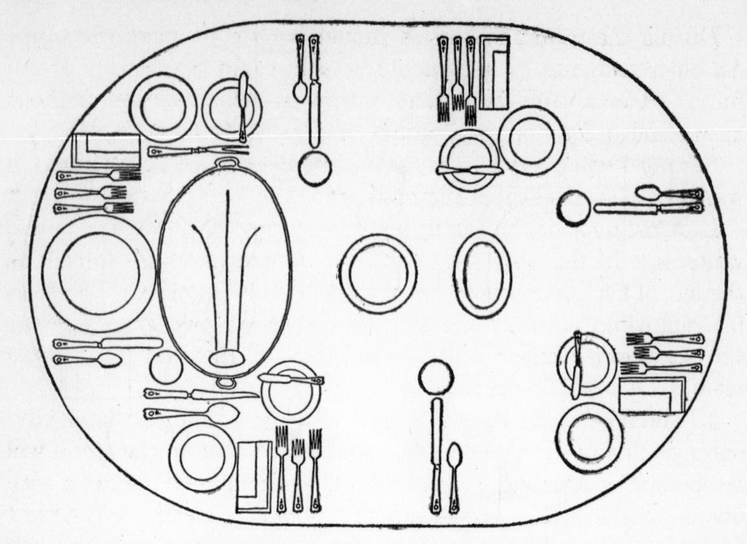

Fig. 33. TABLE SET FOR DINNER

Nut cups are used at formal luncheons or parties. They should be chosen with reference to the color scheme.

Plain place cards are used when a large number of guests are to be seated. In this case the card bears only the name. For special occasions, such as a bride's breakfast, a children's Easter party, a Hallowe'en supper, or a Valentine luncheon, the place card should carry out the special feature of the occasion. The position for a place card is on the napkin or above the cover.

Serving the Meal. The dining room should have, at mealtimes, a comfortable temperature, and the air in the room should be fresh and entirely free of odors from the kitchen. The shades or blinds and curtains should be adjusted so that the light is good and at the same time not uncomfortable for anyone at the table. The chairs should be so placed that the guests may be seated without pulling the chairs back. If the front of the seat is even with the edge of the table, the chair is at a comfortable distance.

Immediately before the meal is announced the glasses should be filled with water, the pitcher filled about three fourths full, and butter placed on the bread and butter plates. The first course may also be placed on the table. Jelly, pickles or olives, celery, and crackers may also be placed when the meal begins.

During the meal the hostess should try not to leave the table. An older daughter or son should be able to do the serving gracefully. Thoughtfulness of the wants of others, speed without haste, and quietness are qualities of a good waitress.

Serving Family Style. A meal may be well served without a waitress. Two accepted methods are:

1. A member of the family may rise from the table and act as waitress. In this case she places her napkin, partially folded, at the left of her cover when she leaves the table to serve. The rules for removing, placing, and passing dishes are the same whether the service is rendered by a member of the family or by a maid.

2. The hostess may serve a meal to a small group without anyone's getting up from the table, provided no dish on the menu will be spoiled by standing. A tea wagon or a small serving table with one or two shelves is necessary. It should be placed at the right of the hostess. On the upper surface all extra silver, dishes, and some of the food, the dessert or salad, for example, may be placed. Other silver and food are placed on the dining table.

The hostess asks members of the group to assist by serving themselves to dishes that are convenient to them, by passing plates or dishes to others, and by passing soiled dishes to the hostess. These soiled dishes may be quietly placed on the lower shelves of the serving table or tea wagon. The host serves the meat and vegetables. The hostess serves the soup, dessert, coffee or tea. The salad may be served by the hostess or may be on the table when the meal begins. A member of the family other than the host or the hostess fills the glasses with water, brings in any hot food, and removes dishes.

Serving a dinner Family (or English) Style. Let us take a typical dinner menu and explain the serving of it by the family style of table service without a maid.

MENU

Vegetable Soup
Roast Beef
Browned Potatoes **String Beans**
Bread **Gravy** **Butter**
Head Lettuce Salad
Fresh Strawberries **Wafers**
Coffee

FIRST COURSE: The soup may be served and on the table when dinner is announced. A plate of crackers will be on the table. The hostess will ask the person nearest the crackers to "please have crackers," who should then offer them to her neighbor, help herself, and pass them.

When all are through eating soup, a member of the family should rise and remove the soup plates. (See Rules for Waiting on the Table, page 122, for directions.) Sometimes the first course, such as tomato or grapefruit juice, may be served in the living room. Then the main course may be on the table when the meal begins.

THE MAIN COURSE: See diagram of table, page 116, for arrangement of the host's cover. The warmed dinner plates should first be brought in and placed in front of the host. Next place a platter containing the roast in front of the host. If the platter is sufficiently large, the potatoes and other vegetables may be placed on it with the roast. Otherwise vegetable dishes should be placed at the side of the platter.

The host carves enough of the roast to serve all at the table. (See carving illustrations, Chapter 28.) He serves the plates, one at a time, with meat and vegetables. He may or may not serve the gravy. As each plate is served, the host passes it, designating the person whom he has served. The carving knife and fork, when not in use, should be placed on the platter.

The hostess may be serving the coffee while the plates are being served. The coffee cups and saucers, cream, sugar, and percolator may be placed on the table at the hostess's cover, as shown in Figure 32, page 115, or they may be placed on a tea wagon or a serving table adjacent to the hostess. If the hostess is not familiar with individual preferences for cream or sugar, she asks each person his preference, or the cream and sugar may be passed at the table for self-service. The coffee is passed by those seated at the table. The coffee may be served with the dessert if preferred.

The gravy, bread, and relishes may be passed at the table. The person near whom each article is placed should offer the food to the person next to him, or serve himself and then pass it, depending upon whether his neighbor is occupied otherwise or not.

If bread and butter plates are used, the butter should be on these plates when the meal is announced. If bread and butter plates are not used, the butter, preferably cut in individual servings and served with a small fork, should be passed at the table.

FIG. 34. DINNER IS SERVED

An attractive set table ready for the guests. The bouillon is on the table.

FIG. 35. MAKING A WELL-MANNERED START

A man helps to seat a woman guest.

FIG. 36. THE SOUP COURSE

Crackers and olives often accompany this course.

FIG. 37. WHEN ONE IS HOST
Carving requires skill and practice. (See Chapter 28.)

FIG. 38. USING THE KNIFE AND FORK TOGETHER; USING THE FORK ALONE

FIG. 39. THE KNIFE WHEN NOT IN USE USING THE BUTTER SPREADER

Fig. 40 SALAD FORKS IN USE AND OUT OF USE

Fig. 41. THE SPOON IN USE AND WHEN LAID ASIDE

The salad, if served with the dinner course, may be on the table when dinner is announced, or it may be placed by some member of the family while the host and hostess are serving at the table, or it may be passed in a large bowl.

When this main course is over, a member of the family may rise and first remove the meat platter and other dishes from which the food was served, next the individual covers, and last the salt and pepper shakers. If necessary, the table should be crumbed: a plate and folded napkin are used.

If the number seated at the table is small, the table may be cleared by passing the used dishes to the hostess for stacking on a serving table near at hand. For a larger group it is much better to have a member of the family "wait on the table," resuming her seat when the serving is finished, to eat the next course.

Water should be poured if needed during the course, but certainly each glass should be filled between courses. Someone may rise from the table to serve water, or it may be placed on the table or conveniently near the table.

THE DESSERT COURSE: The

Fig. 42. WHEN WE LEAVE THE TABLE

bowl of strawberries, cream, wafers, dishes, and silver for serving the berries, may be on a serving table near the hostess, or they may be brought in and placed in front of the hostess. She may serve the berries and pass the plates to those at the table. The wafers and cream may be passed for each person to help himself.

The dishes for the last course are not removed from the table.

Rules for Waiting on the Table. One person can serve eight persons if the compromise style of service is used.

The waitress should come within easy reach of the table, but not close enough to touch it.

Left-hand service seems the simplest form of service to remember, and is used here. Dishes are placed, passed, and removed from the left of the guest. Beverages are placed and removed from the right in order that there shall be no reaching in front of the guest. For a left-handed guest this is reversed.

It is exceedingly bad form for the waitress to reach in front of or in any way inconvenience a guest. It is more convenient for both guest and waitress for the waitress to use the hand farthest from the guest. If serving from the left, use the left hand; if serving from the right, use the right hand.

When two plates are removed at once — as the dinner plate and the bread and butter plate — pick up the farther one (the bread and butter plate) with the left hand and the nearer one (the dinner plate) with the right hand.

In formal service the guest is never left without a clean plate (service plate) in front of him between courses. Service plates are removed as each course is placed, and placed as each course is removed. The service plate is placed or removed with the right hand (from the left side) and the plate containing food or the soiled plate is placed or removed with the left hand.

In serving, the waitress enters the dining room carrying two served plates, one in her right hand, which she places on the serving table. She places the plate in her left hand in front of a guest from the left side. She then takes the plate from the serving table in her left hand and places it in front of the next guest.

In removing plates, go to the left of guests and use the left hand. It is best to remove one plate at a time, and place it on the serving table. The second plate is removed and kept in the left hand. The waitress then goes to the serving table, picks up the first plate, and passes out of the dining room with two plates. Soiled dishes should never be stacked in the dining room when waiting on the table.

The hostess is usually served first and others in succession as they are seated. Some prefer to observe the older custom of serving guests first. In this case the women at the table are served first. It does not matter much one way or the other, since no one begins to eat until all are served.

If all the silver is not placed before the meal is served, everything pertaining to one course must be placed before that course is served.

In clearing the table, the proper order of removal is food first, then soiled dishes, glasses, and silver in order. All unused silver belonging to a course is removed when the course is removed.

In passing food, see that it is held so that the guest may serve himself with ease. Be thoughtful of left-handed guests. How?

The table is crumbed only when necessary. A plate and folded napkin are used.

In filling glasses, do not remove them from the table. A napkin may be used to wipe the lip of the pitcher after each serving, thus protecting the tablecloth and the guest. Water glasses are left on the table throughout the meal.

Seating at the Table. If the hostess has no assistance in serving a meal, she sits at the end of the table that is nearer the kitchen door. If there is a maid, the hostess may sit at the opposite end of the table where she can watch the maid as she enters the room and can easily signal to her. The host sits opposite the hostess.

If a member of the family is serving, her seat should be a position that is accessible to the kitchen door. Guests are seated where they will be most comfortable. Usually a woman guest is seated at the host's right, and a man at the hostess's right.

The Buffet Meal. The buffet meal is an informal way of serving a meal to a relatively large number of persons in a limited space. It is most popular for luncheon or supper, especially for Sunday night supper. (See Chapter 22.)

For a buffet meal no waitress is needed. Two types of buffet service are used. (1) The guests serve themselves from the table where the food, silver, and napkins are arranged; or (2) the hostess requests one or two friends to assist by serving one dish, usually from each end of the table. For example, one person may serve a salad course, or a hot dish, such as creamed chicken in bread cases, and at the opposite end of the table another person may pour the beverage.

The hostess should keep two things in mind if a buffet meal is to be most enjoyable: (1) The food must be such that it can be eaten with a fork. Dishes that slide or tip are too precarious for use when one must hold his plate on his lap, hence knives, and tall glasses are to be omitted. (2) Guests should be seated so they can enjoy an informal grouping. A small table, on which the group may place their glasses, is a most appreciated courtesy.

For a detailed description of a buffet luncheon, see Chapter 29, We Have a Party.

A Cafeteria-Buffet Supper. A much more informal meal is the cafeteria-buffet supper. The guests take a tray and serve themselves, frequently going to the kitchen for the main course. The dessert is served from a table in the dining room. An individual tray service is very comfortable for the guest.

The center of interest in a buffet meal is, of course, the table. The table linen, dishes, flowers, candles, and the food itself are all part of the decoration scheme. The table arrangement affords unlimited opportunities for the artistic hostess to express her skill.

CLASS PROBLEMS

The rules for table service are best understood and remembered if learned through demonstrations and practice. Mock table service is suggested as a preliminary to serving meals.

1. *Breakfast menu*

Fruit
Hot cereal Cream
Eggs Toast
Coffee

Lay the table for this meal and serve it as a mock breakfast, using the family style of service.

2. *Luncheon menu*

Cream of Tomato Soup
Broiled Lamb Chops Rolls
Celery Mashed Potatoes
Stuffed Tomatoes Peas
Charlotte Russe

Lay the table for this meal and serve it as a mock luncheon, using: (1) family style without a maid; (2) compromise style with a maid.

3. *Dinner menu*

Oyster Cocktail
Tomato Bouillon   Crackers
Olives   Celery
Roast Beef   New Potatoes
Asparagus Tips
Lettuce Salad and French Dressing
Frozen Apricots
Mints   Coffee   Nuts

Lay the table for this menu and serve it compromise style without a maid; with a maid.

4. Discuss and compare the difference in serving these menus with and without maid service.

5. Plan a meal which could be served to four persons without the hostess's rising from the table. Assume that there is a tea wagon.

HOME PROBLEMS

1. Set the table for your family meals.
2. Assist with the serving of meals.
3. Act as hostess for a dinner, serving the meal family or English style.

REFERENCES

Bailey, N. Beth (McLean). *Meal Planning and Table Service.* The Manual Arts Press.

Gunn, Lillian M. *Table Service and Decoration.* J. B. Lippincott Company.

Lanman, Faith R., McKay, Hughina, and Zuill, Frances. *The Family's Food.* J. B. Lippincott Company. Chapters XIII, XIV.

Lutes, Della Thompson. *The Gracious Hostess.* Bobbs-Merrill Company.

Niles, Kathryn B. *Family Table Service.* Burgess Publishing Company, Minneapolis, Minnesota.

Stanley, Louise, and Cline, J. A. *Foods, Their Selection and Preparation.* Ginn and Company.

Stewart, Jean J. *Foods: Production, Marketing, Consumption.* Prentice Hall.

Table Service and Etiquette of the Table. Kansas State Agricultural College, Manhattan, Kansas.

Wilmot, Jennie S., and Batjer, Margaret Q. *Food for the Family.* J. B. Lippincott Company.

See also current magazines.

Write to your own State Agricultural College and request any available bulletins on table service.

CHAPTER TWELVE

❧ Where Shall We Eat?

Table Appointments. There should be an atmosphere of cheerfulness and hospitality about the simplest places in which we eat. In summer we like to picnic or to have our meals out-of-doors on the porch. In winter we may have supper before a cheerful fire in the living room, or breakfast in the inviting warmth of the kitchen.

The Breakfast Room or Breakfast Nook. Today the breakfast room or dining alcove is supplanting, to some extent, the dining room in the small house. If the breakfast room is to take the place of a dining room, it should be large enough so that the family will not be crowded at mealtime.

A popular adaptation of the breakfast room is the breakfast alcove or nook in the kitchen, with the Pullman style of table and built-in bench seats. In warm climates, for obvious reasons, a breakfast room is more acceptable than a breakfast nook in the kitchen. The breakfast room may contain built-in cabinets for the storage of dishes and linens, and also storage space in the benches. It may also be used as a children's reading room or playroom, a sewing room, for ironing, or the household office.

The Dining Room. In the large house the dining room is important. When the family is large it is a necessity if meals are to be enjoyed in comfort.

Sunlight and air should be considered in locating the dining room. If it is not placed where the sunshine reaches it much of the day, the color of the walls and hangings should suggest sunlight — yellow, for example. If the room is sunny, softer tones in grays or greens may be a wise choice.

The dining room is usually the most formal room in the house. It ought to have an air of balance and poise and it should be furnished so as to harmonize with the rooms adjoining it. There should be no extra furniture or ornaments; everything should have its own special use. The presence of much furniture interferes with the serving of meals. In addition to the table and chairs there is usually a buffet or server; there may also be a smaller serving table or a tea wagon. A large rug is preferable to smaller ones which roll up and get in the way when meals are served.

The Combination Dining Room. The combination of living room and dining room is a practical arrangement. A gate-leg or refectory table looks well in a living room and is appropriate for the serving of meals. For the serving table, a small table or a spinet desk with the top closed may be used. In order to preserve the informality of a living room, the chairs should not be all alike. Armchairs may be used for the ends of the table, and side chairs for the other places. The side chairs and armchairs may even differ in style, but they should not differ in period. For example, Windsor and ladder-back chairs belong to the same period, but differ in style.

The dining room may also be satisfactorily used as a library or a study room. The built-in cases may be used to hold books instead of china.

Furniture for the Dining Room. Furniture must be lived with a long time, and should therefore be carefully chosen so that it will give the maximum of satisfaction. The general style of the house and the type of furnishings in the adjacent living room should determine the style of furniture for the dining room. For example, if the house is Early American, maple or cherry furniture may be chosen for the dining room. The table may be a gate-leg, drop-leaf, or refectory extension table. If the house is Southern Colonial or Georgian in style, more dignified furniture in mahogany or walnut is called for. If the house is modern in line, the furnishings should also be of modern design. Dining room chairs should be in a style that is appropriate to that of the table.

Table Silver

Choosing Silver. Table silver will usually last a lifetime or longer. It should therefore be chosen carefully.

1. STERLING OR PLATED WARE. Sterling, or "solid silver," is more expensive than plated silver, but it is much more durable, can be passed on for generations, and is one of the most prized of family heirlooms. On each piece of solid or sterling silver is stamped the word "sterling" which signifies that it contains 925 parts of pure metal to 1000 parts of metal. It is not all silver. Another metal is mixed with the silver to give it added hardness. The same pattern of sterling silver may sometimes be purchased in light weight, medium, and heavy weight pieces. The medium and heavy weights

are usually best liked; they are called trade or standard and extra. Sterling silver usually costs quite a little more than the silver it contains. Prices vary with the weight of the silver, and with the pattern selected.

People of moderate means sometimes choose sterling instead of plated flat silver because of its long life. Flat silver consists of knives, forks, and spoons as opposed to hollow ware, such as sugar bowls and cream pitchers.

If one has sterling silver it should be used. Silver that is not used gives little pleasure and is a major care. Careful use really enhances the value of family silver.

Plated silver is made in patterns that compare favorably in beauty with solid silver. Plated silver of good quality will wear well. Its quality is determined both by the *base* and by the plating. A triple plate on nickled silver is very durable. The weight of the plating is more important than the number of platings. Sometimes plated silver is advertised as quadruple plate. This means little unless the weight of the silver plate is given. The best weight plated silver will have 8 or 9 pennyweight of silver per gross of teaspoons, or twice as much silver per gross of tablespoons. One must really examine the specifications in order to determine the quality of plated silver. Brand or trade names mean little, but the specifications given under the trade-mark of a reliable manufacturer may give the consumer useful information.

Inlaid silver is plated silver combined with an inlay of solid silver where the greatest wear comes, for example, on the outer surface of the bowl of a spoon, or at the place at which handles of knives, forks, and spoons touch the table. Inlaid silver is longer wearing and more expensive than the usual plated ware, but less expensive and less durable than sterling.

2. PATTERN. The second important decision to be made is in the choice of a design. Plain silver scratches easily, but ornate silver requires more care. Much time and energy will be saved, therefore, if a plain pattern is chosen.

3. OTHER POINTS IN CHOOSING SILVER:

A satin finish is preferred to a bright finish because of its beauty and because it does not show scratches so easily.

It is well to look at all the various pieces in selecting a silver pattern to make sure of their attractiveness, and also to decide on the desirability of the various sizes and shapes.

Knife blades of stainless steel are available in many patterns of sterling or plated silver. Hollow handle knives are not as durable as the flat-handled kind, but are considered prettier.

In buying silver it is important to buy the product of a manufacturer who has the reputation of being an excellent silversmith.

China

The name "china" has been given to the wide variety of dishes available for table use. The material of which dishes are made originally came from China. Hence the name. But today the china on our tables represents the chinaware of the world. England furnishes Royal Doulton, Minton, Worcester, Spode, and Wedgwood; France charms with Haviland and "eggshell" china; there are novelty wares from China and Japan, and from most of the countries of Europe. American china has only recently succeeded in competing with the wares of foreign countries. Syracuse china is a well-known medium-priced American product; Lennox is a standard high-grade china of American make.

In none of the household furnishings may the housewife better express her individual taste than in her china.

General Rules in Selecting China. Dishes which are to be used for all purposes should be chosen with great care. Since food is ornamental in itself it is more attractive when served on dishes that are not overdecorated. Conventional patterns in china are therefore to be preferred to all-over floral designs. Patterns are put on the china either under the glaze or over the glaze. Under-glaze designs are much more desirable. Gold is always put on over the glaze, hence gold band china that has been used a long time shows the wear on the gold banding.

In selecting china it is wise to see a table laid with the whole set. One plate may be attractive by itself, whereas the effect of the whole set may not be at all pleasing. Dishes are sold in sets and in open-stock patterns. It is wise to choose open-stock patterns, for then your dishes may be replaced for a period of years; but even open-stock patterns are sometimes discontinued. Avoid odd shapes, sizes, and patterns in choosing dishes for general use. If the china is to be used only for the breakfast room, or for a tea service, one may indulge in more unusual patterns. A high price is no guarantee of tastefulness. Very tasteful china may be bought at reasonable prices.

Kinds of China. The kinds of china vary widely in expense and in quality.

1. PORCELAIN AND "BONE CHINA."

The most expensive tableware and that of the best quality is made of porcelain or "bone china." Porcelain is translucent and can be easily distinguished from semi-porcelain ware by holding it to the light. Porcelain is hard and durable, and has a non-absorbent, highly glazed or vitrified surface.

Porcelain china requires handsome linens, silver, and crystal. Even though most of us will not own porcelain china we should all appreciate it for its quality of material, design, and workmanship. The choicest of imported china is porcelain, Minton, Royal Doulton, and Haviland. Lennox is an American-made porcelain.

2. SEMI-PORCELAIN CHINA. Semi-porcelain includes the widest variety in china. Some of the choicest dishes, and also some of the poorest, are semi-porcelain. Much of the best imported china, such as Spode and Wedgwood, is a high-grade semi-porcelain. Syracuse is a good grade of domestic china in semi-porcelain.

A good quality of semi-porcelain is thicker than porcelain china, but it resembles the better china in quality of design and glaze. It is non-porous. Poor grades of semi-porcelain do not wear well; they craze and crack. When we say that dishes "craze" we mean that the glaze on them cracks, admitting grease which discolors the surface in the cracks. Cracked or crazed china is unsanitary and should be discarded.

3. POTTERY OR EARTHENWARE. Pottery is not so durable as the other types of china because it is not so hard. It is not so refined a product either. Pottery is limited in its use to informal settings. It calls for coarse linens of the peasant or hand-woven type, also for glassware to suit. One would not choose pottery if limited to one set of dishes, but if dishes for special use are to be included, pottery is excellent for breakfasts or suppers. Pottery is really a luxury.

In buying pottery, use care in selecting a pleasing but not too brilliant color. The gay combinations that look attractive in the store may not be so attractive with food in them, and one may tire of the strong and varied colors. Well-chosen china will be attractive in design, in shapes, and in materials; suitable for the home in which it is to be used; durable; not too expensive for the budget; and of a pattern that can be replaced.

Glassware

Every table needs at least a little glassware to give it a sparkle. Styles in glassware come and go, but the clear crystal type is always conservative; it may be plain or etched. The articles that are preferable in glass are:

Tumblers or goblets	Punch cups	Finger bowls
Stem glasses for fruit cocktail or dessert	Salt shakers	Candlesticks
	Dessert dishes	

The more expensive glassware is blown glass and is often called crystal. The less expensive is pressed glass. The two names are derived from the processes of manufacture. The quality of glassware is determined by its brilliance, clearness, smoothness, and by the quality of its decoration. The best crystal has a bell-like tone when tapped. Colored glassware is very attractive for special occasions, but when glassware is to be used for all occasions clear crystal is preferable. Plain glassware with little or no ornament is in good taste. Pleasing shapes add to the attractiveness of glassware. Stem ware, such as goblets, is less durable than tumblers. Glassware with a straight edge chips or nicks less readily than does that with a rolled or flared rim.

Glassware is easily broken. It is, therefore, wise not to invest much money in it. The glassware chosen, however, must be in keeping with the silver and china. Elegant dishes require elegant crystal. The attractiveness of modest dishes may be enhanced by the glassware used with them.

Table Linen

The term "linen" is used for all fabrics used on the table — linen, cotton, rayon, and a mixture of any of these called "union linen" is used, but linen is much preferred for the table. Linen damask has a pleasing luster, launders well, and has a smooth and satiny appearance which make it the aristocrat of table linens.

For Dinner and the Dining Room. The white damask linen tablecloth is the most favored for the dining room, and is nearly always used for dinner. The napkins should match the cloths. Simple hand-sewn hems are used. Colored damask in pastel shades may be beautiful, but is not as much favored.

For Breakfast or the Breakfast Room. Simplicity is in good taste for table linen at all times, but it is the dominant note in breakfast linens. A bare table may be used without pads. The cloth may only partially cover the table. Either a square luncheon cloth or a table runner with rectangular place mats will meet with approval. Color is frequently used, especially in the borders. Linens for the breakfast room are often coarse, and embroideries are used. Many very attractive, inexpensive breakfast-room "sets" are available in fabrics of cotton, linen and cotton mixed, and linen. Small napkins are used at breakfast. The napkins usually match the cloth. For an attractive breakfast table, see Fig. 43.

For Luncheon or Supper. The simple linens used for breakfast may also be used for luncheon or supper when this meal is served in the breakfast alcove. For a luncheon served in the dining room, the tablecloth may be laid as for dinner, or the bare table with rectangular place mats may be preferred. Luncheon sets may be quite colorful, or very elaborate, with needlework or inserts of lace, but very simple ones, also, are beautiful and are more practical. Luncheon napkins are medium-sized and preferably match the cloth or plate doilies. Luncheon sets are very practical because of the ease of laundering small pieces of table linen. They are also inexpensive and can be had in a wide variety of designs.

For the Porch or Breakfast Nook. For meals served on the porch or in the breakfast nook sometimes no linen is used. Glass-top tables or linoleum-covered tables are often used without place mats or tablecloths. In the summer we dispense with as much work as possible. The laundering of table linens can be avoided especially in the outdoor dining room.

Very attractive and colorful place mats are available in paper, cellophane, raffia, cork, and other materials. A glass-topped table set with lace paper mats can be very attractive. Paper napkins may also be used.

Points in Purchasing Table Linen. Linen, like jewelry, should be purchased from reliable stores. Even experts cannot tell by casual examination the difference in grades of linen. Buy linen by the weight. Good table linen is closely woven. The double damask is the most durable and the most satisfactory. Cheap damask does not wear well. If good linen is too expensive, a good grade of cotton is preferable to a cheap, poor quality of linen. Colored table "linens" are a fad; it is not wise to invest in expensive material of this type.

Sizes of Table Linens. In purchasing linens the size of the table must be considered. A minimum drop of six to eight inches should

FIG. 43. BREAKFAST ON THE PORCH

be allowed at the sides and ends of the table for damask cloths. A drop of nine to twelve inches is more desirable for more formal use. Linen table damask may be bought by the yard or in pattern cloths. Patterns are usually woven in two, two and one half, or three yard lengths.

A usual size for a luncheon cloth is 54 inches square; for a breakfast or very small cloth, 45 inches square; while cloths for tables as small as card tables are 30 to 45 inches square.

Size of Napkins. Dinner napkins are 22, 24, or even 27 inches square. Luncheon napkins are 18 or 20 inches square, but the size is not arbitrary. When a damask cloth is used for luncheon, small or medium-sized dinner napkins may be used. Breakfast napkins are 14 to 18 inches square. Tea napkins may be 12 to 14 inches square. Rectangular napkins are sometimes preferred to square ones, but this preference is not general.

Other Table Appointments

Containers for flowers are necessary to complete the table appointments. Glass and silver are always the most acceptable containers for flowers. Glazed pottery in colors that are pleasing with the dishes and other appointments are also attractive.

It is necessary to have a variety of shapes and sizes of flower containers in order to make use of a wide variety of flowers, foliage, and berries. The flower holders, called "frogs," are needed also in an assortment of types and sizes as an aid to effective flower arrangement.

In arranging flowers keep in mind the comfort of the guests and do not make it necessary for them to carry on a game of "peek-aboo." Flowers should be either high enough to see under or low enough to see over. The lower arrangement is preferable because it is more informal and one can see and enjoy the flowers to better advantage.

Care of the Dining Room and Its Furnishings

When in use the dining room must be well aired, scrupulously clean, and free from dust. It is best to air the room before each meal. A vacuum cleaner and oil floor mops are useful aids in cleaning. But the room must be not only clean; it must also be attractive. Flowers arranged in low bowls or a simple centerpiece of fruit add a charm to the table both at mealtime and throughout the day. The glass must be sparkling, the china clean, the silver untarnished, the linen spotless.

Between meals the table may be left bare, or it may be ornamented with a bowl of flowers, or a pot and plant with or without a table runner.

Care of Silver. Silver should be sorted and handled with care to prevent scratching. If washed as soon as used, it will need less frequent polishing. To wash silver use hot soapy water, rinse in clear hot water, and dry at once with a clean cloth.

Silver that is tarnished may be cleaned in two ways:

1. A silver paste and soft cloth may be used for polishing. The paste should be removed afterward by washing and scalding.

2. An easy and simple way to clean silver is by a chemical method known as the "electrolytic" method. Two forms of the method are in use: (*a*) Place the silver in an enamelware pan, cover with water, adding one teaspoon of salt and one teaspoon of sodium bicarbonate (baking soda) for each quart of water. Add a strip of aluminum, heat to boiling, and boil one minute. Remove and rub each piece lightly once to give it brightness. (*b*) An aluminum

pan may be used instead of the piece of aluminum, but it should be cleaned with an abrasive powder after use, because this method darkens the aluminum and brightens the silver.

The electrolytic method removes all tarnish, but it should not be used on designs of silver having a "French gray" finish because it will remove that finish, nor with silver that has any gold plating.

Removal of Stains from Table Linens. The stains on table linen are easily removed by the processes of laundering if the cloth is pure linen. It is more difficult to remove stains from cotton.

It is advisable to treat each stain according to its nature, however, before laundering.

Egg white, punch, sugar, and sirup should be soaked in lukewarm water until the stain disappears.

Clear coffee, clear tea, or fruit stains should be spread tightly over a bowl and boiling water poured from a height through the stain.

Cream or beverage stains containing cream, gravies, or clear fat should be washed with cold water and soap. The laundering process will remove traces of the stain.

Stains made by flower stems should be treated with kerosene, then washed with lukewarm water and soap.

For ink or iron-rust stains, use lemon juice or oxalic acid. Wash out the acid with dilute ammonia and wash in several changes of lukewarm water to remove all chemicals.

Gum can be softened with denatured alcohol.

Stubborn stains, such as mildew and old fruit stains, are best treated first with potassium permanganate, then with oxalic acid, and finally washed several times in lukewarm water to remove all traces of the chemicals.

Laundering of table linens. The correct steps in laundering of table linen are:

1. Examine and treat for stains.

2. Soak white linen and cotton pieces in lukewarm clear or soapy water for 15 or 20 minutes. There is no advantage in longer soaking. Colored linens and cottons may be soaked if color is fast to laundering. Rayon or silk should not be soaked.

3. Pieces that have been soaked should be washed in very hot soapy water. Enough soap should be used to make one inch of suds when the water is agitated. Wash in warm soapy water, either in a washing machine or by hand, pieces that have not been soaked, by swishing through the water and not by rubbing or scrubbing.

4. Rinse two or three times in water of the same temperature as the wash water. Do not use bluing. Do not use a bleach.

5. Give linen and cotton that is white a final cool rinse. This expels loose dirt from the fibers and is the real secret of getting rid of "tattletale gray."

Consult also Farmers' Bulletin 1497, *Methods and Equipment for Home Laundering.*

Care of Furniture. Dusting furniture thoroughly and often helps to keep it in good condition. The surface of furniture should be rubbed occasionally with a furniture polish, with wax, or with linseed oil. Use only very soft cloths that are entirely free from grit or dirt. Silk cloths are excellent because they leave no lint.

A good cleaning method to use on the dining-room table top, if it has a hard, smooth, varnish surface, is as follows: Wring a soft cloth out of lukewarm water containing soapsuds made from a neutral soap. Rub top with this, then with a cloth dampened with clear water. Restore the finish by rubbing with a soft cloth on which a few drops of linseed oil, or furniture polish, or wax has been placed. This treatment will remove finger marks from a hard varnished or waxed surface. Clean such surfaces by rubbing with an oiled cloth. Painted or enameled furniture may be washed.

The United States Bureau of Standards recommends a simple furniture polish which may be made by mixing one part of raw linseed oil with two parts of turpentine and adding a little melted beeswax, if desired.

Note: Cloths moistened with linseed oil are especially likely to cause spontaneous combustion. They should therefore be destroyed immediately after use, or kept in a fireproof container.

CLASS PROBLEMS

1. Collect pictures (preferably in color) of dining rooms and breakfast rooms or alcoves. Study and discuss these in class, making a list of the good points and the poor points in each.

2. Arrange for a class excursion to stores or use catalogues for studying furniture and table appointments for the breakfast room, breakfast alcove, and dining room. Note also furniture that might

be used for a dual-purpose dining room. Secure prices and compare costs of each.

3. Select china, silver, glass, and linen for serving six at three income levels: (1) expensive; (2) moderate priced; (3) inexpensive. What is the total cost in each case?

4. Demonstrate flower arrangement for the table.

5. Demonstrate the cleaning of silver by the electrolytic method. (See description, page 135.)

6. Demonstrate the removal of stains from table linen. Prepare Javelle water, oxalic acid solution, and potassium permanganate solutions. Bottle and label. Use for this study Farmers' Bulletin 1474, *Stain Removal from Fabrics.*

HOME PROBLEMS

1. Take entire charge of the care and cleaning of the dining room or breakfast room in your house for one week.
2. Arrange the flowers for the table each day. If wild flowers are available, use them.
3. Care for table linen in your home by removing stains, mending, and perhaps laundering.
4. Polish the silver at home.

REFERENCES

Agan, Tessie. *The House.* J. B. Lippincott Company, 1939. Unit Six.

Bailey, N. Beth (McLean). *Meal Planning and Table Service.* Manual Arts Press, Peoria, Illinois.

Cleaning Equipment and Methods. Bulletin, Good Housekeeping Institute.

Gunn, Lillian M. *Table Service and Decoration.* J. B. Lippincott Company.

House Cleaning, Management and Method. United States Department of Agriculture, Farmers' Bulletin 1834.

Methods and Equipment for Home Laundering. United States Department of Agriculture, Farmers' Bulletin 1497.

Stain Removal from Fabrics, Home Methods. United States Department of Agriculture, Farmers' Bulletin, 1474.

Wilmot, Jennie S., and Batjer, Margaret Q. *Food for the Family.* J. B. Lippincott Company, 1938. Units 31 and 32.

CHAPTER THIRTEEN

❧ The Kitchen

A KITCHEN IS never right by accident. A convenient one is the reward of thoughtful planning, furnishing, and good care. It would be a simple matter if there were specific rules that could be laid down, but the kitchen must be designed with reference to the family, house, locality, work, and workers.

The Importance of Kitchen Planning. There is no one kitchen that can be set up as a model, but some of the modern ideas in kitchen planning are illustrated in the floor plan and illustrations in Figures 44–51.

The farm kitchen requires the most planning, since so many extra activities are usually carried on in or near a farm kitchen. The plan illustrated in this book is for a model farm kitchen, but all of the ideas in the kitchen proper apply to the model town kitchen. An additional utility room has been planned for those activities connected with the work of the farm and with canning.

Use of the Kitchen. The kitchen is a food workshop. It should be sanitary, cheerful, attractive, compact, well ventilated, well lighted, and conveniently arranged. If it is used only for the preparation and serving of food, and for washing dishes and other utensils, it can be quite small. However, some families like to eat at least some of their meals in the kitchen; so a dining corner or "breakfast nook" is desirable. The dining corner can be both compact and very attractive.

A kitchen should have plenty of storage space. Articles should be stored close to the place where they are first used. Equipment for cleaning the kitchen should be out of the way of food preparation. If laundry equipment is kept in the kitchen, as it frequently is nowadays, it should be placed so that it does not interfere with the efficient preparation of meals.

Relation of the Kitchen to Other Parts of the House. The work of the kitchen is closely associated with the dining room, pantry, or

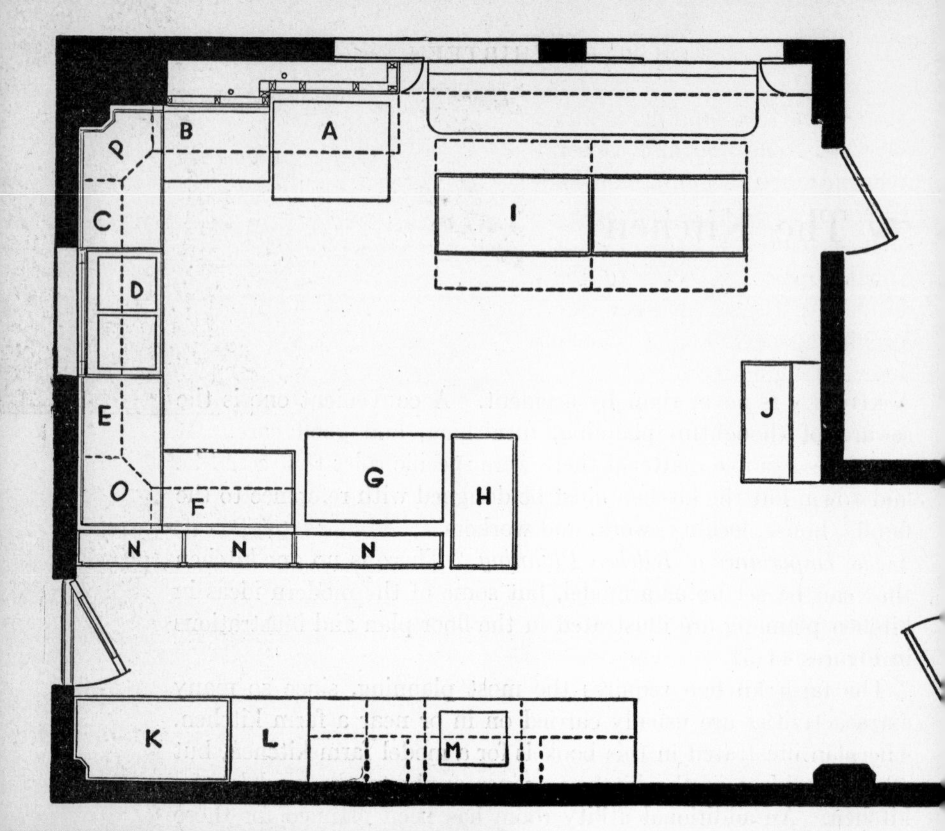

Fig. 44. DIAGRAM OF A MODEL FARM KITCHEN

The floor plan shows three main features: A compact convenient U-shaped kitchen (A to G) Figs. 47–51; an attractive place to serve meals (I), Fig. 45; a desk (J); a utility room (KLMN), Fig. 46, where men enter and wash and hang their outdoor clothes; and places for cleaning supplies and extra storage.

Fig. 45. THE MEAL TABLES WHEN EXTENDED WILL SEAT TEN PEOPLE (I)

4 T. flour
4 c milk

storeroom, fuel supply, laundry or wash room, cleaning closet, rear entrance to house, and incinerator or garbage disposal.

If a pantry is provided, it should open directly into the kitchen. If two pantries are provided, one is a pass pantry between dining room and kitchen. Frequently the breakfast nook serves the purpose of a pass pantry. A pass pantry must be omitted from the small house, but it is very useful in a large house for washing and storing dishes, for placement of the refrigerator, for serving, and for keeping heat and cooking odors from the rest of the house. The kitchen usually opens directly into the breakfast room or the dining room.

A back passageway is a convenience. The kitchen may open into such a passageway and through this one door the wash room or laundry, cleaning closet, cellar, and outside entrance may be reached. A screened back porch with an exit to the yard is almost indispensable. It should communicate directly with the kitchen and in cold weather may be shut in with glass and used for storage. In a southern climate it is a convenient place for doing much work, such as paring vegetables, and it may also be used for serving meals. If there is a basement

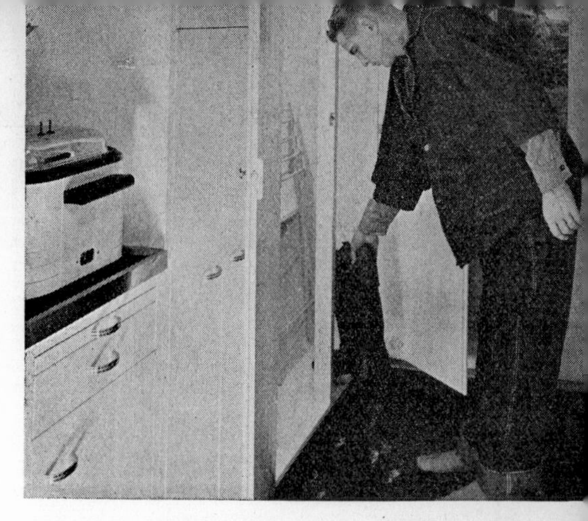

FIG. 46. CLOSET (K) IN UTILITY ROOM

FIG. 47. THE MIXING CENTER (B)

FIG. 48. VEGETABLE PREPARATION (C)

FIG. 49. THE TWO-BASIN SINK (D)

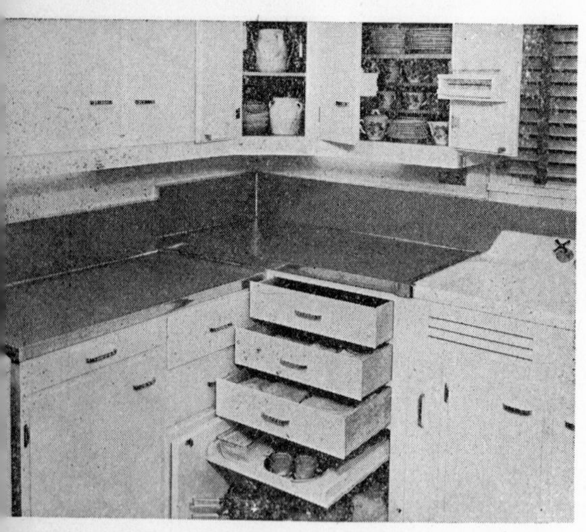

FIG. 50. DISH STORAGE (E) IS AT LEFT

FIG. 51. SERVING CENTER AND STOVE (F)

under the kitchen used for storage of fuel and food, a dumb waiter is a great step-saver.

Size and Shape. It is easier to arrange an almost square or oblong kitchen conveniently. The room should not be very large or very small. One hundred and fifty square feet is sufficient for a kitchen and pantry, if gas, oil, or electricity is used for fuel; or one hundred and twenty square feet for the kitchen without the pantry. If coal or wood is used, the kitchen should be larger; two hundred square feet will give adequate floor space (without a pantry). Ten feet by twelve is a good-sized kitchen for the average house.

Lighting. The number of windows depends upon the wall space and the climate. A kitchen should have at least two windows, preferably on two sides, for ventilation. An outside door may substitute for one window.

The sills of the windows should be high enough to permit the use of the wall space beneath for a table surface or a sink, yet low enough to allow an outside view, and the outlook should be pleasant. A good height for the lower sill of the kitchen window is forty or forty-one inches measured from the floor. The top of the window

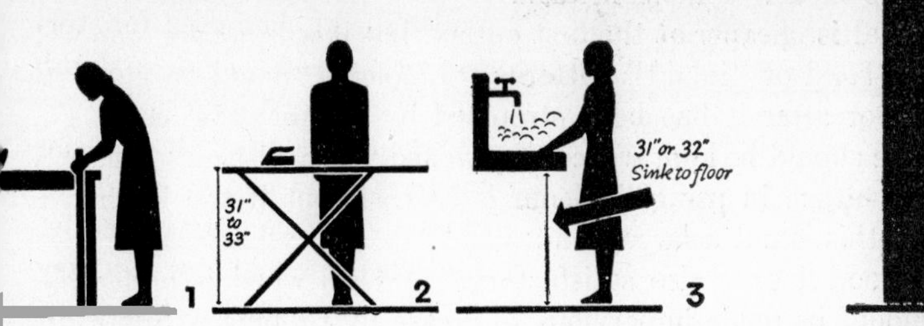

FIG. 52. HEIGHTS OF WORKING SURFACES

should reach to within six inches of the ceiling in order to provide an escape for the heat and odors that rise to the top of the room. Double-hung sash windows are more easily handled than casement windows, though the latter may provide better ventilation and are attractive.

Adequate artificial lighting for the kitchen and for all storage space usually means a central ceiling fixture and special local lighting over each work space, including the stove. Some of the ovens of newer electric stoves, also refrigerators, are well lighted. If these models are used, a good ceiling light should be adequate.

Doors. The location of every door in a kitchen should be considered very carefully. A door means a passageway. We should have as few doors as possible, and they should be grouped on one side or on adjacent sides of the kitchen in order that the worker may not be interrupted by frequent passing through. Adequate cabinet space and convenient arrangement of equipment require large units of wall space unbroken by doors.

From the kitchen there must surely be easy access to the pantry, the dining room or breakfast room, cleaning closet, hall, cellar, laundry, and outside. One door into a back hallway may offer access to several of these places.

Interior Finish

All surfaces in the kitchen should be easy to clean. The surfaces of walls, floors, ceiling, and woodwork should be flat, plain, free from cracks, and non-absorbent. These precautions help to avoid such pests as ants and roaches.

Floors. The kitchen floor must be comfortable to stand on and easy to clean. Linoleum answers both purposes. The printed material is cheaper at the first outlay, but it will not wear so well as the solid or "inlaid" patterns. Linoleum should be glued to the floor after it has been stretched by several days' use. The surface should be kept waxed, shellacked, or varnished. The only disadvantage in using linoleum is its cost, but if the kitchen is small, this is not a large item.

A wood floor is also satisfactory. A hard wood is preferable. It should be made impervious to grease by rubbing with hot linseed oil, or by varnishing. A varnished floor will show wear and spots, but it can be kept looking well if it is refinished about once a year. Small mats of linoleum or rubber may be used at the stove, sink, and table.

Walls and Ceiling. Paint is the best finish for kitchen walls. An oil paint which can be washed with soap and water is best. Water paints are cheaper, but they must be renewed more frequently than other kinds. Enamel is a washable and satisfactory finish. Wallpaper with a special washable surface which is satisfactory for kitchens is now available. Tiling and vitrified brick are good wall finishes if expense need not be considered.

The color of the walls and ceiling should add to the charm of the kitchen. If the room is sunny, tones of gray or gray-green may be used, but if it needs light, yellow, buff, or white should be chosen.

Woodwork. The most satisfactory finish for woodwork or "standing trim," including built-in cabinets, is enamel. The choice of color depends upon the rest of the kitchen. French gray, ivory, and white are much used. Color in woodwork is especially good if there is a breakfast alcove in the kitchen. The surface will be washable if it is treated with stain and linseed oil, wax, or varnish, but the appearance of oil paint or enamel is more attractive.

Care of Painted Walls and Woodwork.[1] Assuming that the kitchen walls and woodwork have a washable painted finish, plain soap and water is a good cleansing agent, and is always on hand in a kitchen. The steps are as follows:

1. Use a light suds, washing a small space at a time.
2. Begin at the bottom and work up to avoid streaking the wall. If the water runs down the clean wet wall, it can be wiped off with-

[1] Adapted from information prepared by the United States Department of Agriculture.

out streaking, but if it runs down a dry dirty wall, it will streak it so it may not be washed off satisfactorily.

3. Use water sparingly.
4. Rub only enough to remove dirt.
5. Wipe dry with a clean cloth.

An Ounce of Prevention. A group of home economists gives a suggestion for saving work on wall washing. "To make painted walls easier to clean the next time" (after cleaning them, of course) "brush on a thin paste made of ordinary laundry starch. The next time you clean the walls you can wash the dirt right off with the starch." [1]

Arrangement of Equipment

Since the basic principle to be considered in arranging a kitchen is to place equipment together that is to be used together, we must think first of the types of work that are to be done in the particular kitchen under consideration. In most kitchens food is stored, prepared, and served, and dishes are washed; in farm kitchens provision must also be made for canning and other preservation of food and for care of milk.

We speak of all kitchens as having four "centers": (1) for preparing food; (2) for serving food; (3) for cleaning up (dishwashing); and (4) for storage of food, dishes, and utensils. In speaking of these centers, we recognize, too, that they are interrelated. We think of the sink as being part of the two centers for dishwashing and food preparation. The storage area, too, is closely related to both the cleaning space and the preparation space, because cleaning up includes storing left-over food, clean dishes, and utensils, and preparing food involves taking it from the places in which it is stored. Can you show other ways in which these parts of the kitchen are related?

1. The food preparation center includes:
   A stove where food will be cooked.
   A sink where it will be washed.
   A counter or table on which mixing is done, vegetables and fruit are pared, and from which serving may also be done (if it is cleared before the meal begins).

[1] Information prepared by the United States Department of Agriculture.

A storage place for utensils used in cooking, mixing, and other preparation processes.

2. The serving center is a place for assembling the meal between the stove, the refrigerator, and the dining table. Here the food is made ready in serving dishes with all the last-minute touches. This is the most variable center. As stated above, the food preparation center may be used for this work. Other possibilities are:

A table or counter surface
A drop shelf
A table on rollers
A counter surface arranged in a pass cupboard for easy serving from kitchen to dining room (or porch)

3. The cleaning center includes:

A sink or other provision for washing dishes (the same sink as in the preparation center)
Storage for cleaning equipment such as dishpans and drying racks
A stove, if water is heated for washing dishes

4. The storage area is interrelated to each of the other areas and includes:

Cabinets for storing staple foods, dishes, utensils and equipment, towels, and cleaning supplies
A refrigerator or other cold storage
Storage for fruits and vegetables

General Suggestions for Arranging the Equipment:

Note how these suggestions are carried out in the model farm kitchen illustrated in this chapter.

1. Have the heights of working surfaces convenient. Suitable heights vary with the worker and the work. For counters, that is, table tops or cabinet tops, and for the rim of the sink and drainboards, a good height is thirty-five to thirty-six inches from the floor. For work such as mixing done when seated on an ordinary chair or low stool, the working surface may be twenty-five inches from the floor; this may be furnished by a sliding shelf, since most people prefer a continuous line for working surfaces in the kitchen. The worker may be made more comfortable by a high stool, but in either case, remember that knee space must be provided to make the worker comfortable when seated. The dining table, and the planning desk when available, should be the usual thirty inches.

2. Have toe space at all places where work will be done, and

knee space where work will be done sitting. Knee space is desirable under the sink. To sit while washing dishes at a thirty-six inch sink a high stool must be used. This knee space can also be used to store the stool when not in use.

3. Have the refrigerator in the kitchen, if possible, and consider nearness to the dining room when locating it. Refrigerators are available with either right-hand or left-hand opening doors. It is important to consider this when buying or placing a refrigerator because it may make a difference in convenience.

4. One good arrangement, especially in a large kitchen, is to place the sink and dish storage with one end at the wall, instead of the side at the wall, the other end extending toward the middle of the kitchen. In many cases this is most convenient, and it may have the added advantages of preventing passageways from breaking into work units, and providing storage space where it is convenient to all parts of the kitchen. In remodeling a large kitchen it is well to consider this plan for dividing the kitchen, so as to separate the food work from other work often done in the kitchen.

5. Have adjustable shelves as far as possible.

6. Have partitions in drawers, preferably removable ones.

7. A shelf or table for receiving groceries near the back door, and a table next to the dining-room door are convenient.

8. Plan to stack only equipment of the same shape and size together.

9. Try storing such space-taking pieces as trays, platters, vegetable dishes, shallow pans, and pot lids on edge, with light partitions (quarter inch plywood is good for these) separating each one into its niche, a sort of filing system.

10. Don't forget spaces for a stool or a chair or two; for the garbage receptacle; and for hanging dish towels, though it is to be hoped you will learn to use very few towels.

11. Have drop-leaf tables for extra table space, with hinged legs that drop as you lift the table.

12. Have a table mounted on special casters or wheels so that it can be moved where needed, and give it its regular place in the room. Often the kitchen two-step ladder or stool can be stored under this table.

13. Have as much continuous counter space around the kitchen as possible.

The Storage Area. Storage space is necessary, but here again no absolute rules apply. The chief considerations are: to store each article near the place where it will be used most; to place the storage facilities where they are accessible, easily cleaned, comparatively free from dust, and not in the way; and to provide a variety of storage places for the different types of articles — shelves, drawers, cupboards, hooks, and racks. The usual storage places are pantries, cabinets, and closets with shelves.

Pantries. Pantries are a convenience but are not essential. In a large house, if supplies are bought in quantity, a storage place is necessary, especially for food that needs to be kept at a lower temperature than that of the kitchen. A north wall is a good location for a pantry.

Cabinets. Cabinets are as necessary in the kitchen as desks, books, and filing cases in an office. The built-in cabinet is preferable, and it should be so built that there are no surfaces to be cleaned behind, under, or on top. Note the illustration showing how this can be achieved.

Cabinets in Units. Cabinets of both wood and metal are available in units so the space arrangement may be planned exactly to suit needs.

The cabinet should be so constructed that the doors of the upper portion, when opened, will not interfere with such articles as a pitcher, a mixer, a percolator, or a quart bottle of milk on the table surface below. This upper part of the cabinet should be a shallow case, ten to twelve inches deep, for storing supplies or dishes. The part below the table top should be much deeper, affording ample space for drawers or for storing large utensils, or for both; twenty to twenty-four inches is a convenient depth for the cabinet bases.

Shelves are a boon in the kitchen. A shelf should be no deeper than is necessary for holding one row of articles. Shelves that are to hold large utensils must, of course, be deep and far apart. The most useful shelves for dishes and supplies, however, are narrow and placed rather close together; for example, the shelf for seasonings, such as salt, pepper, and spices, may be only six inches deep.

Selection of Kitchen Equipment

Stove. Modern gas, electric, and oil stoves are an achievement in engineering and design. In America the design of coal and wood stoves has lagged far behind. In Sweden, however, a very modern wood (or coal) stove is widely used. On this stove the cooking is done on "eyes" or plates just as on an electric range. The consumption of fuel is reduced to a minimum because the combustion is perfect. The result is boiling water in 20 to 25 minutes from the time the fire is built.

The first point to consider in selecting a stove is the fuel to be used. Where electricity and city gas are not available, the choice is among coal, wood, oil, and bottled gas. But whatever the fuel, the stove should be large enough, properly insulated, and easy to clean.

The modern electric and gas stoves leave little to be desired. The heat on the electric stove has been made very flexible with a minimum of three and often five heats. Economy in the operation of both gas and electric stoves has also been made possible by the design of heating units and heat controls. The table-top design is convenient and fits well with the "streamlined" cabinet and sink space. Oven controls are almost universal equipment, and such other conveniences as thrift cookers, lights over the stove and in the oven, glass doors to the ovens, storage drawers, and a clock for timing the cooking, are available for an additional price.

Electric, gas, and oil stoves are usually of enamel. Stain resistant enamel is recommended. Tops of stoves are also available in stainless steel or monel metal, which is more durable but also more expensive. When buying a stove it pays to buy a good one, for it will be the cheapest in the long run. The life of a stove depends upon the care that is given it in its use.

Sink. A porcelain enamel sink is the kind most frequently used and is very easy to clean. The best design has double drainboards, back and sink all in one piece. An overall length of sixty inches is recommended. Rubber mats and rubber-protected dish drainers will avoid breakage of dishes. A cheaper wall sink comes with separate wooden drainboards. Wooden drainboards should be fitted to avoid dirt-catching cracks.

Monel metal or stainless steel sinks and drainboards cast in one piece are expensive but very desirable and will last a lifetime.

Kitchen Table and Table Tops. The working surface may be furnished by a built-in cabinet, a commercial cabinet, or a table. If space permits, a table is desirable in addition to cabinets.

Table and cabinet tops should be of material that is easily cleaned, non-absorbent; will not warp or be cracked by heat; fireproof; resistant to acids and alkalis; reasonable in price; and attractive in appearance. There is no table top that meets all these requirements, but linoleum does so more nearly than anything else. Black linoleum with chromium or aluminum edge is attractive and is easy to care for. These table tops can be purchased separately and installed on either wood or metal cabinet bases.

Wood and porcelain enamel are also used for table tops. Porcelain enamel is the most easily cleaned of all the materials, but it is affected by acids and it chips easily. It should not be difficult to remember to wipe tomato or fruit juice off at once, or to avoid cracking ice or screwing the food chopper on such a table top. The best grade of porcelain enamel is relatively acid-resistant.

If wood is chosen, maple should be used. It may be finished with a waterproof, heat-resistant spar varnish which is durable. Monel metal or stainless steel is highly desirable for table or cabinet tops, but is expensive.

Refrigeration and Refrigerators. It is important that refrigera-

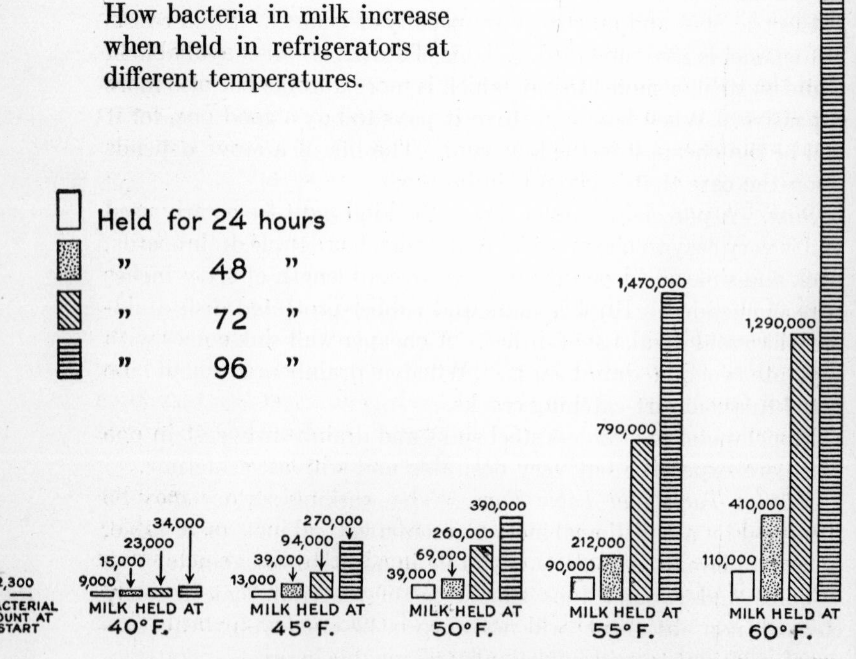

FIG. 53. COLD CHECKS BACTERIAL GROWTH

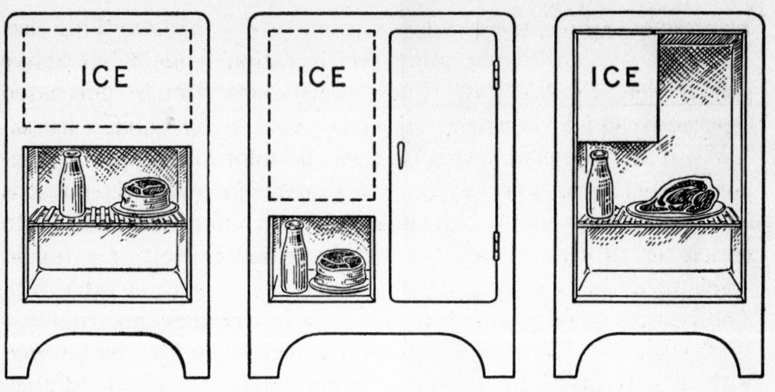

FIG. 54. USING THE TEMPERATURES IN A GOOD REFRIGERATOR

tion be provided in the home to prevent the spoilage of food, both in the interest of economy and as a protection to health. Bacteria spoil food and are injurious to health. Note from the evidence in Figure 53 that the growth of bacteria can be materially retarded at temperatures below 50° F. Reliability of the manufacturer and the temperature maintained in the food compartments should be stressed in buying a refrigerator. A good refrigerator is one that maintains a temperature from below 45° in its warmest part to 42° or below in other portions. The lower the temperatures (above freezing, 32° F.) that the refrigerator maintains, the better.

Next to the temperature, a most important point is the size of the refrigerator. This is indicated in two ways: (1) by the square feet of shelf space, and (2) by the cubic feet or total space. The latter is simpler. A four or five cubic foot box is a very small refrigerator. From seven to nine cubic feet is a moderate to large size for family use. From nine to twelve cubic feet is a very large household refrigerator. Porcelain enamel finish outside and inside is expensive; a lacquered outside finish is satisfactory.

The Ice Refrigerator. There are several styles of ice refrigerators. Both side icing and top icing are satisfactory if the food is rightly placed. The ice chamber should be lined with zinc or galvanized iron, or if wire is used, it should be strong and heavily galvanized. Efficient ice refrigerators maintain a satisfactory temperature and need icing only once or twice weekly.

The Automatic Refrigerator. Efficient automatic household

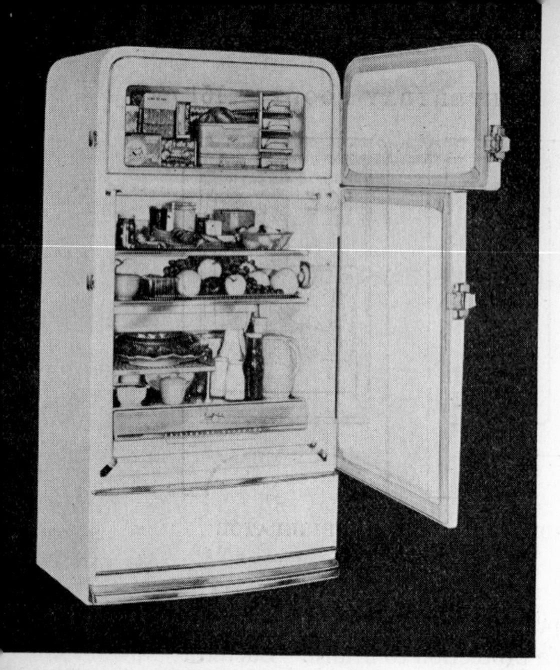

FIG. 55. MANY REFRIGERATORS HAVE HOME FREEZING COMPARTMENTS AS WELL AS SPACE FOR FOOD STORAGE

refrigeration is available wherever there is electricity, gas, or oil. Among the good features are the following:

Conveniently placed temperature control for regulating cold.

Increased capacity for freezing.

Special freezing compartments on some refrigerators for storing frozen foods at below 15° F.

Special containers for foods, such as ventilated pans (humidors) for fruits and vegetables.

Meat compartment for fresh meat.

Moist-air section so that foods are not dehydrated (dried out) are available in some models.

Beauty, and utility outside and inside, such as rounded corners and every facility for ease in keeping the refrigerator clean.

Care of the Refrigerator.[1] To do its work efficiently, a refrigerator must be kept open as little as possible in order to maintain the necessary temperatures for adequate refrigeration.

1. Do not open the door any oftener than necessary.
2. Put food in its proper place. Meat and milk belong in the coldest part of the refrigerator. Fruits and vegetables are kept in the least cold part, and other foods can be placed where most convenient. If one knows where food is in the refrigerator, it saves time and temperature because the door can be closed quickly.
3. Food should be kept covered in the refrigerator. Covers help to keep food clean and odors from spreading from one food to another. Salad ingredients can be kept crisp in covered vessels, and to preserve Vitamin C we cover the orange and grapefruit juice.
4. Do not put anything in the refrigerator that would warm it up. This includes paper bags, egg cartons, extra containers, and warm or hot food. Also, leave out all food that does not require refrigeration. This rule is an economy measure.

[1] Adapted from information prepared by the United States Department of Agriculture.

5. Keep the refrigerator clean. Wipe up food immediately when spilled. Put only clean containers in the refrigerator.

The weekly cleaning of the refrigerator should include defrosting the mechanical refrigerator, because the coating of ice or "frost" on the freezing compartment lowers its efficiency. All refrigerators should be washed inside and out, including all containers and shelves, once a week.

Utensils. Kitchen utensils are used for such a wide variety of purposes that no one material is suitable for the composition of all utensils. There is usually a choice of material for any one utensil.

Material	*Advantages*	*Disadvantages*	*Utensils for which Suitable*
Aluminum (use medium weight)	Attractive Easy to clean (acids) Heats quickly Durable (if a good grade)	Expensive Darkened by alkalis (never boil soda or borax in aluminum) Discolors with some vegetables Does not hold heat	Measuring cup Double boiler Saucepans and covers Cake pans Muffin pans Cast aluminum: Waffle iron Griddle Skillet Frying kettle
Enamelware (Steel coated with glass)	Easily cleaned Cheap (gray) Attractive	Chips readily Will crack with high temperature, as in baking or frying	Saucepans Mixing pans Pudding pans Double boiler Dishpan Bowls Ladle Pitchers Shallow pans Funnels Skimmers
Tinware	Light Cheap Heats quickly	Affected by acids Tarnishes with heat Does not hold heat	Cake pans Biscuit cutter Bread pans (heavy) Muffin pans Potato ricer Baking pans Flour sifter Measuring cup Steamer Wash boiler
Earthenware	Attractive Does not scratch Easy to clean Holds heat Resistant to acids or alkalis	Cannot use directly over flame Breaks rather easily	Baking dishes Custard cups Teapots Bowls for mixing Crocks for supplies

Material	*Advantages*	*Disadvantages*	*Utensils for which Suitable*
Cast iron or wrought iron	Holds heat Not affected by acids and alkalis	Heavy Rusts easily	Griddle Waffle iron Corn stick pans Kettle for frying Skillets Food chopper
Glassware Heat-resistant, such as Pyrex	Attractive Easy to clean Holds heat Not attacked by acids or alkalis	Used only in oven Not suitable for pots and pans Scratches easily Breaks with quick changes of temperature	Pyrex: Measuring cup Baking dishes Custard cups Pie plates Bread pans Fruit knives Refrigerator dishes Double boiler and saucepans Percolator Teapots Plain glass: Lemon squeezer Storage jars for supplies
Stainless steel (look for both words); avoid that labeled just "stainless"	Attractive Does not tarnish or corrode Not attacked by acids or alkalies	Expensive	Mixing spoons Saucepans, lids Knives, forks Griddle, skillet
Steel	A sharp cutting edge All cutlery should be of well-tempered steel	Rusts easily (unless stainless steel) Must be kept sharpened	Knives Spatula Can opener Scissors
Wire	Light Cheap	Hard to clean without a brush Not durable	Dish drainer Broiler Frying basket Soap shaker Toaster Wire eggbeater Strainers
Wooden			Mallet Chopping bowl Spoons Bread board Chopping board Ice-cream freezer bucket
Miscellaneous			Asbestos mats Scales Vegetable brushes

Safety in the Kitchen. The home kitchen is responsible for many avoidable accidents and deaths each year. It would be splendid if boys and girls would join in a serious effort to do away with this unnecessary loss of life. Common kitchen accidents are burns, scalds, injuries from explosions, and falls. Some rules that should be observed in each kitchen are:

Keep handles of pots and pans turned in on the stove, never out from the stove. Little children have been scalded to death because this simple precaution was not observed. Practice keeping handles in their place in the school kitchen.

Keep little children out of the kitchen as far as possible. It should be possible for a mother to have a safe place to leave a child, such as a play pen or a room with a low gate across in place of the door, while she is busy preparing meals.

Light coal, wood, and gas stoves with care. Kerosene should not be used in lighting fires. Skill in lighting coal and wood fires without any such aid as kerosene may be developed easily. When lighting a gas burner, light the match before turning on the burner. If the range has a pilot light, and for some reason a burner fails to light when you turn it on, turn it off immediately and light the burner with a match. Check to see if the pilot light has gone out. When lighting a gas oven, find where the match should be applied and learn to apply it without looking in the oven. Light the match, turn the gas on full, apply the match.

Take good care of matches. Keep in earthenware, pottery, or metal containers or in a metal cabinet; keep away from heat; keep out of children's reach.

Teach children that a stove is hot and something to avoid.

Avoid using materials that burn near a stove, even discarding ragged pot holders because they catch fire easily. Avoid having curtains near a range, even an electric one.

Avoid slippery floors. Clean up anything spilled on the floor as soon as it is spilled.

NEVER have gasoline in the kitchen. This is one of the most explosive materials known. The best rule is never to permit gasoline in the house. There are no little accidents with gasoline. They are all terrible ones.

Remember that the range is meant to withstand heat, so that if something on the range catches fire, leave it there and turn off the heat.

Have only sturdy chairs and tables in good repair in the kitchen.

Water is a conductor of electricity, therefore do not make a circuit by touching an electric switch or appliance with one hand when the other hand is on the faucet or in the water. Never touch an electric switch with wet hands or when standing on a wet surface.

Labor-Saving Devices. The simplest labor-saving device is the most effective. Raised table and sink heights, stainless steel paring knives, oven-heat regulator, rotary eggbeater, electric mixers, loose-bottom cake pans, and wire or wooden racks for draining dishes are examples of simple labor-saving devices that should be found in the kitchen. The size of the family and the amount of work to be done determine whether special equipment saves or makes labor.

Some so-called labor-saving devices save labor in one process only to entail labor in other ways. In a small family, for example, a bread mixer or a dishwashing machine may make more work than it saves. There is greater need for a few well-selected simple tools than for a large number of devices that increase the task of the housekeeper and occupy space that could be used to better advantage. Important considerations in determining the advisability of purchasing any tool or device are:

1. Does it do the work it is supposed to do?
2. Can a net saving of time and energy be counted on when the care of the device is taken into consideration?
3. How often would it be used?
4. Is it well made and easy to handle and to clean?

Kitchen Conveniences. Every kitchen should have a clock and a bookshelf.

The greatest convenience is plenty of hot water.

An incinerator for garbage is convenient for a city kitchen.

The gas or electric meters should be placed where they may be read by the inspector even when the family is absent.

The asbestos-wrapped water heater will prevent overheating of the kitchen if the asbestos is at least one inch thick.

Gas, electricity, or oil is preferable for cooking to wood or coal.

Electric service outlets are needed in the kitchen for percolator, dishwasher, iron, and various other utensils. Droplights over working surfaces are convenient.

A folding wall ironing board should be placed in the kitchen if there is not a separate laundry.

FIG. 56. THE PLAN OF THIS KITCHEN WAS BASED ON THE LETTER "U"
The sink is at the center of the U, the refrigerator and range at either end.

A dishwashing machine is advantageous if a large number of dishes are to be washed.

A drying rack and a spray for rinsing the dishes save much labor, if the spray has a heat-resisting hose.

Covered glass jars or dishes are excellent for storing supplies. Aluminum foil and oiled silk or plastic covers for foods and dishes are useful, especially in the refrigerator.

Hooks or racks are desirable for the most frequently used utensils; also, for electric cords.

Paper towels and wax paper are desirable.

CLASS PROBLEMS

1. Draw a plan to scale for a suggested remodeling of your kitchen. Justify suggested changes.

2. Discuss the fuels available in the community and the advantages and disadvantages of each. Emphasize relative costs.

3. Divide the class into groups for investigating the advantages of certain equipment.

SUGGESTED INVESTIGATIONS

Dishwashing machines	Coal or wood stoves
Water heaters	Materials for utensils
Refrigerators	Electric stoves
Electric refrigerators	Gas stoves
Small electric equipment	Oil stoves
Home freezers	Bottled gas

SUGGESTED METHOD

a. Visit stores to study the types of equipment available.
b. Procure advertising literature and prices. Study advertising in current magazines and list the advantages which manufacturers claim for their products.
c. Make inquiries of housekeepers who use such equipment.
d. Invite someone from the commercial field to explain special articles.

4. Learn to read a gas meter and an electric meter.

5. Investigate the cost of the same kitchen floor in pine, in hard wood, and in linoleum.

6. If you had thirty dollars to spend on kitchen equipment, how would you spend it for your own kitchen, and why?

HOME PROBLEMS

1. Clean your home kitchen.
2. Take an inventory of the utensils in your home kitchen. List the articles that need replacing, the articles that are not used, and the new articles that are needed. Find out what these articles would cost.
3. What utensils in your home kitchen are the most used? What are the least used?
4. Clean the cabinets, pantries, and closets used as kitchen storage space in your house.
5. Check your home kitchen to see if it can be made a safer place.
6. Clean (and defrost) a refrigerator.
7. Plan rearrangement of your kitchen in accordance with the principles of good kitchen planning.

REFERENCES

Agan, Tessie. *The House.* J. B. Lippincott.

Balderston, Lydia Ray. *Housewifery.* 5th edition. J. B. Lippincott Company. Plumbing, Built-in Cabinets, Furniture Arrangement, Meters, Equipment, and Labor-Saving Appliances, Storage, Cleaning, Household Pests.

Gray, Greta. *House and Home.* J. B. Lippincott Company.

Bulletins published by the Bureau of Human Nutrition and Home Economics.

How to Choose and Use Your Refrigerator. AIS-56.

How to Make your Electric Cords Last Longer. AWI-20.

Home-built Electric Dehydrater. AWI-76.

A Step-saving U Kitchen. Miscellaneous Publication 646.

Write your State College of Agriculture for bulletins on kitchen planning and care.

CHAPTER FOURTEEN

❧ When You Go to Market

Isn't it fortunate that we're not all alike? And that our ways are different? It would be strange if we all liked to do the same things in the same way, including eating the same food obtained and prepared in the same way. Many possible choices are open to most of us in the methods we may use to obtain our foods and in the foods we may have. In other parts of this book we have turned our thoughts to meal planning and to types of food as well as to the preparation of meals. Here we turn to the problem of buying or obtaining the foods, and our aim is to become wise in the ways of trading money for good value in food. We'll do well to recognize the number of possible choices and to gain a good basis for deciding for ourselves how we are to do this important job. That it is important, we all know. More often than not, families find that a third or more of their money is spent for food; so it is important financially. We know, too, how important food is to health. Then there is the pleasure of eating. It is a good idea, certainly, to make our own decisions in a matter that affects so greatly our pocketbook, our health, and our happiness.

Some people may think that they have little or no choice in this matter, perhaps because of limited funds, or perhaps because there are only one or two stores in which it is convenient for them to buy food. Perhaps they may be so busy that they have given little thought to this problem. Things have conspired against them until the result may almost be called a rut — a food rut. You're not going to let that happen to you. Start in the opposite direction right now. All those who plan and buy food for themselves and their families can make food choices in such a way that their decisions can count toward good meals. The members of their families can help, too.

Before you get very far in this chapter, try to recall what you have learned already about buying foods. You may remember some of the suggestions made in other chapters of this book. You may have learned about buying food by reading newspapers and magazines. You have bought certain kinds of food yourself; for instance, candy, ice cream, and soft drinks. You may be fortunate enough to have experience in buying other foods.

You know, for example, that candy is sold in bars, by the pound, and by the piece of candy, and also that different kinds of candy can be found on sale. When you have bought candy in wrapped bars or packages, have you noticed the list of ingredients on the label? If you haven't, do so next time you buy.

One way to increase your knowledge about buying foods is to talk to homemakers about ways they buy and how they learned them. They can always tell you some of the easier ways or more economical buys, and they may suggest that they have learned such things the hard way.

Meanwhile, gather a food exhibit to which you can refer as you study this chapter. Mark each food with its amount and price. Store perishable foods by proper methods. Here is a suggested list:

Bread: 3 or 4 loaves of different kinds (enriched white, whole wheat, rye, etc.), different sizes, and different brands

Cocoa: 2 or 3 packages of different sizes and brands

Meats: 3 or 4 pounds of different cuts of beef, veal, lamb, or pork; for example, round steak, chuck, T-bone, neck

Canned goods: 6 to 10 cans of fruit, vegetables, soups, juices, etc., in different sizes and with different types of labels
1 kind of canned food in each of three grades, A, B, and C
1 or 2 cans of different kinds and brands of canned meat

Cereal: 3 to 6 packages of ready-to-cook and ready-to-eat breakfast cereal

Potatoes: different varieties

Citrus fruit: different sizes of oranges, grapefruit, and lemons

Leafy green vegetables: different varieties

Labels from packaged foods, including candy

Several forms of the same food: for example, canned, fresh, frozen, and dried peaches

Food-Buying

You will find there are four general questions that often bother those who buy food for their families. They are:

1. How much money should our family spend for food?

2. How should the food money be divided among the different kinds of food?

3. How can we know which store or stores to patronize?

4. What are some good rules for me to follow in buying food?

These questions are so general that they permit only rather general, broad answers, but the general answers can be applied according to the conditions affecting individual families.

How Much Money? Homemakers naturally wonder how much money they should spend for food. To get an adequate diet, the majority must spend from one fourth to one half of their income. It is not surprising that they do not want to over-spend on food, because money is needed for so many other things as well. But the question is not an easy one to answer.

As you know, a nutritious diet is made up of foods in all seven food groups (see Chapter One). Look through the lists of foods in the Basic Seven groups and you will see some in each group that are relatively inexpensive and others that are expensive. If the family dislikes the inexpensive ones, food costs will mount. So the amount spent on food varies with the tastes of the family. It also varies, of course, with the size of the family and the number of growing children.

The cost of food also varies considerably because of changes from time to time in food prices. When food prices are high, more money must be spent than when they are low. For example, in an "average" city in 1948 it took $18 to buy the same food that $9 bought in 1936.

A family that lives on a farm or has a garden may spend considerably less money for food than a city family. And a homemaker who knows how to preserve foods when they are plentiful may be able to save substantial sums.

How Use the Money? There is no one rule that helps all families answer general question number two: "How should the food money be divided among the different kinds of food?" Again, family likes vary, family needs vary, food prices vary, and home production and preservation of food vary. Here is an example of the problem. As you know, grapefruit, oranges, and tomatoes are nutritionally similar. There are times when one grapefruit costs fifteen cents, a dozen oranges cost thirty cents, and a dozen tomatoes cost fifteen cents. At such times those who buy grapefruit would have to spend more for the same nourishment, or get less nourishment for what they spend, than those who purchase oranges or tomatoes. Home-grown tomatoes, properly canned, might cost least of all.

If your family buys all the food it uses, you would do well to follow the rule given by a famous food scientist. He advised homemakers to be sure that "at least half the expenditure for food is for fruits, vegetables, milk, cheese, cream, and ice cream."[1] More detailed suggestions on how to be thrifty in apportioning your food dollars follow:

On *milk*, spend enough to get at least 3 cups for each adult and 4 cups for each child. Provide whole milk, or, if you buy skim milk or buttermilk, provide some butter or margarine to take the place of cream. The butter or margarine will supply needed fat, as well as Vitamin A.

On *fruits and vegetables*, spend at least a fifth of the money, stressing green and yellow vegetables and potatoes, as well as inexpensive fruits. Fruits in general are expensive. You can see that if a fifth of the family's food money is spent on expensive fruits, the amount of fruit obtained will be small — often too small to provide enough of the nutrients that fruits supply. If you buy fruits that are in season, you will probably get greater value from the proportion of money allowed for fruits.

On *breadstuffs and grain products*, you may spend as much as one fifth of each food dollar. Have a variety of these products, mostly whole-grain and enriched foods. These foods can well be used in an economical diet, but it takes a resourceful meal planner to provide pleasing meals with the large amount of these that a fifth of the food money would buy.

In buying *meat*, keep costs down to one fourth or one fifth of the dollars spent on food. Meat, though important, is very expensive. It is relatively the most expensive food group. For this reason, expenditures for meat must be watched carefully by the majority of families.

On *appetizers*, such as coffee, tea, and sauces, keep expenditures as low as one tenth of the food costs.

How Choose Stores? For many families there is only one store, or perhaps two, in which it is convenient to buy food. Other families [illegible]ly have a number of stores conveniently placed but also hav[illegible]ty of different kinds or types of stores from which to cho[illegible] we learn by experience, it is a good idea to shop

[1] [illegible] C., and Lanford, Caroline Sherman. *Essentials of Nutri-* [illegible].

FIG. 57. TWO TYPES OF STORES

Compare the advantages to be gained by serving oneself, as in the upper picture, with the advantages to be gained by using the services of a clerk, as in the lower picture.

Each store in which food for families is sold should have two characteristics. These two characteristics are:

1. A STOCK OF THE KINDS AND QUALITIES OF FOOD MOST NEEDED BY THE FAMILY. Of course store managers respond as well as possible to requests that indicate family needs. Therefore family buyers should be careful and thoughtful in performing their buying job. Thorough knowledge of what they are trying to do, as well as alertness and tact, are certainly desirable.

2. PROPER CARE OF EACH FOOD, INCLUDING SCRUPULOUS CLEANLINESS. Order should prevail; decayed fruits and vegetables should be separated from food on sale; displayed food should be well above the floor (18 inches or more); such food as meat and eggs should be kept in a refrigerator; clerks' hands should be clean and a good place to wash them should be provided. It is a great help when homemakers express appreciation of such conditions.

Differences Among Food Stores. Other characteristics may be needed by some families, but not by others. These should be considered thoughtfully when choosing stores to be patronized. They are:

1. AN OPPORTUNITY FOR THE FAMILY FOOD BUYER TO OBTAIN INFORMATION. Many wish to ask questions and obtain suggestions. In some stores a great deal of buying assistance is available.

2. METHOD OF INDICATING PRICES. Some would prefer to buy in stores where prices are prominently displayed. Did you notice how prices were displayed when you obtained the foods to help in the study of this chapter?

3. SELF-SERVICE OR ASSISTANCE FROM CLERKS? Self-service has advantages, and there are advantages in being served by trained sales clerks. Clerks can make helpful suggestions and can locate foods sought quickly. Self-service stores may charge somewhat lower prices. Self-service stores make it possible for family buyers to feel free to study information on labels without wasting a clerk's time, and for them to notice varieties in foods and in brands.

4. CASH SALES OR CHARGE? Advantages of paying cash are avoidance of debt and the possibility of lower prices. Charging makes it possible to buy without carrying much money.

5. DELIVERY SERVICE OR CASH AND CARRY ONLY? Delivery increases the store's costs and, therefore, usually increases food prices at stores where delivery service is provided. However, using your own automobile may cost more than the difference in prices.

APPROXIMATE MEASURE OF ONE POUND AND ONE OUNCE OF SOME COMMON FOOD ARTICLES

Product	Measure		Product	Measure	
	1 *oz.*	1 *lb.*		1 *oz.*	1 *lb.*
Apples, dried		4 c.	Marshmallows		60
Baking powder	2½ T.	2½ c.	Molasses		1⅓ c.
Beans, navy		2¼ c.	Mustard	4 T.	
Bread crumbs	¼ c.	4 c.	Oil — peanut — corn, cottonseed	2 T.	2 c.
Butter	2 T.	2 c.	Raisins or dates		2⅔ c.
Chocolate, unsweetened	1 square	16 squares	Rice, brown or white	2 T.	2⅛ c.
Cinnamon	4 T.		Sugar, brown	2⅔ T.	2⅔ c.
Cloves	4 T.		Sugar, confectioner's	3½ T.	3½ c.
Cocoa	4 T.	4 c.	Sugar, powdered	2⅔ T.	2⅔ c.
Coffee, ground	4 T.	4 c.	Sugar, white	2 T.	2 c.
Cornstarch		3½ c.	Tea	⅜ c.	6 c.
Flour, bread or pastry	¼ c.	4 c.	Vanilla	2 T.	
Flour, graham		3¼ c.	Walnuts	¼ c.	4 c.
Figs		2½ c.			
Lard	2 T.	2 c.			
Liquid	2 T.	2 c.			
Macaroni	½ c.	6 c.			

BUYING GUIDE

FOOD	NUMBER SERVINGS
Almonds, shelled (lb.)	30 (12 nuts each)
Apples, fresh (lb.)	3
Apples, dried (lb.)	18
Apricots, dried (lb.)	16
Artichokes, (qt.)	3
Asparagus, (No. 2 can)	5 to 7
Asparagus, (1 bunch)	4
Bacon, (lb.)	25 thin slices
Bananas, whole (lb.)	3
Bananas, slices, (lb.)	5
Beans, snap	4 to 8
Beef, round steak, (lb.)	4 to 5
Sirloin, (lb.)	2
Porterhouse, (lb.)	2
Ground meat, (lb.)	4 to 5
Beets, (lb.)	4 to 5
(3 beets per lb.)	
Bread, (lb. loaf)	15 slices
(Pullman loaf)	30 slices
Cabbage, raw (lb.)	10 to 12
Cooked, (lb. raw)	5 to 6
(Solid head)	5 to 8
Carrots, (lb.)	3
Cauliflower, small head or lb.	4
Celery, (1 bunch or 3 stalks)	8 to 12
Cheese, American, (lb.)	20 1 inch cubes
Cheese, cottage, (lb.)	8
Chicken, small broiler	2
Large	4
Med. fryer	6
Roast, (lb.)	2
Chicory, (head)	4
Cocoa, (½ lb.)	60 cups
Coffee, (lb.)	40 to 50 cups
Corn, canned (cup)	3
Green, per ear	½ to 1
Cream, thin, (pt.)	15 to 18
Cream, whipped, (pt.)	25 (dipped t. or 16 (dipped T.)
Cream, heavy, after whipping (pt.)	40 (dipped t. or 25 (dipped T.)
Cucumber, 1 med. in salad	4
Sliced	2 to 3
Custard with pt. milk	4
Dates, (lb.)	2⅔ c.
Eggplant, med.	6 to 8
Figs, dried (lb.)	7
Fish, (lb.)	3
Grapes, (lb.)	4
Greens, (lb.)	2 to 3
(pk.)	6 to 8
Ham, uncooked, (lb.)	6
Ham, cooked, (lb.)	8 to 10
Huckleberries, (lb.)	6 to 8
Ice cream, (qt.)	7 to 8
Ice, (qt.)	7
Jelly, (½ pt. glass)	3 to 5
Lamb, (lb.)	4 to 5
Lettuce, (head)	4
Lemon juice, (1 lemon)	3 T.
Lima beans, fresh shelled, (lb. or qt.)	5
Liver, (lb.)	4 to 5
Onions, (lb.)	3
Orange juice, (1 orange)	⅓ c.
Oysters, (pt.)	4
Parsnips, (lb.)	4 to 6
Peaches, (lb.)	3 to 4
Peanuts, (lb.)	25 (10 peanuts each)
Pears, (lb.)	3
Peas, green in shell, (lb.)	2 to 3
Pecans, (lb.)	30 (12 nuts ea.)
Plums, (lb.)	7 to 9 plums
Pork, (lb.)	3
Potatoes, (lb.)	3 to 4
Prunes, (lb.)	10 to 12
Raisins, (lb.)	16 (1 oz.)
Raspberries, (qt.)	6 to 8
Rice, (lb.)	12 to 16
Salad, (lb.)	3
Spinach, (lb.)	3
Strawberries, (qt.)	6 to 8
Sweet potatoes, (lb.)	3
Tea, (½ lb.)	175 to 250
Tomatoes, fresh whole, (lb.)	3
Sliced, (lb.)	5 to 6
Turnips, (lb.)	3
Veal, (lb.)	3 to 4

A Guide to Common Container Sizes

CONTAINERS	APPROXIMATE NET WEIGHT	APPROXIMATE CONTENTS IN CUPS	APPROXIMATE NUMBER OF SERVINGS	USES
8Z TALL	8 OZ.	APPROXIMATELY 1 CUP	SERVES 2	USED PRINCIPALLY FOR FRUITS; ALSO FOR SOME SPECIALTIES. (SOMETIMES REFERRED TO AS BUFFET)
NO. 1 TALL CAN	16 OZ.	APPROXIMATELY 2 CUPS	SERVES 3 TO 4	USED FOR SALMON, SHELLFISH AND HERRING. ALSO FOR SOME VEGETABLES, FRUITS, JUICES, FISH PRODUCTS, AND SPECIALTIES.
NO. 303 JAR / NO. 303 CAN	16 OZ. TO 17 OZ.	APPROXIMATELY 2 CUPS	SERVES 3 TO 4	USED PRINCIPALLY FOR VEGETABLES AND FRUITS; ALSO FOR SPECIALTIES.
NO. 2 CAN	1 LB. 2 OZ. TO 1 LB. 4 OZ.	APPROXIMATELY 2½ CUPS	SERVES 4 TO 5	MOST POPULAR CONTAINER FOR VEGETABLES. ALSO USED FOR FRUITS, JUICES, AND SPECIALTIES.
NO. 2½ CAN / NO. 2½ JAR	1 LB. 12 OZ. TO 1 LB. 14 OZ.	APPROXIMATELY 3½ CUPS	SERVES 6 TO 7	MOST POPULAR CONTAINER FOR FRUITS. ALSO USED FOR SPINACH, TOMATOES, BEETS, PUMPKIN AND SOME JUICES.
NO. 3 CYL.	1 QT. 14 OZ. TO 1 QT. 15 OZ.	APPROXIMATELY 5¾ CUPS	SERVES 8 TO 12	USED FOR JUICES (SOMETIMES REFERRED TO AS NO. 5)

FIG. 58. EXAMINE YOUR COLLECTION OF CANNED FOODS IN RELATION TO THIS CHART

Ways of Buying Food. A buyer's own ways of making food purchases may have an important influence on what the family gets. There are a number of practices that a buyer would do well to adopt, although the importance of each practice varies with the individual. Here are ten suggestions that usually are helpful:

1. Learn to recognize good quality in fresh foods. Desirable characteristics of fresh fruit are suggested on pages 46 and 47; similar characteristics of fresh vegetables are given on page 194. Signs of quality in fresh meat are discussed in Chapter 24.

2. Have a list, of course, each time food is bought. It is an unnecessary source of irritation for all concerned for a homemaker to forget some item that is badly needed. Forgetting can be reduced to a minimum if the buyer takes the little trouble required to make lists and has one with her when she shops. A pad and pencil in the kitchen are good insurance against forgetting.

3. Know how much you need. Experience helps family buyers to know how much they should buy. The buying guide on page 166 and the table of approximate measures on page 165 will be helpful in deciding how much to buy before going to market. A notation of amounts is desirable on the shopping lists. It is even more important when some member of the family besides the usual food buyer does the shopping. It is troublesome to buy either too much or too little.

4. Ask questions, definite ones. Even the most experienced homemakers find themselves wishing to know more than they do, and no one should, therefore, feel foolish about a need for more information. The family buyer should remember how important each detail of food buying is to the family concerned.

5. Study the different forms in which some foods are available. Learn the characteristics of the different forms (such as dried, fresh, and frozen), and understand conditions that make one a better buy than the others. If a food can be bought either fresh, canned, dried, or frozen, the choice should be made from the standpoints of nutritive value, flavor, waste, convenience, comparative costs, and family preferences.

6. Buy in season those foods that are more plentiful, that have a better flavor, and that may be more nutritious when in season. This practice is economical and results in having a food at times when it is especially good.

7. Read, understand, and compare information found on the

labels of the same or similar types of food. Make a list of kinds of information on the label, such as size of pieces, number of pieces, recipes for using the product, heaviness or lightness of sirup, net weight, and grade. Rate each kind of information according to your opinion of its importance. Then make a list of all the information you would like to find on each label. Do you usually find the most important items?

8. Know grades of canned fruits and vegetables, meats, fresh fruits, and vegetables, and eggs, and good uses of each grade, so that if you find graded food in your store you can buy the one that is suited to the use you wish to make of it.

9. Watch for good value at moderate cost or at low cost. Value in relation to cost varies from time to time so that a habit of comparing values and prices is indispensable to the expert buyer.

10. Study food advertising. Many definite facts of interest to the food buyer are found in advertising. Of course, some space in advertising is given to "glamour," that is, color, illustrations, striking slogans. In spite of this, we can often find some real information about new foods and some new information about old foods. Recipes are often included. Advertising that is found in newspapers should have special attention. It lists food and prices currently featured in local stores. In studying such advertising, note all indications of amount and quality, as well as prices.

How to Save Money

A few pages back you were asked to look over the foods in the Basic Seven food groups, to note which ones were expensive and which relatively inexpensive. A wise buyer knows the less expensive foods in each group. This knowledge helps her to economize. She is able to buy generously the cheapest foods in each nutritive group. For example, some cheap foods in these groups are:

Group 1: Green and yellow vegetables — cabbage, carrots, collards, beet tops, turnip greens.

Group 2: Tomatoes and citrus fruit — canned tomatoes most of the time, but sometimes small juicy oranges and in midsummer, fresh tomatoes.

Group 3: Potatoes — white potatoes in U.S. No. 1 or No. 2 grade. Dried fruits — prunes, apples.

Group 4: Milk and milk products — buttermilk, canned milk, dried milk.

Group 5: Meat — cheap cuts having little waste, low grades, specialties such as kidneys.
Eggs — cold storage eggs from June to March.
Dried vegetables and nuts — peanuts, peanut butter, soybeans, dried beans of several kinds.

Group 6: Grain products — cornmeal, oatmeal, graham crackers, soda crackers.

Group 7: Fat — compound lard.

Some Economy Helps

1. Prefer foods with little or no waste, or foods with less waste, at the same or nearly the same price. Which cuts of meat in your collection have the most waste? Does this waste make the edible part more or less expensive than that of other cuts? Is there more waste in peeling one variety of potato than another? Is there more waste in the head of lettuce or the head of cabbage in your collection?

2. Stress the forms in which food is lower in cost. If part will not be eaten, but will instead find its way into the garbage can, of course the part suitable for the family table will be higher in cost per pound than the price indicated. Fresh fruit and vegetables in season are often plentiful and low in price. Canned fruit and vegetables are often inexpensive and little or none should be wasted.

3. Ready-to-eat foods are relatively high priced. This is true of such foods as breakfast cereals and of the many different "mixes" for muffins, pancakes, and others.

4. Keep low grades in mind. Often a low grade at a low price is an economical buy, and well suited to the use that will be made of it. Sliced peaches, Grade C, are good in pie, for example. Read the descriptions of grades of canned foods on page 296 and suggest purposes for which each grade is most suitable. Study grades of meat on page 263 in the same way.

5. When it is economical, buy in large quantity. Such a food as oatmeal is usually cheaper per pound in a large package than it is in a small one. It may be economical to purchase a large piece of meat, and cut it into smaller pieces suited to preparation in different ways. Of course, proper storage is necessary. Such meat should usually be stored frozen, with proper wrappings. Ask an experienced butcher to show you how a large piece can be cut at home for different uses. However, buying in large quantities is

FIG. 59. THE DIFFERENCES BETWEEN GRADE A, B, AND C TOMATOES CAN BE SEEN IN THESE PICTURES

The nutritive value of the three grades is the same.

not always thrifty. A purchase of a luxury food, such as olives, in a large quantity, even at a reduced price, often results in extravagant use; buying perishable food cheap and then allowing part of it to spoil is uneconomical.

6. Study actual cost of food in different size packages at various prices. Look back to page 71 and see how much this may mean, even with inexpensive food. Then take some examples from your food collection, such as different size packages of cocoa. Use the table on pages 172 and 173 to find the actual cost per pound in different size packages.

7. Keep records of your food purchases, both the amounts you buy and the prices you pay. Such records help the family to get its money's worth. It is a simple matter to keep good records and to use less than a half hour a week for them, after the habit of doing this systematically once a week is established. If records are studied and used as a guide in future buying they are invaluable.

TABLE FOR DETERMINING COST

HOW TO DETERMINE COST PER POUND: Read the label on the can or package to learn weight of contents. If weight is stated in pounds or in fractions of a pound, reduce to ounces, remembering that there are 16 ounces in a pound. (Thus, 1 lb. 2 oz. is 18 ounces.) Find this figure in the first column, headed "Weight of Contents." Find the price you paid for the can or package in the top row of figures (as 16¢). Follow down the column of figures given under the price until you reach the line of figures extending to the right

Weight of Contents of Package in Ounces	Cost per Pound of a Food Which has Specified Price per Package											
	5¢	6¢	7¢	8¢	9¢	10¢	11¢	12¢	13¢	14¢	15¢	16¢
1	$.80	$.96	$1.12	$1.28	$1.44	$1.60	$1.76	$1.92	$2.08	$2.14	$2.40	$2.56
2	.40	.48	.56	.64	.72	.80	.88	.96	1.04	1.12	1.20	1.28
3	.27	.32	.37	.43	.48	.53	.59	.64	.69	.75	.80	.85
4	.20	.24	.28	.32	.36	.40	.44	.48	.52	.56	.60	.64
5	.16	.19	.22	.26	.29	.32	.35	.38	.42	.45	.48	.51
6	.13	.16	.19	.21	.24	.27	.29	.32	.35	.37	.40	.43
7	.11	.14	.16	.18	.21	.23	.25	.27	.30	.32	.34	.37
8	.10	.12	.14	.16	.18	.20	.22	.24	.26	.28	.30	.32
9	.09	.11	.12	.14	.16	.18	.20	.21	.23	.25	.27	.28
10	.08	.10	.11	.13	.14	.16	.18	.19	.21	.22	.24	.26
11	.07	.09	.10	.12	.13	.15	.16	.17	.19	.20	.22	.23
12	.07	.08	.09	.11	.12	.13	.15	.16	.17	.19	.20	.21
13	.06	.07	.09	.10	.11	.12	.14	.15	.16	.17	.18	.20
14	.06	.07	.08	.09	.10	.11	.13	.14	.15	.16	.17	.18
15	.05	.06	.07	.08	.09	.11	.12	.13	.14	.15	.16	.17
16	.05	.06	.07	.08	.09	.10	.11	.12	.13	.14	.15	.16
17	.05	.06	.07	.08	.08	.09	.10	.11	.12	.13	.14	.15
18	.04	.05	.06	.07	.08	.09	.10	.11	.12	.12	.13	.14
19	.04	.05	.06	.07	.08	.08	.09	.10	.11	.12	.13	.13
20	.04	.05	.06	.06	.07	.08	.09	.10	.10	.11	.12	.13
21	.04	.05	.05	.06	.07	.08	.08	.09	.10	.11	.11	.12
22	.04	.04	.05	.06	.07	.07	.08	.09	.09	.10	.11	.12
23	.03	.04	.05	.06	.06	.07	.08	.08	.09	.10	.10	.11
24	.03	.04	.05	.05	.06	.07	.07	.08	.09	.09	.10	.11
25	.03	.04	.04	.05	.06	.06	.07	.08	.08	.09	.10	.10
26	.03	.04	.04	.05	.06	.06	.07	.07	.08	.09	.09	.10
27	.03	.04	.04	.05	.05	.06	.07	.07	.08	.08	.09	.09
28	.03	.03	.04	.05	.05	.06	.06	.07	.07	.08	.09	.09
29	.03	.03	.04	.04	.05	.06	.06	.07	.07	.08	.08	.09
30	.03	.03	.04	.04	.05	.05	.06	.06	.07	.07	.08	.09
31	.03	.03	.04	.04	.05	.05	.06	.06	.07	.07	.08	.08
32	.03	.03	.04	.04	.05	.05	.06	.06	.07	.07	.08	.08

PER POUND OF A FOOD [1]

from the figure for weight of contents. This figure is the cost per pound. For example, if a package weighs 18 ounces and its price is 16 cents, the cost per pound is 14 cents.

This table also may be used for determining cost per pint of liquid sold by the fluid ounce, since there are 16 fluid ounces in a pint. For example, if 2 fluid ounces of vanilla cost 23 cents, the cost per pint is $1.84.

COST PER POUND OF A FOOD WHICH HAS SPECIFIED PRICE PER PACKAGE

17¢	18¢	19¢	20¢	21¢	22¢	23¢	24¢	25¢	26¢	27¢	28¢	29¢	30¢
$2.72	$2.88	$3.04	$3.20	$3.36	$3.52	$3.68	$3.84	$4.00	$4.16	$4.32	$4.48	$4.64	$4.80
1.36	1.44	1.52	1.60	1.68	1.76	1.84	1.92	2.00	2.08	2.16	2.24	2.32	2.40
.91	.96	1.01	1.07	1.12	1.17	1.23	1.28	1.33	1.39	1.44	1.49	1.55	1.60
.68	.72	.76	.80	.84	.88	.92	.96	1.00	1.04	1.08	1.12	1.16	1.20
.54	.58	.61	.64	.67	.70	.74	.77	.80	.83	.86	.90	.93	.96
.45	.48	.51	.53	.56	.59	.61	.64	.67	.69	.72	.75	.77	.80
.39	.41	.44	.46	.48	.50	.53	.55	.57	.60	.62	.64	.66	.69
.34	.36	.38	.40	.42	.44	.46	.48	.50	.52	.54	.56	.58	.60
.30	.32	.34	.36	.37	.39	.41	.43	.45	.46	.48	.50	.52	.53
.27	.29	.30	.32	.34	.35	.37	.38	.40	.42	.43	.45	.46	.48
.25	.26	.28	.29	.31	.32	.33	.35	.36	.38	.39	.41	.42	.44
.23	.24	.25	.27	.28	.29	.31	.32	.33	.35	.36	.37	.39	.40
.21	.22	.23	.25	.26	.27	.28	.30	.31	.32	.33	.34	.36	.37
.19	.21	.22	.23	.24	.25	.26	.27	.29	.30	.31	.32	.33	.34
.18	.19	.20	.21	.22	.23	.24	.25	.27	.28	.29	.30	.31	.32
.17	.18	.19	.20	.21	.22	.23	.24	.25	.26	.27	.28	.29	.30
.16	.17	.18	.19	.20	.21	.22	.23	.24	.24	.25	.26	.27	.28
.15	.16	.17	.18	.19	.20	.20	.21	.22	.23	.24	.25	.26	.27
.14	.15	.16	.17	.18	.19	.19	.20	.21	.22	.23	.24	.24	.25
.14	.14	.15	.16	.17	.18	.18	.19	.20	.21	.22	.22	.23	.24
.13	.14	.14	.15	.16	.17	.18	.18	.19	.20	.21	.21	.22	.23
.12	.13	.14	.15	.15	.16	.17	.17	.18	.19	.20	.20	.21	.22
.12	.13	.13	.14	.15	.15	.16	.17	.17	.18	.19	.19	.20	.21
.11	.12	.13	.13	.14	.15	.15	.16	.17	.17	.18	.19	.19	.20
.11	.12	.12	.13	.13	.14	.15	.15	.16	.17	.17	.18	.19	.19
.10	.11	.12	.12	.13	.14	.14	.15	.15	.16	.17	.17	.18	.18
.10	.11	.11	.12	.12	.13	.14	.14	.15	.15	.16	.17	.17	.18
.10	.10	.11	.11	.12	.13	.13	.14	.14	.15	.15	.16	.17	.17
.09	.10	.10	.11	.12	.12	.13	.13	.14	.14	.15	.15	.16	.17
.09	.10	.10	.11	.11	.12	.12	.13	.13	.14	.14	.15	.15	.16
.09	.09	.10	.10	.11	.11	.12	.12	.13	.13	.14	.14	.15	.15
.09	.09	.10	.10	.11	.11	.12	.12	.13	.13	.14	.14	.15	.15

[1] Reprinted by courtesy of New York State College of Home Economics, Cornell University.

How to Keep Records

Good food records may be kept if the following steps are taken:

1. Keep the cash slips from each purchase. It helps if the food is bought only once a day or less frequently. The slips may be your order list with the prices paid added to the list, or it may be the grocer's check list of prices with notes made on it to help you know better what the foods were. The cash slips may be kept in a box used only for this purpose, or slipped on a nail or spike that is reserved for them.
2. Set aside ten or fifteen minutes each week for the keeping of records. Choose a time which you are fairly sure can be regularly kept for this, and a time when you are rested and will do a good job. A good time for most homemakers is soon after breakfast.
3. Provide yourself with a book or cards on which to place the written record. Beginners often like to try the cards.
4. Have on hand a good pencil that, preferably, is used just for this purpose. Sometimes it takes a chain to keep the pencil and record together.

Fig. 60. Whether you shop in person or by telephone, always check your purchases with the grocer's receipt

You see that it does not require much time or expense; system is more important than anything else. The final record should give a complete description of each purchase. A complete description tells how much, what, and the cost, as "10 lb. sugar, .89" or "5 lb. flour, .40." Dollar signs just take up space and sometimes look like 3's or 8's, so omit them. You should use all the abbreviations you can; write five cents, .05, and five dollars, 5.00. Do you see things that can be learned from complete records? One family found that they could buy the 400 lb. of sugar they used each year at a saving of $3.65 a year by buying it in large quantity. Can you suggest something else that can be learned from food purchase records? Perhaps you would like to try keeping the records of food purchases at school so that you will have practice in doing it.

How to Save Time

No one has enough time for all there is to do. Some homemakers, such as mothers of very small children, are especially hard pressed for time. They need to squeeze out minutes from other things in order to devote time to their children. Some time economy tips are:

1. ARRANGE YOUR LIST IN THE ORDER IN WHICH YOU EXPECT TO BUY. If you will buy staples first, put them at the top of the list.

2. WRITE AMOUNTS, KINDS, BRANDS, GRADES ON YOUR LIST.

3. MAKE EACH BUYING TRIP COUNT AND LIMIT THE NUMBER OF TRIPS. There just aren't any days that are longer than twenty-four hours, and it is a part of good management to use time to good advantage. Also, better variety can be obtained when enough time is taken to buy a number of foods needed, including, for example, two or three kinds of vegetables instead of buying one at a time. Where adequate storage is available, once-a-week purchasing of staples and twice-a-week purchasing of perishables is desirable. Not only are time and effort saved in buying less often, but they are also saved in caring for foods at home and storing them properly. Fluid milk must be bought each day or every other day.

4. BUY AT A CONVENIENT TIME. Buying at rush hours is wasteful of precious minutes, as a rule, and may result in frayed tempers, so that it is wise to avoid such times if possible. If there is a hurried feeling, the buyer may find that "haste makes waste."

5. PHONE YOUR ORDER OCCASIONALLY IF YOU ARE REALLY HARD PRESSED FOR TIME. If you adopt this practice, do a good job.

Have your list well prepared and in the same order as suggested above. Such a list saves time in the long run, and avoids confusion. Give the order slowly and distinctly. Plan carefully any questions you need to ask. Be sure there is understanding at both ends of the phone. It helps to know the clerk personally if it is necessary to order by telephone. Try to shop in person about every other week or at least once a month. Shopping in person makes it possible to get ideas, check and compare prices.

Laws to Protect Our Food

It isn't surprising that our federal government takes an interest in our food and has made some regulations about its labels, about the packages in which it is sold, and about the way it is advertised. In the chapter on meat you will see that there is a special federal law about its care. Our United States Government makes regulations about what goes from one state to another (interstate commerce) and each state government makes regulations about what remains within the states (intra-state commerce).

The Food, Drug, and Cosmetic Act. Fifty years ago there were no federal food laws. In those days, packaged foods were often adulterated. For example, coffee might have roasted grain ground with it or even pecan shells. Foods were sometimes falsely labeled. But today the United States Food and Drug Administration enforces laws against adulteration and misbranding of food. It has power to do so under the Federal Food, Drug, and Cosmetic Act of 1938 (which replaced the Federal Food and Drug Act of 1906).

The following is a brief summary of the provisions of the 1938 Act. As you read it, study the labels on the packages in the collection of food you made. Notice how they conform to the different provisions of the Act.

Adulterations forbidden by the Federal Food, Drug, and Cosmetic Act are as follows:

1. Including in food any substance injurious to health.
2. Including decomposed or filthy substances.
3. Packing food under unsanitary conditions.
4. Removing, substituting, or adding substances or concealing inferiority in any way.
5. Using coal tar dyes that have not been certified by the Food and Drug Administration.
6. Including non-edible substances in candy.

Misbranding of Foods is also forbidden by the Federal Food, Drug, and Cosmetic Act. Misbranding includes the following practices:

1. Having false or misleading labels. This includes claims, illustrations, and all parts of the labels. If canned dried peas should have an illustration of green peas on the label, it would be called misbranding. All printed matter with or in the package is considered part of the label.
2. Using the name of another food.
3. Imitating another food, unless the label says clearly that the food is an imitation.
4. Making or filling the container so as to be misleading about the amount it contains.
5. Omitting from the label the name and address of the manufacturer, packer, or distributor.
6. Failing to state accurately the quantity of the contents in terms of weight, measure, or count.
7. Failing to place all required information in a place on the label that is prominent and easy to see.
8. Failing, when quality is indicated, to have it conform to United States Department of Agriculture standards for the claimed quality.
9. Failing to disclose the presence of artificial coloring or flavoring or chemical preservative.

Violations of these provisions are still found sometimes, but the effect of the law has been to reduce the adulteration and misbranding of foods that go into interstate commerce. (Ask the manager or clerk of a store what foods he sells that come from across the state borders.) The fact that violations are still found is an indication of the need for vigilance on the part of the federal government. Such vigilance protects honest business from unfair ways of others, besides protecting the health and purses of those who buy.

The Federal Law about Advertising. Advertising of food is regulated by the Federal Trade Commission. As the Federal Trade Commission is a federal agency, it has jurisdiction only over foods in interstate commerce, but its power extends to national advertising in magazines, over the radio, and in newspapers sold in more than one state. Penalties are largest for advertising which makes misleading health claims, but all misleading advertising is forbidden.

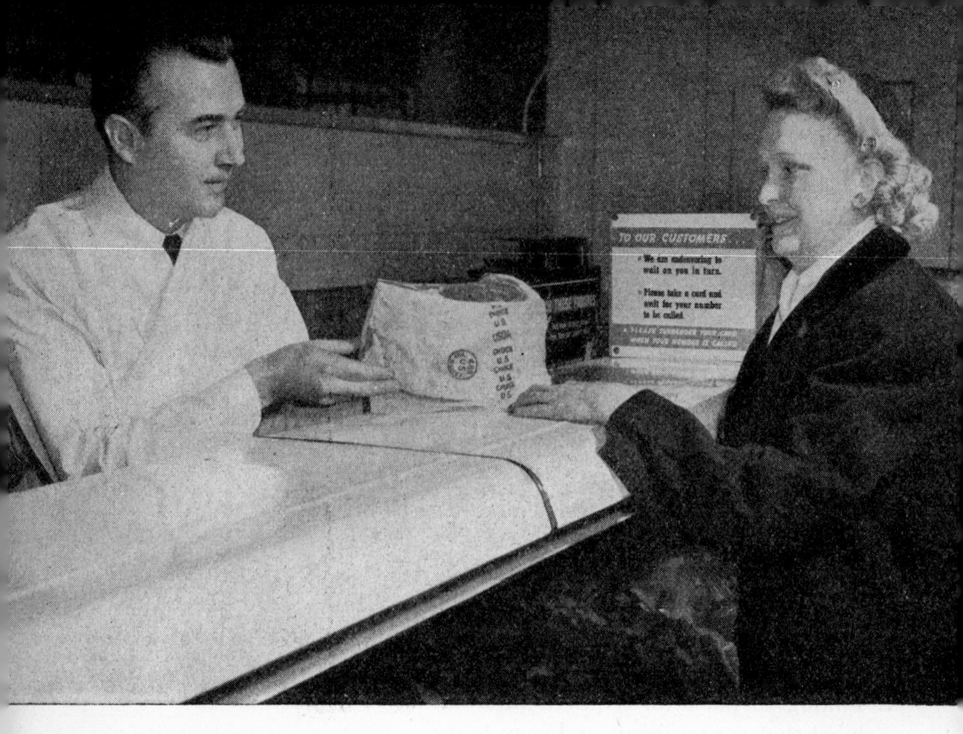

FIG. 61. THE HOUSEWIFE IS CHOOSING A BEEF RIB ROAST WHICH BEARS THE GRADE STAMP "U.S. CHOICE"

The round stamp on the meat indicates that the meat was also inspected and passed by U.S. government inspectors for wholesomeness.

Federal Meat Inspection Act. Meat inspection, as authorized under the Federal Meat Inspection Act, is responsible in large part for the cleanliness and sanitary handling of the large quantity of meat that goes through interstate commerce. This regulation of meat supplies is discussed in Chapter 24, Meat. Meat animals are inspected before slaughter; the methods of slaughter are inspected; the meat is inspected after slaughter; methods of handling it are inspected as long as the meat remains in the plant; and the plant itself must be properly constructed and cleaned.

State and City Regulations. States and cities have regulations about the storage and distribution of food within their limits. States have laws and have established departments of food and health to enforce the laws. Cities have ordinances and have established departments of health and in some cities, food departments to enforce the ordinances. There are also special regulations about sanitation in stores, eating places, and about the care of special foods, such as meat.

CLASS PROBLEMS

1. Figure the cost per pound of several packages of food. Use the Cost-Weight Table for determining cost per pound. Estimate how much of these foods a family might use in a year, choose economical purchases, and estimate annual savings.

2. Divide the class into seven groups. Have each group select one of the Basic Seven groups of food. In each of the Basic Seven groups, find which individual foods cost least per pound, which cost moderate amounts, and which are expensive. Tell the class what you have learned.

3. Get five or six packages of different kinds of food. Read the labels and compare them with the list of points that should be included on a good label.

4. Investigate your state's laws about food. Obtain the food ordinances of at least two cities. Are their regulations similar? Do you find any that are unimportant to families that buy food?

HOME PROBLEMS

1. Select three or four foods on which to compare prices in different stores. Suggestions are graham flour, canned beans, oranges, packaged crackers, canned peas, olives. Try to price the same quantity and quality of each. What is responsible for differences in price in different stores?

2. What does your newspaper tell you about food? Read news sections carefully for items, remembering that they may be small. Read the advertising carefully. Make a list of the information. Divide the list into general facts and definite ones. Did the advertising indicate quantity and quality?

3. Ask a homemaker about some of her problems in buying food. Can you begin now to learn to solve such problems?

4. Ask a neighbor or a friend what foods his or her family likes and what the family dislikes. Do their likes and dislikes affect the amount of money that must be used to buy their food?

REFERENCES

Better Buymanship Bulletins. A series of pamphlets on family buying problems, including a number of helpful ones on foods. Send for price list. Household Finance Corporation. Headquarters, 919 North Michigan Avenue, Chicago, Illinois.

Consumer Reports. A general monthly publication on family buying. 17 Union Square West, New York City.

Consumers' Research Bulletins. A general monthly publication on family buying. Washington, New Jersey.

Donham, S. Agnes. *Marketing and Housework Manual.* Rev. ed. Little, Brown and Company.

Federal Food and Drug Administration, Washington, D.C. Send for digest of the Federal Food, Drug, and Cosmetic Act and ask about recent popular publications.

Gaer, Joseph. *Consumers All.* Harcourt, Brace and Company, New York.

Monroe and Henry. *It Pays to Buy Food Wisely.* Cornell Bulletin for Homemakers 237, Mailing Dept., N.Y. State College of Agriculture, Ithaca, New York.

Nicholas, F., and Trilling, M. B. *You and Your Money.* Lippincott.

Public Affairs Pamphlets. A series of popular pamphlets, including a few on food. Send for price list. Public Affairs Committee, Inc., 22 East 38th Street, New York City.

Sherman, Henry C. *Food Products.* Fourth edition. The Macmillan Company.

Bulletins and pamphlets of the United States Department of Agriculture as follows:

Popular Publications for the Farmer and Homemaker, List No. 5.

The ABC of Canned Fruit and Vegetable Labeling, Miscellaneous Publication No. 460.

A Consumer's Guide to U.S. Standards for Farm Products, Miscellaneous Publication No. 553.

Containers for Fruit and Vegetables, F.B. 1821.

A Fruit and Vegetable Buying Guide for Consumers, Miscellaneous Publication No. 167.

How Families Use Their Income, Miscellaneous Publication No. 653.

The Inspection Stamp as a Guide to Wholesome Meat, Miscellaneous Circular 64.

Helping Families Plan Food Budgets, Miscellaneous Publication No. 662.

CHAPTER FIFTEEN

What Shall We Have for Luncheon or Supper?

THE NUMBER OF MEALS per day is a matter of custom. If you will make inquiries of travelers in other lands, you will learn that eating habits in different countries of the world vary. In this country we eat one light meal (breakfast), one moderate meal (lunch, luncheon, or supper), and one heavy meal (dinner). It is the moderate meal that we have under discussion here, whether that meal is eaten at noon or at night. In cities the members of the family usually eat the noon meal "in town" or at school. This meal is light or moderate, and often hurried — in fact, a "lunch." Even in small towns and rural districts the school children often eat a lunch at school. Thus noon is the more favored time for the moderate meal of the day. Little children, however, should always have their heavy meal at noonday.

Luncheon. Luncheon is frequently a meal of individual choice and hence of individual responsibility. No matter how well the housewife may plan for the health of her family, every person should know how to choose food wisely, because most of us eat away from home sometimes and all of us choose, to some extent, what we eat at home.

Luncheon is the meal that interrupts the day's work. It is often a hurried meal; hence it should be simple and easily digested. Even when the family eat luncheon at home, it should be remembered that the housewife has a full working day, and the noon meal should be easily prepared and simply served in order to conserve her time and energy.

Because of its informality a large number of people may be entertained easily at a "buffet luncheon." A formal luncheon on

FIG. 62. WHAT SHALL WE HAVE FOR LUNCHEON?

the other hand is really a dinner, but is served at noon instead of in the evening.

Relation of Luncheon or Supper to Other Meals of the Day. Because a well-balanced diet is necessary for health, menus should be planned first to meet the body needs and secondly to please the eye and the palate. The three meals of the day must be considered together in planning, to secure a balance of dietary essentials.

It was suggested that one fourth of the daily requirement be supplied by breakfast. Luncheon or supper may well supply about one third of the total number of calories and dinner the remainder. Some persons, however, eat approximately the same amount for each meal.

Daily Food Requirements of High-School Girls and Boys. Boys and girls in high school are growing rapidly and entering into many school activities. They need good wholesome food which is well prepared and served attractively. The daily energy requirement for high-school girls is about 2400 or 2600 calories; for boys from 3200 to 3800 calories. Liberal amounts of minerals and vitamins will be needed for the best physical development during this period. To meet these needs boys and girls should include in the daily diet the following foods:

One quart of milk.
One raw fruit, preferably citrus or tomato.
Two or more vegetables in addition to potatoes; raw vegetables, green and yellow vegetables should be used frequently.
Whole-grain cereal products.
One egg.
One serving of meat, or meat substitute; liver and fish should be served occasionally.
Butter at every meal.
Other foods, such as simple desserts, extra servings of vegetables, cereal products, and fruits will be needed to furnish needed calories.

From Table V in the Appendix you can estimate the calories needed for yourself and your family. From Table VI in the Appendix you can estimate the calories you receive from the food you eat.

The following table shows what a fourteen-year-old girl ate one day during a fall semester. Check to see if she has met her daily food requirements in calories. Has she included all of the food essentials listed on page 182?

A DAY'S DIETARY FOR MARY DOE, A FOURTEEN-YEAR-OLD GIRL

Breakfast	*Measure*[1]	*Calories*[1]
Tomato juice	¾ cup	40
Wheatena	¾ cup	100
Top milk	¼ cup	100
Whole milk	1 cup	170
Whole-wheat raisin toast	1 slice 3¾ × ⅜ × ½	100
Butter	1 T	100
	Total.........	610
Luncheon		
Cream of pea soup	¾ cup	114
Crackers (soda)	4	100
Peanut butter sandwich	1	152
Cocoa	1 cup	200
Oatmeal cookies	1	133
Apple	1	80
	Total.........	779
Dinner		
Beef loaf	1½ slices 4″ × 6″ × ⅛″	150
Brown sauce	3 T	50
Baked potato	1 medium	100
Turnip greens	½ cup	30
Raw carrot strips	3 T	15
Cornmeal muffins	2–2½″ in diam.	266
Butter	1 T	100
Baked custard	⅔ cup	200
Milk	⅝ cup	100
	Total.........	1011
	Grand total....	2400

Some Factors in Planning Luncheon and Supper. There is more variety possible in luncheon menus than in breakfast menus. The same factors influence what we eat at each meal: age, sex, occupation, state of health, habit, and season.

The characteristic luncheon dishes are: soups, especially cream

[1] Figures are from Rose, M. S., *Feeding the Family*, 1940. The Macmillan Company.

soups; vegetables; salads; breads; sandwiches; beverages; a main hot dish, such as a cheese, egg, or combination meat and vegetable dish; and fruits or other desserts.

A luncheon menu containing all or most of these dishes is a *heavy* luncheon. A luncheon consisting of several of them is a *medium* luncheon. A luncheon consisting of two or three of these items in simple combinations is called a *light* luncheon or a lunch.

Heavy Luncheon	*Medium Luncheon*	*Light Luncheon*
Cream of tomato soup	Cheese soufflé	Lettuce and tomato salad — French dressing
Meat loaf with vegetables	Lettuce with French dressing	A roll
Head lettuce and Thousand Island dressing	Rolls	Tea or milk
Rolls	Milk, tea, or coffee	Baked custard
Milk or coffee	Prune whip	
Pie		

Seasonal Specials for Luncheon. One of the delights of a change in season is the welcome variety that it brings in menus. With the first cold weather you are pleased to find for luncheon a bowl of savory soup, or a casserole of steaming scalloped oysters, delicately browned, but what could be less tempting in July? Spring has its delights in an array of fresh vegetables, and we think with pleasure of the tinkle of ice in our glasses in summer.

One of the most important factors in planning a luncheon menu is the climate or season. Following are some of the foods appropriate for hot and cold weather:

Dishes	*Cold Weather*	*Hot Weather*
Soup	All kinds, especially cream soups	Jellied consommé or bouillon
Main hot dish	Fish and oysters, meat, cheese, eggs, sausage, gumbo, stews, chowder	Often lacking
Vegetables	Potatoes, cauliflower, cooked onions, cabbage, rice, celery, carrots, greens, winter squash, canned vegetables, dried vegetables. Vegetables prepared with sauces	Spinach, summer squash, corn, asparagus, new peas, string beans, radishes, tomatoes, cucumbers, shallots, new potatoes, okra. Vegetables served simply
Salads	Not used as main dish; a side dish for the main course, as slaw	As main dish; all kinds, chiefly fruit, vegetable, or egg

Dishes	*Cold Weather*	*Hot Weather*
Breads	Hot rolls, or toast, or nut bread	Hot rolls or crackers with cold dishes
Sandwiches	Toasted or hot sandwiches	All kinds
Beverages	Hot chocolate, cocoa, or for adults, coffee, tea	Iced drinks of all kinds, especially fruit juices, ginger ale, cold milk, iced tea
Desserts	Pie, cake, dried fruit, fruit roll, puddings, ice cream	Ices, berries, cantaloupe, fresh fruits: cherries, plums, peaches, pears
Total calories	(maximum)	(minimum)

CLASS PROBLEMS

1. Look through your local newspaper for a week for food advertising and bring clippings of them to class if possible. On what day of the week are the best sales offered? Are brand names found in these advertisements? Are the brands those that are used and liked in your home? Do you know the usual price of any of the items? Can you account for any specially good price? Is it offered only in large quantity? Is there a good local supply? Is it the height of the season? Do the advertisements give you any information about grade, size of package, etc.? Which item would it be helpful to see before deciding on a purchase? For which items might additional information be found on the label?

2. Keep a record of what you eat for lunch for one week. Indicate the minerals and vitamins in each food. How many calories were furnished in each meal?

3. Procure menus for the noon meal from several eating places in your locality. Suggested places: the grill room or the coffee shop in a hotel; a tea room; a dairy lunch; a restaurant; a school cafeteria. From these menus make out a list of typical luncheon dishes.

4. Suggest several one-dish luncheon or supper menus.

HOME PROBLEMS

1. For three days keep a record of what you eat for breakfast, luncheon, and dinner. What portion of your total calories do you eat at each meal?
2. On Saturdays help at home with the noon meal.
3. Plan the market order for Saturday food shopping.
4. Help with the marketing — study grades, standards, labels, weights, and quality in relation to price.

REFERENCES

A Guide to Good Meals for the Junior Home Maker. United States Department of Agriculture, Miscellaneous Circular 49.

Bogert, L. Jean, *Nutrition and Physical Fitness.* W. B. Saunders Company.

Diets to Fit the Family Income. United States Department of Agriculture, Farmers' Bulletin 1757.

Lanman, Faith R., McKay, Hughina, Zuill, Frances. *The Family's Food.* Chapters I, II, and III. J. B. Lippincott Company.

Rose, Mary Swartz. *Feeding the Family.* The Macmillan Company.

When Disaster Cuts Down Home Grown Food, Make Food Money Protect Health, 1938. Children's Bureau.

See current magazines for luncheon menu suggestions.

CHAPTER SIXTEEN

❧ The Vegetable Luncheon

Cook Book References

Food Value

In this chapter and the six chapters that follow, the discussion continues to center around the meal that is called luncheon if it is served at noon and supper if it is served later in the day. In this unit it is assumed that this meal will be a noon meal and hence a luncheon. If, however, it is a supper, the suggestions offered are equally appropriate, except, of course, for the school lunch, which is always a noon meal.

Kinds of luncheons. In addition to calling a luncheon light, heavy, or medium, there is another and perhaps more typical way of classifying luncheons, such as: the vegetable plate, the hot dish luncheon, the cold salad plate luncheon, the picnic lunch, the school lunch, the dairy lunch (usually a glass of milk and a sandwich). In this chapter we shall consider especially the vegetable luncheon at which vegetables constitute the main dish.

Vegetables are an ideal food for luncheon. Wise is the person who makes the vegetable luncheon a habit. One can feel that he has eaten a "square" meal when a vegetable luncheon is chosen, without having the uncomfortable, stuffy feeling that goes with overeating. Vegetables give us a bountiful supply of the much-needed minerals and vitamins, without overloading on calories, and yet they lend themselves to delectable combinations with butter or cream sauce and breads so that those who need extra calories can

FIG. 63. CREAM OF CORN SOUP IS ONLY ONE OF THE MANY WAYS IN WHICH VEGETABLES AND MILK CAN BE COMBINED FOR LUNCHEON

easily have the required amount in the vegetable luncheon.

Vegetables offer attractive combinations. Tempting the appetite is up to the one who plans and prepares the combinations of vegetables. A vegetable plate may be second to none in attractiveness. Picture, for example, snowy-white cauliflower with a cheese sauce, fresh green asparagus, and half of a broiled tomato on toast, attractively arranged as a vegetable plate.

WHAT HOT VEGETABLE DISHES SHALL WE HAVE FOR LUNCHEON?

Soups. Soups offer an opportunity for including vegetables in the luncheon menu They are easy to prepare, cheap, well-liked, easily varied, digestible, suitable for all the members of the family, and are especially acceptable in winter. There are two kinds of vegetable soups — cream and stock.

Some idea of the variety of vegetable soups for the luncheon can be gained from the following partial list of cream soups:

Asparagus	Pea	Onion
Celery	Tomato	Potato
Corn	Mushroom	Spinach

Cream soups are doubly valuable in the luncheon menu because they combine milk and vegetables.

Mixed vegetable soup made with meat stock is also good. For the method of making vegetable soups, consult the Index for cook book references in this and other cook books.

A satisfying noon meal is a bowl of cream vegetable soup, whole-wheat bread, and one

FIG. 64. A VEGETABLE PLATE IS AN OPPORTUNITY FOR A SKILLFUL COOK TO DISPLAY HEP. ART

The menu for this tempting vegetable luncheon plate is new parsley potatoes, lima beans, yellow squash, stuffed tomato.

other food, perhaps a salad or a dessert.

In the farm home it is a wise provision to include in the summer canning plenty of vegetable soup mixture. This will be relished by the family when cold weather comes and fresh vegetables are not plentiful and will be a convenience to the homemaker in planning the noon meal on a busy day.

FIG. 65. THE VEGETABLE LUNCHEON SERVED FAMILY STYLE

Menu: Corn on the cob, broiled tomatoes, broccoli with Hollandaise sauce, cucumber and watercress salad. What would you supply to complete the menu? The salad bowl adds its charm.

The vegetable plate. The vegetable plate gives an opportunity to serve vegetables either simply cooked or "dressed up" a bit — as creamed, stuffed, scalloped, baked, fried, and au gratin dishes, vegetables find a welcome place on a luncheon plate. A variety of sauces served with vegetables offers additional appetizing possibilities.

If ingenuity is exercised in the preparation of vegetables, they can be served in a great variety of ways and made so tempting that all the family will like them. Frequently certain vegetables are unpopular because they are prepared in uninteresting or unpalatable ways. Vegetable cookery in the average family offers much room for improvement.

A suggestion of some tempting ways of serving vegetables which you may want to try your skill at combining into distinctive vegetable plates are:

- Asparagus au gratin
- Boston baked beans
- Broiled tomatoes
- Glazed carrots
- Cauliflower with Hollandaise sauce
- Scalloped egg plant
- Broiled mushrooms
- French fried onion rings
- Creamed onions
- Stuffed peppers

Figure 64 shows a tempting vegetable plate. You can learn to plan others equally or more tempting. Cooked fruits are sometimes served as a vegetable. Crisp bacon adds a contrasting flavor to a vegetable plate, but at an increase in expense.

Why We Should Eat More Vegetables

Eat More Vegetables. If Nature were in business and wrote advertising slogans to sell her bounties she would promote vegetables, with fruits, as a first aid to good looks, and such a claim would be legitimate, for beauty comes from within. Vegetables, like fruits, are important sources of those food materials which are Nature's contribution to good health and good looks. Healthy skin, hair, eyes, body vigor are all a part of being attractive. It is a good rule to make vegetables the main dish for one meal daily. Why should we eat at least two vegetables daily? Should some vegetables have preference over others? Let us see.

How do Vegetables Help to Keep us Well?

1. Vegetables appeal to the appetite because of their variety of color, shape, flavor, and texture.

2. All vegetables contain cellulose and woody fiber which are valuable as laxatives.

3. Vegetables are important sources of the three minerals in which the diet is most likely to be deficient: iron, phosphorus, and calcium. Iron is abundant in such green leaves as spinach, dandelion greens, turnip greens, beet tops, mustard, and other greens. Calcium and phosphorus are found in collards, mustard, carrots, and turnip tops. Many other vegetables are also valuable sources of these minerals.

4. Vegetables are important sources of Vitamins A and C, and of thiamin, riboflavin, and niacin. The vitamin content of vegetables is highly important to our well-being.

Vitamin A, necessary for normal growth and good nutrition, is found in yellow vegetables, especially in sweet potatoes, carrots, yellow corn, and yellow squash. Green leafy vegetables, such as turnip greens and spinach, contain large amounts of Vitamin A. Here, as in many vegetables, the yellow color is covered up by the green pigment. The thinner and greener the leaf the richer the content of Vitamin A. This rule also applies to the iron and calcium content of vegetables. Head lettuce is not so rich in Vitamin A as is unbleached lettuce, and the same is true of cabbage and celery. It occurs, for example, in tomatoes, string beans, new peas, and in growing stems and shoots, such as asparagus.

Vitamin B_1 or thiamin, which is so necessary for proper growth, maintenance of appetite, good digestion, and an undisturbed nervous system, is fairly evenly distributed in all kinds of vegetables, but the amount is small in all of them. This vitamin is soluble in water, and is often lost when vegetables are cooked in water and the water drained off.

For Vitamin C (ascorbic acid) vegetables rank with the fruits. In fact, they are the only other important source in our food. Except for tomatoes, the best sources are the fresh green leaves and shoots, all rapidly growing parts of the plant: green cabbage, spinach, turnip greens, young onions, asparagus, and green lettuce. Since Vitamin C is easily destroyed by storage or cooking, these foods are most valuable when eaten raw and fresh from the garden.

Vegetables are a good source of riboflavin (Vitamin G), but even more important is their content of niacin. This substance was discovered so recently that tables of its occurrence have not been made yet, but a member of the U.S. Public Health Service has said that he never finds a case of pellagra in a family which has a backyard garden.

Vegetables do not contain Vitamin D. We need to depend on other sources for this vitamin.

Consult Chapter 1 and Table IX in the Appendix for further information on vitamins and their functions.

CLASSIFICATION OF VEGETABLES

1. *According to composition:*

Classification	*Examples*	*Qualities*
"Green" vegetables	Spinach Lettuce Squash "Greens," as beet, turnip, etc. Tomatoes Artichokes Asparagus Broccoli	High in water, vitamins, and minerals. Little starch or protein
Starchy vegetables	Beans Peas Corn Potatoes Soybeans	Contain important quantity of starch, or proteins, or both. Good supply of minerals and not so rich in vitamins as green vegetables.

2. *According to flavor:*

Mild vegetables	Carrots Lettuce Potatoes Beans Celery Artichokes	Delicate in flavor, therefore fit easily with any other foods and lend themselves to various ways of cooking
Strong vegetables	Cabbage Onions Green pepper Cauliflower	Strong flavor due to volatile oil which can be modified by method of cooking. Will pass off in steam if cooked in uncovered vessels.

The classification of vegetables is less important than their composition. It does have significance in meal planning and in cookery. One green and one starchy vegetable, or one mild and one strong vegetable, make pleasing combinations. Two green or two mild vegetables are acceptable, but two starchy vegetables or two strong ones are to be avoided in a single meal.

3. *Form in which marketed.* Vegetables are also classified as fresh, dried, canned, or frozen vegetables.

Fresh vegetables are better sources of Vitamin C than are cooked, dried, or canned vegetables except tomatoes. A large amount of the Vitamin B_1 may be found in the liquid with canned fruits and vegetables, instead of in the food. These are lost when the liquid is discarded.

Dried seeds, such as peas, contain notable amounts of Vitamins B_1, G, and niacin.

Dried and canned vegetables are equivalent to fresh vegetables as sources of minerals and cellulose. Some dried seeds, such as peas and beans, are cheap sources of protein and fuel.

Frozen vegetables are much like fresh vegetables in taste and composition. They are in a very convenient form because all the waste has been removed and the vegetable is ready for cooking.

Effect of Freezing on Vegetables and Fruits. The information on the effect of freezing on the food value of fruits and vegetables is increasing rapidly. It should be remembered that freezing is a relatively new process for preserving fruits and vegetables in the home. A great deal of research on this modern means of preserving fresh foods is now being carried on.

The studies that have been made on frozen vegetables (and

fruits) concern their Vitamin C (ascorbic acid) content. According to these studies,[1] freezing itself appears to have no destructive action on the vitamin content of foods. This is important because certain vegetables are a major source of Vitamin C, and this vitamin is needed daily since the body does not store much of it.

Losses sometimes attributed to freezing generally occur before the foods are frozen or are a result of improper handling during and after freezing. For example, the manufacturing operations concerned with shelling, washing, and blanching of Lima beans and peas have often been found to result in a loss of as much as 50 per cent of the ascorbic acid. Slow freezing, slow thawing, or storage of the frozen product above 0° F. (a temperature lower than zero is preferable) adversely affects the vitamins. Commercially frozen foods, however, are frozen by a process known as *quick freezing* in which the temperature is rapidly lowered to as low as —60° F. By this method vitamin content, flavor, and texture are preserved.

Frozen foods, especially vegetables such as peas, beans, and spinach, have been found to lose ascorbic acid if allowed to stand after thawing, and it is generally recommended that cooking be started while they are still in the frozen condition. Fruits which are to be used uncooked should be served immediately after thawing.

Some Vegetables Deserve Special Notice. Vegetables as a group are valuable for the addition of minerals and vitamins to the diet, but some individual vegetables in the group are more important than others and should be specially emphasized.

Look up in Table VI, Appendix, the minerals and vitamins in a serving of turnip greens, spinach, tomatoes, cabbage, lettuce, carrots, white potatoes, sweet potatoes, and dried beans.

Energy Value of Vegetables. Table VI (The Nutritive Value of Foods), Appendix, shows that most vegetables do not yield a high return in calories. Potatoes, dried beans, and peas, however, are an exception. For persons who desire to reduce, or who do not wish to gain more weight, the low fuel value of vegetables is important. Vegetables are "filling," and they satisfy the appetite without piling up calories if they are served without much cream, butter, or other fat.

We may summarize the importance of vegetables in the diet by a quotation from Dr. Sherman: "If we take account of the fact

[1] *Food and Life, Yearbook of Agriculture,* 1939, United States Department of Agriculture.

that we must purchase phosphorus, iron, at least three kinds of vitamins, as well as protein and energy in our food, we see that money spent for fruits and vegetables yields fully its proportionate return in nutritive value, as we now understand it, if not in calories and protein."[1]

Buying and Caring for Vegetables

Buying Vegetables. We need different kinds of vegetables. We must be careful not to buy or eat one kind of vegetable to the exclusion of others. A daily supply of vegetables that will be adequate for body needs will be supplied by:

First: potatoes, or sweet potatoes
Second: tomatoes, or citrus fruits, or both
Third: green and yellow vegetables
Fourth: one other vegetable

Other vegetables not falling in these classifications may be used to supplement the total amount of vegetables in the diet. For economy or convenience dried and canned vegetables may be used.

Economy in buying vegetables is necessary in most families and may be achieved by using vegetables that are in season and by choosing the less expensive ones in each of the groups. Serving cheaper vegetables in various pleasing ways is a challenge. The resourceful homemaker, for example, uses cabbage or inexpensive greens generously in place of more expensive green vegetables. Frozen vegetables are sometimes cheaper than fresh ones. Canned and dried vegetables are sometimes cheaper and more convenient to use than fresh ones, the times when they are cheaper varying in different sections according to the seasons. For true economy the local market must be studied carefully as the seasons change. Why?

Fresh vegetables that are in season are usually superior in quality, and are more economical than those that are out of season. For the calendar of seasons for vegetables, see Chapter 26, Vegetables and Fruits for Dinner.

It is often possible to buy vegetables direct from the producer. Good roads and automobiles make possible trips to a curb market, or to the country to combine pleasure and foraging.

Crispness, soundness, and tenderness are watchwords in select-

[1] From H. C. Sherman: *Food Products* (3d ed.) pp. 407–408. Reprinted by permission of The Macmillan Company, publishers.

ing young fresh vegetables. Fragrance is an indication of good quality in many vegetables, as in most fruits. Fresh, young vegetables are superior in flavor and in Vitamin C to old or wilted vegetables. Vegetables that are not fresh may be detected by the limpness of the leaves and the flabbiness and wrinkled condition of the vegetable. Specks or spots also indicate inferiority.

Choose vegetables that are displayed and handled under sanitary conditions.

The surest way to buy fresh vegetables is by grades — U.S. Government Grades. Graded fresh vegetables are available and are in general use in the wholesale market, but except for potatoes the consumer does not yet have the privilege, in most places, of buying fresh vegetables by grades. For Grades for Fresh Vegetables see Chapter 26, Vegetables for Dinner.

Caring for Vegetables. Most vegetables do not store well, and it will be remembered that storing decreases the Vitamin C content. These are two important considerations that favor daily marketing for vegetables. Fresh vegetables should, in general, be stored in a cool place in such a way that air may circulate through them. They should be above the floor level, preferably a foot or more.

Very perishable vegetables, such as tomatoes and shelled English peas, should be stored in a refrigerator to prevent spoilage. All stored vegetables should be inspected at intervals in order to find and discard any beginning to spoil. Various types of spoilage spread rapidly and can be prevented if the first spoiled vegetables are discarded. Fresh vegetables should always be washed before they are used and before they are placed in a refrigerator. Frozen vegetables should be kept frozen in the ice compartment of an automatic refrigerator, or in a special compartment provided for frozen foods until it is time to cook them.

Vegetable Cookery

Underlying Principles. When we cook vegetables, we are interested in knowing the methods which will prevent loss of their mineral and vitamin content and which will produce products that are pleasing in flavor and attractive in shape, color, and texture. Vegetables may be steamed, baked, or boiled.

1. Calcium, iron, phosphorus and other minerals, Vitamins B_1 and G and niacin are soluble in water. If vegetables are boiled, use as small an amount of water as possible. The water can be

concentrated and served with the vegetables or saved and used in gravies, sauces, and soups.

2. Vitamin C is not only soluble in water, but is quickly affected by exposure to air, heat, and soda. Points to remember in cooking vegetables are:[1]

Don't put through a sieve while hot.

Don't use soda in cooking green vegetables.

In boiling foods, start the vegetables in boiling water, and raise the temperature back to boiling as soon as possible.

Don't use long cooking periods such as stewing or simmering when shorter methods are just as good.

Use as little water as possible.

Frying foods causes a great loss of Vitamins A and B_1 as well as C.

Vegetables should be prepared just before cooking so that the cut surfaces shall not be exposed to the air for a long time.

Frozen foods, especially spinach, peas, and beans, rapidly lose Vitamin C if allowed to stand after thawing. Start cooking frozen vegetables while they are still frozen. They require much less time to cook than fresh vegetables. Serve raw frozen foods immediately after thawing.

3. If you wish to preserve the green color in vegetables, cook them in an uncovered vessel instead of using soda.

4. Cook vegetables as short a time as possible. For boiling, vegetables should be dropped into rapidly boiling salted water and should be cooked only until tender. Overcooked vegetables are unpalatable. Steaming is a good method of cooking mild vegetables.

5. Vegetables need careful seasoning, all require salt. Butter, cream, milk, pepper, paprika, and cayenne are all useful seasonings.

6. The flavors of strong vegetables are modified by cooking in uncovered vessels. Steaming is not suitable for strong vegetables. Why?

7. Directions often call for parboiling vegetables as a preliminary step. By this is meant cooking them beforehand in boiling salted water, until they are partially tender.

8. Certain vegetables (potatoes, sweet potatoes, squash, etc.) are very well liked when baked.

[1] Adapted from *Food and Life, Yearbook of Agriculture*, 1939, page 205. United States Department of Agriculture.

9. Prepare vegetables for cooking by washing them thoroughly and removing all spots or unsound portions. Pare thinly, if at all.

10. Dried vegetables require soaking. They should be cooked in the water in which they were soaked in order to prevent further loss of minerals. Dried vegetables require longer cooking than fresh vegetables.

11. Canned vegetables have a milder and fresher flavor if not heated in the water in which they have been canned. However, as this water contains soluble minerals and vitamins, it may be concentrated and poured over the vegetables, or saved and used in soups.

12. Bread crumbs are a great help in preparing vegetable dishes. Left-over bread may be toasted, or dried in the warming oven, then rolled into crumbs and stored in glass jars. Scalloped and stuffed vegetables are very little trouble to prepare if the bread crumbs are on hand.

CLASS PROBLEMS

1. Review Chapter 4 on Fruits and discuss the similarity of fruits and vegetables in their food value and their place in the diet.
2. Prepare a program of production of vegetables on the farm for the use of a farm family. Show the months when each fresh vegetable will be available and the months when canned, dried, or stored stock must be used. Find the differences, if you can, between the prices of these vegetables when sold at the farm or at wholesale prices, and at retail prices.
3. Visit the market and study the buying of vegetables.
4. Visit grocery stores and study the labels on canned vegetables.
5. Make a comparison of the price and quality of various vegetables in the following places: markets, groceries, cash-carry stores, vegetable wagons, near-by farms, curb markets, or in any other places dealing in vegetables.
6. Exhibit one-hundred-calorie portions of available vegetables.
7. Estimate the calories in one serving of vegetable dishes prepared in the class. See Table VI in Appendix.

HOME PROBLEMS

1. Purchase the vegetables for your family for one or two weeks.
2. Learn to eat at least two vegetables which you do not now eat.

3. List the vegetables that you eat each day for a week. Have you obtained a daily supply of Vitamin C?
4. Plan the vegetables for your family's meals for one week.
5. Prepare at home several luncheons using vegetable dishes as the center of the meal.

REFERENCES

A Fruit and Vegetable Buying Guide for Consumers. United States Department of Agriculture, Miscellaneous Publication No. 167.

Bogert, L. Jean. *Nutrition and Physical Fitness.* W. B. Saunders Company.

Chaney, Margaret S., and Ahlborn, Margaret. *Nutrition.* Houghton Mifflin Company.

Conserving Food Value, Flavor and Attractiveness in Cooking Vegetables. United States Department of Agriculture, Circular 265.

Halliday, Evelyn G., and Noble, I. *Hows and Whys of Cookery.* The University of Chicago Press.

Heseltine, Marjorie, and Dow, Ula M. *The Basic Cook Book.* Houghton Mifflin Company.

Home Storage of Vegetables. United States Department of Agriculture, Farmers' Bulletin 879.

Justin, Margaret M., Rust, Lucile O., and Vail, Gladys E. *Foods,* Unit 2. Houghton Mifflin Company.

Lanman, Faith R., McKay, Hughina, and Zuill, Frances. *The Family's Food.* J. B. Lippincott Company.

Monroe, Day, Kyrk, Hazel, and Stone, Ursula B. *Food Buying and Our Markets.* M. Barrows and Company. Discussion of Buying Vegetables in Chapters XV, XVI.

Proximate Composition of Fresh Vegetables. United States Department of Agriculture, Circular 146.

Rose, M. S. *Foundations of Nutrition.* The Macmillan Company, 1938. 3d edition.

Sherman, H. C. *Food Products.* The Macmillan Company.

Soybeans for the Table. United States Department of Agriculture, Leaflet 166.

Stewart, Jean J. *Foods: Production, Marketing, Consumption.* Prentice Hall.

CHAPTER SEVENTEEN

❧ The Hot Dish Luncheon or Supper

Cook Book References

Soufflés, etc.	*Page* 441	Meat and Vegetable Stew	*Page* 472
Casserole Dishes	*Page* 444	Croquettes	*Pages* 449, 472
Luncheon Loaves	*Page* 445	Fritters	*Page* 449
Creamed Dishes	*Page* 443	Oysters	*Page* 450
Chowders and Gumbos	*Page* 446	Hot Sandwiches	*Page* 451
Macaroni and Cheese	*Page* 442		

Food Value

Nutritive Value of Foods	*Table* VI, *Appendix*
Food Value in Shares	*Table* VIII, *Appendix*
Minerals and Vitamins	*Tables* IX, X, *Appendix*

The Hot Dish Luncheon Offers a Variety of Main Dishes. For most of the year, hot food is preferred for the noon meal. A hot luncheon offers a wide enough variety to meet any taste. Most restaurants and coffee shops list the hot plate lunch as the "business man's lunch." It usually consists of a main hot dish, plus a vegetable, bread, and a beverage. In general, the main hot dish will be nourishing and appetizing, but not so filling that it leaves one too "stuffy" to feel like going back to work at school or job.

1. *Variety in Food Materials.* In hot dishes the following food materials may be used as a foundation: eggs, meat, fish, oysters and other shellfish, poultry, cheese, nuts, vegetables, macaroni, spaghetti, or rice.

2. *Variety Made Possible by Method of Cooking.*

Note the following suggestions:

Soufflés
Casserole or ramekin dishes
Au gratin dishes
Stuffed vegetables
Scalloped dishes
Creamed vegetables or meat
on toast
in timbale cases
in bread cases
Gumbos
Chowders
Oyster stew
Meat and vegetable stews
Croquettes
Fritters
Meat turnovers
Seasonings and sauces:
Curried dishes
Brown sauce
Pimiento
Mushroom sauce
Hollandaise sauce
Cheese sauce

From this list, select the ones that are unfamiliar to you and look them up in a good cook book (see page 387) to find what ingredients they contain and how they are made.

Food Value of Hot Dishes. The main dish for luncheon may vary in food value all the way from supplying all the elements of good nutrition in one dish, to a single article of food, supplying adequately only one or two food nutrients. The tendency is toward food combinations which provide all the essentials.

Many of the materials used in the main hot dish have been discussed in previous chapters, but a few important articles of food have not yet been included. Chapters on meat, fish, and poultry are given in the dinner unit which follows. In the luncheon menu these protein foods usually appear as left-overs.

Omitting meat, fish, and poultry for later consideration, and eggs which have already been studied, we may discuss here: cheese, macaroni and spaghetti, and shellfish.

Cheese

1. *Production.* Cheese is a staple article of diet, and is one of the oldest prepared foods known. Cheese making in America has become an important industry. Much of the finest flavored and most expensive cheese is imported from Europe.

2. *Composition and Food Value.* Cheese, when made from whole milk, may be said to be slightly more than one third water, slightly more than one third fat, and slightly less than one third protein, with a high proportion of minerals, especially calcium and phosphorus.

The protein of cheese is the protein of milk, partially digested, and is a complete protein. The fat is milk fat, little changed except that it is less finely divided and hence not so quickly digested. The mineral content varies somewhat according to the amount of salt added. Cheese is always relatively high in calcium and phosphorus and also contains some iron. Cheese is a good source of Vitamin A; a small amount of Vitamin G is present.

Cheese is a concentrated and inexpensive food. A one-inch cube of yellow cheese yields approximately one hundred calories. It should be regarded primarily as a staple article of diet rather than as an accessory to pie, or as a last course after a heavy meal. The practice of serving cheese at the end of an already heavy meal, the fact that cheese by itself is not easily masticated, and the further fact that fat digests less rapidly than sugars and starchy foods, have led to the erroneous belief that cheese is hard to digest.

Cheese Cookery. It is important to know that cheese is easily overcooked either at high temperatures or by long cooking. Overcooked cheese is lumpy, stringy, and tough.

Macaroni and Spaghetti

Macaroni, spaghetti, vermicelli, and noodles are paste foods made from hard wheat. These products contain a rather high percentage of protein (ten to thirteen per cent), but are chiefly carbohydrate (seventy-five per cent). They may be considered as breadstuffs. When they are baked with cheese and milk a very economical and nutritious dish is the result. In fact these foods with cheese are a staple diet in Italy.

The quality of uncooked macaroni cannot be easily judged. When cooked, good quality macaroni will keep its tube shape and will swell to twice its original size. It will be firm but tender, not pasty and sticky, and will not have the "starchy" or "musty" taste of poor quality macaroni.

Shellfish

The shellfish most commonly used for food are oysters, clams, scallops, lobsters, crabs, shrimp, and crawfish.

1. *Oysters* are the most important shellfish and are the most widely used for food. They are found in shallow water on the Atlantic and Gulf coasts. Oysters are considered in season from September to May. They are more plump at this time than at any other.

2. *Composition and Food Value.* See Table VI, Appendix.

Because the chief food value of shellfish is in the protein they contain, they are comparable to meat and are interchangeable with meat in the diet. Fresh oysters contain Vitamins A, B_1, C, and G.

Sea food contains some small amount of iodine. Shellfish differ from most animal foods in containing carbohydrate. This is in the form of glycogen (animal starch) and is responsible for the sweet taste.

3. *Buying Shellfish.* Oysters can be shipped fresh better than other shellfish. They are removed from the shell and frozen or shipped on ice in double sealed cans. Canned oysters are also available. Small oysters (blue points) are best for cocktails and

FIG. 66. MEAT AND VEGETABLE PIE

stews; large oysters are preferable for frying. The best oysters are creamy in color and plump. Small oysters are cheaper than larger ones. Oysters are sold by the pint or quart and also by the hundred.

Whether shellfish are economical or not depends upon the locality and the season. Crabs, shrimp, and lobster are plentiful in the summer and are cheaper then. Oysters are cheaper and more plentiful in winter. Except on the coast, shellfish cannot be considered an economical food.

4. *Preparation.* Oysters are liked best raw, broiled, baked on the half shell, scalloped, stewed, and fried. Crab and lobster are most often served in salad, but they are also served hot with various sauces — creamed, or à la Newburg. Crabs are also stuffed, or "deviled." Shrimps are served creamed, fried, with tartar sauce or as creole shrimp, which is a shrimp dish with tomato sauce. Clams are served in various ways, especially steamed or in chowder.

Oysters, shrimps, and crabs are especially well liked as an appetizer, appearing on the menu as cocktails.

METHODS OF PREPARING THE MAIN HOT DISH

1. *Left-Overs.* Many of the most palatable and attractive luncheon dishes are made of "left-overs." An economical housewife will take care of all left-over food and will serve it to her family in a form as acceptable, if not more acceptable, than when it first appeared on the table.

Use of Left-Overs. In using left-overs, change the form, texture, flavor, and appearance as much as possible. Left-over roast beef, for example, may make an excellent dish without arousing suspicion that it is the same meat. Avoid using left-over material for the following meal.

Uses for left-over meats: loaf, meat pie, croquettes, turnovers, creamed meat on toast, baked hash, stuffed vegetables, and sandwiches.

Uses for left-over vegetables: fritters, soufflés, salads, au gratin and scalloped dishes.

2. *Soufflés.* A soufflé is a baked dish similar to omelet in that it is made light by the use of stiffly beaten egg whites. Cheese, fish flakes, asparagus, and cooked vegetables can be made into soufflés.

There are two kinds of soufflés: (1) those that require white sauce to build or hold the material together; for instance, all dry materials, as meat, fish, cheese, or rice, are combined with white sauce; (2) those for which the material does not require binding with white sauce: vegetables, such as corn, potato, squash, or fruit.

3. *Casserole or Baked Dishes.* There are too many casseroles and baked dishes to list them all, but the following are among the most interesting:

Meat turnovers — ground cooked meat baked in a turnover made of biscuit dough rolled thin. Served with brown sauce.

Italian hash — chopped cooked meat, macaroni, cheese, tomato or brown sauce.

Meat and tomato pie — cooked ground meat, boiled potatoes, tomatoes, mushrooms (perhaps), bread crumbs.

4. *Au Gratin Dishes.* A cooked food, usually a vegetable, may be prepared with white sauce, covered with buttered crumbs or cheese, or both, and browned in the oven. Au gratin dishes may be prepared several hours before use and cooked just before serving. Cauliflower or potatoes are favorite au gratin dishes.

5. *Omelets* are popular hot dishes for luncheon. An omelet is really an egg soufflé cooked in a frying pan. Omelets suitable for luncheon are cheese, parsley, ham, or Spanish omelets.

6. *Creamed Dishes.* Creamed dishes consist of vegetables, meat, or fish heated in a white sauce. They may be varied by the addition of pimiento, green pepper, onion, celery, or parsley. Creamed foods may be served on toast, in timbale cases, or in bread cases.

7. *Stuffed Vegetables.* Tomatoes, green peppers, potatoes, eggplant, and summer squash are the most practical vege-

FIG. 67. A HOT LUNCHEON

Menu: Creamed eggs on toast, peas, broiled tomatoes, cocoa.

FIG. 68. SOMETHING DIFFERENT IN A LUNCHEON PLATE
Menu: Bacon and meat broiled on a skewer, rice, and stuffed cucumbers.

tables for stuffing. The stuffing may consist of the vegetable pulp or ground meat, or both, mixed with bread crumbs and liquid and seasoned to taste.

8. *Chowders.* See recipe, page 446.

9. *Gumbos.* See recipe, page 447.

10. *Croquettes.* Croquettes of meat, fish, or fowl, usually consist of the cooked ground meat, seasoned well and held together by a thick white sauce. Croquettes of potato or rice may be mixed with raw egg yolk instead of with white sauce. Croquettes are fried in deep fat. For rules for deep-fat frying, see page 447.

Fried Foods. It is well known that physicians often advise against eating fried foods. Especially, children and persons with impaired health should avoid fried foods. They are difficult to digest because fat digests slowly. It should be mentioned also that the unstable Vitamin C does not survive frying. While it is not wise for anyone to make a practice of eating fried foods, there is no denying that when properly prepared they are very tempting.

CLASS PROBLEMS

1. Choose six main dishes for luncheon that you would like to prepare. Have them as different in type as possible. Score each for food value. Plan the menu to accompany each of the main dishes. Prepare in class as many of them as possible with their accompaniments and serve. Judge your results and your method of management.

2. Find out the kinds of cheese and the price of each in your local market. If possible, examine and taste the different varieties.

3. Verify the statement that cheese is a concentrated and economical food by comparing the amount and cost of hundred-calorie portions of cheese with hundred-calorie portions of other foods.

4. As the various hot dishes are prepared in class, estimate the food value of the recipes, the cost, and the number of servings. List the cost and calories of one serving. Check for minerals and vitamins.

5. Given any hot dish for luncheon, discuss the advisability of completing the meal by the addition of a soup; a salad; a bread; a beverage; a dessert.

6. Plan three hot plate luncheon menus in which the main hot dish is a way of using left-overs. Prepare and serve these in class. Evaluate.

HOME PROBLEM

For a month care for and use the left-over food in your home, planning and preparing such dishes as your family will enjoy.

REFERENCES

Lanman, Faith R., McKay, Hughina, Zuill, Frances. *The Family's Food.* J. B. Lippincott Company. Chapters VIII and XIII.

Sherman, Henry C. *Food Products.* The Macmillan Company. Chapter IV for cheese; Chapter VII for shellfish.

Stewart, Jean J. *Foods: Production, Marketing, Consumption.* Prentice Hall.

Todoroff, A. *Handbook of Food Selling.* The Grocery Trade Publishing House. Sections 4, 5, 13, 18.

Bulletins:

Aunt Sammy's Radio Recipes Revised. Bureau of Human Nutrition and Home Economics, United States Department of Agriculture.

Care of Food in the Home. United States Department of Agriculture, Farmers' Bulletin 1373.

Making American Cheese on the Farm for Home Consumption. United States Department of Agriculture, Farmers' Bulletin 1734.

Making and Using Cottage Cheese in the Home. United States Department of Agriculture, Farmers' Bulletin 1451.

Neufchâtel and Cream Cheese, Farm Manufacture and Use. United States Department of Agriculture, Farmers' Bulletin 960.

Any good Cook Book. See page 387.

CHAPTER EIGHTEEN

❧ Salads and the Cold Plate Luncheon

Cook Book References

Salads	*Page* 484
Salad Dressings	*Page* 488
Salad Accompaniments	*Page* 489

Food Value

Food Value in Shares	*Table* VIII, *Appendix*
Vitamins in Foods	*Table* IX, *Appendix*
Minerals in Foods	*Table* X, *Appendix*

THE COLD PLATE LUNCHEON holds high favor in the summer, but it also lends itself to the menu at all seasons, for it may be combined most acceptably both with hot beverages and with cold. A salad plate is the most popular of all cold plate luncheons. As an illustration of how the same salad may be adapted to menus in different seasons, note the following combinations:

When the thermometer is high:

Tuna Fish Salad
Crisp Crackers Iced Tea
Lemon Ice

When the thermometer is low:

Tuna Fish Salad
Hot rolls Hot Chocolate
Hot Grapefruit
(half of grapefruit — browned in oven)

Salads add to the menu a freshness, an attractive color note, and a pleasant acid flavor. They also offer an easy means of getting much-needed foods into an otherwise inadequate diet.

Salads for Luncheon. So great is the variety in salads that we may serve one salad as a light side dish at dinner and another as the main dish for luncheon. The dinner salad should always be light; a salad green with a simple dressing is preferable.

A mixture of salad greens with a French dressing is the perfect accompaniment for cold sliced meat, such as ham, corned beef, or chicken.

Food Value of Salads and Their Place in the Diet. The food value

FIG. 69. SALADS FOR LUNCHEON
Salads are always acceptable if attractively served and well seasoned.

of a salad is no more and no less than the sum total of the food values of its various ingredients.

Fruit and vegetable salads may make an important contribution to the mineral and vitamin content of the diet. The fact that raw fruits and vegetables are well liked in salads gives an opportunity to include in the menu foods rich in Vitamin C. The salad greens themselves are to be thought of as important foods and not as a garnish. To retain the maximum amount of Vitamin C, materials should not be cut or sliced for salads until just before serving, since it will be recalled that Vitamin C is easily lost by exposure to air.

Starchy vegetables, meats, nuts, cheese, and rich salad dressings give us salads of high fuel value. Salads are not usually rich in protein, but meat, fish, poultry, egg, and cheese salads are exceptions. By their Vitamin B content, they also help maintain good digestion. Green and yellow vegetables add Vitamin A. Lemon juice makes an acceptable dressing which is rich in Vitamin C.

Because of the cellulose, acids, and fats which they contain, salads are laxative.

We should not forget that salads are economical. In fact they may save both time and money. Choice left-over vegetables, fruits, and meats may be used in salads.

Salads are often rich combinations of food. For growing children or for adults with weak or impaired digestion, the vegetable or fruit salads with little dressing are preferable. Very small children should receive their raw, leafy vegetables in sandwiches without dressing. Sandwiches are simpler combinations than salads and are easier for small children to eat. Without highly flavored salad dressing, they are more likely to be thoroughly chewed. Sandwiches made of raw, shredded, tender cabbage, grated carrots, or lettuce and brown bread are suitable.

SALAD MATERIALS

1. *Body of salad:*

Vegetables	Meat	Fish
cooked	all kinds	tuna fish
raw		salmon
Fruits	Nuts	crabs
cooked	Cheese	shrimp
raw	Gelatin	sardines
dried	Poultry	
canned		

2. *Salad greens:*

Lettuce	Chicory	Watercress
Cabbage	Endive	Parsley
Celery	Romaine	Other greens in season

3. *Salad dressings:*

French	Cooked or boiled	Peanut butter
Whipped cream	Thousand Island	Cheese
Mayonnaise	Spanish	Russian

4. *Garnishes:*

Lettuce	Diced carrots, beets,	Radishes
Parsley	tomatoes, apples	Nuts
Hard-cooked eggs	with skins	Tomato
Olives	Green pepper	Pimiento

5. *Accompaniments:*

Breadstuffs	Beverages (hot or iced)	Miscellaneous
bread sticks	tea	cheese balls
rolls or toast	coffee	celery
toasted crackers	milk	radishes
Swedish wafers	fruit juices	olives
cheese straws	chocolate	nuts
hot biscuits	cocoa	plain or salted
muffins		potato chips
sandwiches		

Variety in Salads. The foregoing list of salad materials shows five ways in which the salad plate may be varied. The most usual ways to vary the salad are by the material which make up the body of the salad, or by the dressing, or both. Even if lettuce is the only salad green available, considerable variety can be achieved. For example, note the variety in the types of salad listed on page 210.

FIG. 70. THE COLD PLATE FOR LUNCHEON OR SUPPER
Menu: Sliced tomatoes, sardines, cottage cheese, fresh fruit salad, clover leaf rolls, milk.

Salad Body	*Dressing*
Mixed cooked vegetables	French
Mixed fruit in gelatin	Whipped cream
Celery, apple, nut	Cooked
Sliced tomatoes	French or mayonnaise
Salmon	Mayonnaise
Frozen fruit	Dressing mixed with the salad and frozen
Grapefruit and avocado pear	French
Canned or fresh pears	Creamed cheese
Head lettuce	Thousand Island
Lettuce (head or leaf)	Roquefort cheese
Leaf lettuce	Peanut butter in "boiled" dressing

If a variety of greens is also available, the range of combinations is even wider. A book could be written on salad combinations. The only limiting factors are the material at hand and one's own ingenuity.

Variety in salad plates is produced not only by the ingredients in the salad itself but by the ensemble or accompaniments. In considering the impression of variety given by salads, one must also include such interesting variations as color in the food itself, the garnish and even in the dishes and table appointments. The serving of food always allows for an artistic touch, but when salad is the main course at a luncheon in the spring or summer, there is endless opportunity for designing a beautiful table.

There is also an opportunity to vary the way the salad is served. For example, it may be served on individual plates, or from the salad bowl by someone at the table, or the salad bowl may be passed for each one to serve himself. For a buffet meal a favorite way of arranging the salad is to place individual servings on a large platter or chop plate. Each person may serve himself, or a hostess may serve each guest's plate as he passes the buffet service table.

Dessert for the Salad Luncheon. The dessert that is to follow a salad should be rather carefully chosen. With a fruit salad we may have a starchy dessert. For example: grapefruit salad, cheese straws, tea (for adults), chocolate pudding. A fish salad calls for a light, tart dessert. Lemon ice or some other fruit ice is relished after shrimp salad. After a light vegetable salad with bread sticks, a rich dessert may sometimes be served; for example, butterscotch pie.

Follow a rich meat salad with a light dessert in some such combination as chicken salad, hot rolls, fresh cherries.

The kind of dessert to be used with a vegetable salad will vary. If potato salad (starchy) is served, a light dessert of fruit (gelatin or sherbet) is acceptable. If the salad is of green vegetables, the dessert may be richer — perhaps a carbohydrate plus fruit, such as strawberry shortcake.

Preparation of Salads. How can we make sure of having good salads?

1. The lettuce, or other green used, must be clean, crisp, tender, and fresh.

2. Cooked vegetables are usually cut in small pieces of uniform size and shape; raw vegetables, such as cabbage, carrots, or lettuce, are shredded; raw carrots are also grated. Surplus fat and gristle should be removed from cooked meat.

3. Before assembling the salad, all the materials should be drained. Watery fruits or vegetables cause the salad dressing to become watery.

4. Salad ingredients should be chilled in advance of the preparation of the salad. Salads should always be served cold. The combining of the various ingredients should be done immediately before serving. This is necessary at any time if the best results are to be had, but it is essential in some cases because fruits cause

mayonnaise to separate. Chopped fruits and vegetables should be prepared just before serving. Lemon juice prevents the darkening of the cut surfaces of apples and bananas. English walnuts turn dark and develop a disagreeable taste in the presence of acids. Lettuce wilts in contact with oil.

5. Silver or stainless steel knives are best for preparing fruits or vegetables for salads.

6. Meat, vegetables, and fish prepared for salads are improved in flavor by "marinating." To "marinate," allow the cut materials to stand in French dressing; the dressing is drained off before the salad is made.

7. Garlic or onion flavor adds an indefinable touch to some salads, such as potato salad or celery salad. The cut edge of a "clove" of garlic may be used to rub the bowl in which the salad is prepared. Vinegar in which small pieces of garlic are kept gives an excellent flavor when used in preparing mayonnaise or French dressing. A mild onion flavor for the salad dressing can be obtained by scraping the cut surface of an onion with a knife. Chopped raw onion or garlic should not be put in salad, because it is objectionable to many people.

8. A simple edible garnish is most attractive. Custom no longer demands that the garnish be left uneaten and often the garnish is a valuable source of vitamins and minerals. Parsley, a most attractive garnish, is one of the best sources of iron. Suggestions for suitable garnishes are given on page 209.

9. Salads make their appeal through quality rather than quantity. Serve small to medium-sized portions, compactly arranged. The lettuce should never cover the plate or hang over the edge.

In serving, rather plain china is to be preferred, for salads add a decided color note of their own to the table, and ornate china detracts from the charm of the food.

Salad Dressings. An acid and seasonings are ingredients of all salad dressings. The acid is usually lemon juice or vinegar. Lime juice is also good.

Cooked dressing contains milk, starch, egg, vinegar, and butter or cream plus seasonings. Variations in cooked dressing are made by the addition of thick sour cream, whipped cream, or peanut butter. This type of dressing is used on any salad, but especially on mild fruit, vegetable, or gelatin salads.

French dressing is the most easily prepared and the simplest oil dressing. It is a well-blended mixture of oil and vinegar, seasoned more or less highly, and may be used on any salad. It is especially suitable for green salads, such as slaw, lettuce, or cress. It is also used frequently on acid fruits. Almost any seasoning may be added to French dressing.

Mayonnaise is an emulsion of oil with egg yolk or whole egg; lemon juice or vinegar, salt, pepper, cayenne, and paprika are commonly used seasonings. Though used on all kinds of salads, mayonnaise is preferred on fish, meat, and egg salads. It is a rich dressing and is used more frequently at luncheon and on special occasions than at dinner. Why?

Of the numerous variations in mayonnaise, the most favored is Thousand Island dressing, which is mayonnaise with finely chopped olives, sweet pickle, pimiento, and sometimes chili sauce, onion or cucumber.

The fat of the oil used in salad dressing furnishes its chief food value, since in one serving of dressing the quantity of egg or milk would be so small as to be of almost negligible food value. In a whipped-cream dressing the value consists not only in its fat but in the amount of Vitamin A that it offers. From one to two tablespoons of salad dressing may be considered a hundred calories.

Accompaniments for Salads. At dinner, salad is an accompaniment to the meat course, but at luncheon and at parties where it is a course in itself, salad constitutes the main dish and is served with a variety of tempting accessories.

1. The most usual salad accompaniment is a sandwich or hot bread. Sandwiches should be small and dainty and the filling should present a contrast to the salad. Variety in sandwiches is produced by the filling, the kind of bread used, and by using toasted or fresh bread. Cheese straws or cheese balls are delicious with some salads, especially those of mild flavor.

2. The season has much to do with the choice of beverages to accompany salads. If the salad is not very rich, cocoa or chocolate with whipped cream may be relished. Children should drink water or milk or a fruit beverage.

3. There are many other miscellaneous accessories that may be served with a salad course. Some suggestions are salted nuts, olives, potato chips.

Nuts as Food. Nuts, often regarded as a relish or an accessory, are by composition and food value really a staple food.

There is some variation in the composition of nuts, but in general they are rich in protein and in fat. Nuts are comparable to meats in the amount and the kind of protein that they contain. They are deficient in Vitamins A and C. Many nuts are good sources of Vitamin B_1. Peanuts are good sources of Vitamin G and niacin, the pellagra-preventive factor. Almonds are particularly good sources of calcium and most nuts are good sources of phosphorus. The high energy content of nuts is indicated by the small size of one-hundred-calorie portions of various nuts. If you will estimate the cost of one hundred calories in the form of nuts, you will find that they are an economical source of fuel.

CLASS PROBLEMS

1. Suggested salad lessons: (See the next chapter for breads to accompany salads.)

    1. Orange salad, French dressing
       Hot cheese biscuit   Tea
    2. Red cabbage salad, Thousand Island dressing
       Clover leaf rolls   Iced chocolate
    3. A meat salad or fish salad with fresh raw vegetables, Mayonnaise   Fresh nut bread   Lemonade
    4. A fruit salad day
       Members of the class prepare different fruit salads.
       These recipes may be collected by the class.
       Score the salads prepared. Plan accompaniments.
    5. A vegetable salad day
       Proceed as for Lesson 4.
    6. A meat or meat-substitute salad day
       What salad foundations would be included here?
       Proceed as for Lesson 4.
    7. Serve a salad luncheon buffet style.

2. Collect attractive pictures of salads. Colored advertisements in many magazines make good material. Mount them on cardboard approximately six by nine inches in size. These cards will serve several purposes: (*a*) they will give suggestions for serving; (*b*) they furnish room on the back of each card to check the salad as a source of minerals and vitamins.

3. Plan several "hot-weather specials," with salads as the main course, for luncheon. Introduce as much variety as possible and give your reasons for each choice.

4. Justify with specific data the statement that nuts are economical sources of energy.

5. Plan four low-cost salads which you can serve at home.

6. From the list of accompaniments on page 209 complete the menu for a salad plate luncheon for each of the salads given on page 210.

HOME PROBLEMS

1. Study your family dietary and see if it needs improving by the addition of fruits and vegetables. Answer this question by keeping and analyzing a record of the menus for a week. State your reasons for your conclusions.
2. Prepare attractive salads for six or eight people from suitable left-overs.
3. Practice making salad dressings at home.
4. Make salad accompaniments for your family.
5. Prepare a salad for refreshments for a group of your mother's friends or of your own.
6. Purchase salad greens for two weeks.
7. Plan and prepare, several times, seasonable luncheons or suppers for your family, with salad as the main course. Introduce as much variety as possible. Calculate the cost and the calories.

REFERENCES

Current magazines. Any good Cook Book. See page 387. See also references in Chapters 4, 16, 11.

Heseltine, Marjorie, and Dow, Ula M. *The Basic Cook Book.* Houghton Mifflin Company.

Sherman, H. C. *Food Products.* The Macmillan Company. Chapter XI.

Todoroff, A. *Handbook of Food Selling.* The Grocery Trade Publishing House, 1936. Section 8.

A Fruit and Vegetable Buying Guide for Consumers. United States Department of Agriculture, Miscellaneous Publication 167.

Making and Using Peanut Butter. United States Department of Agriculture, Circular 384.

Nuts and Ways to Use Them. United States Department of Agriculture, Miscellaneous Publication 302.

CHAPTER NINETEEN

❧ Breads for Luncheon and Supper

Cook Book References

Quick Breads	*Page* 401
Yeast Breads	*Page* 452

Food Value

Nutritive Value of Foods	*Table* VI, *Appendix*
Food Value in Shares	*Table* VIII, *Appendix*

Breads

Of all the enticing odors that come from a kitchen none is more inviting than that which fills the air on baking day. And freshly baked homemade bread tastes as good as it smells. When you take out of the oven a well-shaped, lightly browned, delicately fragrant loaf of bread, or a pan of rolls which you yourself have created, your pride is pardonable and your achievement real.

Both yeast breads and quick breads are suitable for luncheon.

The great variety of breads that may be used for supper or luncheon, and the variety of other dishes suitable to these meals provide hundreds of good luncheon and supper combinations.

Quick Breads for Luncheon or Supper. First review Chapter 7. The same principles apply in making all quick breads. Most of the quick breads acceptable for breakfast are used for luncheon, and in addition there are many others. Breads that include nuts, cinnamon, raisins, sugar, and molasses are especially acceptable for luncheon.

Shall We Make or Buy Our Bread? Baking day is not the household institution it once was, for bread baking is an industry that modern machinery has partially taken from the household.

Let us answer the question of whether we shall make or buy bread by saying that we shall do both. Let us discover what each is like, and learn both about buying wisely and about baking at home. Homemade bread is still a favorite, and every housewife can obtain variety in her menus at small expense by the use of rolls or bread made at home. The fact that such breads are homemade is no guarantee of excellence, but the ability to make good yeast bread is a matter of especial pride with housewives.

FIG. 71. CINNAMON ROLLS IN THE MAKING

Flour for Breadmaking. To make good yeast bread, an elastic dough is necessary in order that the dough will rise and produce light bread. Wheat flour is almost universally used for bread because it possesses this quality. The elasticity of wheat flour is due to gluten. You have only to make a dough of flour and water to see the characteristics of gluten.

Rye bread is the second most common bread. Various other flours are used in breadmaking, but wheat flour is the basis for the bread, only a small portion of the substitute flour being used.

Kinds of Wheat Flour. Wheat flour may vary either according to the kind of wheat used, or according to the part of the grain used, or according to whether or not it is bleached in the process of manufacture.

1. *Kinds of Flour Due to Variation in Wheat.* Soft wheat produces a flour relatively rich in starch and poor in gluten. This flour is termed pastry flour and is preferred for baking-powder mixtures.

Hard wheat produces a flour relatively rich in gluten and poor in starch. This flour is called bread flour and is preferred for mixtures that are leavened with yeast.

The baker buys bread flour for his yeast mixtures. Some housewives keep both bread and pastry flour, but it is much more usual to buy only a general purpose flour for household uses. Most of the flour sold for household purposes is a blend made from hard and soft wheat. Good yeast bread and good baking-powder products can be made from the same flour.

2. *Kinds of Flour Determined by the Part of the Grain Used.*

Graham flour, whole-wheat flour, white flour, and wheat bran are variations produced in the milling process. The parts of the wheat grain vary in composition: (*a*) the bran contains chiefly cellulose and mineral matter; (*b*) the aleurone cells, a layer just inside the bran, contains minerals, especially phosphorus and iron, and Vitamin B_1; (*c*) the endosperm, by weight about 82 per cent of the grain, consists chiefly of starch and protein (gluten); (*d*) the germ contains fats and minerals.

White flour, or "patent" flour, is made from the endosperm. The removal of the other parts of the grain improves the keeping qualities of the flour, but lowers the nutritive value, as practically all of the minerals, cellulose, and Vitamins B_1, G, and niacin (the pellagra-preventive factor) are removed. Graham and whole-wheat flour are made from the entire grain. Some dark wheat flour, however, has had the germ removed so that the keeping qualities will be improved. Such flour may not be called whole- or entire-wheat flour.

3. *Flour Varies According to Whether or Not It is Bleached.* There is a difference of opinion as to whether bleaching is desirable or not. Some people are beginning to prefer the creamy appearance of unbleached flour. On flour shipped in interstate commerce there must be a label stating that it is bleached if this is the case.

Ingredients of Yeast Breads. The usual ingredients of homemade yeast breads are flour, liquid, yeast, sugar, fat, and salt. Other ingredients, such as raisins, nuts, or spice, are added for variety.

Flour means wheat flour unless otherwise specified. This flour makes a light, porous loaf. Flour made from corn, oats, barley, buckwheat, rice, potatoes, and soybeans may be substituted for part (up to one fourth or one third) of the weight of the wheat flour.

Flour makes up about 57 per cent of the weight of a loaf of bakers' bread, and it makes up a somewhat larger proportion of homemade bread. This means that about ten ounces of wheat flour are used in a one-pound commercial loaf and about twelve ounces in a homemade loaf. For bread sold in interstate commerce, the United States Food and Drug Administration requires that all of the flour used in making bread labeled "whole wheat," "entire wheat," or "graham," be whole-wheat flour. White bread may not contain more than 3 per cent of other starchy substances, such as cornstarch. For bread made and sold entirely within a state this federal law does not prevail.

Liquid. Water or milk or both may be used. For home baking part or all milk is preferred, because it improves somewhat the flavor, the nutritive value, and the keeping qualities of the bread. For reasons given below in the discussion of yeast, water should be boiled and milk should be heated almost to the boiling point (scalded) and cooled before adding the yeast. In commercial baking dried milk is often used. The Food and Drug Administration limits to 38 per cent, or about one third, the amount of moisture permitted in the bread sold in interstate commerce.

Yeast. Yeast is used in breadmaking because of the changes it produces in dough. These changes make bread light. From sugar and starch in solution yeast produces alcohol and carbon dioxide gas. The bubbles of gas, held in the dough by the elastic gluten of the flour, cause the dough to rise as they are formed, and the dough becomes light. The heat of cooking then vaporizes the alcohol and drives it and the gas out of the bread, hardens the gluten in its stretched form, and kills the yeast.

Yeast needs food, warmth, and moisture in order to grow. These same conditions are also favorable to the growth of other organisms. For this reason, a strenuous effort should be made to keep all organisms except yeast out of the mixture by heating the liquid and sterilizing the utensils used. This effort is rewarded by obtaining bread of superior flavor; carelessness results in the sour or musty flavor of poor quality bread. The food that produces quick yeast growth is sugar, but yeast uses flour as food too. The temperature at which yeast grows best is 80 or 85 degrees F., or slightly above room temperature.

Yeast may be bought as compressed yeast or dried yeast, or it may be obtained from a home-prepared "starter." Two kinds of dried yeast are available: old-fashioned cake yeast and fast-rising dry yeast. The fast-rising kind is a new product that is being used rather widely. One package of this dry yeast equals one compressed yeast cake. Dried yeast should be soaked in cold or lukewarm water in which some sugar has been dissolved. The appearance of gas bubbles indicates the beginning growth of the yeast.

Some housewives prepare a liquid yeast, called a "starter," by keeping a piece of dough from one baking to another. The problem in handling the starter is to keep it free from organisms other than yeast. This is accomplished by keeping it cold and carefully covered in a utensil that has been sterilized with boiling water.

If properly made and kept, the starter may be used for several weeks. It is used in the same manner as compressed yeast. Good directions for starters may be found in Farmers' Bulletin 1775, *Home-Made Bread, Cake, Pastry.*

Sugar. Because yeast uses sugar more readily than it does flour, the addition of sugar hastens the rising of the sponge or dough. Molasses or sirup may be used in place of sugar, particularly in dark breads.

Fat. Any kind of cooking fat that has a pleasing flavor or little flavor is useful as shortening. Fat in correct proportions makes bread products tender. To insure good proportions, follow a reliable recipe and measure accurately.

Salt. Salt is added for flavor, preferably only after the yeast growth is well started.

Buying Yeast Breads. We need the following information about all yeast bread we buy: the weight in ounces or in pounds and ounces, and it is better to know the exact weight, rather than, for instance, that it is "over fourteen ounces"; the kind and amount of ingredients; the sanitary conditions in the bakery; the kind of paper in which it is wrapped, since it is reported that some waxed paper will impart a flavor to the bread; and the date on which the bread was baked.

Judging Yeast Bread. Something of the quality of yeast bread may be learned by inspecting the loaf and a slice from the loaf. The loaf should be oblong and symmetrical, with an evenly rounded top. The color of a slice of white bread should be creamy or white, with no gray tinge, and no streaks. It should have a slight luster. A creamy shade results from the use of milk or unbleached flour.

The grain of a slice should show thin cell walls, elongated upward. It should be even and have no large holes, no streaks, or extreme closeness. The texture should be elastic, fairly soft, and springy. Very soft texture indicates the bread has not been baked sufficiently long to keep well.

The flavor of white bread should be that of good materials, well blended, and well baked, and should have no suggestion of sourness, yeast, mustiness, or any other off-flavor. Graham and whole-wheat bread should have a whole-grain or "nutty" flavor.

The score card on page 453 in the Cook Book shows one way in which bread may be judged.

Place of Bread in the Diet. Though white bread is of value principally for its fuel, it is also important for protein. White bread, unless made with milk or enriched flour (see below), is a poor source of minerals and vitamins. Whole-wheat bread is important for its laxative property, which is due in part to the fat of the germ and in part to the cellulose. Whole-wheat bread is also a good source of iron, phosphorus, and thiamin. The yeast adds some thiamin and riboflavin to yeast bread. Vitamins A, C, and D, unless added, are lacking in most grain products.

Enriched Flour. Enriched flour looks like ordinary white flour, but contains the same minerals and vitamins as the whole-wheat grain. Flour may be called "enriched" if it meets certain standards set by the United States Government authorities. Specified amounts of thiamin, niacin, riboflavin, and iron must be added and specified amounts of Vitamin D and calcium may be added. The Federal Government recommends that all flour be enriched, and about one half the states in this country have laws requiring the enrichment of all flour and bread sold.

Because of its increased food value, enriched flour is to be preferred to other flour for use at home. Bakers use unenriched flour, but add the specified amounts of vitamins and minerals to the dough. The bread that results is called "enriched bread." Of course, even enriched bread and bread made with enriched flour should not replace eggs, milk, fruits, or vegetables, but a generous use of bread with milk is to be encouraged in the interest of economy and a good diet. Simple suppers of milk, bread, fruit, and vegetables are excellent for small children.

CLASS PROBLEMS

1. What types of flour and of breads are for sale in your local stores? Investigate.
2. If there is a flour mill in your locality, make arrangements, if possible, to see the mill in operation.
3. Find out what variety or varieties of yeast can be bought in your community.
4. Find out the latest government regulations concerning enriched flour and bread. To do so, write to the Information Service of the Bureau of Human Nutrition and Home Economics, U.S. Department of Agriculture, Washington, D.C., and to your state home demonstration service.

5. After the class has made bread and understands the process, visit a local bakery.

6. Weigh or measure a one-hundred-calorie portion of bread. Calculate the cost and compare it with the cost of one-hundred-calorie portions of other products.

7. Make various yeast breads in the laboratory. Score the products in class. Bread lessons may be combined with other lessons — those on salads, vegetables, or school lunch, for example.

HOME PROBLEMS

Much home practice is necessary if you are to become a good breadmaker.

1. Practice at home, making rolls for luncheon or supper.
2. After you have had success with rolls several times, try making bread.
3. If your family uses homemade bread, begin by assisting in the process of making it. Practice kneading especially.
4. Prepare some variations of yeast bread, such as nut bread, raisin bread, brown nut bread, or cinnamon rolls.
5. Prepare various quick breads for luncheon or supper.
6. Care for the bread, including left-over bread, in your home.

REFERENCES

Halliday, E., and Noble, I. *Hows and Whys of Cookery.* University of Chicago Press.

Home-Made Bread, Cake, Pastry. United States Department of Agriculture, Farmers' Bulletin 1775.

Lanman, Faith R., McKay, Hughina, Zuill, Frances. *The Family's Food,* Chapter XI. J. B. Lippincott Company.

Rose, M. S. *Foundations of Nutrition.* The Macmillan Company.

Sherman, H. C. *Food Products,* Chapter VIII. The Macmillan Company.

Stewart, Jean J. *Foods: Production, Marketing, Consumption.* Chapter III, 1938. Prentice-Hall.

Good Cook Books. See page 387.

CHAPTER TWENTY

❧ The School Lunch

Cook Book References

Sandwiches	*Pages* 451, 459
Cookies	*Page* 502

Food Value

Nutritive Value of Foods	*Table* VI, *Appendix*
Food Value in Shares	*Table* VIII, *Appendix*
Vitamins and Minerals	*Tables* IX *and* X, *Appendix*

Is the school lunch important? From the standpoint of health, the school lunch is no more important than any other meal, but it is more difficult to provide the right foods for this meal and to serve it in a wholesome setting.

Many school boys and girls eat the noon meal at school. Hence it is their responsibility to choose foods wisely. Proof that all boys and girls do not rise to this responsibility is found in the way many spend their money for candy and soft drinks instead of for more needed foods.

What would you think of a man who set out for an automobile trip without providing gasoline and oil, or who, on his way, failed to dodge nails or glass in plain sight in the road? He sounds too stupid to be real, and yet boys and girls do worse than that to their own machinery when they buy such things as lollipops, soft drinks, candy, pie, pickles, and doughnuts instead of milk, vegetable soups, fruits, and other simple foods which they need for growing, for going, and for keeping fit. No machinery is so delicate as the human mechanism, and yet none is so much abused.

Balancing the Diet at the School Cafeteria is Your Responsibility

When you eat meals at home the person who plans the meals is mainly responsible for whether or not the diet is balanced. It is true that by not eating some food included in the menu you may upset the balance. But at school when the choice is entirely yours, the responsibility for balancing the diet is also entirely yours. How can you judge whether or not you have made a wise choice?

Measuring the Diet in Scientific Terms. In order to judge a diet scientifically, food materials, such as apples, oranges, milk, bread, vegetables, meat, and sweets, must be interpreted in calories, protein, iron, phosphorus, calcium, and vitamins. For this interpretation a unit of measure is necessary. A famous nutritionist has devised a unit called a share which is an interesting and easy method of figuring exactly how much food you are receiving in relation to your daily need for calories, calcium, protein, minerals, and vitamins. She thinks of a share as a thirtieth of an average man's requirement for the day. This makes a share a different weight for every one of the substances (protein, calcium, iron, etc.) a man requires, but if we have a table, such as Table VIII, in the Appendix, in which the amounts in food are expressed in the same way, it is easy to count up, for example, how many of the thirty shares have been eaten for breakfast and how much is left to eat before the day is over. In the Appendix, Table VIII, you will find the actual weight which a share of each food constituent represents, but it is more important to remember that each is a thirtieth of the man's requirement.

How Many Shares do Young People Need to Balance the Diet? The table on page 225 shows the food requirements of growing boys and girls in terms of shares of energy (calories), protein, calcium, phosphorus, iron, and Vitamins A, B_1, C, and G.

A share of energy is 100 calories. When you studied Unit 1 you estimated your calorie requirement. If you divide this by 100 it will give you your energy requirement in shares.

To use the table, find in the first column the number of energy shares which is right for you. Reading across the page in this line you can find the number of shares you require in protein, calcium, phosphorus, iron, and Vitamins A, B_1, C, and G.

Suppose you need 2300 calories or 23 shares of energy. This number is not given in the column of energy shares; therefore, we take 25 as the nearest number given, and, reading across the page, find how many shares you need of protein, the three most important minerals, and the four vitamins which have been definitely estimated in shares.

A growing body needs more building materials than an adult body needs. This need is shown in the shares of each of these materials required in a day. When an adult person requires 3000 calories he requires 30 shares of all the other foods needed by the body; that is, one share for each one hundred calories needed. From the table below you will see that when a growing boy or girl needs 3000 (30 shares) calories he needs 43 shares of calcium. In other words, he needs more calcium in proportion to his total calories than does an adult if his diet is to be balanced with his body needs. A wise selection of food yields the right number of calorie shares and more, rather than less, of the other shares.

TOTAL FOOD REQUIREMENT IN SHARES [1]
(Boys and Girls 10–18 Years of Age)

Energy	Protein	Calcium	Phosphorus	Iron	Vitamins			
					A	B_1	C	G
20	20	43	23	20	20	20	30	20
25	25	43	25	26*	25	25	30	25
30	30	43	30	30	30	30	30	30
35	35	43	35	35	35	35	35	35
40	40	43	40	40	40	40	40	40
45	45	45	45	45	45	45	45	45
50	50	50	50	50	50	50	50	50

* 28 shares of iron are recommended for girls.

One may furnish the right number of calories for the energy needs of the body, but short-change the body on building materials and other needed nutrients. Let us see how this works in the school cafeteria.

Measuring the School Lunch in Terms of Shares. Two illustrations present themselves from a school cafeteria. Billy and Betty are twins. They each have a job of growing up and they each have the responsibility for selecting their lunch in the school cafeteria. An examination of a typical day's selection of food by each of these two shows how much more Billy gets for his money than does Betty. Note that each of them has spent the same amount of money.

Billy's tray explains part of the reason why he is so healthy. He eats a well-balanced meal with plenty of Vitamin A for growth. Betty, his twin sister, is not so tall for her age and sex, and not so robust; in fact she is finicky about her food, and this very fact is no doubt partly responsible for the difference in physical development between Betty and Billy.

[1] Philadelphia Dairy Council. Adapted from *Laboratory Handbook of Dietetics*, by Mary S. Rose. The Macmillan Company. Used by permission.

A typical lunch for Billy is:

Plate lunch $.27
- Meat balls with brown gravy
- Spinach
- Gingerbread
- Whole-wheat bread
- Butter
- Milk

Lunch chosen by Betty from the counter in individual items:

Date nut sandwich	.10
Gingerbread	.10
Chocolate milk	.07
Total	.27

A nutritionist has submitted the following measures of Billy's and Betty's lunches in terms of shares:

	* *Total Shares Needed in One Day*	* *Shares in Lunch Chosen by Billy*	* *Shares in Lunch Chosen by Betty*
Calories	25	7.5	5
Protein	25	7.5	6
Calcium	43	15.9	15.6
Phosphorus	25	15.2	8.7
Iron	25	14.9	6.2
Vitamin A	25	135.3	5.2
Vitamin B_1	25	14.7	9.3
Vitamin C	30	28.0	2.5
Vitamin G	25	15.4	4.0

* The lunch is expected to furnish between one fourth and one third of the food shares needed for the whole day. See Table VIII, Appendix.

A Graphic Comparison of Two School Lunches

Billy and Betty spent the same amount of money, but the charts (Figure 72) show that they got about the same amount of only one nutrient — calcium. In every other respect Billy got more food value for his money than Betty did. Betty depended on her preferences, but Billy depended on the skill of a trained dietitian, for he selected a plate lunch planned by a dietitian.

Getting Your Money's Worth. In addition to your responsibility to your body you also have a responsibility to your pocketbook when you buy food. Most people do not have all the money they want or need, but one can make what he has go farther by good management. The school lunch is an excellent place to learn a lesson in money management. Getting your money's worth in food means getting the most of what the body needs for the amount of money spent. Measuring food in shares for a given expenditure will show the extent to which wise expenditures have been made. A study of the foregoing table, which compares the shares which

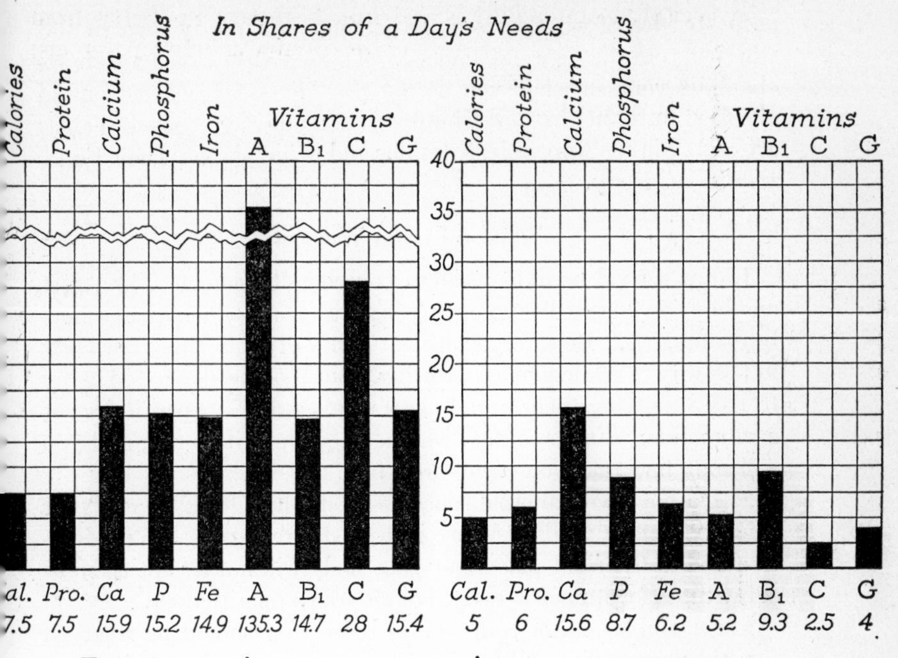

FIG. 72. BILLY'S LUNCH AND BETTY'S LUNCH IN SHARES OF A DAY'S NEEDS

Billy and Betty purchased for fifteen cents when they bought their school lunches, shows that Billy got his money's worth, but that Betty made a relatively poor investment.

On closer examination of this table it can be seen that Billy got more for his money in the following ways:

½ more calories
⅙ more protein
nearly twice as much phosphorus
2½ times as much iron
more than 25 times as much Vitamin A
(the extra can be stored by the body)
1⅔ times as much Vitamin B_1
more than 10 times as much Vitamin C
nearly 4 times as much Vitamin G

If you will select a cafeteria lunch, or better still, list all the food that you usually eat on a typical day, and estimate it in shares, as we did for Billy's and Betty's lunches, you can get a fairly accurate idea of whether you are getting your money's worth and whether your diet is well balanced. To see just how you are short-changing yourself when you do not provide enough of any one of the food nutrients, review Chapter 1. In addition, consult Tables IX and X in the Appendix, Vitamins and Minerals and Their Function in the Body.

School-Lunch Wisdom

1. Eat a good breakfast before you come to school. Breakfast and lunch in one meal is an outrage against the good health of school boys and girls. Be sure you are not guilty of neglecting your body in this way. While you are growing, your food needs are too many to risk supplying them in only two meals a day. Appetite is not a safe guide. Eat breakfast whether you want it or not, and you will soon find that you enjoy breakfast.

2. Do not give valuable space to foods that do not serve your primary dietary needs. Many such foods are harmless in moderation and in the right place, but your body will not accept them as substitutes for its needs even though your appetite does.

For example, tea or coffee takes room that should be reserved for milk; or a lollipop, if eaten first, may destroy all appetite for a bowl of vegetable soup.

3. Choose simple, easily digested foods.

4. Have at least one vegetable in the lunch, preferably a green vegetable. This is important because many boys and girls lack the needed amount of vegetables in their daily food.

5. Take time to enjoy your meal and to masticate it thoroughly. Do not gulp down your food in order to run out and play.

6. Check your daily calorie requirement and see that for lunch you eat one third or more of the calories required for the day.

The average boy or girl from twelve to sixteen years of age needs between 750 and 1200 calories for luncheon.

7. Eat your lunch in as pleasant surroundings as possible. Be sociable and enjoy your friends at lunch time. In the school lunchroom never forget to be courteous. A well-mannered person is more easily told by his behavior in the school lunchroom than by his behavior when he is remembering his "company manners."

8. Use the best knowledge you have in selecting foods at all times, but remember that at the school lunch hour the responsibility is entirely yours.

FIG. 73. CHOOSING LUNCH IN THE SCHOOL CAFETERIA

9. Remember to drink water at school. Of the total daily requirements, four glasses should be drunk between meals.

10. Cleanliness is important at all times. Food served at school should be clean and served under sanitary conditions. The school lunchroom should be screened. Take care that flies do not contaminate your lunch. Wash your hands before eating.

11. Practice economy. Economy means getting the most for your money. Are you getting the most in body needs and in good health for the money and time that you spend on the lunch hour at school?

12. A light lunch after school is desirable for hungry boys and girls, particularly if the school lunch has been a box lunch. Milk, bread and butter, and fresh fruits are acceptable.

The School Cafeteria. A well-managed school cafeteria affords the following advantages:

1. The food is hot and is therefore more tempting than a cold lunch.

2. The cafeteria is a convenience and allows adequate time for lunch.

3. It may be a place for relaxation and good-fellowship.

4. An opportunity is afforded for useful education in good manners and in the wise selection of food.

5. The school cafeteria may make possible the supplying of

needed food that is lacking in meals at home. Milk and vegetables are examples.

6. The school cafeteria is an economical place to eat. Usually, when you buy prepared food, you have to pay for food, service, equipment, rent, and management. The school cafeteria, however, charges you only for food and simple service; the other items are included by the school board in the school budget.

The Lunch Brought from Home. The box lunch has some obvious handicaps:

1. It is troublesome to carry a lunch box or basket to and from school.

2. The packing of the lunch usually adds to the work at a time of day when everyone is busy.

3. Variety is necessarily limited in a school lunch because of the trouble in carrying the food and because much food is not good when prepared and packed four or five hours before it is eaten.

4. Throughout much of the school year the weather is cold and cold food is not tempting. Except for hot drinks carried in a thermos bottle, it is impossible to provide hot food in a box lunch.

5. It is difficult to provide needed foods in a box lunch.

Suggestions for Pleasing Box Lunches. Do not try to have many kinds of food in one lunch. Including too many foods in one lunch makes it difficult to have variety from day to day.

SANDWICHES:

1. Sandwiches are easy to carry, easy to prepare, and are well liked — hence they are staple articles for the school lunch box.

FIG. 74. OFF TO SCHOOL — WITH GOOD SUPPORT
Lunch: Milk, brown bread sandwiches (cheese and nuts), drop cakes, and an apple.

2. Use good bread. It is best to have sandwich bread a day or more old. Day-old bread can be bought at some bakeries for half price. Bread made at home with milk, however, has more food value.

3. Secure variety in sandwiches by varying the size and shape; by varying the kind of bread; by varying the filling.

4. Sandwich fillings should be seasoned mildly. Suitable fillings are:

Peanut butter with chopped lettuce, celery, or carrots.
Shredded lettuce or cabbage with salad dressing (brown bread).
Peanut butter, mixed with cream to soften and to improve flavor.
Chopped egg.
Chopped nuts or nut paste.
Chopped meat (it is better to eat meat in the middle of the day than at night, hence it is permissible in the lunch) if the lunch box can be kept in a cold place so the meat will not spoil.
Cheese — especially cottage cheese.
Dried fruits — made into a paste by chopping and softening with milk or by steaming. Nuts may be added.
A little crisp bacon broken up in salad dressing (finely chopped lettuce or cabbage may be added).
Jelly or marmalade.

Fruits and Vegetables. The lunch would be monotonous without fruit. Preferably include a juicy fruit. An orange, apple, or ripe banana is easy to carry. Cooked fruit may be carried in a covered jelly glass or in a small screw-top jar. A tomato is a good substitute for an orange. Why?

Chopped raw vegetables — lettuce or cabbage, for example — should not be forgotten, because they are important in supplying Vitamin C.

Sweets. Cookies are made to order for the school lunch. They have one advantage over sandwiches — they can be made in some quantity and kept for several days. A cooky jar filled weekly is a great aid from day to day in preparing the school lunch.

Other simple sweets which may be used are cake — preferably sponge cake or drop cakes — gingerbread, wafers, zwiebach, dried fruits, baked custard, and one or two pieces of candy — for eating last.

Beverage. When the lunch is brought from home, it is often difficult to provide a beverage. Milk or chocolate milk is often available, however, in the school cafeteria for those who bring

FIG. 75. PACKING THE SCHOOL LUNCH

their lunch. This is usually more convenient than bringing milk from home, for there is not always a cool place at school in which to keep it.

Thermos bottles may be used for milk or a hot drink like cocoa, but they require care in cleaning and transporting. If a thermos is used, milk should be very cold when it is put into the bottle.

Packing the Lunch Box. The secrets of satisfactory packing are to keep all flavors separate and to prevent the food from becoming mashed. If you are packing a lunch for someone else, put in a surprise now and then, such as a stuffed egg or a salad.

Waxed paper, paraffin cups or cartons, glass jars or glasses with closely fitting lids insure the separation of flavors. Sandwiches, cookies, and in fact each article of food, should be wrapped separately in waxed paper. Paper napkins and drinking cups should be included. An extra paper napkin for spreading the lunch on the desk will prove convenient. Heavy things should be placed at the bottom, and the box or container should be carried in the same position in which it is packed. This last is easy if the box has a handle.

Cleanliness and daintiness are essential. The lunch box or basket itself, and any glass containers used, should be scalded every day and sunned frequently. This will keep them clean and sweet.

The school lunch should be carefully planned. It is undesirable to pack the lunch from left-overs at the breakfast table. Why?

Early morning is such a busy time that every effort should be made to have all food and supplies possible ready for packing before morning comes. A little thought will discover how much can be got ready the night before, and conveniently placed so that the time needed for finishing the preparation and packing of the lunch in the morning will be very short. Such foods as fruits, desserts, and sandwich fillings, and all supplies, such as paper napkins and wax paper, can be made ready the night before and the box lined ready to be filled. Forethought of this sort often is accompanied by forethought in making the lunch more appetizing.

The Lunch Box Supplemented at School. Many schools, which have no cafeteria or lunchroom, supplement the lunch brought from home with milk or one hot dish or both. This requires little equipment. If a school has a home economics department, no additional equipment is needed. Occasionally home economics classes prepare a hot dish as a supplement to the school lunch.

The foods listed below are the most satisfactory and suitable dishes to use in supplementing a lunch brought from home. Can you tell why?

Milk	Meat and vegetable stews
Creamed vegetable soups	Cocoa
Vegetables	Custard

Much valuable information on this type of school lunch is available in bulletin form. If this is the best way of solving the school lunch problem in your school, home economics pupils can procure practical help from the bulletins listed at the end of this chapter.

CLASS PROBLEMS

1. Each pupil may keep a record of what he or she eats for lunch on school days for five days. Also keep a record of the other two meals.
   a. What proportion of the total number of calories required do you eat at school?
   b. Is your noon meal well chosen when considered with the other meals eaten in the day? Give reasons for your opinion.
   c. Write a theme on the topic: "My School Lunch as It Is and As It Should Be."

2. In your school should home economics pupils assume any responsibility for the school lunch? In order to answer this question make a study of the situation. For example:
   a. If your school is a small one and there are elementary grades in the same building, it will be easy to acquaint yourself with the school lunch practices of the group by observing the lunches these children eat. Discuss these observations

in the light of the school lunch needs of the group. Determine whether any responsibility for improvement of the situation rests with the home economics pupils as a group through a class project or as individuals through home projects. Make practical plans for discharging this responsibility.

b. If there is a school lunchroom or cafeteria at your school, make a study of the situation.

(1) What is offered for lunch? Is it suitable? Make suggestions for improvement. Would it be advisable to appoint a committee to co-operate with the lunchroom manager? In what ways?

(2) Do the boys and girls select their food wisely? Make note of what a considerable number of students' trays contain.

Would it help for the home economics class to conduct an educational campaign in the lunchroom?

Suggestions: Count the shares of calories, protein, minerals, and vitamins per serving for foods offered, and place them on the board with prices. (See Tables VI to X in Appendix.)

3. For two weeks plan the school lunch for the same individual with the lunch from home supplemented at school by milk or one hot dish.

4. Demonstrate the packing of school lunches prepared at home.

5. Can you eat more economically at school than you now do and improve your diet? Prove your statement.

6. Check the following suggested lunches for the food materials needed by the body:

a. School Cafeteria:

(1) Cream of tomato soup, crackers; rolls; fruit; plain cake.
(2) Meat and vegetable stew; bread and butter; sweet chocolate.
(3) Lettuce sandwiches; milk, bread and butter; cookies.
(4) Creamed eggs on toast; boiled onions; cup custard.

b. Lunch Boxes:

(1) Egg sandwich, an apple, cookies.
(2) Date and raisin sandwiches, a tomato, stuffed egg.
(3) Jelly sandwich, cookies, candy.
(4) Cheese sandwich, stuffed egg, baked custard.

7. Prepare various kinds of sandwiches.

8. Prepare simple cookies and cakes. Suggestions:

Oatmeal cookies	Hermits	Gingerbread
Tea cakes	Date squares	Jelly roll

9. Select two of the kinds of sandwiches you have made and one kind of cookies and plan a practical and good school lunch which includes them.

HOME PROJECTS AND HOME PROBLEMS

1. Plan, prepare, and pack your lunch for a month (if you take a lunch from home).
2. Plan, prepare, and pack the lunch for a younger child. Count the calories and the cost, and score for protective foods.
3. Record for one week what you eat at lunch in the school cafeteria, choosing what you usually eat without any special emphasis on the choice. Record the cost. Estimate the calories. Check also for growth and protective foods.
4. Record for one week what you eat at lunch in the school cafeteria, consciously choosing your lunch to illustrate your knowledge of foods and costs. Record the cost; estimate the calories. Check these lunches for growth and protective foods. Have you improved in meeting your responsibility for your health?
5. Plan, prepare, and pack a picnic lunch.
6. Make cookies several times at home for your school lunch.
7. In the school cafeteria, taste unfamiliar dishes and try to learn to like some of them.

REFERENCES

Food for Children. United States Department of Agriculture, Farmers' Bulletin 1674.

Menus and Recipes for Lunches at School. United States Department of Agriculture, Miscellaneous Publication 246.

Nutrition in Childhood. 1937. Public Health Reprint 654, Children's Bureau.

Rose, M. S. *Feeding the Family.* Chapters X, XI, and XII, 1940 edition. The Macmillan Company.

Rose, M. S. *Foundations of Nutrition.* Chapter XXIV, 1938 ed. The Macmillan Company.

Sources from which bulletins and circulars are available:

Bureau of Human Nutrition and Home Economics, United States Department of Agriculture, Washington, D.C.

The State Agricultural College in your State—Extension Service.

Children's Bureau, Department of Labor, Washington, D.C.

CHAPTER TWENTY-ONE

❧ Luncheon or Supper Desserts

Cook Book References

Cakes and Cookies	*Page* 491
Pastry	*Page* 506
Puddings, Custards, Fruit Desserts	*Page* 512
Gelatin Desserts	*Page* 519
Frozen Desserts	*Page* 521

Food Value

Food Value in Shares	*Table* VIII, *Appendix*
Vitamins and Minerals	*Tables* IX *and* X, *Appendix*

Choosing a dessert. The rest of the meal influences the choice of a dessert, but a safe guess is that fresh fruit is the best dessert of all for the noonday meal. After lunch most of us return to study or to other work and overeating makes us feel like doing neither.

Fresh fruit makes an attractive ending for a meal, is a convenience for the busy housekeeper, and is a first aid to good nutrition. Fresh fruit is the undisputed choice of Europeans and of people of many other countries, such as Mexico. We, in the United States, however, seem to be the only people who have the habit of eating at luncheon rich sugar-laden desserts that add so many extra calories to the diet and so much extra work for the homemaker.

There is no real line of demarcation between luncheon and dinner desserts. The choice of a dessert for luncheon does not preclude the appropriateness of that same dessert for dinner on some other day. Since luncheon is usually a lighter meal than dinner, a heavier dessert is often permissible at the former meal. In this text most of the richer desserts are included in the luncheon sweets and the lighter ones in the dinner sweets.

That Sweet Tooth. The ice-cream parlors, soda fountains, candy shops, and pastry shops bear testimony to the universal love of sweets. Americans average more than one hundred pounds of sugar per person annually!

The greatest difficulty about this taste for sweets is that constant vigilance is needed to keep it from playing havoc with looks and with health. The danger is not so much in liking sweets as in over-indulging this appetite and omitting such foods as milk and vegetables.

Sugar

Sugar, Sirup, and Honey. To the chemist there are six sugars instead of one, and each has a name. Cane and beet sugar are chemically the same sugar, called sucrose. When we speak of sugar, we usually refer to sucrose. White sugar is ninety-nine per cent pure sucrose. Brown sugar contains some molasses, hence it is richer in minerals and is slightly less concentrated than white sugar. Sugar is also available as powdered sugar, sometimes called confectioner's sugar, and as loaf sugar which is much favored for hot beverages.

The consumer who wants to know what he is buying needs to know something of the rather large number of sirups on the market. Federal standards and grading have been established for a number of these sirups.

A number of different sirups are obtained from sugar cane. The one given the highest rating for quality is top sirup or cane sirup.

Grades of products from sugar cane listed in order of quality are:

1. Cane sirup — excellent.
2. Light molasses — excellent.
3. Dark molasses — good.
4. Barbados molasses — used chiefly in animal foods.
5. Black strap molasses — not good for human food.

Molasses is a by-product of the sugar industry. Cane molasses is edible, but beet molasses is not.

Sorghum or sorgo sirup comes from the sorghum plant which is similar to sugar cane. Its flavor is similar to that of cane sirup, but it has an additional tang, easily recognized by those who know this sirup.

Corn sirup is manufactured from cornstarch. Light corn sirup has about 10 per cent of sugar sirup (from either cane sugar or beet sugar) added to it. Dark corn sirup usually has refiners' sirup added to it to darken it. Corn sirup does not crystallize readily and is, therefore, a good choice for candy making or for cake frosting. The sugar in corn sirup is not so sweet to the taste as cane sugar.

Maple sirup is obtained from the sap of certain varieties of maple trees, and is much prized for its flavor. Pure maple sirup, to be labeled as such in interstate commerce, must come entirely from maple trees, and contain not over 35 per cent water, and weigh not less than 11 pounds to the gallon.

Mixtures of maple sirup usually contain cane-sugar sirup and are labeled "maple and cane." Such mixtures vary greatly in the proportions of maple sirup and sugar sirup they contain. Some mixtures contain more cane-sugar sirup than maple sirup. When more than 50 per cent of the product is cane-sugar sirup, the label must read "cane and maple."

Honey, the sweetest of all sugars, as sold in interstate commerce under the regulations of the Food and Drug Administration, must be made entirely of the natural product of the honey bee. Its flavor and color vary with the flower or flowers from which it comes. Extracted honey is the honey separate from the comb; section-comb honey is taken directly from the hive and may be sold in whole or cut sections; bulk comb or chunk honey consists of pieces of comb with extracted honey poured over them and is commonly sold in glass jars.

The Food Value of Sugar and Other Sweets. Sugar is a pure product, free from adulterations and cheap in price. Sugar owes its food value entirely to one element — carbohydrate; it contains no minerals and no vitamins. Hence it is an extremely one-sided article of food, serving only to supply energy.

Molasses contains, besides sugar, a high concentration of minerals, being rich in both calcium and iron.

Two tablespoons of sugar furnish one hundred calories.

One hundred calories of other sweets:

Molasses, 1½ tablespoons	Candy, .7 oz. (1 or 2 pieces)
Honey, 1 tablespoon	Jelly, 2 tablespoons
Sirup, 1½ tablespoons	Preserves, 2 to 3 tablespoons

Place of Sugar in the Diet. The average diet could be improved by reducing the sugar consumed by perhaps as much as one half. Why is this true?

1. Sugar blunts the appetite for more needed foods.
2. Sugar is irritating to the mucous membrane of the stomach.

This irritation is lessened if sugar is taken in small quantities, diluted with other foods. Concentrated sweets should not be eaten between meals. Not only is sugar itself irritating, but it ferments easily in the stomach. The gas formed produces physical discomfort, and the products of fermentation irritate the digestive tract.

3. Because sugar is well liked, it is easily eaten in excess. Each pound of surplus body weight means that surplus calories have been eaten. It is much easier to do without the surplus calories in the first place than to reduce the surplus weight afterwards. Sweets add calories rapidly.

It must not be concluded from this discussion that sugars and sweets are unwholesome. It is the excess that is unwholesome.

Dessert Discretion

1. The wholesomeness of sweets depends on the energy needed and on the quantity and concentration of the sweets that are eaten.

2. Sweets should be diluted. Thus sugar in a drink is preferable to a piece of candy. Sugar is still more wholesome if combined with other ingredients, as in cookies, and is even better as a part of a meal.

3. Sweets should be eaten last in order not to dull the appetite for more useful foods.

4. Simple sweets are to be preferred to rich combinations. When rich combinations are served to adults, there should be a simpler dessert for the children. Richness is due to both fat and sugar.

5. A very rich dessert cannot be justified after a heavy meal. It may occasionally assume the proportion of the main dish if it is used with a wise combination of foods. For example, apple pie, a glass of milk, and a slice of cheese may at times constitute a satisfactory lunch for an adult.

6. Sweets should not be eaten between meals. They irritate the stomach and take the place of more needed foods.

7. Overweight people should beware of desserts containing much fat or sugar; they must be stingy with the calories. A good rule to adopt is little or *no* sweets.

8. Thin people may eat desserts provided they do not upset their digestions with too much sugar or fat.

Fig. 76. FRUIT SHORTCAKE

9. The most desirable desserts are those that combine a high food value, other than calories, with digestibility, such as custards, fruits, milk desserts, cornstarch puddings, cereal or bread puddings.

10. When pies are served, those with the crust cooked separately and with a minimum amount of crust are preferable.

Desserts for Luncheon

Sponge Cakes. Sponge cakes contain no butter or other fat; the egg furnishes the liquid, though a tablespoon of water or milk is sometimes added. The leavening agent is air beaten into the egg whites. Sponge cakes are of two types — yellow and white. Yellow sponge cake is plain sponge cake and is made with both the white and the yolks of eggs. White sponge cake is called angel food cake. Jelly roll and chocolate roll are variations of sponge cake. For the method of making and baking sponge cakes see page 500.

Cookies. See Chapter 20. See recipes, pages 502–505.

Fruit Whips. (Recipes, page 516.) There are two types of fruit whips: (1) cooked, (2) uncooked. The pulp of almost any fruit may be used. Cooked prunes, dried apricots or peaches, apple sauce, or fresh bananas are the fruits most commonly used. Cooked fruit whips are in reality fruit soufflés and are served either hot or cold. Uncooked fruit whips are served cold.

Fig. 77. DUTCH APPLE CAKE IS AN UPSIDE-DOWN CAKE

Baked Fruits. (Recipe, pages 390–393.) Apples, bananas, and pears are baked and served hot or cold.

Fruit Roll. (Recipe, page 517.) Any kind of cooked dried

fruit or uncooked fresh fruit may be used. The roll may be baked or steamed and served in its own juice or with hard sauce. Apple dumplings are really fruit rolls. They may be varied in many ways, as with brown sugar, with raisins, with nuts.

Shortcakes. (Recipes, page 517.) A shortcake is a fresh fruit, sweetened and sometimes crushed, served between layers of cake, pastry, or rich biscuit dough topped with whipped cream. Shortcakes are rich and should be served only with a light meal. Almost any fresh fruit is good for the purpose.

Puddings. (Recipes, pages 512–515.) Puddings are made of egg, sugar, and milk to which are added various dry ingredients such as nuts, berries, fresh or dried fruits, bread crumbs, rice, flour, and some other materials. They are mixed either as custards, or as cakes, and may be either steamed or baked. No general rules are possible because of the wide variety.

Pastry. (Recipes, pages 506–511.) Pastry is rich and should be used sparingly. Pies may be eaten with little inconvenience by active people. Children should not be given pie at all, but some of the filling may be baked separately in custard cups for them. Good pastry is

FIG. 78. CUSTARD PIE WITH MERINGUE

FIG. 79. FRUIT PIE

FIG. 80. TARTS

crisp and flaky. Pies are preferable which have the crust cooked separately. Fillings may be highly nutritious.

Custards. (Recipes, page 515.) Custards are made of milk, are sweetened and flavored in various ways, and are thickened with egg or with egg and a starchy substance — cornstarch, flour, tapioca, or rice. They are among the simplest and best desserts from the standpoint of digestion and nutrition. Custard desserts may be enjoyed by all members of the family.

Fruit. Fruit should be used frequently as the luncheon dessert, especially in summer.

CLASS PROBLEMS

1. Plan luncheons that might be followed by a heavy dessert, a moderate dessert, and a light dessert, suggesting the dessert in each case and stating the reason that it is recommended.
2. Imagine the following family: father, overweight, employed in a sedentary occupation; mother, normal weight, occupied with housework; sixteen-year-old daughter, with a fickle appetite and inclined to be underweight; fourteen-year-old boy, normal weight, very active. Discuss dessert habits for this family.
3. Ask a doctor and a dentist to talk to the class on the subject of eating sweets.
4. Prove to yourself that sugar is irritating to the mucous membrane of the digestive tract by holding a piece of hard candy in one place in your mouth until it dissolves.
5. Exhibit one-hundred-calorie portions of various sweets.
6. Review chapters on eggs, milk, fruits, cereals.
7. Make a collection of colored pictures, mounted on white cards, to illustrate attractive desserts.
8. Prepare sponge cake, angel food cake. (Recipes, pages 500–501.)
9. Prepare cooked fruit desserts:

   Prune whip, page 516 — Peach or berry roll, page 517
   Apple dumpling, page 516 — Shortcakes, pages 517

10. Prepare puddings and sauces:

    Plum, page 512 — Chocolate bread, page 514
    Cornstarch, page 512 — Rice, page 513 — Sauces, pages 439–440

11. Make pastry and pies. (Recipes, pages 507–511.)
12. Prepare custards such as boiled, baked, caramel, chocolate. (Recipes, pages 515–516.)

13. Compute the calories and the cost per serving of all desserts prepared in the laboratory. Which are low cost? Moderate? Expensive?

14. Secure luncheon menus from books and magazines and discuss the suitability of the dessert for the rest of the meal.

15. Arrange a fresh fruit plate for dessert. Compare it with other desserts in attractiveness, in ease of preparation, and as a source of vitamins and minerals.

HOME PROBLEMS

1. Try to reduce the amount of sweets that you eat, substituting for them, if you need the calories, other and better foods.
2. If you are overweight, try omitting desserts from your meals, and reduce any other excess of sweets.
3. Try to omit eating all sweets between meals.
4. Make a one-crust pie (the crust baked separately) to show your family how good one-crust pies are. Apple-sauce pie is suggested for the first experiment. Next try a chocolate or lemon-filling pie with meringue.
5. Bake a sponge cake at home. If successful, try an angel food cake. If not successful, try plain sponge cake again, after discussing with your teacher the probable causes of your failure.
6. Bake various fruit desserts at home.
7. Make custards for your family luncheon or supper.
8. Prepare chocolate bread pudding and several other puddings at home.
9. Plan the sweets for your family meals for one week.

REFERENCES

Any good Cook Book. See page 387.

Apple Recipes. United States Department of Agriculture.

Halliday, Evelyn G., and Noble, I. *Hows and Whys of Cookery.* University of Chicago Press.

Homemade Bread, Cake and Pastry. United States Department of Agriculture, Farmers' Bulletin 1775.

Honey and Some of Its Uses. United States Department of Agriculture, Leaflet 113.

Ice Creams Frozen Without Stirring. United States Department of Agriculture, Department Leaflet 49.

Sherman, Henry C. *Food Products.* The Macmillan Company. Chapter XIII.

CHAPTER TWENTY-TWO

❧ How Will You Plan a Luncheon or a Supper?

For Courtesy at the Table — *See Chapter* 10
For Table Service — *See Chapter* 11
For Where Shall We Eat? — *See Chapter* 12

WHAT ARE THE CHARACTERISTICS of an enjoyable luncheon? It is fascinating to learn of the many different food combinations that may be used for this meal, but you know that an enjoyable meal is far more than an interesting combination of food. You are not learning merely to prepare good combinations of food and to serve them properly, you are learning one of the most appreciated arts of homemaking, for good meals are associated with gracious living.

What will make your luncheons remembered? Tastiness, daintiness, and yes, an element of surprise, that something different from "what we had yesterday," are qualities of really good meals. But add to these the charm of an unflurried hostess, a light, airy room, a pretty table, and congenial companionship and you have a meal that satisfies.

Since practice makes perfect, on with our plans for luncheon. The luncheon may not be perfect at first, but we are making progress when we are able to prepare better and better meals.

Planning is Always an Important Element in Meals that Satisfy. Thoughtful planning of meals is the best of all labor-saving devices for the home. In general, the same rules that make breakfasts a success (Chapters 2 and 9) apply in planning the working schedule for luncheon or supper. These general rules of good management never vary:

1. Have before you the clear and definite purpose of good nutrition with a minimum expenditure of time, energy, and money, and with a maximum of excellence in cookery.

2. Make careful plans. These include plans for menus, recipes, marketing lists, the purchasing of foods, and a working schedule.

3. Carry out your well-laid plans, adjusting them to circumstances as the need arises.

4. Learn from your experiences. Experience is the best teacher only when you examine your experiences and profit from them.

What Will You Plan for Luncheon or Supper? Because of the almost endless variety that invites you in planning menus for luncheon or supper, this is the meal that should balance all the day's meals. Any lack in breakfast or dinner in meeting the daily food requirements can be made up, with a little thought, at luncheon or supper. Points to keep in mind here are:

1. Since luncheon dishes offer so many tempting ways to use fruits, vegetables, and milk, this is an excellent time to make sure of an adequate supply of minerals and vitamins — the protective foods on which all too often we short-change ourselves.

2. What one eats is controlled in large measure by appetite. Plan, therefore, to tempt appetites with food attractively served in pleasing combinations.

3. Careful planning of simple meals is the key to economy.

4. A good planner uses foods that are in season. This is in the interest of economy, variety, and quality.

5. When food makes a second appearance on the table, make a new dish of it, and make it more attractive than when first served. Made-over food is so much more acceptable than left-over food.

6. The menu should include as few dishes as possible. The meal in one dish is favored. How much less trouble it is to serve baked macaroni and cheese than it is to provide separate dishes to furnish the necessary amount of protein, fat, and carbohydrate! What would complete such a meal?

7. Dishes which can be prepared ahead of time are a great convenience. If the work is planned and systematized, most of the preparation for luncheon can be made at the time the kitchen work is being done after breakfast; supper may be prepared during the preparation of dinner.

8. Much labor can be saved if, in planning meals, the needs of the entire family are considered; then there will be little need for preparing special dishes. Where adaptations are necessary they can be made with little effort if they have been planned ahead of time. The most frequent adaptations called for in the ordinary family are caused by the differences in food for adults and for children. The table on page 246 illustrates how adaptations can be made with no special purchases or extra labor.

Foods Especially Desirable for Adults and Children	Adaptations	
	Adult	*Children*
Milk	Hot breads	Stale bread
Eggs	Scalloped or au gratin vegetables	Buttered vegetables
Soups	Tea or coffee	Milk
Bread and other cereal food	Stuffed tomato	Stewed tomato
Vegetables, simply prepared	Salads, rich dressings	Sandwich of shredded lettuce or cabbage
Leafy vegetables	Banana salad	Baked banana
Sandwiches	Apple dumplings	Baked apple
Simple desserts, as cookies, sponge cake, gelatin	Pie	Stewed fruit or custard
Fruit	Shortcake	Berries
	Peach cobbler	Stewed peaches
	Croquettes	Creamed meat

9. As suggested in connection with breakfast, the utensils to be used should be planned so that the same utensil is not wanted for two purposes at the same time.

Plan to use the oven for more than one thing at a time. Custard and potatoes may be baked at the same time even though potatoes require a moderate oven and custard must have a slow oven. The potatoes may be put on the top rack and the custard set below in a pan of water. Can you think of other examples?

For the discussion of courses for a formal luncheon see Chapters 23 and 29.

Buying the Food. Most of the staples used for luncheon or supper are also bought for the breakfast menu.

Every good manager plans for the unexpected. An emergency or reserve shelf stocked with staples is an excellent device for every household. The pantry should contain at all times food materials for such emergencies as unexpected company; the groceryman's failure to send the right supplies or to send them on time; the unexpected absence of the cook or the housewife, and other occasions.

Serving the Luncheon or Supper. For full information on table service, see Chapter 11, Table Service. As a rule, family service is used for luncheon or supper. Luncheon cloths or place mats and small napkins are suitable for this meal. Decorative china, primarily intended for breakfast sets, may also be used at luncheon. Plain china, however, is always correct for all meals.

The Family Luncheon. The family luncheon usually is a simple meal of one or two courses. The first course, including the beverage, may be on the table when the meal begins. It is important that the meal be served promptly if school children or employed members of the family eat at home at noon.

A tea wagon or a serving table is a convenience. The salad or the dessert course may be placed on the tea wagon; its lower tray is convenient for holding used dishes.

Light Luncheon	*Moderate Luncheon*
First course:	First course:
Vegetable plate or cream soup *or*	Soup or appetizer { fruit / shellfish / tomato juice }
Hot dish luncheon *or*	
Cold plate	
Second course (sometimes):	Second course (main):
Salad or dessert or fruit	Hot dish luncheon *or*
	Vegetable plate *or*
	Salad
	Third course:
	Dessert or salad

The Formal Luncheon. With feminine members of the family luncheon is a favorite way of entertaining their friends. The table for a formal luncheon may be laid either with doilies or a tablecloth. More or less elaborate table decorations are employed, and color schemes are usually carried out. The menu for a formal luncheon is similar to that of a dinner, and the service used is formal service, Russian style. (See Chapters 11 and 15.)

Supper. The evening meal is the meal of most leisure and social interest for the family. The home supper should be simple, especially if there are children in the family. Supper is delightfully informal. In summer a supper may be served on the porch. In winter, if the family is small, a tea table, an electric grill and toaster, and an open fire make the evening meal a cozy contrast to the raw winter night. On Sunday night, suppers are the usual practice.

At breakfast there is a rush for school or work, and sometimes all the members of the family do not breakfast at the same hour. At lunch the day's work is interrupted for a hurried meal; often each member of the family eats in a different place. This is not the case with the evening meal; this is the time of day when members of the family see one another. The setting for this meal should be pleasing, and the food should be wholesomely selected and prepared, and attractively served. The most important consideration, however, is not the food but the family. Dinner or supper offers the chief opportunity for family intercourse. Save the most interesting occurrence in your day to relate to the others at the evening meal. Remember that the others, too, have something to tell, and give them the opportunity to tell it. Make the evening meal, whether it be supper or dinner, an occasion of good food, good humor, good manners, and good companionship.

The Buffet Supper. The buffet supper is much favored for the Sunday night meal for the family. Sometimes one wishes to entertain guests for supper. The buffet supper offers a way of serving a large group with a minimum of effort, without maid service.

One autumn afternoon a family party of seven, ranging from grandmother and grandfather to the youngest child, motored to a country home to have supper with friends. In the living room a log fire crackled cheerfully in the large fireplace. There was no flurry or effort; the hostess was smiling and serene and stayed in the living room with her guests. The children played awhile on the floor where toys were in abundance, but the center of attraction for them was their fifteen-months-old host.

After the two families had visited together awhile, and the travelers had rested from their long drive, supper was announced by the hostess, who had left the group ten minutes before. The dining-room table was a picture. Four gleaming candles made the affair a party, and the children voiced immediate approval. A small table in the corner of the room was set for them. The food provided for them — we shall let you imagine that — was just what children should eat, and the table looked very festive. They began their meal with no thought of what the grown-ups were having.

At one end of the large table for the grown-ups, there was a platter with salad arranged on lettuce leaves in individual servings. At the other end of the table a platter edged with parsley bore a baked country ham — sugar-cured of course — with a golden-brown crust dotted with cloves. If the other dishes that so bountifully filled the table were recorded here your mouth would water. As the guests entered they passed the host who stood and carved the ham, serving it on large plates from a stack in front of him. Each guest received a plate from him and then moved around the table, serving himself from the other dishes on the table as he went the rounds. The hostess placed a serving of salad on each plate. Each guest took, from the well-arranged table, the necessary silver, a napkin, and a glass of water and proceeded to the group of comfortable chairs about the cheery living-room fire. The hostess followed them and brewed tea at a tea table. A chair arm, a piano bench, or a small table proved convenient for holding glass or teacup. The food had been so selected that no knife would be needed; even the ham was so tender that it could be cut readily with a fork.

The children could be seen through the door at their table in the dining room, but they entertained themselves. They returned to the living room when the sweets were passed. Each of the little visitors was allowed to pass the sweets and nuts to the grown-ups. Their mother suggested that they might each eat two pieces of candy. They carefully selected pieces of generous size and made sure they had their favorite kinds.

Then they settled to quiet play in the center of the circle, and the adults lingered over the teacups and the sweets. The men of the party collected the dishes and returned them to the dining room. The baby was made ready for bed, and he threw a kiss to each guest. On the way home one of the little girls expressed the sentiment of the entire family: "Mother, isn't living fine and don't we have a good time!"

Don't you wish you could have been there? Why not try the plan at your own home?

Because the buffet luncheon also offers a convenient way of serving a larger group than can be seated in the dining room, it is a favorite way of entertaining informally. For a full discussion of this type of party see Chapter 29, We Have a Party, pages 315–325.

CLASS PROBLEMS

1. Plan a luncheon of each type — vegetable, hot dish, cold plate. Describe the family which is to eat each meal and state the season for which it is planned. How would you modify these menus for use at supper instead of luncheon? Emphasize variety at moderate cost.

2. Contrasts make menus pleasing. Contrasts may be in flavor, texture, crispness, freshness, and color. Study the luncheon menus on page 250 and point out the contrast, or the lack of contrast, that makes each one pleasing or monotonous.

a. Cream of Celery Soup — Toasted Bread Sticks
Orange and Date Salad
Hot Rolls — Milk or Iced Tea

b. Cheese Soufflé — Berry Muffins
Baked Potato — Chocolate with Whipped Cream

c. Chicken Croquettes — Hot Biscuit
Baked Tomato Stuffed with Rice — Milk
Strawberries and Cream

d. Cream of Tomato Soup — Bread
Creamed Chicken on Toast — Scalloped Potatoes
Baked Custard — Milk

3. As a class, plan four luncheons that meet the needs of the class. Divide your number into groups, each group to plan the working schedule, the market order, and the serving of the luncheons. Collect the food to be served and discuss points in selecting each one. Have class discussion of the plans.

4. Each group will prepare and serve the luncheons as planned. Discuss the results.

5. Groups exchange menus to see if the second group can improve on the plan of the first by preparing the same meal as well or better, in less time.

6. Plan a menu for luncheon and make out the working schedule so that the housewife may have the morning uninterrupted for sewing until within a half hour of the time for serving luncheon to her family, which consists of four children and her husband, who does desk work.

7. Plan a supper that this same housewife mentioned in Problem 6 could serve to her family. Assume that she had been to town and must serve the supper shortly after her return, without having time to change to a house dress. The family prefers a hot dish for supper.

8. Plan an emergency shelf for your family. After class discussion of this problem, you will find a trip to the grocery store by each member of the class interesting. Procure prices of foods for the shelf. Discuss plans made by various members of the class.

9. Plan a Sunday night supper for your family.

10. Plan a menu suitable for the family buffet supper party described on pages 248–249.

HOME PROBLEMS

Luncheon or supper projects have no doubt already suggested themselves to you.

1. How monotonous it must be for the housewife never to have a surprise at mealtime. She delights the family with surprises in the menus, but she always knows the menu herself. Since you are in school, it will not be very convenient for you to cook the noon meal, but if the evening meal at your home is supper, why not plan, prepare, and serve the family supper for a week? If you cannot have full responsibility, you can plan the menus and do the marketing, and you can help prepare such dishes as salads or desserts. Can you surprise and delight your mother and family with some special dish or menu?
2. Entertain a group of your friends at an informal luncheon which you plan, prepare, and serve.
3. Plan and prepare a Sunday night buffet supper for your family.
4. Add to the pleasure of mealtime in your home by your own good humor, good manners, and interest in other members of your family.
5. Plan and purchase the articles for an emergency shelf in your pantry.

REFERENCES

Current magazines for luncheon and supper suggestions.

Bailey, N. Beth (MacLean). *Meal Planning and Table Service.* Chapters III, IV. Manual Arts Press.

Rose, Mary Swartz. *Feeding the Family.* Chapters IV, XII, XIV. The Macmillan Company.

Government Bulletins:

A Guide to Good Meals for the Junior Home Maker. United States Department of Agriculture, Miscellaneous Circular 49.

Diets to Fit the Family Income. United States Department of Agriculture, Farmers' Bulletin 1757.

Getting the Most for Your Food Money. United States Department of Agriculture.

Any good Cook Book. See page 387.

For other references on Table Service and Table Manners, see references for Chapters 10 and 11.

CHAPTER TWENTY-THREE

What Shall We Have for Dinner?

See Chapters 1, 3, 15

DINNER IS A MORE LEISURELY and dignified meal than breakfast or luncheon; and since it is usually the main meal of the day, its menu is likely to be heavier than that of the other meals. The heartiness of dinner, as well as the kind of food selected, depends on the menu of the earlier meals of the day.

Planning the Three Meals of the Day. The inexperienced manager plans each meal as a unit; this procedure necessitates balancing each meal. The experienced manager plans the meals for the day, or even for the week, as a unit. It makes no difference which meal is planned first; all three of the meals of the day should be considered together. Moreover, all the members of the family must be considered in each day's plans; for what the family needs is the sum of what the individuals need, and this in turn is determined chiefly by weight, age, activity, and state of health. Perhaps the easiest way to plan the day's meals is to consider breakfast first, because the menu for breakfast varies little from day to day, and dinner next. The luncheon menu can be so planned as to supply the deficiencies in the other two meals.

Menus that Please, and Why. In all the foregoing chapters we have emphasized the food value of various articles of food, and their place in the diet. When every day's food is planned in accordance with the food needs of the body, the meal problem has only begun to be solved. It is possible to work out one day's or one week's dietary to perfection, but what happens if the family does not like it, or grows tired of it? Pleasing the family day in and day out calls for a knowledge both of nutrition and the art of menu planning and of cookery.

What are the tricks of the trade by which simple, well-balanced meals can be made attractive? Variety in menus is necessary, but how can it be achieved? Herein lies much of the art of cookery and meal planning.

1. Food should be well cooked. Poorly cooked food is universally disliked.

2. Foods are appreciated chiefly for their flavor. Each food should be prepared in such a way as to capitalize its flavor if that flavor is well liked, or to modify it if it is objectionable. To illustrate: no cook can improve the flavor of a good cantaloupe, so why scoop it out in little balls and change its flavor in a cocktail or a salad? Onions are too strong for many people; here it is worth time and trouble to modify the flavor through parboiling and scalloping with toasted, buttered bread crumbs.

3. A few foods should be served at a time. One who eats at a hotel occasionally is delighted with the long menu; choosing from his bill of fare is a pastime, but the multiplicity of dishes is the very thing that tires the person who habitually eats at the hotel. He must order from the same long menu each day, and what was variety the first day has soon become monotony.

4. Surprises are enjoyed. Do not have a certain menu or a certain dish regularly on any one day. Although it is poor economy to use foods out of season, watch the markets and surprise your family with seasonal foods at the first of the season. You can recall how you relish the first appearance of oysters in the fall; or the first fresh home-grown strawberries in the spring.

5. A new food should be prepared in a familiar and well-liked way. Introduce only one strange food, or one new dish, at a time.

6. No two foods should be prepared in the same way at the same meal. Rice croquettes and chicken croquettes do not please if served together. Imagine the monotony of fried oysters, fried eggplant, and banana fritters in the same menu!

7. Contrast is one of the most useful devices for producing menus that please. Many contrasting combinations of foods are so well liked that they are acceptable universally. Examples are: crisp crackers or croutons served with soup, butter with bread.

Some pleasing contrasts in food are:

Soft and solid textures — Hot and cold temperatures
Mild and strong flavor — Definite and indefinite shape
Sweet and acid flavor — Small sizes and larger sizes
Mild and tart flavor — Colorful and colorless food
Different methods of cooking, such as scalloping and boiling.

FIG. 81. GRAPEFRUIT AS A FIRST COURSE

Utilizing the suggestions for contrasts in food, list familiar examples of pleasing combinations of foods.

8. The same food, except such staples as bread or milk, should not be served twice in the same day.

9. Many courses for a family dinner should be avoided. The same courses for successive days may become monotonous. Soup served every day, even with variation in kind, grows tiresome.

The Dinner Menu. Dinner is served in courses. The heartiness of any one course is inversely proportioned to the number of courses served. A diner can manage six or eight courses only if none is very rich, and if he eats lightly of each.

Order of Courses. Courses follow a well-established sequence that gives the appetizing foods first and those that dull the appetite last. Contrast between the courses is needed. A warm soup or an acid fruit is served first because it not only helps to insure a relish for the rest of the meal, but it stimulates the flow of the gastric juice, thus preparing the stomach for the reception of food.

The meat or meat substitute, with vegetables, is the main course and deserves prominence because it furnishes a greater variety of the foods needed by the body than do the other courses.

A salad course accompanies or follows the main course for two reasons. The succulence of the dish, and the fact that it is cold, make it a pleasing contrast to the main course. Salads, like soups, are appetizing and serve to stimulate the appetite.

As stated in a former chapter, sweets dull the appetite. At the end of a meal this can do no harm. Most of us like to finish our meal with sweets, and so the dessert course comes at the end of the meal.

A small cup of coffee is frequently served after the dessert, usually without cream or sugar. The flavor of coffee at the end of a heavy meal is relished because it removes the sweet taste of the dessert.

It should be remembered that the formal meal with its sequence of courses is a tax on the digestive system. It should never be indulged in by children and only at intervals by adults. When there are many courses the portions served should be small, and in order to enjoy all the courses, one should eat sparingly of each.

Types of Dinner Menus. Dinner is the meal at which we most frequently entertain our friends. There is a wide variety in the number of courses and in the type of food that is served. In very formal dinners each food with its accompaniments may constitute a course. The family dinner should, however, be simple, consisting of two or three courses.

FAMILY DINNER (light)	SPECIAL DINNER (moderate)	FORMAL DINNER (heavy)
Soup or fruit cocktail	Cocktail (fruit or	Cocktail (fruit or shellfish)
(sometimes)	shellfish) or	Soup
Main course:	Soup	Entrée or fish
Meat	Meat course	Meat
Vegetables	Salad course	Salad
Salad	Dessert	Dessert
Bread	Coffee (with main	Coffee, cheese, crackers
Dessert	course or dessert)	Mints and nuts

MENU FOR A FAMILY DINNER

Baked Chicken
New Potatoes Hard Rolls and Butter
Head Lettuce with French Dressing
Orange Charlotte
Coffee, Cream, and Sugar

MENU FOR A SPECIAL DINNER

Bouillon Crackers Olives
Leg of Lamb with Mint Sauce
Stuffed Potato Buttered Peas
Hard Rolls, Butter
Lettuce with Thousand Island Dressing Swedish Wafers
Frozen Apricots Sponge Drops
Coffee (with the dessert or main course)

A BANQUET MENU (FORMAL)

Oyster Cocktail
Chicken Consommé Crackers Olives
Broiled Trout Julienne Potatoes
Roast Turkey
Dressing Cranberry Sauce
Buttered Cauliflower Peas in Timbale Cases
Cucumber and Lettuce Salad
Frozen Custard Rolled Wafers
Coffee (demi-tasse)
Roquefort Cheese Water Crackers
Mints Salted Nuts

The formal dinner requires expert service, and is seldom used in homes. The plan is followed for banquets and for the formal entertaining which is usually left to larger groups than the family and is best carried out by the expert staff of a hotel or a club. The discussions in this book are for family dinners.

The Selection of Dinner Foods. The cocktail may be of shellfish with a highly seasoned sauce. Fruit cocktail, if acid, may be served. This course is intended as an appetizer; hence sweet fruits are not so acceptable as those with a tart flavor.

Soup for dinner should have little fuel value. A clear soup, bouillon or consommé, is used as an appetizer. Crackers, olives, pickles, or radishes may accompany either soup or cocktail. It is not usual to serve both soup and cocktail in the same home dinner.

The main course at dinner consists of meat, fish, poultry, or game accompanied by one or two vegetables. Potatoes are the best liked vegetable, and are served daily in many parts of the country. In some localities, however, rice is preferred to potatoes. The second vegetable should be a watery or succulent variety, such as spinach, turnips, or broccoli.

Plain bread and butter are served, as a general rule, with a home dinner. Hard rolls, called dinner rolls, are well liked.

A salad instead of the second vegetable may be served with the meat. A green salad, such as slaw, lettuce, watercress, or Swiss chard, with French dressing, is preferable. Heavy salads are not used at dinner.

The choice of the dessert depends on the rest of the dinner both as to flavor and heaviness. This course, like the salad, should be light. Fruit ices are acceptable. Sometimes fresh fruit is served. That is the only dessert used in Mexico and is also familiar in Southern Europe. Rich desserts are distinctly American. A light dessert, offered in small servings, is acceptable and makes a pleasing contrast in the menu.

Coffee is served with the main course, or with the dessert, or after dinner.

A choice of cheeses, with hard crackers, is frequently served as the last course instead of a dessert. A highly flavored cheese stimulates the digestive juices and is an aid to good digestion.

A Comparison of Luncheon and Dinner Menus. There is no hard-and-fast line between the dinner and the luncheon. Many dishes are interchangeable in these menus.

It is a wise provision, both from the standpoint of nutrition and economy, to serve meat only once a day. The dinner menu is usually the best place for it.

The two menus may contain the same number of calories, though frequently the dinner menu contains slightly more than one third the total number of calories required and the luncheon about one third, with the breakfast furnishing less than one third (about one fourth).

Vegetables, salads, and desserts are lighter and more simply prepared for dinner than for luncheon. Luncheon is usually made up of a few dishes, hence they may be rich. Dinner comprises two or more courses, and so each dish must be simple.

When We Dine Out. An excellent way to study dinner menus is from the menu cards of hotels or restaurants. Everyone should know how to order from a menu card. At hotels and restaurants three types of menus are available.

1. *A la Carte Menu.* This menu is a veritable catalogue of foods for dinner. It is very confusing to be faced with the job of ordering from such a menu. A la carte service is the most expensive service.

2. *Table d'Hôte Dinner.* This is a menu offered complete at a set price by the hotel. In a very large hotel there may be more than one table d'hôte menu for any one meal, but there is usually only one. This menu usually permits of some choices.

3. Club dinner menus, which are a combination but abbreviated version of à la carte and table d'hôte. In this type of menu there are usually several combinations offered for the main course, designated by numbers. The individual then chooses his soup, bread, beverage, and dessert; thus the main course is table d'hôte and the rest of the meal is à la carte. This is a very popular type of menu, since it gives some individual choice, but does not force as many decisions as does an à la carte menu.

CLASS PROBLEMS

1. Review Chapter 3, What Shall We Have for Breakfast, and Chapter 15, What Shall We Have for Luncheon or Supper.

2. Bring to class hotel dinner menu cards, both à la carte and table d'hôte; from these select a light, a moderate, and a heavy dinner.

3. Each member of the class should check the menus selected by her for a balanced meal. Check also for pleasing contrasts. Have you made as good menus as the steward did?

4. How should an overweight person order his dinner from the hotel menu cards? An underweight person? Explain. Order dinner for a child four years of age.

5. Plan a light, a medium, and a heavy dinner for your family.

6. Plan a dinner for a family of four (2 adults and 2 children) that you consider moderate in cost. How would you change the menu to make it a low-cost but adequate meal? How change the menu if cost is no consideration?

HOME PROBLEMS

1. For one week plan the dinners for your family, illustrating as well as you can ways of making the menu pleasing.
2. List the food you eat for dinner for three days. Estimate the calories. Do you eat a third or more of your calories at dinner? Is your habit in this matter justified?
3. Be very careful as to your personal cleanliness at all meals. Take special pains to be ready for dinner.
4. Try to do your part to make dinner a pleasing event in your family.

REFERENCES

Dinner menus in current magazines. Special articles on dinner or dinner combinations in current magazines. Hotel menu cards.

Bailey, N. Beth (MacLean). *Meal Planning and Table Service.* The Manual Arts Press.

Rose, Mary Swartz. *Feeding the Family.* Chapters IV, XIV, 1940. The Macmillan Company.

Diets to Fit the Family Income. United States Department of Agriculture, Farmers' Bulletin 1757.

See other references at end of Chapters 3, 9, and 16 of this text. Any good Cook Book. See page 387.

CHAPTER TWENTY-FOUR

❧ Meat

Cook Book References

Meat Cookery, *Page* 461

Food Value

Nutritive Value of Foods	*Table* VI, *Appendix*
Food Value in Shares	*Table* VIII, *Appendix*
Vitamins and Minerals	*Tables* IX *and* X, *Appendix*

KINDS OF MEAT. In this chapter the term meat includes beef, veal, pork, mutton, and lamb.

Economic Importance of Meat. We eat approximately twice as much meat as Europeans do. An average of one of every three dollars spent by American families for food is spent for meat. Why are we willing to spend so much for meat?

Why We Like Meat. Meat is almost universally liked because of its richness of flavor and because it satisfies the appetite. The cook likes meat because it is easy to prepare, and because, also, a large roast provides cold meat for later meals with almost no labor of preparation involved. Variety in menus is obtained merely by using a different cut of meat, or by varying the kind of meat and the method of cooking.

COMPOSITION AND FOOD VALUE OF MEAT

Meat is about half water. The protein content varies from one sixth in fat cuts to one fifth in lean cuts. There is a wide variation in the fat content, from one tenth in very lean meat to one third in pork. The calories in each pound of meat are proportional to the fat content, pork chops yielding twice as much fuel as round steak and more than twice as much as veal. See Table VI, Appendix.

Protein. The protein of meat is "complete." In your reading you may have seen the term *amino acids.* These are the smaller units of which proteins are made. The body must have a certain assortment of amino acids in order to build or rebuild its protein tissues. A complete protein contains all of these required amino acids. Incomplete proteins lack one or more of the amino acids required for building body proteins. Incomplete proteins are useful, but they must be supplemented by complete proteins.

Energy Value. Meat contains fat, which is an excellent fuel food. A good diet contains both fat and carbohydrate. The energy value of meat may be overrated if judged from figures giving composition, because when meat is trimmed for cooking a large part of the fat is discarded, and at meals much of it may be left on the plate.

Minerals. Meat contains a good quantity of iron, phosphorus, and sulphur. Liver should receive special mention for its iron, and also for its copper content. Copper in small amounts is needed by the body in its utilization of iron.

Vitamins. Meat is a poor source of several vitamins. It cannot be counted on for Vitamin C because the presence of that substance varies with the food that was fed to the animal and because Vitamin C is not stored to any great extent in the body of the animal.

The parts of the animal which are commonly used for food contain little or none of Vitamin A, but this vitamin is present in the vital organs that are not so generally used for food, such as the heart, kidney, sweetbreads, and especially the liver. Lean pork, kidney, liver, brains, lean beef, and lean mutton are important sources of Vitamin B_1. Liver contains small amounts of Vitamin D. Meats, especially liver and other organs, are good sources of Vitamin G and niacin.

Extractives. The flavor of meat is due to extractives. They have no food value, but are an aid to good digestion, since they stimulate the flow of the digestive juices, especially the gastric juice.

The Digestibility of Meat. Meat is quickly digested. The connective tissues which determine the toughness or the tenderness of meat are easily dissolved by the gastric juice. Tough cuts of meat, if properly cooked, seem to be as easily digested as the tender cuts. Experiments show that the protein of meat is about as easily digested as that of milk or eggs. Lean meat is more quickly digested than meat with an excess of fat.

Place of Meat in the Diet. Meat is an important food, but it is so expensive that it is easy to spend too big a share of the food money for it. Instead of purchasing meat with one dollar out of each three dollars spent for food, it would be better to spend for meat only one out of four or five dollars. An excess of meat in the diet may replace other needed foods. In the interest of economy and good health American families should spend less for meat and more for fruits and vegetables. Meat must be supplemented by foods that furnish carbohydrate, vitamins, cellulose, and minerals. We need fear no shortage of protein if we eat daily one serving of meat, one egg, or one meat substitute, two glasses of milk, with bread, cereals, and occasionally beans, peas, and nuts. Fruits and vegetables furnish in abundance the food substances lacking in meat.

Children need adequate supplies of protein to take care of their rapid growth: considerably more in proportion to their weight than do adults. Part of this is provided by the quart of milk a child consumes. One serving of meat a day, an egg, and cereal products in addition to the milk will furnish sufficient protein for the growing child. Lean beef, bacon, lamb, veal, chicken, fish, and liver are suitable for young children.

The Care of Meat

All moist protein foods spoil easily. Meat, therefore, requires scrupulous care from the time that the animals are selected for slaughter to the handling of the meat in the home.

Federal Meat Inspection. The Federal Government exerts a rigid control over sanitary conditions in the meat industry, when the product of the packing houses is handled in interstate or foreign shipment.

The Federal inspection is twofold in nature. First the animals are inspected before and after slaughter to insure the use of only those that are healthy. Some animal diseases, such as trichinosis in pork and tuberculosis in beef cattle, are communicable to human beings. Under the veterinary inspector all diseased animals are condemned and kept from the market. The sanitary inspector also has supervision of the handling of the meat that is suitable for food. There are rigid sanitary restrictions concerning the plant and the workers. The meat is handled rapidly, is kept at a low temperature during the handling, and is stored at approximately freezing temperature.

Each side of beef, veal, pork, lamb, and mutton is inspected and if edible is then stamped "Inspected and Passed." You will see this government stamp on the meat in your market.

State and Municipal Control. Meat which is slaughtered and sold within a state does not come under the Federal Meat Inspection

Act. Moreover, the Federal Act does not control the conditions in wholesale or retail establishments handling meat after it reaches a state or city. It is essential, therefore, that every state and every municipality exert rigid control in order to insure the sanitary handling of meat. Investigate the regulations and their enforcement in your community.

Care in the Home. As soon as meat is brought to the house, it should be placed in the refrigerator. Unless the meat is already very cold, do not place it in a glass or other heavy dish with a glass cover or heavy cover because it does not cool rapidly enough. Place in the refrigerator uncovered or covered loosely with wax or parchment paper, or in a dish with wax paper over it. Uncooked meat should be stored in the coldest part of the refrigerator (at 45° F. or below). Cooked meat may be stored in a somewhat less cold section of the refrigerator, and in a covered container or loosely covered with wax paper.

How to Buy Meat[1]

How to Judge Amounts Needed. In general one pound of meat provides three good servings, but when there is little bone and little other waste, one pound serves four or five people. The following list of amounts and numbers of servings may be used as a guide to how much to buy:

One pound of round steak provides three or four servings.
One pound of calves' liver gives four or five servings.
A four-pound leg of lamb gives ten to twelve servings.
One pound of lamb or veal chops gives three chops.
Two pounds of pot roast provides about eight servings.
Two pounds of pork spare-rib serves four persons.
Two pounds of ham serves six to eight persons.

When buying meat for such dishes as stew and meat pie where vegetables are used, one pound of meat is sufficient for four or five servings.

Grades of Meat. Meat is always graded, in the wholesale market, according to market preference; that is, the preferences of the persons who buy meat. The kind that will bring the highest price is called prime, the next in the list, choice. The differences in price

[1] The tables on the characteristics of cuts of beef, veal, lamb and mutton, and pork are used by permission from *Ten Lessons on Meat for Use in High Schools*, National Live Stock and Meat Board, Chicago.

in the same town for the same cuts are due to differences in grade. It is difficult for those who are unskilled to detect the grades. The main differences that we would detect between a steak from a choice animal and one from a medium animal would be in the matter of fat, and toughness or tenderness.

United States grades of meat are:

Steer and heifer:	U.S. Prime or No. A1	Excellent, not usually available in retail market
	U.S. Choice or No. 1	Excellent for special guest meals
	U.S. Good or No. 2	Good for general use
	U.S. Commercial or No. 3	Good for general use
	U.S. Utility or No. 4	Fair for general use (low in price)
Lamb, veal, and mutton:	Same grades as steer and heifer through Grade 2, but Grade 3 is known as U.S. Medium or No. 3, and Grade 4 is known as U.S. Plain or No. 4	
Pork:	U.S. No. 1	
	U.S. No. 2	
	U.S. No. 3	
	U.S. Culls	
Stag and bull:	Same grades as steer except prime grade is omitted	

In some cities meat is sold by grades in retail stores. You may have seen meat that is stamped US CHOICE in a strip, repeated many times from the top to the bottom of a side of beef. Such meat has been graded by the U.S. Department of Agriculture. This service may be used by any packing plant for a service charge of one tenth of a cent a pound or less. United States grades for meat begin with Prime, but there is such a small proportion of meat of this grade that Prime is seldom seen on the retail market. It is sold almost exclusively to hotels and restaurants that are able to pay and charge high prices.

Beef. Good beef is firm, well mottled or marked with fat, and has a characteristic bright red color. The fat (suet) should be creamy white and firm. There should be no disagreeable odor. The beef is cut lengthwise into halves and each half in turn into a forequarter and hindquarter.

BEEF CUTS

Cut	*Characteristics*	*Methods of Preparation*
Neck	Juicy and well flavored.	Soup, stewing, and corning
Chuck	Good quality meat. The steaks are more or less	Roast; fifth rib, oven roast Steaks

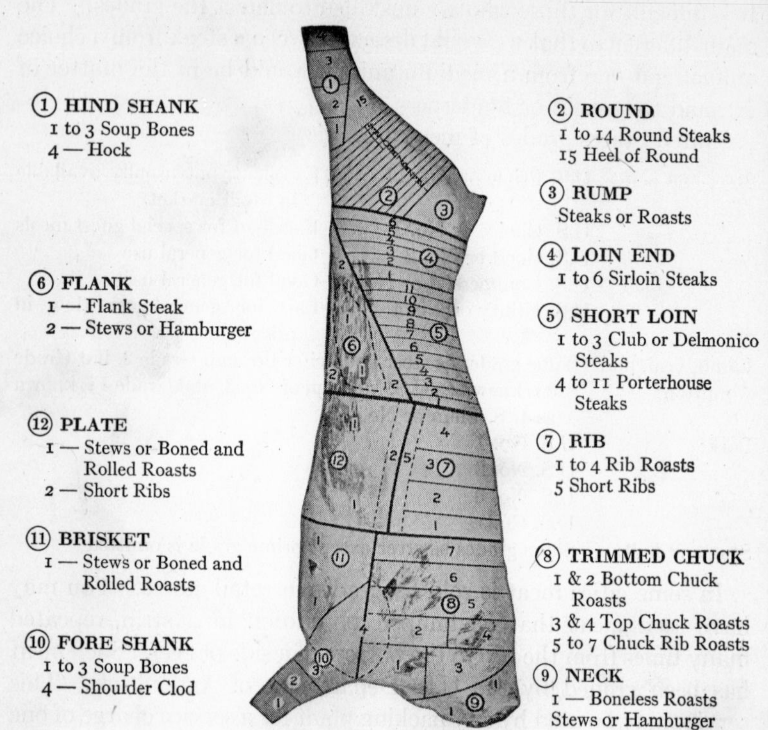

Numerals in circles ① refer to wholesale cuts and major subdivisions of such cuts. Other numerals refer to retail cuts

WHOLESALE CUTS AND SUBDIVISIONS

ALL PERCENTAGES BASED ON CARCASS WEIGHT

① to ⑥ Hindquarter	48.0%	⑦ to ⑫ Forequarter	52.0%
① to ③ Round and Rump	24.0	⑦ Rib	9.5
① Hind Shank	4.0%	⑧ & ⑨ Chuck	22.0
② Buttock	15.0	⑧ Trimmed Chuck	17.0%
③ Rump	5.0	⑨ Neck	5.0
④ & ⑤ Full Loin Inc. Suet	20.5	⑩ Fore Shank	5.5
④ Loin End	7.0	⑪ Brisket	6.5
⑤ Short Loin	10.5	⑫ Plate	8.5
Kidney Knob	3.0		
⑥ Flank	3.5		

FIG. 82. BEEF CHART, WHOLESALE AND RETAIL CUTS

Cut	*Characteristics*	*Methods of Preparation*
	rectangular in shape and contain cross-sections of shoulder blade, backbone, rib, but often the last two are trimmed off. Contains more connective tissue than cuts from the hindquarter contain. The lean is composed of more muscles, too, the fibers of which run in various directions, so that steaks cannot be cut across the grain. Low in fat, but with a rather high percentage of bone.	Pot roasts Stews Boiling
Rib	Roasts from this cut are rich in flavor and very tender. A comparatively large muscle known as the "eye" and the rib bones make it easy to identify the prime rib roasts.	Oven roasts
Plate Plate Navel Rib ends	Lean and fat are deposited in alternate layers in plate cuts. These cuts usually contain ends of ribs and sections of breastbone. The presence of the latter is a sure indication that the cut is from the plate. The fat is sweet and well suited to forming a part of boiling meat.	Boned, rolled, sold either fresh or corned Rib ends roasted as "short ribs" Stews Pot roasts Corning Boiling
Fore shank	Bone and gristle, varying amounts of lean.	Soups Stews
Round — rump and shank off	Round or oval in shape with a small round bone and a large proportion of lean meat. Tender, juicy, and well flavored. The "top of the round" is the most tender portion of the steak and can be distinguished from the "bottom round" because	Pot roasts Steaks: Swiss Spanish Rolled

Cut	*Characteristics*	*Methods of Preparation*
	it consists of one large muscle while the "bottom round" is made up of two.	
Rump	Is a somewhat wedge-shaped, solid, juicy piece of meat of good quality.	Pot roasts Steaks Corning Stews
Hind shank	Bony, connective tissue and some meat.	Soups Stews
Loin	Sirloin steaks are oblong in shape and contain sections of the backbone and hip-bone. Is more tender than the round. The porterhouse steak contains a T-shaped bone. The meat of the main portion is of very high quality but the strip end is rather coarse. The club steaks are similar to porterhouse, but they contain no tenderloin. The loin contains the choice cuts of the hind quarter.	Steaks Roasts
Flank	Flank steaks are boneless and there are but two in each carcass. Consists of flat, rectangular muscle weighing 1 to 2½ pounds. Muscle fibers run lengthwise, making it necessary to "score" the steak across the grain.	Stewing Broiling Braising
	VEAL CUTS	
Breast	Meat of good quality	Roasted, stuffed and roasted
Shoulder	Solid meat of good quality	Roasted, boned, stuffed and roasted
Chuck	Meat of good quality	Steaks, roasts
Leg	Solid meat of good quality, very little waste	Roasts, steaks (called cutlets)

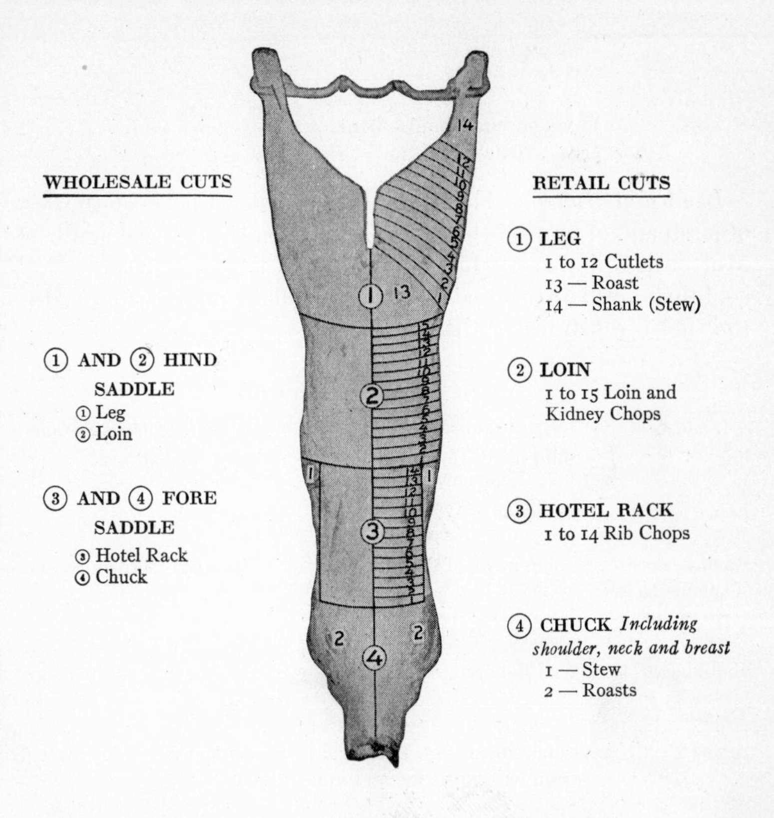

Numerals in circles ○ refer to wholesale cuts. Other numerals refer to retail cuts

YIELDS OF WHOLESALE CUTS AND SUBDIVISIONS

① AND ② HIND SADDLE — 49%		③ AND ④ FORE SADDLE — 51%	
① Legs	40%	③ Hotel Rack	6.5%
② Loin	9%	④ Chuck	44.5%

FIG. 83. VEAL CHART, WHOLESALE AND RETAIL CUTS

Cut	*Characteristics*	*Methods of Preparation*
Loin	Choice meat	Loin chops, roasts
Rib	Bone and fat. Lean meat, excellent quality	Rib chops, roasts
Shanks	Fore and hind shanks, bone, gristle, little meat	Stews, soups

Lamb and Mutton. There is the same contrast between the flesh of lamb and of mutton that there is between that of veal and beef. Mutton is a dull red, while lamb is much lighter in color. Both contain fat well distributed and white and flaky in character. Mutton suet is much firmer than beef suet.

LAMB AND MUTTON CUTS

Cut	*Characteristics*	*Methods of Preparation*
Leg	Solid meat, fine quality	Roasted, boiled
Loin	Choice meat	Chops, roasts
Rack — corresponds to rib chops	Bone, meat of fine quality	Chops, roasts, crown roasts
Shoulder or chuck	Well-flavored, tender meat	Stews, braised, stuffed and roasted
Breast	Bone, meat not so fine in grain as that in leg and loin	Boned and rolled for roast Stews
Flank	Good quality meat	Roast, stews

Pork. Pork is finer grained and lighter in color than the flesh of other animals. It should also be firm to the touch. The fat of pork is softer than that of other animals; it is also more plentiful.

Feet	Bone, skin, fat, not much meat, but this little is delicate	Stewed, boiled, broiled, fried in deep fat, pickled
Hams	Solid meat, little bone	Fresh: steaks and roasts Cured: baked, broiled, boiled
Fat back	Large percentage of fat, very little lean	Salt pork: pan-fried, combined with other foods

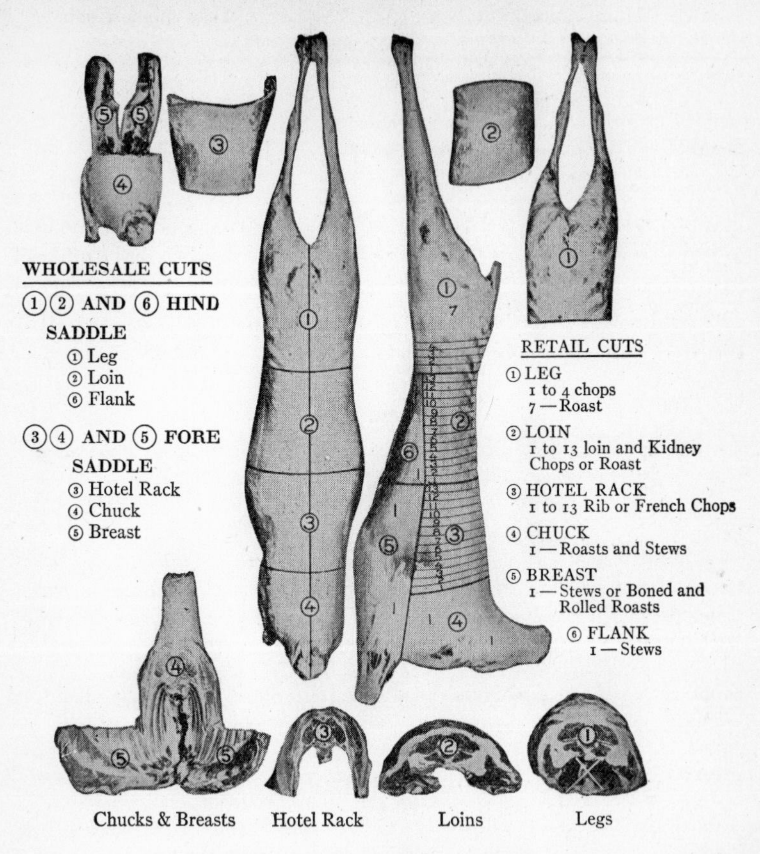

Numerals in circles ⊙ refer to wholesale cuts. Other numerals refer to retail cuts

YIELDS OF WHOLESALE CUTS

Per Cent of Carcass		Subdivisions — Per Cent of Carcass	
① ② & ⑥ Hind Saddle	50.0%	① Legs	33.0%
③ ④ & ⑤ Fore Saddle	50.0%	② & ⑥ Loin and Flank	17.0
		③ Hotel Rack	12.0
		④ Chuck Inc. Neck	23.5
		⑤ Breast Inc. Shank	14.5

FIG. 84. LAMB CHART, WHOLESALE AND RETAIL CUTS

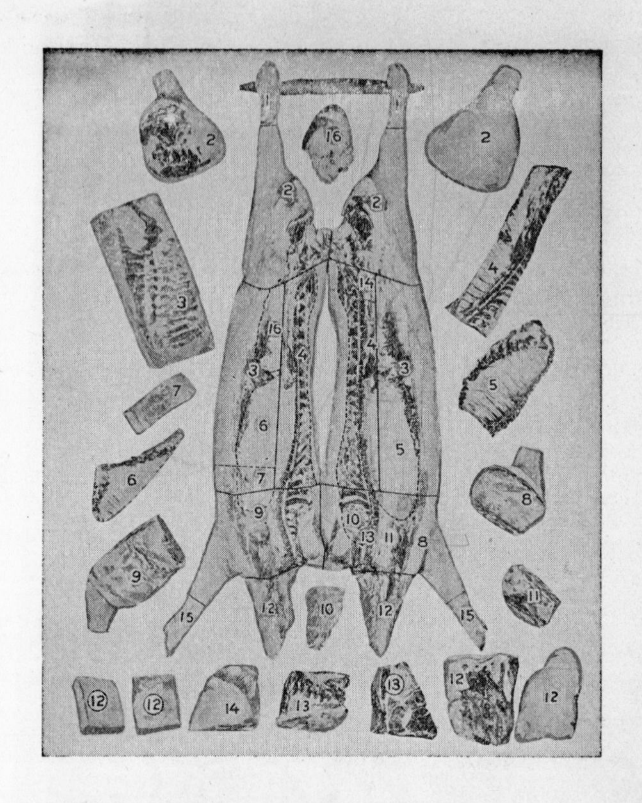

WHOLESALE CUTS — PERCENTAGE OF CARCASS

Cut	%	Cut	%	Cut	%
1-Hind Feet	1.00%	7-Brisket	2.25%	(12)-Jowl Butts (*trimmed*)	2.25%
2-Hams	19.000	8-Picnic	7.50	(13)-Boneless Butt	3.05
3-Clear Bellies	16.50	9-N.Y. Style Shoulder	16.00	13-Boston Butt	5.20
4-Pork Loins	12.75	10-Neck Bones	.35	14-Loin Butt	4.00
5-Spare Ribs(*f.s.*)	2.50	11-Picnic Butt	3.02	15-Fore Feet	.92
6-Spare Ribs(*h.s.*)	1.50	12-Jowl Butts(*untrimmed*)	3.75	16-Leaf Fat	3.52

FIG. 85. PORK CHART, WHOLESALE AND RETAIL CUTS

Cut	*Characteristics*	*Methods of Preparation*
Clear bellies	Fat and lean.	Bacon: broiled or pan-fried
Loins	Leading fresh pork cuts. Contain backbone, ribs, and tenderloin. Small amount of fat on outside. Tender, lean meat.	Roasts, chops
Picnic shoulder (formerly called California hams)	Large percentage of lean meat. Well flavored. Sold fresh or smoked.	Fresh: roasted Smoked: cooked like ham
Butts — cut from top of shoulder and from the jowl	Boston butts — ends or top pieces cut from heavy shoulders for making picnic ham. Include end of shoulder blade. Picnic butts — surplus fat and skin are removed and the shank cut off close to the breast.	Steaks, roasts
	Lean butts — consist of lean, boneless portion of Boston butts between blade bone and neck bone.	Fresh: roast Sweet: pickled and smoked like ham
	Dry salt butts — made from jowl, edges trimmed smooth and the piece flattened out.	Cured
Spare ribs	Lean and fat. Good flavor.	Baked or boiled
Tenderloin	Choice, lean, tender, boneless. Sold as part of loin roast or separately.	Broiled, pan-fried, stuffed and baked
Fat	From one tenth to one third of the hog carcass is made into lard.	Frying, shortening

General Methods and Principles of Meat Cookery

Tender Cuts of Meat. Tender cuts of meat are taken from the parts of the animal where the muscles are little used. All cuts of lamb and pork are tender; also the cuts from the bone and rib of beef. The tenderloin is the tenderest part of an animal. It is often removed whole and sold as a fillet, or as fillet steaks. The

FIG. 86. BROILED STEAK, BAKED POTATOES, AND FRENCH FRIED ONION RINGS

tender cuts of meat are more juicy and contain less connective tissue than the tougher cuts and therefore require less cooking. Although more desirable, they are more expensive. Tender cuts are required for broiling, pan-broiling, or roasting. Tender meats can be made tough and dry by poor cooking.

The best methods of cooking tender cuts are roasting, broiling, or pan-broiling. The U.S. Bureau of Human Nutrition and Home Economics recommends constant temperature roasting. In this method the meat is cooked at a constant temperature of 275 to 375 degrees F. in a shallow uncovered pan. Advantages are that a full flavor is developed and moisture is retained, so that the cooked meat is juicy and well flavored. It used to be considered that first searing the meat surface retained the moisture, but this has been found to be untrue. The time of cooking is influenced by the weight of meat, the degree of cooking desired (pork should always be cooked thoroughly and there is some evidence that it is safer to cook all meat thoroughly), and the constant temperature at which it is cooked. No salt is added until late in the cooking, because salt prevents browning and causes moisture to be extracted from the meat.

See recipes in the Cook Book for roasting, broiling, and pan-broiling, pages 461–465.

Cooking of Less Tender Cuts. Less tender cuts include from beef the chuck, brisket plate, round, and flank. Rump may be tender or tough depending on the animal. The best methods to use for these cuts

FIG. 87. BEEF MAY BE BOTH INEXPENSIVE AND SAVORY

FIG. 88.
I. BAKED HAM SLICE WITH PINEAPPLE
II. BOILED HAM

are stewing or braising. In each method the meat may first be seared to develop surface flavor and then cooked by moist heat for a long time (simmered, steamed) or it may be cooked with moist heat in the pressure cooker for a short time. Devices to soften the meat tissue may be used, such as first cutting it in small pieces, pounding or chopping it, or by adding acid in the form of tomato juice or vinegar. The length of time of cooking depends on the weight of the meat and the use of softening devices.

Cooking Very Tough Portions and Bones for Soup. Very tough cuts for soups and stews should be so cooked as to get flavor from the meat. For stews, the small pieces may first be dipped in a little flour and then seared to develop flavor and add thickening to the stew; for soups the meat may be partially seared and then cut into small pieces, and with bones added cooked at a low temperature (simmered) for a long time.

For recipes and time and temperature of meat cookery, see pages 461–475.

Meat Specialties. Delicacies to food connoisseurs or those who like different dishes are certain gland and muscle parts not so well known as the regular steak-chop-and-roast cuts. The best known gland meats are kidneys, liver, and sweetbreads, and other specialties that are economical and delicious, when properly cooked, are brains, tripe, heart. Calf liver is more expensive than lamb or beef liver. Liver is rich in iron and copper; kidneys in Vitamins A, B, C, and G, as well as iron and copper, brains have an excellent supply of Vitamin C and a good supply of Vitamin B_1. All these foods are favorites in other countries and are also coming into favor rapidly in the United States.

FIG. 89. MIXED GRILL — POTATOES, LIVER, SAUSAGE, LAMB CHOP, BROILED TOMATOES

How would you complete the menu for this dinner?

Select liver that is bright-colored and fairly firm; beef kidneys that are a bright brownish-red in color, lamb kidneys tending toward purple, and calf kidney slightly lighter than beef; brains that are fairly firm.

Gravies and Sauces. Some of the choicest flavor of the meat cooks out of it. This is usually conserved in sauces or gravies, which are necessary with the tougher cuts of meat. Why?

Meat Preservation by Canning. See Chapter 33.

Ways of Reducing the Expenditures for Meat

In most families, meat expenses need to be kept down, because meat is our most expensive food. These expenses should be kept to one fourth of the total spent on food, or if possible to one fifth.

1. Purchase meat in such a way as to take advantage of differences in price, owing to local conditions, but avoid buying meat in an unsanitary market just because it is cheap.
2. Use less expensive cuts, including glands and other specialties.
3. Avoid a meat containing a high proportion of fat, bone, and gristle, as they are largely waste. Buy cuts, such as round steak, rump, and flank steak, that have much lean meat and little waste.

Learn to estimate the cost per pound of meat that is actually eaten, as well as the price at which it is purchased.

4. Ask for trimmings from the meat you purchase and use them for flavoring soups and other dishes.

5. Serve combination dishes called meat extenders. These consist of meat mixed with other food. There is a long list of them, including meat pies, stews, hash, meat soups, and meat with such foods as rice, potatoes, grits, or macaroni.

6. Serve meat only once a day or, if necessary, only two or three times a week.

CLASS PROBLEMS

1. Find out the laws governing the handling of meat in your state. Find out whether your state and county maintain inspection of establishments handling meat.

2. If possible visit two types of cold storage plants for meats.
   a. A commercial packing-house cold storage plant.
   b. A locker freezing plant where farm people store meat produced on the farm.

3. Look up the Federal Meat Inspection Act (Sherman, *Food Products*, Chapter VI, and Appendix B). Find out what the meat inspection regulations are in your community.

4. In preparation for a meat-cutting demonstration, study the chart showing the cuts of meat. If possible, arrange to have a meat-cutting demonstration in the laboratory at school. A butcher may come to class and cut a side of beef that is to be used in the cafeteria. If this cannot be arranged, go to a market for a demonstration.

5. Visit markets. Note sanitary conditions. Learn to distinguish pork, lamb, mutton, veal, and the various cuts of each.

6. Plan dinner menus for one week, varying the kind of meat.

7. Plan dinner menus for one week, using beef, but varying the method of cooking.

8. Prepare tender cuts of meat.

9. Prepare meat stock and clear soups. (See page 424.)

10. Prepare tougher cuts of meat in various ways. (See page 471 in recipes.)

Demonstrate the use of such utensils and devices as:

Thrift or deep-well cooker
Dutch oven
Casserole

11. Demonstrate such methods of making meat tender as:

Stewing
Using tomato juice — Spanish steak, page 471
Pounding — Swiss steak, page 471
Grinding — Hamburg steak, page 465

12. Prepare meat in combination with other foods in dishes known as meat extenders.

Meat and vegetable stews, page 472
Meat and dumplings, page 474
Liver and onions, page 474
Liver and bacon, page 474
Meat pie, page 474
Meat turnovers, page 412

13. Prepare various sauces or gravies, pages 436–439, with the dish each should accompany.

Brown gravy
Mint sauce
Tomato gravy
Milk gravy
Maître d'hôtel butter
Mushroom sauce

HOME PROBLEMS

1. Test your knowledge and develop a discriminating judgment of meats by purchasing the meat for your family for a month.
2. Plan the meat for your family meals for one week. Try to satisfy them with meat in the menu only once each day.
3. Keep accounts or study the accounts of food expenditure in your household for two weeks. What per cent of the expenditure is for meat, for milk, for fruits, for vegetables?

   Is the expenditure for meats desirable? Justify your statement, making suggestions for improvement if you deem improvement necessary. Try to reduce your meat bill.
4. Prepare some of the less tender cuts of meat at home.

REFERENCES

Accepted Foods and Their Nutritional Significance. American Medical Association. Section VII.

Heseltine, Marjorie, and Dow, Ula M. *The Basic Cook Book.* Houghton Mifflin Company.

Justin, Margaret M., Rust, Lucile O., and Vail, Gladys E. *Foods.* Houghton Mifflin Company.

Lanman, Faith R., McKay, Hughina, Zuill, Frances. *The Family's Food.* J. B. Lippincott Company. Chapter X.

Rose, Mary Swartz. *Feeding the Family.* The Macmillan Company. References on place of meat in the diet.

Rose, Mary Swartz. *Foundations of Nutrition.* The Macmillan Company.

Sherman, Henry C. *Food Products.* The Macmillan Company. Chapter VI and Appendix B.

Stanley, L., and Cline, J. A. *Foods, Their Selection and Preparation.* Ginn and Company. Chapter XIII.

Government Bulletins. United States Department of Agriculture. Available from the Superintendent of Documents, Government Printing Office, Washington, D.C.:

Beef Grading and Stamping Service. Leaflet 67.

Care of Food in the Home. Farmers' Bulletin 1374.

Commercial Cuts of Meat. Circular 300.

Lamb and Mutton on the Farm. Farmers' Bulletin 1807.

Market Classes and Grades of Dressed Beef. Farmers' Bulletin 1246.

Meat Dishes at Low Cost. Miscellaneous Publication Number 216.

U.S. Graded and Stamped Meat. Leaflet Number 122.

Bureau of Human Nutrition and Home Economics, Department Leaflets:

17 *Cooking Beef According to the Cut.*
28 *Lamb As You Like It.*
45 *Pork in Preferred Ways.*
48 *Reindeer Recipes.*
66 *Rabbit Recipes.*
81 *Cooking Cured Pork.*
74 *Boning Lamb.*

CHAPTER TWENTY-FIVE

❧ Poultry and Fish

Cook Book References

Poultry	*Page* 475
Fish	*Page* 481

Food Value

Nutritive Value of Foods	*Table* VI, *Appendix*
Food Value in Shares	*Table* VIII, *Appendix*
Minerals and Vitamins	*Tables* IX *and* X, *Appendix*

Poultry

Poultry includes chicken, turkey, duck, goose, pigeon, squab, and wild birds. Chicken is the most commonly used.

In larger cities poultry is handled through cold storage facilities, but in smaller localities it is often purchased alive, or freshly killed and dressed, from local markets.

Poultry does not come under the Federal Meat Inspection Act, but the Department of Agriculture will inspect poultry for dealers who request it. Such inspection is an aid to the consumer. The government has made a thorough study of the handling of poultry and advises that if it is killed before shipping, the feathers be removed, but that it be shipped without further dressing because it remains in better condition when not drawn (removal of the entrails) before shipping.

Chickens are sold according to their age as broilers, as roasting chickens, as fryers, and as fowls, hens, or capons. A broiler is a very young chicken, usually about three months old. A fryer is a larger chicken, three to six months old, but young enough to be tender. Fully grown chickens are usually called fowls, capons, and hens. Hens are the older birds and are not tender.

Selection of Live Poultry. The following should be sought in selecting a live bird:

Heavy weight for size	Bright red comb
Feathers in good condition	Breastbone well covered with flesh

Selection of Dressed Poultry:

1. *Age.* Young birds have soft, smooth, yellow feet, a flexible breastbone; very little fat under the skin or on the entrails and vital organs; many pin feathers, but few hairs. Older birds have rough feet; hard or tough breastbone; a good deal of fat under the skin and about the entrails and vital organs; few pin feathers, and long hairs.

2. *Freshness.* The flesh of fresh unfrozen poultry should be firm, but neither stiff nor flabby. It should give to the touch. The skin should be whole and clear in color. Frozen poultry is, of course, hard like ice.

3. *Waste.* The edible meat of poultry represents about 55 to 66 per cent of its dressed weight, when dressed weight is taken to mean that the bird is plucked and bled, but not drawn. This means that we can count on about 50 to 60 per cent of live weight to be edible meat. Therefore, poultry is more expensive per pound of edible meat than it seems from the purchase price per pound. It is often considered the most expensive of the flesh foods in city marketing. However, poultry is a meat which may be raised at home in rural or small-town areas, and under these circumstances is not expensive. Good roads and curb markets also make country produce more accessible and more reasonable for the city dweller in many areas.

WEIGHTS OF DRESSED POULTRY

Broilers	1 to 2 pounds
Fryers	2½ to 3½ pounds
Baking chickens or roasters	3½ to 5 pounds
Capons	6 to 9 pounds
Duckling	3 to 4 pounds
Turkey	8 to 20 pounds (12 to 14 pounds a good size)

Frozen poultry should be marketed while still frozen and thawed just before cooking. Any frozen food material, especially meat and fish, spoils rapidly when thawed. See page 566 for instructions about thawing poultry. Cook poultry immediately after it has thawed. Poultry may be thawed as part of the cooking process. It takes longer, of course, to cook unthawed poultry.

Composition and Food Value of Poultry. In composition and food value, poultry does not differ in any important respect from other meat. It is chiefly a protein food and the protein is complete. The fuel value varies according to the amount of fat present.

Poultry, like meat, is lacking in calcium, but contains a good amount of iron and phosphorus. Chicken is an excellent source of Vitamin B_1 and a fair source of niacin.

The light meat is composed of more tender fibers than beef and pork, and contains less fat than the darker meat. For these reasons it is preferred for persons with weak digestion.

Poultry is a fairly good source of iron and phosphorus. In the diet, poultry is interchangeable with other meat.

The Dressing of Poultry. Dressing poultry involves three distinct processes — killing, picking, and drawing.

The best way to kill a chicken is by cutting the throat and thrusting a sharp knife through the roof of the mouth and out through the top of the head. This destroys the part of the brain controlling the muscles that hold the feathers, and thus, by releasing the feathers, renders the bird easy to pick.

See directions on page 475 for picking, drawing, and trussing poultry.

Ways of Cooking. Because flavor depends on extractives, the fundamental principles of cooking poultry are the same as those for cooking meat. For tough chickens long, slow cooking is required and methods and utensils similar to those used for tough cuts of meat are used. Young chicken is usually broiled, fricasseed, smothered, or fried. Older chickens are baked, roasted; fowl is boiled for salad or croquettes, stewed with dumplings, or stewed for chicken pie.

Either the constant temperature method or the searing method may be used for baking poultry. The constant temperature may be between 300° and 350° F.; by the searing method the poultry is baked at 400° F. for 20 minutes, then the temperature is lowered to 275° F. and the baking continued. Many factors, such as the size, age, sex, and proportion of fat, influence the length of the cooking period. In baking, the

FIG. 90. FRIED CHICKEN

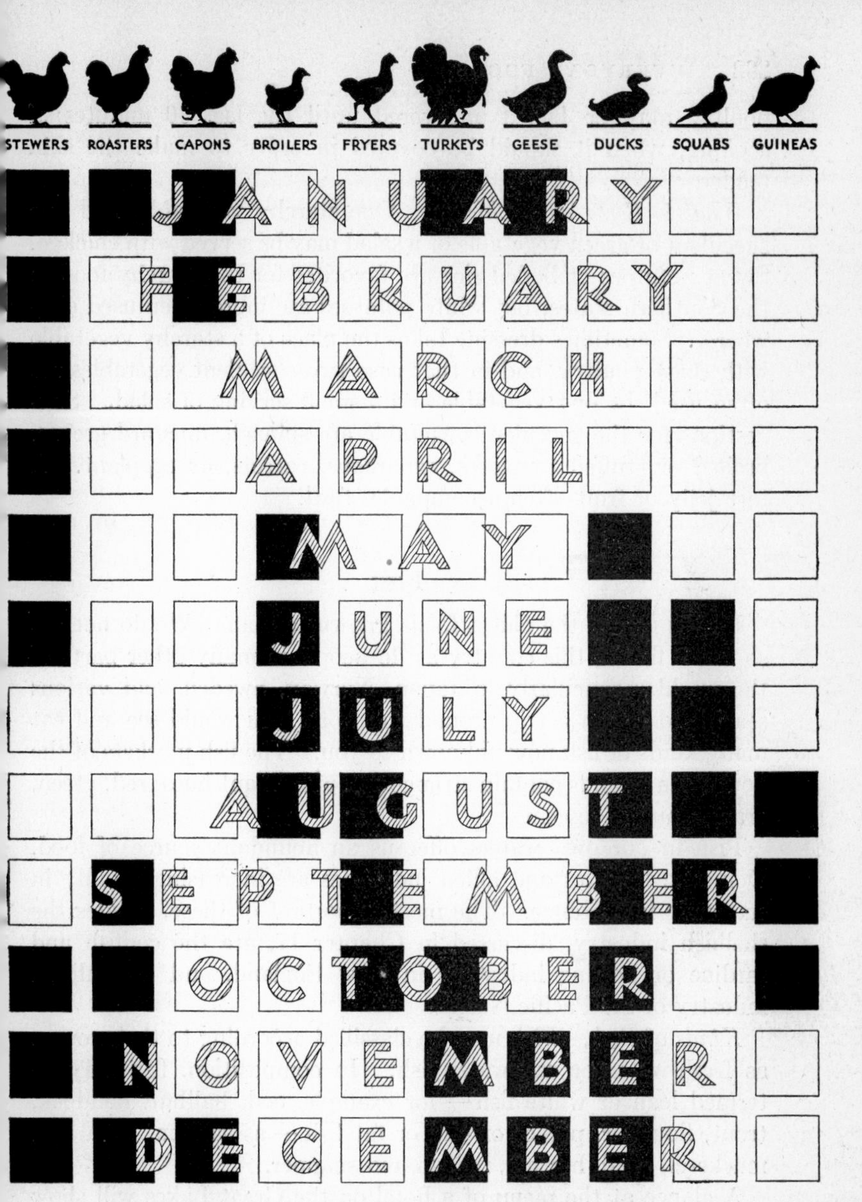

FIG. 91. FRESH POULTRY CALENDAR

The black squares indicate the months in which the supply of the given poultry is greatest and consequently the price may be expected to be lowest

poultry may be baked uncovered until the last 30 minutes of cooking, when it should be covered in order to make the skin tender.

What to Serve with Chicken. One starchy vegetable, and one succulent or green vegetable or a salad may be served with chicken. Sweet potatoes or boiled rice are favorites for the starchy food in the Southern states, but white potatoes are more often used elsewhere. Sometimes dressing takes the place of a starchy vegetable with roast poultry, and in that case two succulent vegetables are often used, or one vegetable and a small serving of salad. Suggestions for the succulent vegetable are spinach, mustard greens, broiled or stuffed tomatoes, asparagus, carrots, or eggplant. A tart jelly or fruit often accompanies fowl.

Fish

Fish is one of the oldest foods known to man. We do not eat so much fish in this country as do people in many other parts of the world, particularly in Japan, Norway, Sweden, and various sea islands. On a trip around the world you would see and eat many kinds of fish now unknown to you. The fish markets of the South Sea Islands contain strange fish of brilliant hues: red, green, orange, and iridescent.

Fish in our own waters offer us an abundant source of food. Domestic fisheries and allied industries are increasing rapidly in economic importance. The most important of these, besides the shellfish industry, discussed in Chapter 17, are the codfish and sardine or herring industries in New England, and the salmon industry of the Pacific Northwest.

Kinds of Fish. Fish may be classified according to their source as fresh-water or salt-water fish. In composition, fish may be termed lean or white fish — for example, cod, halibut, haddock, trout, flounder, perch; or oily or fat fish — as salmon, tuna fish, mackerel, shad, herring, redfish, red snapper.

A glance at the menu of a hotel on the Great Lakes will show you the usual fresh-water fish and ways of serving them. A dinner menu card from a seashore hotel will give the favorite kinds of salt-water fish and ways of serving them. You will notice on each menu some fish that is not found in the region.

FISH ON DINNER MENU

(A hotel on the Great Lakes)

Lake Erie Whitefish
Broiled Lake Trout, Anchovy Butter, Spinach
Halibut, Florentine or Fried, Beet Salad
Planked Lake Trout
Jumbo Frog Legs Sauté with Mushrooms, Bacon à L'Espagnole
Soft Shell Crab, Fried or Sautéed, Cole Slaw
Half Lobster, Julienne Potatoes
Scallops Fried

FISH ON DINNER MENU

(A hotel on the Gulf of Mexico)

Baked Fillet of Red Snapper
Grilled Gulf Trout Maître d'hôtel, Potatoes
Select Oysters Fried in Bread Crumbs
Baked Red Snapper à la Portuguese Potatoes Maître d'hôtel
Shrimps Creole with Rice
Broiled Spanish Mackerel
Tenderloin of Trout, Tartar Sauce
Broiled Red Fish Maître d'hôtel
Boiled Finnan Haddie with Potatoes Maître d'hôtel
Crab Meat au Gratin
Salt Mackerel, Broiled or Boiled

Composition and Fuel Value of Fish. See Tables VI, IX, and X in Appendix.

Place of Fish in the Diet. Fish like meat varies in composition. Some varieties have much more fat than others and are consequently higher in fuel value. The chief nutrient in fish is protein. The protein of fish is complete and is therefore interchangeable with meat in the diet. About one fifth of the edible portion of fish is protein. Fish contains less iron than meat. Like meat and poultry, fish, as a group, is deficient in calcium and vitamins. Salmon and oysters contain Vitamins A and D. Sardines and codfish are good sources of Vitamin B_1. Some salt-water fish contain iodine, a substance quite rare in foods, but necessary in the diet. Lean fish, like the white meat of chicken, is more quickly digested than beef; but fat fish, such as salmon, is digested about as readily as pork.

In some localities fish is an economical food, but its price varies with the distance from the source of supply and with the season. There is every reason to believe that fish will increase in importance as a food for the family table. Transportation facilities make it practicable to market fish in good condition at great distances from the source of supply.

Buying and Caring for Fish. Freshness is the all-important quality in selecting fish. Fish deteriorates rapidly, and is at its best with regard to flavor when just fresh from the water. It must be shipped and marketed on ice or in a frozen condition. When frozen, it should not be thawed until ready for cooking. The ice that forms in the tissues breaks down the connective tissue, thus allowing rapid spoilage after thawing. Frozen fish may be thawed in cold water.

Fresh fish is recognized primarily by its firm and rather rigid flesh. A finger pressed on the flesh should not leave a dent. Other characteristics are clean, red gills, bright eyes, no disagreeable odor, and scales that tend to cling to the skin but remove easily. Wise purchasers look for the less expensive fish, and remember that canned fish is equal in food value to fresh fish of the same variety.

When fresh fish reaches the house, it should be dressed, if this is not already done, and chilled immediately. Because of its strong odor, it should be placed preferably in a closed container, but both the fish and container should be thoroughly chilled. Otherwise, wrap fish in wax or parchment paper before placing in the coldest part of the refrigerator. If fish is to be kept for even a day or two, it should be frozen.

Buying Canned Salmon. The price of canned salmon is no indication of its food value. Many people seem willing to pay more for salmon that is rich in flavor, firm in flesh, and deep in color, but there is little difference in food value. Varieties of canned salmon in order of their descending price are: Chinook, red, coho, pink, and chum. Before purchasing, read the labels and compare the net weights with prices of different grades.

Methods of Cooking Fish. Cooking improves the flavor and appearance of fish. It requires less cooking than meat because it has less connective tissue. If overcooked, it will fall to pieces.

Ways of Preparing Fish for Dinner. Fish may be cooked in many ways of which the most important are:

Baked	Fried	Steamed
Broiled or grilled	Planked	Boiled

When boiled, fish loses both flavor and form, and therefore other methods of cooking are to be preferred except when the fish is being prepared for salad, for scalloped dishes, or chowder.

Planked fish is served on the plank on which it is cooked.

What to Serve with Fish. Fish is rarely served without lemon or some sauce. These additions give the dish an attractive appearance and offer a pleasing contrast to the fish flavor. The vegetable should be carefully chosen, because not all vegetable flavors combine well with fish.

1. Sauces for fish. (See recipes.)

Egg, p. 438	Maître d'hôtel, p. 439	Cucumber, p. 439
Tartar, p. 489	Drawn butter, p. 439	Mock Hollandaise, p. 438
	Tomato, p. 438	

2. Vegetables that are preferred with fish.

Potatoes, prepared in various ways	Tomatoes	Green salads
	Carrots	Cucumbers
Asparagus	Celery, cooked or uncooked	Radishes

3. A bread-crumb dressing is served with baked fish.

4. Garnishes.

Lemon sliced and dipped in chopped parsley or paprika

Parsley	Cucumbers	Radishes
Watercress	Pickles	Tomato

Crisp bread offers a pleasing contrast to the soft texture of fish. Hard rolls or bread sticks may be served with it. In the South crisp corn sticks or corn muffins are usually served with fish.

CLASS PROBLEMS

1. Visit the local market to see what poultry and what fish are available in your community and the conditions under which these foods are sold.

2. Plan the main course of dinner menus that will be suitable for January, March, July, September, November, and December containing poultry that you think will be reasonable in price at that time; containing poultry that might be higher in price.

3. Plan the main course of dinner menus as in Problem 1, but use fresh-water fish, and salt-water fish.

4. Find local prices for poultry at different seasons and estimate roughly the cost of edible meat by assuming that it will be about 50 per cent of live weight and 58 per cent of dressed weight.

5. Send to the Production and Marketing Administration, United States Department of Agriculture, Washington, D.C., for description of grades of dressed poultry and, in a visit to market, look at graded poultry if it is sold there and if not, see if you can recognize characteristics of different grades.

6. As a main course for dinner, prepare combinations of poultry or fish with suitable vegetables and breadstuffs. Serve attractively, paying special attention to sauces with the fish.

HOME PROBLEMS

1. Dress a chicken for baking, one for frying, and one for broiling.
2. If the opportunity presents itself in your household, dress a duck, a squab, a turkey, or other birds.
3. Prepare a baked chicken for Sunday dinner.
4. Purchase chicken and fish for your family several times. Find out the price per pound of each, also cost per serving.
5. Plan and prepare three dinners with chicken as the meat.
6. Plan and prepare a dinner with baked fish as the meat.
7. Prepare fish for your family — if they eat fish — in two other ways. Include the preparation of the sauce to serve with the fish.
8. Prepare corn sticks or crisp bread sticks for a fish dinner.

REFERENCES

Heseltine, Marjorie, and Dow, Ula M. *The Basic Cook Book.* Houghton Mifflin Company.

Lanman, Faith R., McKay, Hughina, Zuill, Frances. *The Family's Food.* J. B. Lippincott Company. Chapter X.

Rose, Mary Swartz. *Foundations of Nutrition.* The Macmillan Company.

Sherman, Henry C. *Food Products.* The Macmillan Company. Chapter VII.

Stanley, Louise, and Cline, J. A. *Foods, Their Selection, and Preparation.* Ginn and Company. Chapter XV.

The Story of Salmon. Carlisle Packing Company, Seattle.

Ward, Artemas. *Encyclopedia of Foods.* Artemas Ward, New York. Description of many varieties of fish; special articles on salmon.

Circulars from the United States Department of Commerce, Bureau of Fisheries, on caviar, salmon, haddock, the bowfin, the sable fish, sardine, and other fish.

Marketing Poultry. Farmers' Bulletin 1377.

Poultry Cookery. United States Department of Agriculture.

CHAPTER TWENTY-SIX

❧ Vegetables and Fruits for Dinner

Cook Book References

Vegetable Cookery	*Page* 425
Vegetable Salads	*Page* 485
Cooked Fruits	*Page* 390
Fruit Salads	*Page* 486

Food Value

Nutritive Value of Foods	*Table* VI, *Appendix*
Food Value in Shares	*Table* VIII, *Appendix*
Vitamins in Foods	*Table* IX, *Appendix*
Minerals in Foods	*Table* X, *Appendix*

VEGETABLES, AND TO A LIMITED degree, fruits are used as the accompaniment for meat or a meat substitute in the main course of the dinner menu. Vegetables and fruits are also used in salads, but vegetables are preferred to fruits for dinner salads.

The following menus suggest what vegetables are served for dinner.

JUNE DINNER MENU FROM AN OHIO HOTEL

Vegetables

Green Peas
Asparagus
Buttered Beets
New String Beans
Buttered Carrots
Fresh Lima Beans
Corn on the Cob
Spinach
Potatoes: Mashed, Creamed, au Gratin, Baked, French Fried, New Potatoes in Cream

FEBRUARY DINNER MENU FROM A TEXAS HOTEL

Vegetables

Brussels Sprouts
Cauliflower in Cream
Buttered Beets
Buttered Young Carrots
Boiled Onions in Cream
Fried Eggplant
Fresh Peas
Asparagus Tips, Drawn Butter
French Artichokes, Drawn Butter
Green Stringless Beans
Fresh Spinach
Stewed Sugar Corn
White Turnips, Butter Sauce

Potatoes

Sweet Potatoes, Baked, Fried, Candied
White Potatoes, Baked, O'Brien, au Gratin, Hashed Brown, Julienne, Lyonnaise,

Rice

Steamed, Boiled, au Gratin, Spanish, Creole

Pleasing Vegetable Combinations at Dinner. The à la carte menus give a general idea of what vegetables are appropriate for dinner, but offer no suggestion as to good combinations. What vegetables are properly served with the various dinner meats? The following are suggested as some of the tried and true combinations.

Broiled Steak	*Roast Beef*	*Grilled Lamb Chops*
Mushrooms	Scalloped potatoes	Peas
Baked potato	Broiled tomato	Browned potatoes
Combination salad (lettuce and tomato)	Slaw, Spanish dressing	Watercress, French dressing

Baked fish	*Roast Pork*	*Baked Chicken*
French fried potatoes	Candied sweet potato	Rice
Spinach	Cinnamon apples	Cauliflower
Cucumber salad, French dressing	Mexican slaw	Head lettuce, French dressing

From these combinations it may readily be seen that the type of meat used for the dinner menu in some measure determines what specific vegetables are to be used. A starchy vegetable, a succulent vegetable, and a green salad represent the general choice in each of these menus. It is not necessary to have both the second vegetable and the salad.

Comparison of Vegetables for Luncheon and Dinner. At dinner the number of courses is greater than at luncheon, and because of the number of dishes each dish should be simply prepared. For luncheon the problem is to make the vegetable dishes sufficiently rich to serve as the main dish. For dinner the problem is so to choose and prepare the vegetables as accompaniments to meat, the main dish, that they will add to the attractiveness of the meat. A creamed or scalloped vegetable is useful at dinner if the meat is meager in quantity, if a dry or cold meat is served, or if there is difficulty in using the milk allowance.

Important Sources of Vitamins and Minerals

Potatoes

White Potatoes. The white potato, although a native of South America, is often called the Irish potato because it is a staple article of diet in Ireland. It is the most widely used vegetable in our country. Many families use potatoes daily.

The potato owes its popularity to various factors: (1) it is a mildly flavored food that blends with almost all other foods; (2) in texture it is a pleasing contrast to the solid form of meat and to the softness of other cooked vegetables or the succulence of salad plants; (3) potatoes are easily cooked and may be served in a variety of ways; (4) they are easily digested; (5) they are "filling" and inexpensive.

Composition and Food Value of White Potatoes. Potatoes are an excellent and cheap source of fuel due to the carbohydrate, chiefly starch, which they contain. In this respect they may be compared with grain products and bread. They contain only a small amount of protein, but what they have is a valuable kind.

Potatoes are rich in a variety of minerals. Potassium is the most abundant mineral, but this is not usually lacking in any mixed diet that contains one fruit and one vegetable. White potatoes are a good source of iron, and are important in this respect because they are eaten in such quantities. Phosphorus in considerable amount is also found in this vegetable.

Potatoes may be considered a good source of Vitamins B_1 and C. There is not so high a Vitamin C content as in oranges, tomatoes, raw cabbage, or onions; nevertheless, because it is eaten in such quantities, the potato may be considered an important source of this vitamin.

New potatoes are waxy, due perhaps to the presence of some sugar and more protein than the old ones contain.

Sweet Potatoes, in some respects, are similar in food value to white potatoes. They are good sources of Vitamins B_1 and C. As might be supposed from their yellow color, sweet potatoes are rich in Vitamin A. Sweet potatoes contain sugar and are somewhat higher in fuel value than are white potatoes. Sweet potatoes are not so good a source of iron as are white potatoes.

Suggested Ways of Preparing Potatoes. Potatoes are cooked (1) to soften the cellulose; (2) to cook the starch; (3) to develop the flavor.

In a restricted diet it is advisable to cook potatoes in the skin in order to avoid loss of valuable minerals. This is not important in a mixed diet containing fresh fruits and raw vegetables. Why?

Some of the well-liked ways of serving white potatoes are:

Baked	Riced with butter	French fried
Boiled	Hash browned	Shoestring
Creamed	Julienne	Stuffed
Mashed	Chips	O'Brien
Scalloped	Soufflé	au gratin

Sweet potatoes are served more frequently with pork, fowl, and game than with beef. Some of the well-liked ways of serving sweet potatoes are:

Baked	Mashed and baked with nuts or marshmallows	Sautéed
Glazed		Soufflé
Candied		

Rice

Use of Rice. Rice is frequently served instead of potatoes as the starchy vegetable for dinner. It is cheap, nutritious, easily digested, blends well with other foods, and is easily cooked.

Only one starchy vegetable should be served at dinner. If rice is used it should be as a substitute for potatoes, not in addition to them. The same is true of macaroni, hominy, grits, and even of dried peas and beans. Why? In the Orient rice is the chief staple article of diet, and in the food supply of the world it is a much more important article than wheat or potatoes.

The rice most used by Americans is white or polished rice. It consists of the endosperm only and is chiefly starch and protein with only a trace of fat and minerals. Brown rice is the whole grain, and is therefore more nutritious. It contains minerals, fat, and a considerable amount of Vitamins B_1 and G. The market demand for brown rice is increasing. Brown rice requires a longer cooking period because of its tough outer coat.

Rice may be substituted for potatoes in a mixed diet, but potatoes are preferable in a restricted diet. Why?

Suggestions for Cooking Rice. Like other cereals, rice is cooked in boiling salted water. Care must be taken not to overcook it. When thoroughly done the grains should stand apart. To accomplish this result three things are necessary: (1) the rice used should be head rice (whole grains); (2) it should be cooked rapidly;

(3) when thoroughly cooked it should be drained in a colander and allowed to stand a few minutes in this utensil, covered with a folded cloth.

FIG. 92. BOWL SALAD OF VEGETABLES

Rice is cooked with other foods as in the following combinations: soups, or broths; stuffed tomatoes or peppers, with meat; curried rice, Spanish rice, and creole rice.

Cooked Fruit in the Dinner Menu. Some cooked fruits that are often served with the meat and vegetable course instead of a second vegetable are: baked bananas, apple sauce, spiced apples or pears, pineapple sautéed, fruit fritters, and cranberries. These fruits are often served with pork or with poultry:

Turkey and Cranberries
Pork Roast and Apple Sauce or Spiced Apple
Baked Ham and Pineapple Slices (sautéed)
Roast Chicken and Baked Bananas or Pears

Fruits in the form of jams, jellies, preserves, or pickles appear in the dinner menu as accompaniments to any meat.

OTHER VEGETABLES OR FRUITS IN THE DINNER MENU

Dinner Salads. Light salads are appropriate for dinner. A salad green, or a combination salad of lettuce with cucumbers or tomatoes, is good. Lettuce, romaine, cabbage, Chinese cabbage, watercress, endive, and celery are some of the vegetables favored for raw vegetable salads at dinner. The dressing should not be rich. French dressing is preferred.

A light, acid fruit salad, such as grapefruit salad with a light dressing, is also served at dinner. If the salad is served as a separate course, crisp crackers may be served with it. Gelatin salads, such as tomato aspic, are acceptable in the dinner menu.

Nutritive Values of Vegetables and Fruits. The nutritive value of vegetables and their importance in the diet is discussed in Chapter 16. This chapter should be reviewed in connection with the study of vegetables for dinner. For nutritive value of fruits see Chapter 4. Vegetables and fruits in the diet are all improtant for their valuable mineral salts, for their vitamins, and for their cellulose.

Cutting and slicing avocado

Peeling orange and grapefruit

Slices of orange and sections of grapefruit

Finished salad

FIG. 93. PREPARATION OF GRAPEFRUIT AND AVOCADO SALAD

SUMMARY OF VEGETABLES AS IMPORTANT SOURCES OF VITAMINS [1]

Vitamin A	*Vitamin B_1*	*Vitamin C*	*Vitamin G*
Artichokes, globe**	Beans, wax, green and Limas	Artichokes, globe**	Beans, Lima*
Asparagus, green**	Beets	Asparagus**	Beets*
Beans, green	Cabbage	Broccoli	Beet Tops**
Beet greens	Carrots	Brussels sprouts	Cabbage*
Broccoli	Collards	Cabbage	Carrots*
Brussels sprouts**	Cress, garden	Cauliflower	Cauliflower*
Cabbage, green	Broccoli*	Collards	Collards*
Carrots	Brussels sprouts	Cucumbers**	Kale**
Chard	Eggplant*	Dandelion greens	Lettuce*
Collards	Kale	Endive**	Mustard greens**
Dandelion greens	Kohlrabi	Kale	Peas*
Dock	Leeks	Kohlrabi	Spinach*
Escarole	Lettuce	Leeks**	Turnip greens**
Kale	Mushrooms	Mustard greens	Watercress*
Lettuce, green	Onions	Parsnips**	
Mustard greens	Parsnips	Peas, green	
Okra**	Peas	Peppers, sweet	
Peas, green	Potatoes*	Potatoes**	
Peppers, sweet	Spinach	Onions**	
Spinach	Tomatoes	Radishes	
Squash, yellow	Turnips	Rhubarb**	
Sweet potatoes	Turnip greens	Rutabagas	
Tomatoes, red and yellow	Water cress	Spinach	
Turnip greens		Sweet potatoes**	
Watercress		Tomatoes	
		Turnips	
		Turnip greens	
		Watercress	

*Fair; **good; others excellent

SUMMARY OF VEGETABLES AS IMPORTANT SOURCES OF CALCIUM, PHOSPHORUS AND IRON [1]

Calcium	*Phosphorus*	*Iron*
Artichokes, globe or French	Artichokes, globe or French	Beans, common or kidney
Beans, snap or string	Beans, common or kidney	Beans, snap or string, Lima
Beans, common or kidney	Beans, Lima	Beet greens
Broccoli	Broccoli	Broccoli
Cabbage	Brussels sprouts	Brussels sprouts
Cauliflower	Cauliflower	Cabbage, green outer leaves
Carrots	Celeriac	
Celery	Chickpeas	
Celeriac	Collards	

[1] *Food and Life, Yearbook of Agriculture*, 1939, United States Department of Agriculture.

Calcium	*Phosphorus*	***Iron***
Chard	Corn, sweet, green	Chard
Chicory	Cowpeas, black-eye peas	Collards
Chickpeas	Cress, garden	Cowpeas
Collards	Kohlrabi	Endive
Cress, garden	Lentils	Escarole
Dandelion greens	Parsnips	Kale
Endive	Potatoes	Leaf Lettuce
Escarole	Pumpkin	Lentils
Kale	Peas	Mustard greens
Lettuce	Soybeans	Peas
Mustard greens	Spinach	Salsify
Okra	Turnip greens	Soybeans
Parsnips		Spinach
Romaine		Turnip greens
Rutabagas		
Salsify		
Soybeans		
Turnips		
Turnip greens		
Watercress		

Vegetables Vary with the Seasons. It is important to know when a vegetable is in season in order to include it in the menu when it is best in quality and most economical in price. The vegetable calendar on page 295 is general for the United States. It will vary, of course, with a given locality. The frontispiece shows how appetizing vegetables can look.

Buying Vegetables and Fruits by Grades

Grades of Fresh Vegetables and Fruits. Government grades have been prepared for a large number of fresh vegetables and fruits, and descriptions of each of them may be obtained from the Production and Marketing Administration, United States Department of Agriculture. Grades of vegetables are more commonly used than are grades of fresh fruits. It has been estimated that three fourths of all white potatoes are sold in containers plainly marked with their grade, though consumers do not always know what grade they are buying, unless they see the bag or basket in which the potatoes were shipped. Watch for the grades in buying potatoes. Consumers in the future will buy more and more by grades, but this aid to the consumer will not come until consumers generally demand it.

[1] *Food and Life, Yearbook of Agriculture,* 1939.

FRESH VEGETABLE CALENDAR

Showing months in which quality of fresh vegetables is usually excellent and price is low

	Jan.	Feb.	Mar.	Apr.	May	June	July	Aug.	Sept.	Oct.	Nov.	Dec.	When buying look for
Asparagus		X	X	X	X	X							Stiff stems Tight buds
Beans, snap							X	X	X	X	X		Crispness
Beans, Lima						X	X	X	X				Crispness
Beets			X		X	X	X	X	X	X			Medium size Crispness
Brussels sprouts									X	X	X	X	Crispness Tight buds
Cabbage	X	X	X	X	X	X	X	X	X	X	X	X	Firmness No spots
Carrots	X	X	X	X	X	X							Firmness
Cauliflower	X	X	X						X	X	X	X	Crispness Whiteness
Corn						X	X	X	X	X			Full ears Evenness
Cucumbers					X	X	X	X	X				Straightness Crispness
Eggplant			X	X				X	X	X			Firmness
Kale	X	X			X				X	X	X	X	Crispness
Lettuce				X	X	X	X	X					Crispness Firm heads
Onions	X	X	X	X	X	X	X	X	X	X	X	X	
Parsnips			X	X						X	X	X	Firmness
Peas				X	X	X	X	X					Crispness Full pods
Potatoes, Irish	X	X	X	X	X	X	X		X	X	X	X	Firmness No soft spots
Potatoes, sweet	X	X	X	X					X	X	X	X	Firmness
Spinach	X	X	X	X	X	X				X	X		Crispness
Squash						X	X	X	X	X	X		Firmness
Tomatoes					X	X	X	X					No spots Heaviness
Turnips	X	X	X						X	X	X	X	Firmness Medium size

FIG. 94. OFFICIAL UNITED STATES GRADES FOR CANNED FRUITS AND VEGETABLES

The wholesale trade in vegetables is conducted on a basis of grades. If the grocer from whom you buy vegetables can buy by grades, the consumer should also have this aid. The first step for consumers is to know for what commodities grades and standards are available and next to demand that these commodities be sold to the consumer by these grades.

Grades for Canned Goods. Canned goods are now available with the grade plainly marked on the label.

UNITED STATES GOVERNMENT GRADES OF CANNED GOODS

Grade	*Description*
Grade A (or U.S. Fancy)	Fancy as name implies No more nutritious than lower grades Flavor good Liquid little colored Pieces firm
Grade B (or U.S. Extra Standard or Choice)	Not so fancy in quality as Grade A Flavor not so good as A but good Pieces in can not so firm Liquid more color Nutritive value equal to better grade
Grade C (U.S. Standard)	A standard product Recommended for general use Food wholesome Nutritive value same as A or B Consistency, Flavor } Good but not excellent

All wholesale purchase of canned goods, as, for example, for school cafeterias, is made on the basis of grades. Graded canned goods are to be found on the market in almost all sections of the United States, though not all of the canned food is graded. As you become acquainted with your market facilities, you will be interested to notice the extent to which it is found in your locality.

CLASS PROBLEMS

1. Review the chapters on Fruits and on Vegetables and Salads, Chapters 4, 16, and 18.
2. Visit stores and markets to study fruits and vegetables, and ways in which marketed. Can fresh vegetables or fruits be bought by grade in your market?
3. Plan the vegetables and salads for dinner for a given family, using the following meats in the various menus: baked hen, roast leg of lamb, fried trout with tartar sauce, Swiss steak, pork chops. Justify your choice.
4. Prepare potatoes in some of the ways suggested on page 290. Laboratory lessons on potatoes should be combined with the lessons on meat to make a main course for dinner.
5. Prepare sweet potatoes in some of the ways suggested on page 290. This lesson may be combined with the lesson on preparing various cuts of pork.
6. Prepare rice as a dinner vegetable, pages 290.

Boiled rice
Steamed rice, brown or polished
Italian baked rice
Tomatoes stuffed with rice

HOME PROBLEMS

1. Purchase the vegetables for your family for a week.
2. Plan the luncheon and dinner vegetables for two weeks.
3. Prepare potatoes in at least six different ways.
4. Prepare for one week the second vegetable either as a hot vegetable or as a salad for dinner.
5. Substitute brown rice for potatoes in your dinner menus now and then. If rice is more frequently used in your home, substitute potatoes for it now and then.
6. Prepare baked bananas, apple sauce, and spiced apples. These are appropriate when served with pork or chicken in place of a vegetable.

REFERENCES

See references for Chapters 4, 16, 18.
Any good Cook Book. (See page 387.)
Articles and other material in current literature on vegetables, potatoes, rice, and meat and vegetable combinations.

Bogert, L. Jean. *Nutrition and Physical Fitness.* Chapter V. W. B. Saunders Company.

Halliday, E. G., and Noble, I. *Hows and Whys of Cookery.* The University of Chicago Press.

Justin, Margaret M., Rust, Lucile O., and Vail, Gladys E. *Foods.* Houghton Mifflin Company.

Rose, Mary Swartz. *Foundations of Nutrition.* The Macmillan Company.

Sherman, Henry C. *Food Products.* Chapter IX. The Macmillan Company.

Stanley, Louise, and Cline, J. A. *Foods, Their Selection and Preparation.* Chapters V and VI. Ginn and Company.

Government Bulletins:

Cooking American Varieties of Rice. United States Department of Agriculture, Leaflet 112.

Food and Life. Yearbook of Agriculture, 1939. United States Department of Agriculture.

Preparation of Beets, Carrots, and Turnips for Market. United States Department of Agriculture, Farmers' Bulletin 1594.

Proximate Composition of Fresh Vegetables. United States Department of Agriculture, Circular 146.

The Iron Content of Vegetables and Fruits. Stiebling, H. K. United States Department of Agriculture, Circular 205.

Vitamin Content of Foods. United States Department of Agriculture, Miscellaneous Publication 275.

CHAPTER TWENTY-SEVEN

❧ Dinner Desserts

Cook Book References

Frozen Desserts	*Page* 521
Gelatin Desserts	*Page* 519
Butter cakes and fillings	*Pages* 491, 498

Food Value

Food Value in Shares — *Table* VIII, *Appendix*

FOR MOST OF US, keeping the dessert till the end of the meal means saving the best for the last. Sweets are universally liked and if we eat them discreetly there is no reason why we should not enjoy them all our days. It is not the use of sweets but their abuse that is to be condemned. Their place in the diet and the menu is discussed fully in Chapter 21.

Comparison of Desserts for Dinner and for Luncheon. There is no essential reason why the same dessert may not be used either for luncheon or for dinner. Because dinner is the heavier meal it is wiser and more pleasing to serve a light dessert. The richer desserts were treated in the luncheon discussion.

In this chapter the desserts discussed for dinner are: frozen mixtures, gelatin dishes, and butter cakes. This is an arbitrary division of luncheon and dinner desserts. Many desserts given here are suitable for either a luncheon or a dinner menu. A frozen dessert may appear in a luncheon menu, or a fruit whip in a dinner menu with equal propriety, but rich pudding or pie is more appropriate for luncheon than for dinner. Why?

FROZEN DESSERTS (pages 521–527)

Frozen desserts are refreshing. Though chiefly appropriate in warm weather, frozen mixtures are acceptable in menus the year round. If wisely chosen and eaten with discretion they may be enjoyed by both children and adults. In the diets of invalids simple frozen mixtures are almost invaluable.

FIG. 95. WHEN THE MENU IS NOT TOO HEAVY, CAKE IS A GOOD DESSERT

FIG. 96. STRAWBERRY SUNDAE

FIG 97. CANTALOUPE À LA MODE IS A FAVORITE DESSERT

Water Ices. An *ice* consists of fruit juices, water, and sugar. Any fruit ice frozen to a coarse mush is called a *frappé.*

Sherbets are made by freezing a water ice to a mush, adding gelatin or beaten egg white, and then completing the freezing.

When milk replaces part of the water in a sherbet, gelatin or egg white is usually omitted and the dessert is called *milk sherbet.*

Frozen Punch is a water ice distinguished by high flavor. Spices are often used. A mixture of fruit juices is common.

Ice Creams. Milk and cream are the foundation for ice cream. There are almost endless variations. *Plain ice cream* is thin cream, or a mixture of cream and milk, sweetened, flavored, and frozen. *Fruit creams* are made of crushed fruit pulp, and thin cream, heavy cream, or custard sweetened and frozen. *Frozen custards* are soft custards to which flavoring and thick cream are added before they are frozen. Caramel and maple are favorite custard flavorings. Chopped nuts or candied fruits may be used in custard creams.

Fancy Creams. Rich, highly flavored custards containing candied fruits and nuts are called *frozen puddings.* They are frozen in molds. *Mousse* consists of heavy cream, whipped, sweetened, flavored, and frozen in molds. Maple, caramel, and chocolate mousse are favorites. *Parfait* is a custard with whipped cream, frozen in molds. It is not frozen so hard as frozen pudding or mousse.

Any ice cream may be served with such additions as chocolate sauce, caramel sauce, marshmallow sauce, chopped nuts, crushed fresh fruit, candied fruit, preserved fruit, whipped cream, or a mixture of two or more of these. When so served it is called a *sundae.*

Methods Used in Freezing. There are fundamentally two methods of freezing desserts: (1) by stirring steadily during the freezing process, (2) without steady stirring during the freezing process. The ordinary ice-cream freezer with a dasher makes a frozen dessert of smoother texture than mixtures frozen without steady stirring. This is because the dasher beats air into the mixture and the crystals as they are formed are smaller.

In freezing without stirring the size of the crystal can be regulated somewhat by air beaten in before freezing, by the texture of the mixture, and by the rapidity of freezing. A fairly rich mixture, the ingredients of which have been carefully combined, frozen as rapidly as possible insures the best product in freezing without stirring. The mechanical refrigerator offers a convenient means of providing frozen desserts. Recipes especially designed for freezing without stirring should be used. (See pages 525–527.)

Buying Ice Cream. Buying ice cream has become a consumer problem, since more than three quarters of a billion pounds are sold each year. In buying ice cream, we should have satisfactory answers to three questions:

1. Is it pure? Ice cream is entitled to be passed as pure when:

The milk or cream, or the "ice-cream mix" used, is pasteurized.
The ice cream is free both of visible dirt and of disease bacteria.
The place where the ice cream is made is sanitary.
Artificial flavors and colors, if used, are harmless.
The bacteria per cubic centimeter are limited to 30,000 to 50,000.

2. What are the ingredients in the ice cream? The most important ingredients to be checked are: milk fat, milk-solids-not-fat, and air. The fat content is a measure of the amount of cream that has been used (or not used); the milk-solids-not-fat indicates the milk in the ice cream; and the air shows how much the volume has been increased by beating and by the freezing process. Standards for butterfat and milk solids vary, but the butterfat probably

should not be less than 12 per cent, except in the case of chocolate-flavored ice cream, ice cream with nuts in it, and the like. The total milk solid content, including fat and solids-not-fat, should probably be not less than 20 per cent. Air is whipped into ice cream during the freezing process. The amount of air should be such that the finished product weighs not less than 4½ pounds per gallon. This is at least 1 pound 2 ounces per quart and 9 ounces per pint.

Other ingredients usually found in commercially produced ice cream are sugar, flavoring, and gelatin. Fat, sugar, and flavoring are the ingredients that should create the flavor in ice cream. Gelatin is used to help make the product smooth. If too much gelatin is used, the ice cream becomes very slick and slippery. The Federal government specifications limit gelatin to one half of 1 per cent and sugar to 14 per cent in ice cream purchased by the government agencies. Eggs may also be used in the ice cream usually referred to as "French ice cream."

3. Should you buy hand-packed ice cream or ready-packed ice cream? There are two ways to buy ice cream; one is in bulk and the other is ready-packed. When ice cream is packed to order, it is often more expensive than ready-packed ice cream both because of the extra handling and because of the quality of the ice cream used. Containers of hand-packed ice cream may contain a little more or less than the measure you specify according to how tightly or loosely the carton is packed. When next you buy ice cream, buy some of each kind, and compare the kinds for weight, cost, fluffiness, flavor, smoothness, and number of servings.

Gelatin Desserts. (*See page* 519.)

Source and Food Value of Gelatin. Gelatin is a protein extracted commercially from the bones, ligaments, and tendons of either sound young beeves or healthy calves. Because it is an incomplete protein, gelatin alone cannot support the growth or the repair of tissue. If supplemented with a complete protein it has value.

Gelatin is easily digested and is of value in cookery for invalids. It may be bought either in granular form as pure gelatin or combined with sugar, flavoring material, and coloring matter. Such gelatin powders contain about 12 per cent gelatin.

Another form in which gelatin may be purchased, in the wholesale market especially, is sheet gelatin; that is, in bulk. Gelatin is cheaper in this form, but is not so convenient to use, because it must be substituted for granulated gelatin by weight, and all the recipes call for gelatin by spoons. If an accurate scale is available these equivalents can be figured out. The saving may not be worth the trouble unless a large quantity of gelatin is consumed.

Good pure gelatin, when dissolved by itself in hot water after soaking in cold water, is practically odorless while hot and is transparent.

Properties of Gelatin. Gelatin will not dissolve in hot liquid until it has first been allowed to swell in cold water. This is a general characteristic of all gelatin except specially prepared products. It melts at a high temperature and "jells" or becomes solid at a low temperature. It will not stiffen until it is cold, but after it stiffens it may be placed in a warm room without melting.

The proportion of gelatin to liquid varies somewhat according to the character of the final product, but a general proportion is two tablespoons of gelatin to one quart of liquid (including the cold liquid in which it is soaked).

Partly stiffened gelatin, before it is so stiff that the edges break apart, can be beaten into a foamy mixture about double its original volume. When it has been beaten until foamy, whipped cream or egg white may be added.

Fresh pineapple contains an enzyme that digests gelatin. Use pineapple cooked or canned in gelatin.

The General Rules for Gelatin. (See recipes, page 519.)

BUTTER CAKES. (*See pages* 492–498.)

Cakes are classed as butter cakes and as sponge cakes. For sponge cakes see Chapter 21.

FLOUR. A good cake flour (soft wheat) gives the most satisfactory results. "Enriched flour" has the most food value.

BINDING AGENT. It is important to have one egg as a binder in a cake mixture; this first egg is often not considered as part of the leavening agent. Additional eggs improve the texture of a cake.

LEAVENING AGENT. For the relation between flour, leavening agents, and eggs, and rules for the substitution of soda and acid for baking powder, see Breakfast Breads, Chapter 7.

SUGAR. The sugar is largely responsible for the texture of cake. If used in the correct proportion, it makes a light and grainy texture. Contrast the texture of cake with that of muffins, and then contrast recipes in this respect. When too much sugar is used the cake is so tender that it crumbles when removed from the pan.

FAT. Fat also is partly responsible for the texture of cake, though not in so great a degree as sugar. If too little fat is used the cake will not be light, but too much fat makes it heavy and gives it a tendency to greasiness.

LIQUID in cake is usually milk, but fruit juices, sour milk, whey, or a mixture of water and milk may be used.

Preparations for Cake-Making. Pans should be lightly greased, or greased and floured. All surplus flour should be shaken from the pans. For loaf cake it is well to fit a greased paper in the bottom of the pan. Be sure the pans are clean, otherwise the cake will stick in spite of greasing and flouring. The oven should be ready for use when the cake is ready for baking. Assemble all ingredients and utensils before beginning to combine the cake. All measurements must be accurate if good results are to be expected. Because egg whites will not beat if any fat or egg yolk is present, break the eggs one at a time over a cup or small bowl.

Methods of Mixing and Baking Cakes (see recipes, pages 491–501 ff.).

Substitutions and Modifications of Ingredients in Cake:

FLOUR. Cake recipes call for soft-wheat flour. If a hard-wheat flour is used the amount should be reduced by two tablespoons per cup of flour. A good substitute for cake flour is seven eighths of a cup of bread flour plus two tablespoons of cornstarch well mixed and sifted together.

EGGS. If the number of eggs is to be reduced in a cake recipe, the leavening agent and the liquid must be increased. For each egg omitted add two tablespoons of liquid and one half teaspoon of baking powder. Two yolks or two whites are considered the equivalent of one egg. If yolks are used alone, add a little extra baking powder. Use one fourth teaspoon baking powder for each extra yolk. It is not well to substitute for eggs in a rich cake.

CHOCOLATE. Chocolate contains both fat and starch. It should therefore replace some of the fat and some of the flour if added to a recipe that does not call for chocolate. One ounce of chocolate (one square) is the equivalent of one tablespoon of fat and one tablespoon of flour. The chocolate should be melted and stirred into the batter just before the egg whites are folded in.

COCOA. Cocoa calls for the reduction of the flour in a recipe. For each one fourth cup of cocoa, reduce the flour one tablespoon. The substitution of cocoa in a recipe written for chocolate will not alter the amount of flour needed, but the fat should be increased one half tablespoon for each one fourth cup of cocoa used.

NUTS. For each cup of nut meats added, the fat in a recipe may be reduced two tablespoons.

Testing the Cake. When the cake is done it will: (1) shrink from the sides of the pan, and (2) spring back when the center of the surface is touched lightly with the finger.

Causes of Failure in Cake-Making. Failure in cake-making may be due to wrong proportions of ingredients through poor recipe or inaccurate measurements; careless baking; or the use of poor ingredients.

FAILURES IN CAKE-MAKING AND THEIR CURES

Errors in Cake-Making	*Results*	*Instructions for Good Results*
Too much fat	Crumbly or greasy cake Undersized, rough edges	Plain: ¼ c. fat to 3 c. flour Rich: ½ c. fat to 3 c. flour (never more than 1 c.) (any fat except lard)
Sugar		
Too much	Fall in center Heavy Sugary crust	Plain: 1 c. sugar to 3 c. flour
Too little	Dry Coarse, tough crust Will not brown well	
Liquid (milk)		
Too much	Heavy streaks — cake falls	Plain: 1 c. liquid (milk) to 3 c. flour
Too little	Coarse, dry cake — cracked crust	
Baking powder		
Too much	Crumbly, porous cake with sticky crust	
Too little	Heavy, undersized cake	
Baking		
Oven too slow	Undersized, heavy cake, close grain, pale sticky crust	Have oven ready when cake is put in
Oven too hot	A coarse, thick cake, with a hump in the middle	Layer cake 325° F. for 25 min.
Uneven heat	A cake irregular in shape and texture	Loaf cake or tube pans, 325° F. for 40–45 min. Pound cake 300° F. for 60 min.

Cake Fillings. Cake fillings are chiefly sugar. They may be classed as cooked or uncooked.

1. *Uncooked fillings* consist of powdered sugar made into a smooth paste with water, fruit juice, cream, or butter.

2. *Cooked fillings.* Boiled icing and chocolate and caramel frostings are the most common. A thermometer is useful for all sugar cookery. See pages 498–499 for proportions and temperatures. Cream of tartar or a few drops of vinegar are sometimes added to insure a creamy texture.

Cake frostings may be varied through the addition of such materials as coconut, pineapple, nuts, dried fruits, candied fruits.

Cake is a substantial food and should be considered a dessert in itself and not merely an accompaniment to desserts. When cake is used to accompany other desserts, small servings of the plainer kinds without frosting are preferable. Cookies are best for this purpose.

CLASS PROBLEMS

1. Review Chapter 21 and plan desserts for dinner and luncheon menus to show essential differences.

2. Calculate the one-hundred-calorie portions of all gelatin and frozen desserts made in the laboratory (see recipes, pages 519–527). Estimate the calories in one serving; also check each recipe for vitamins.

3. Estimate the cost of preparing frozen mixtures at home and compare with the cost of commercial ice cream.

4. Visit an ice-cream factory. Note its sanitary condition. Ask what ingredients are used.

5. Calculate the calories in various fountain specials, such as banana split, double chocolate malted milk, chocolate nut sundae, butterscotch sundae. Discuss the advisability of eating these, especially between meals.

6. Explain "latent" heat in freezing. This is a problem in physics, which the physics teacher will be glad to explain.

7. Try freezing ices and creams in a freezer that stirs the mixture; in a "vacuum freezer" that freezes without stirring; and in the freezing trays of an automatic refrigerator. What are the relative merits of each method?

8. Prepare various gelatin desserts and estimate their calorie value and vitamin content (see recipes, page 519).

9. Prepare various kinds of butter cakes. Class discuss and score results. (See recipes, pages 492–498.)

10. Experiment with a standard cake recipe (page 493), modifying it by the use of: chocolate, cocoa, nuts, various fats, all egg yolks, all egg whites. Compare the recipes thus obtained with recipes from cook books.

11. Frost cakes with cooked and uncooked fillings.

HOME PROBLEMS

1. Form the habit of eating frozen desserts slowly.
2. Train yourself not to eat rich foods between meals.
3. Prepare a custard ice cream for dinner.
4. Prepare milk sherbet for dinner.
5. Prepare a fruit ice cream for dinner or for party refreshments.
6. Prepare two types of gelatin desserts at home.
7. Make a charlotte for Sunday dinner.
8. Bake a standard cake three times at home. Bake it once as a loaf cake, once as a layer cake, once as cup cakes.
9. Make three kinds of cake at home. Suggestions: white cake, gold cake, spice cake, chocolate cake.
10. Make boiled icing for a loaf cake.
11. Make chocolate filling for a layer cake.
12. Plan and prepare the dinner dessert for your family for two weeks.

REFERENCES

Halliday, E. G., and Noble, I. *Hows and Whys of Cookery.* The University of Chicago Press.

Sherman, Henry C. *Food Products.* The Macmillan Company. Pages 228, 229 and 235–236 for gelatin.

Stanley, Louise, and Cline, J. A. *Foods: Their Selection and Preparation.* Ginn and Company. Chapters IX, XIV, XX.

Any good Cook Book. See page 387.

Government Bulletins:

Homemade Breads, Cakes, and Pastry. United States Department of Agriculture, Farmers' Bulletin 1775.

Ice Creams Frozen Without Stirring. Bureau of Human Nutrition and Home Economics, United States Department of Agriculture, Leaflet No. 49.

CHAPTER TWENTY-EIGHT

❧ The Preparation and Serving of a Good Dinner

References

For Table Customs, see Chapter 10
For Table Service, see Chapter 11
For Serving Other Meals of the Day,
see Chapters 9 and 22

"DINNER IS SERVED." What welcome news, and with what pride it would be said if one might add, "and I have prepared this good dinner." Have you noticed that it is the highest praise to call a dinner "good"? You are finding how such praise can be deserved for the food you prepare and the way in which you serve it. What do people mean when they say, "That dinner was good"? The same food can be used to produce dinners that no one likes particularly, and to produce "good dinners" that are relished. What do people usually like at dinner time?

You have noticed a great preference for having dinner at home rather than in a public place. This is because informality, privacy, the companionship of a small group in our own homes, and last but not least, home-cooked foods are especially enjoyed. A home atmosphere should be cultivated. An attractive table; somewhat subdued light, if dinner is served at night; family members who have rested for a few minutes before the meal and refreshed themselves with at least clean hands and faces; the avoidance of interruptions; simplicity; the serving of food at the table by host and hostess, all contribute to the atmosphere of a good dinner at home.

The feeling of graciousness is always enhanced by an easy manner on the part of the host and hostess. Now is the time for you to learn to have an easy manner after you have been busy with dinner preparations. Interesting, pleasant, and gay conversation may well be the rule, and each member in the family can be encouraged to learn the art of good table conversation. Be sure that you do your full part to make dinner "good."

But in addition to all of these other considerations, the food itself must be good. This does not indicate that the food should be elaborate, rare, or served in an elaborate manner. In fact, homes in which family and friends enjoy dinners most are quite often homes in which pride is taken in the simplicity of food and of service. Many people like variety in their food, but the secret of this is having only a few foods in one dinner so that others may be used in other dinners. Above all, the enhancing of natural flavors with perfect cookery is the way to gain the admiration of others for your skill as a cook. Do you agree that these are conditions liked by you and your family at dinner time? Would you change some of them, and add others?

If you have been practicing in your home, as suggested in each chapter, your family will not be surprised some day to see mother start out in her "best bib and tucker," as carefree as a guest in her own home, content in the knowledge that an experienced cook is in the kitchen, and that a good dinner is in store. Why not plan to have your mother as your dinner guest? For such an occasion the dinner must be well planned, well prepared, and well served. Before this home project is undertaken, it is well to summarize here some important points in planning, preparing, and serving the dinner.

The Dinner Menu. In the preceding lessons you have studied the dinner menu in detail. A few questions will serve to emphasize the principles involved.

1. Is the menu a balanced meal when the other meals of the day are considered?
2. Is the menu planned for the group that is to be served?
3. Has account been taken of the adults and children?

For example, if coffee is planned for the adults, is milk provided for the children? The menu should be planned so that little or no special preparation is required for individuals. If children cannot have a rich dessert, why not serve a simple one for all?

4. Has the expenditure for food been considered sufficiently? The two items that have the widest range of price are the meat and the vegetables or fruits. Should cheaper meats be used? Are the fruits and vegetables seasonable and reasonable in price? Has enough milk been provided so you can safely economize elsewhere?

5. Is the menu pleasing? Has due regard been taken of the food preferences of the family? Is there variety in the courses and in the dishes? Are there pleasing contrasts in flavor, texture, temperature, method of cooking, shape, size, color?

6. In the interest of conserving time and energy, is the menu simple?

7. In the interest of good digestion and comfort, does the menu consist of combinations of food that can be easily digested? Is the order of the menu the best from the standpoint of good nutrition and good digestion? Will the family be well fed, but not overfed?

The Working Schedule. There is no essential difference between planning a good working schedule for breakfast, for luncheon, and for dinner.

Dinner is a more complicated meal than the other two because of its multiplicity of courses and dishes. More food must be served hot for dinner than for other meals. For these reasons it is perhaps especially necessary to make a careful working plan for the preparation of dinner. On the other hand, your greater skill from practice in cooking and serving simpler meals and individual dishes should offset the greater difficulty involved.

You now have a good notion of the length of time required to prepare any given dish. You should also be skillful in doing several things at one time — that is, in managing.

Pertinent suggestions are:

Plan what can be done ahead of time. Salads, most desserts, the setting of the table, and other tasks will suggest themselves in connection with the working out of any given menu.

See that all supplies are on hand before you begin work.

Plan the utensils you will need so that the right thing is available at the right time.

Hot breads may be heated or kept hot in the top part of a double boiler if the lid is tight. This is also a good use for the "thrift cooker" if the range is one of the newer type electric ranges.

Mashed potatoes or other vegetables that might burn on if left over the direct heat may be kept hot by putting the covered pan into a pan of boiling water.

Keep in mind the order in which the meal is to be served and have your schedule so arranged that everything will be ready when it is needed and as it should be — the hot things hot and the cold things cold. Some dishes can be allowed to stand and some must be served as soon as done.

Can you save time and work with a fireless cooker?

Division of the Working Schedule or Plan. Divide the working plan into four parts:

1. Those things that may be done ahead of time, such as setting the table and arranging flowers.

2. Those things that must be done at the beginning of the preparation: (*a*) in order that the dishes may be cooked at the proper time; (*b*) in order that certain dishes may be ice-cold; (*c*) for proper blending of flavors.

3. Those things that may be prepared in between, such as short cooking of vegetables, preparing a beverage or a sauce, mixing biscuit dough. Here is the best place for finding time to freshen one's appearance in order to make sure of being a presentable hostess.

4. Late and last-minute things. Late things are those that come shortly before serving. Examples are such activities as baking biscuits, combining salad, mashing potatoes. Last-minute tasks are those that must be remembered in the final minute before serving, such as pouring the ice water, placing butter on the table, putting cracked ice in the glasses for lemonade or iced tea, and serving the meal.

The writing out (in brief) of the plan for work is a short cut to becoming a skillful manager. Plan to have your kitchen as nearly in order as possible when the preparation is completed. Remember that you are not only the cook, but a member of the family, and plan to have your appearance attractive and your good disposition in evidence when dinner is served. If you can accomplish these things your pride in yourself will be pardonable.

Serving the Dinner. The service for a family dinner may be more formal in style than the service used for breakfast or luncheon, and still be very informal. The degree of formality is partly a matter of taste and partly a matter of how much help is available. A really formal meal cannot be served without competent help. Let us assume that in an average family there is no maid service and that the family prefers dinner served in family style. For details of this service, see Chapter 11.

Carving

In family style of table service the carving is done at the table by the host, but every housewife should know how to carve. Frequently she must do the carving in the kitchen and even more frequently she must teach others to carve. The task requires skill and confidence, but confidence comes with skill. One cannot acquire skill in carving by studying descriptions of carving or by watching a skillful carver, but both of these are helpful. If you would be skillful at carving you must understand how it is done and you must watch someone else do it; but in addition you must use every opportunity to practice on your own account.

For most pieces of meat there is only one correct way to carve. This depends always on the direction in which the fibers run and on the position of the joints.

The advantages of good carving are many. Chief among them

is getting the meat to the person served in the best condition possible for the particular cut of meat. Each portion should be placed neatly on the platter and then on the plate with the best side up. The remainder of the meat should not be jagged and rough, but should be inviting enough to tempt one to a second helping.

The following points are important in all carving:

1. The knife must be sharp, thin, and of the proper size.
2. The fork should be provided with a guard (in case the knife slips). Its correct use holds the roast firmly. An expert carver seldom has to move the fork until the carving is finished.
3. The platter should be large enough to make it possible to carve without accidents to the tablecloth.
4. The roast should be placed in the correct position (see Figs. 99–103).

FIG. 98. CARVING A PORTERHOUSE STEAK

A slice of the tenderloin and of the wide muscle should be served to each person.

FIG. 99. CARVING A ROLLED RIB ROAST

The slices should be of even thickness. Note the position of the knife.

FIG. 100. CARVING A LEG OF LAMB

Notice the position of the knife in relation to the bone.

CLASS PROBLEMS

1. Study table service for home dinners. See Unit Three, Chapter 11.

FIG. 101. CARVING A WHOLE HAM

Enough slices should be cut to serve the table before cutting the slices from the bone.

2. Plan market order, working schedule, and table service for the following menus to be served to a given family without maid service. Assume that milk is to be served with the meal to each child under fourteen years. Indicate items in the menu that you would omit for the children.

a. Baked Chicken
Grapefruit Spinach
Baked Potato Hot Biscuit
Sliced Tomatoes
Coconut Cake

b. Bouillon, Toasted Crackers
Swiss Steak
Stuffed Eggplant
Rice Bread and Butter
Head Lettuce
French Dressing
Orange Charlotte

FIG. 102. THE FIRST STEP IN CARVING A TURKEY OR CHICKEN

Notice the importance of knowing the position of the joint.

3. Estimate the cost of the above menus at current market prices. Suggest changes that will make the meal more economical.

4. Assume that you are to eat the dinners listed in Problem 2. Plan your breakfast and lunch on each of these days so that you will have a well-balanced meal considering fuel, protein, vitamins, and phosphorus, calcium, and iron. Assume that lunch is brought to school one

FIG. 103. THE SECOND STEP IN CARVING A TURKEY OR CHICKEN

Cutting thin slices from the breast.

day, eaten at the school cafeteria one day, and eaten at home one day.

5. Prepare and serve several dinners, planning carefully the menu, recipes, market list, utensils, and preparation schedule. Evaluate your results.

6. Estimate the number of calories you eat for each meal for three days. Do you eat one third of your total number, more, or less, for dinner?

7. Practice carving whenever the opportunity arises.

HOME PROBLEMS

1. Plan and prepare dinner for your family for a week or two.
2. Plan all the meals for your family for two weeks. Purchase all supplies; keep a record of expenditure.
3. Practice carving.
4. Have your mother for a guest for several Sundays.
5. Entertain some of your mother's or father's friends at dinner. You act as cook and waitress.

REFERENCES

Current magazines. See References for Chapters 9, 10, 11, 22.

Bailey, N. Beth (McLean). *Meal Planning and Table Service in the American Home.* Manual Arts Press.

Hadida, Sophie C. *Manners for Millions.* Doubleday, Doran and Company.

Heseltine, Marjorie, and Dow, Ula. M. *The Basic Cook Book.* Houghton Mifflin Company.

Justin, Margaret M., Rust, Lucile O., and Vail, Gladys E. *Foods.* Houghton Mifflin Company.

Lutes, Della T. *The Gracious Hostess.* Bobbs-Merrill Company.

National Livestock and Meat Board. *Ten Lessons on Meat.*

Table Service and Etiquette of the Table. Kansas State Agricultural College.

Wilmot, Jennie S., and Batjer, Margaret Q. *Food for the Family.* J. B. Lippincott Company.

Young America's Cook Book. Home Institute of New York Herald Tribune. Charles Scribner's Sons.

Write your State College of Agriculture and request any available bulletins on meal preparation and serving.

CHAPTER TWENTY-NINE

❧ We Have a Party

EVERYBODY LIKES A PARTY. Many of us enjoy parties most when we are hosts and have invited our friends to make merry with us. We may or may not choose a special day for the occasion. The ways in which we most like to entertain are luncheons, suppers, dinners, "parties," teas, receptions, and best of all those informal affairs when our home is the gathering place for the crowd. For all of these occasions food puts on frills and plays a most important part in the good times.

THE BUFFET LUNCHEON

A buffet meal is popular for luncheon, for Sunday evening suppers, or for late suppers. Buffet service is very much more used in Europe than in America. If you have the opportunity to eat at a Swedish restaurant (they are becoming popular in our larger cities), you will probably have the pleasure of serving yourself from a buffet table laden with many new and tempting dishes. As an illustration of planning and serving a buffet meal we have chosen a luncheon at school.

Home economics classes enjoy entertaining, and the buffet luncheon offers a most convenient way for entertaining a comparatively large group. Let us assume that the football team is invited to luncheon as guests of a home economics class. The luncheon is to be served buffet style in the school dining room, made attractive with seasonal decorations.

Plans for the Luncheon. The preliminary preparation calls for the selection of recipes, the estimate of quantities needed, and of course the making-out of shopping lists and a trip to the market to do the shopping. The kitchen preparation should be carefully planned so that everyone is busy, and everything ready when serving time comes.

The two-course menu chosen is as follows:

Celery Olives
Scalloped Oysters Cranberry Salad
Fried Eggplant Hot buttered rolls
Hot Chocolate
Lime Sherbet and Cookies
Salted Nuts Mints

The success of the luncheon will depend not only upon the plan but upon the way it is carried out. The standards are good cooking, attractive service, and gracious hospitality. Every member of the class must discharge her duties as hostess by making everyone feel at ease. The guests also have a part in making the event festive by entering into the occasion and enjoying, first, the good company; second, the hospitality that is extended; third, the attractive surroundings; and last, but not least, the good food.

For a buffet luncheon the table must be a festive affair. This means, of course, that one must take into account the table appointments that are available. Let us assume that, for this particular home economics department, dishes, linen, serving dishes, and silver are available, or may be borrowed from the cafeteria, for a group of thirty at a two-course luncheon, so a two-course luncheon it shall be. In making the plans it is to be kept in mind that all of the food is to be prepared to the queen's taste (even though it is to be served to kings this time), and served in the most attractive and effective manner.

Decorations. Since this luncheon may be anywhere in the United States the decorations will have to be decided in accordance with the location of the school. They may be chosen from a variety of native plants and home garden flowers available. The most usual decorations available for a November table are autumn leaves, red berries such as bittersweet, chrysanthemums, asters, or dahlias, but perhaps, in the South, zinnias or even roses may be in bloom.

Table Linen. The table is the center of attention at a buffet luncheon. If the table is of beautiful wood, beautifully finished, linen mats and table runner may be used, but if the table is not in the pink of perfection, a tablecloth would be preferable. It is sometimes easier to get a good arrangement of the buffet service if a cloth is used. Since a buffet table will contain so much of interest, the tablecloth should be a background for the food and should, therefore, be unobtrusive, but it may be festive. In this case a white tablecloth is chosen with a simple but attractive cut-work embroidery pattern.

Serving. The general plan is to have the first course served at the table by two hostesses, one at each end of the table. The second course is to be served from the laboratory and passed to the guests by members of the class assigned to this particular responsibility. The table is arranged so that a guest comes to one end of the table where a hostess, who is seated, serves his plate with scalloped oysters and eggplant. The plate is large enough, dinner size, to hold the food and a glass or cup. The guest passes behind the chair of the hostess, receives his plate on the hostess' right and passes down the long side of the table, serving himself to celery, olives, and hot rolls.

At the other end of the table another hostess serves the cranberry salad, which is arranged in individual servings, each held in a cup of lettuce. The salad is on a large chop plate and is served with a salad fork and spoon. The guest continues his journey around the chair of the second hostess and down the other side of the table, taking a fork, a spoon, and a napkin which are conveniently arranged for him.

Thoughtful planning calls for a seating arrangement whereby the guests may sit in groups with some convenient place, perhaps a small table, for chocolate cups or water glasses. The plate is large enough to hold one or the other of these but not both. Sometimes enough card tables are used to seat all the guests. With this plan the linen, silver, and water glasses may be arranged on the card tables before the meal is announced.

One of the hostesses serves each group with chocolate from a tray, the cups having been filled in the kitchen. The tray also contains a bowl of whipped cream for the guest to serve himself. If the luxury of tables is not available, the saucers are sometimes omitted; the guest takes a cup from the tray and places it on his plate.

Hot rolls are also passed during the meal, once or oftener. Guests will also appreciate water (which can be served from a tray). Water glasses should be refilled from a pitcher by some vigilant hostess.

When the course is served, the dishes are removed from the table so that the table continues to look attractive during the meal.

At the ends of the table in place of the serving dishes a tray with water pitcher and glasses may be placed conveniently where guests may serve themselves.

When all the guests have finished with the first course, the hostesses remove plates and chocolate cups, one dish in each hand, taking them to the kitchen. Guests should keep their napkins. After all the soiled dishes are removed, the water glasses are refilled and the second course is served, with the lime sherbet and the cookies making an attractive plate. Mints, carrying out the color scheme, and nuts are passed by two of the hostesses. Up to the time they are served, the mints and nuts have been on the side table and have contributed to the decorative scheme for the room.

After the meal is eaten the plates and napkins may be placed by the guests on the table, or removed to the kitchen by the hostesses. One can easily take a plate and a napkin in each hand.

Learning from Experience. The buffet luncheon is not complete until the class has discussed it in terms of its good points and the points that need improving. The major purpose of any activity at school is to learn from it. The learning from this experience is not complete until the experience has been evaluated from the standpoint of the manager, the cook, the hostess, and the guest. For details of table service and etiquette see Chapters 10 and 11.

The Formal Luncheon

Girls and women frequently entertain their friends at a more or less formal luncheon. A color scheme may be carried out in the table decorations. If more than ten or twelve guests are invited, they may be seated at small tables.

A FORMAL LUNCHEON MENU

(Color scheme: yellow and green; flower: jonquil)

Grapefruit
Cream of Pea Soup   Crackers
Chicken Croquettes (Parsley)   Hot Rolls   Butter Balls
Spinach Timbales with Hard-Cooked Egg
Buttered Young Carrots   Iced Tea   Mint Sprigs
Sweet Pickled Peaches
Orange Sherbet   Rolled Wafers
Mints   Coffee   Nuts

The menu is served in Russian style. (See Chapters 10 and 11.)

FIG. 104. FORMAL LUNCHEON FIRST COURSE

JUST A PARTY

At a tea or a party the refreshments are incidental and should therefore be light. The hostess must put much time and thought into the entertainment for a party. Parties for special occasions are easy to plan and are effective. A Halloween party, for example, is easily made a success.

Frozen desserts or cold drinks are the most usual "refreshments" for a party. Some entertainment, as games or dancing, is provided. One form of refreshments that has proved very popular is a "milk bar" at which various milk drinks are served according to choice: milk shake, chocolate milk, buttermilk, sweet milk, malted milk. The setting resembles a counter in a drugstore.

If the guest list is small, the refreshments may be more in the nature of a supper served either buffet style or with the plates served from the kitchen. For refreshments at afternoon parties two courses are sometimes served: a salad course and a dessert, usually a frozen dessert. For evening parties one course is preferable. This may be either a salad or a frozen dessert.

SUGGESTED REFRESHMENTS FOR A SUPPER PARTY

Afternoon	*Evening*
No. 1 (Summer) Fruit Salad Cheese Balls Iced Tea Brown Bread Sandwiches Peppermint Candy Ice Cream	No. 1 (Summer) Strawberry Ice Cream Cookies Mints Nuts
No. 2 (Winter) Turkey Croquettes Peas Hot Rolls Hot Tea Sponge Cake Salted Nuts	No. 2 (Winter) Creamed Chicken and Mushrooms on Toast Salted Nuts Coffee Mints

The refreshments at children's parties are important, but they must be simple. Candles, favors, and small hard candies contribute to the menu, but it is not usually complete without ice cream and cake. Plain ice cream and cookies that are not over-rich are preferable. The cookies may be in fancy shapes.

The Tea

The term tea may indicate a cup of tea and a few sandwiches or cakes served on the spur of the moment to afternoon callers, a very informal gathering of a few intimate friends for a fireside meal, or it may mean a rather formal gathering of a large number of people.

If you want to introduce a guest to your friends, or to extend a courtesy to a large group of people, giving a formal afternoon tea is a comparatively easy plan. At a formal tea the hostess and a few of her friends whom she has requested to receive with her greet the guests as they arrive. After passing this group the guests chat with other friends and acquaintances. Music adds to the occasion. Guests make a tea successful by enjoying one another's company.

One goes to the dining room for refreshments. The tea table may be lighted by candles if lighting is needed. Attractive dishes of nuts, candies, sandwiches, and cakes are arranged on the table. It is customary for one or two friends of the hostess to sit at the ends of table and pour. Sometimes young girls serve all the refreshments, but at other times each guest goes to the tea table

Fig. 105. A FORMAL TEA TABLE

Fig. 106. TEA FOR MOTHER'S CALLERS

and receives a cup of tea or glass of punch served by the person presiding at the tea table, and is expected to serve herself from the other dishes on the table. The food served at a tea should be dainty and attractive.

Afternoon tea is served in some homes if callers drop in. It consists of the simplest sandwiches, perhaps cookies, and tea.

Invitations to a tea may or may not be written. By telephone is a convenient and much used way of inviting guests to a tea. Even if invitations are received no written acceptance or refusal is necessary. The way to show one's appreciation of an invitation to a tea is to accept in person by appearing at the tea attractively attired and in a convivial mood.

The informal tea in some localities means a fireside supper. Sunday evening is the chosen time. A tea table, an electric toaster, and a "tea kettle" add to the charm of the repast.

A Reception

A reception is frequently held in the evening and demands full dress. Engraved invitations are used.. The occasion is either the visit of some distinguished guest, or the presentation to society

FIG. 107. OPEN HOUSE FOR YOUNG MERRYMAKERS

of a débutante, a bride, or some other significant person. Receptions are also given as the formal entertainment of clubs, colleges, or other social groups. The country club or a hotel is more frequently used for receptions than the home.

WHEN THE LATCHSTRING HANGS OUT INFORMALLY

After a football game or a skating party, or just when your crowd drops in, something to eat is in order. Try serving steaming spiced cocoa (recipe, page 393) in pottery cups. Have a bowl of red-skinned apple wedges on the table. Salted peanuts are inexpensive and appetizing. Or perhaps the boys have learned to like tea. Serve it in man-sized pottery mugs with thick slices of lemon or orange, decorated with cloves, and with stick cinnamon or cinnamon stick candies to stir with. With tea, toasted sliced doughnuts are grand or perhaps you prefer raisin and nut sandwiches. Cream cheese spread on rounds of brown bread makes another good choice. If only the girls come, more dainty refreshments will be appreciated. Try French coffee — half coffee and half hot milk poured into dainty coffee cups, or a cup of hot Oriental punch (recipe, page 397). With these beverages nothing could be better than a plate full of Toll House chocolate cookies (recipe, page 502).

A Kitchen Party

The modern version of the chafing-dish party. Keep your guest list small and congenial. Draw slips for duties. Array each guest with a kitchen apron or a gay dish towel. Let the boys try their hand at cooking. Here is a suggested menu that provides simple dishes, yet gives each guest something to do:

Spaghetti and Cheese (recipe, page 442)
Carrot and Cabbage Slaw
Bran Muffins Butter Apple Jelly
Hot Chocolate
Taffy Red Apples

Sunday Night Suppers for the Family

Surprise the family with Sunday supper served around the fireplace in the living room. Place the plates on trays or have the family get their food cafeteria style in the kitchen. Here is a menu using left-overs from Sunday noon which can be quickly prepared.

Creamed Vegetables (left-over peas, asparagus, potatoes hard-cooked eggs, heated with white sauce No. 2)
Whole-Wheat Bread and Butter
Fig Preserves
Hot Chocolate Oatmeal Cookies

Fancy Cakes

Fancy cakes, salted nuts, and open sandwiches go with parties.

Decorated Cookies. Use a rich dough. Cookies to be decorated should be rolled thin and cut in various shapes. Brush the surface with egg white and decorate with any of the following materials:

Granulated sugar, plain or colored.
Very small candies.
Blanched almonds, in conventional designs or as petals for flowers.
Citron or angelica for leaves of flowers.
Angelica for stems of flowers.
Small pieces of candied cherry, ginger, orange peel, currants, raisins, or nuts, used in various ways.

Cookies may be cut in fancy shapes. Animal cookies or gingerbread men especially delight children.

Rolled Wafers. Wafers are appropriate, dainty accompaniments for frozen desserts, gelatin desserts, or beverages (recipe, page 504).

Fig. 108. SIMPLE FOODS ARE ACCEPTABLE AS REFRESHMENTS ON A WARM AFTERNOON

Marguerites, *kisses*, and *macaroons* are served with frozen desserts, custards, gelatin dishes, or with beverages at tea. For recipes and variations see page 504.

Lady fingers or *sponge drops* are shaped from sponge-cake batter (page 500) by means of a pastry tube and bag. With a little practice one can easily acquire the necessary skill.

Lady fingers are served especially with chocolate desserts. They are also suitable cakes for children's parties.

Fancy frosting. With a set of pastry tubes and a pastry bag, very attractive cake decorations can be made by a skilled person. The very elaborate decorations of wedding and birthday cakes are made in this way.

Nut Confections

Salted nuts, sugared nuts, and glacéed nuts are useful as accompaniments for afternoon tea, party refreshments, buffet luncheons, and on other occasions (recipes, pages 530, 531).

Fig. 109. ICE CREAM AND COOKIES

Open Sandwiches

Open sandwiches can be made highly decorative, hence they are much prized for tea. Plates of dainty open sandwiches make a tea table most appealing, and they taste as good as they look.

Cut one-fourth-inch slices of one or two days old bread. Remove the crust. Cut in fancy or simple shapes as desired. Cut in angles, rounds, triangles, stars, hearts, spades, clubs, diamonds, rings, shamrocks, and any other fancy shapes. Cover with creamed butter or a thick salad dressing and any desired filling. Decorate with stuffed olives sliced thin, pimiento, green pepper, nut meats, hard-cooked eggs, candied cherries or orange peel, and other colorful edibles. Serve on flat plates or trays or on a bed of shredded lettuce. Do not stack.

CLASS PROBLEMS

1. Serve the luncheon menu on page 318 as a mock luncheon, using formal table service.
2. Plan a Valentine luncheon with appropriate color scheme and table decorations. An Easter breakfast.
3. Give a formal luncheon at school as a class project. It is suggested that some special day be the occasion of the luncheon.
4. Plan a party, including decorations, entertainment, and refreshments.
5. Plan a party for a child's birthday.
6. Plan a kitchen party.
7. The class should give a tea to some group in school. Plan and execute the tea as a class project. Make the fancy cakes, open sandwiches, mints.
8. Plan an afternoon party for a group of your school friends.
9. Plan an evening party for a group of school boys and girls.
10. Notice fancy cookies and cakes displayed at bakeries. Discuss and demonstrate decorations.
11. Make fancy decorated cookies. Use recipe for crisps, page 504.
12. Make rolled wafers (recipe, page 504).
13. Make marguerites, kisses, or macaroons (recipe, page 504).
14. Demonstrate the use of pastry bag and tubes.
15. Prepare salted nuts, sugared nuts, or glacéed nuts.

REFERENCES

Any good Cook Book. See page 387.

Bailey, N. Beth (McLean). *Meal Planning and Table Service.* The Manual Arts Press. Chapters V and VI.

Lutes, D. T. *The Gracious Hostess.* The Bobbs-Merrill Company.

Post, Emily. *Etiquette.* Funk and Wagnalls.

CHAPTER THIRTY

❧ Festive Occasions

NOW AND THEN we celebrate a special family festival, or go somewhere, perhaps on a trip. We may consider under two groupings these special occasions when, now and then, food plays an important part. There are feast days when the family ties are especially strong and which usually only intimate friends share with us. Thanksgiving, Christmas, fireside suppers, and picnics are the chief of these. At times we go away from home for a vacation trip. We may then eat in dining cars, hotels, and restaurants, tea rooms, and various other public places.

OUR FAMILY FESTIVALS

Thanksgiving Dinner. The term "Thanksgiving dinner" suggests a table laden with plenty. Roast turkey, cranberries, pumpkin and mince pies are some of the characteristic dishes for Thanksgiving. Except in the unchanging preference for turkey, the Thanksgiving menu shows many variations. Chrysanthemums, autumn leaves, and fruits are traditional table decorations.

In the interests of health and economy a simple menu may be served without sacrificing any of the spirit of the occasion.

A HOME THANKSGIVING DINNER MENU

Fruit Cocktail
Celery Olives

Roast Turkey Jellied Cranberry Sauce
Dressing Giblet Gravy
Grilled Sweet Potatoes Mashed Turnips
Lettuce Salad French Dressing

Pumpkin Pie or Caramel Ice Cream
Mints

On family festival days people away from home are likely to be lonesome. At such times hotels and ships try to make up for the lack of family and friends by supplying a superabundance of good food for the Thanksgiving dinner. Such a menu from a large hotel will serve to show a list of dishes that are almost traditional for a Thanksgiving dinner. It is not recommended that a dinner include all of these, or that one eat all of them even if the menu does include them.

AN ELABORATE HOTEL THANKSGIVING MENU

Scallop Cocktail
Tomato Bouillon
Crisped Paprika Crackers
Celery Olives Salted Nuts
Roast Stuffed Turkey
Chestnut Dressing Giblet Gravy
Jellied Cranberry Sauce
Grilled Sweet Potatoes
Onions in Cream Mashed Turnips
Frozen Punch
Romaine Salad French Dressing
Creamed Cheese Balls Crackers
Pumpkin Pie Whipped Cream
Fruit Nuts Cluster Raisins
Café Noir

Garnishing plays a very special part in the serving of food for the Thanksgiving or Christmas dinner; garnishes indeed are important in making food attractive at all times. Food must please the eye as well as the palate. The ingenious cook wins hearty approval by an added touch here and there.

General Rules for Garnishing Foods. The purpose of a garnish is to add to the attractiveness of a dish, hence it must not be made too conspicuous or used

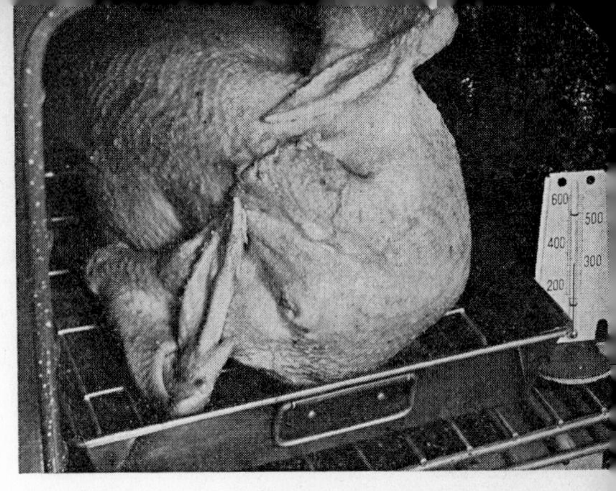

FIG. 110. PUTTING THE TURKEY IN THE OVEN

FIG. 111. BASTING THE TURKEY

FIG. 112. TURNING THE BIRD

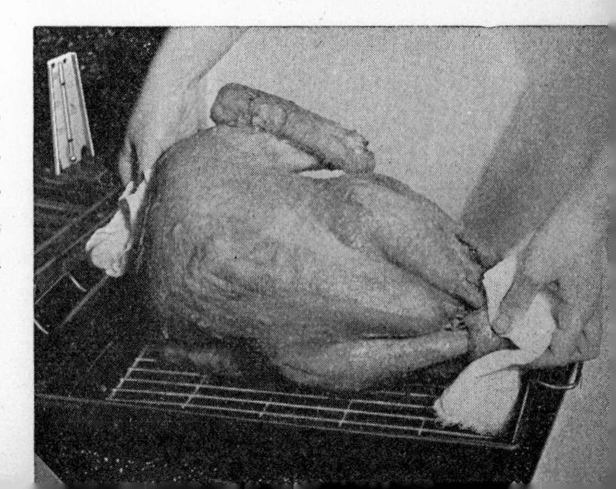

in too great quantity. Well-cooked food, served in attractive dishes, at a table well laid with linen and silver, needs little decoration. Food is attractive in itself. The browned surfaces of cooked foods and the colors of such foods as tomatoes, radishes, and carrots need no adorning.

Garnishes that come in contact with the food should be edible. Flowers or ribbons are not appropriate on the plate with food.

GARNISHES APPROPRIATE FOR COURSES OR DISHES

COCKTAIL:

Catsup, parsley, mint leaves, celery, olives, radishes.

SOUP COURSE:

Chopped parsley or diced vegetables.
Whipped cream on bouillon or cream soup.

MEAT DISHES:

Parsley is the traditional garnish for turkey.
Mint for lamb.
Cloves for baked ham.
Spiced apples, or apple rings and cooked prunes for pork.
Sliced lemon for fish.
Lemon dipped in chopped parsley or paprika, or both, for fish.
Sliced tomatoes, lemon, radishes, lettuce, hard-cooked eggs for cold cuts of meat.
Potato roses or Duchess potatoes for planked steak or fish.
Vegetables cut in fancy shapes or diced.
Toast points.

SWEETS WITH THE MEAT COURSE:

Jellies, spiced cherries, cranberries, pickled peaches are only some of the colorful and attractive accompaniments for the main course at dinner or luncheon.

VEGETABLE DISHES:

Cheese grated
Browned bread crumbs
Pimiento
Chopped parsley

SALADS: Salad vegetables and fruits are themselves highly decorative.

DESSERTS: Desserts, like salads, are themselves highly decorative.

Fresh whole fruits; as strawberries
Cherries (red or green)
Candied fruit
Candies
Nuts
Whipped cream

BEVERAGES: Iced beverages are attractive with sliced orange or lemon, cherries, or a sprig of mint in the glass.

If finger bowls are used, one blossom in the water is attractive.

Christmas Dinner

The Christmas table must look different from any other! Holly, poinsettias, small Christmas trees gay with tiny ornaments and lights in one color, or in all colors, miniature winter scenes with artificial snow glistening in the light, especially candlelight, and with tiny reindeer, a sleigh, and jolly old Santa, of course, make possible this achievement. Let your imagination go and you can work out a novel table decoration for the Christmas table that will win the hearty approval of all.

The Christmas menu is not unlike that of Thanksgiving. Turkey is usually the main course, but roast goose also has a time-honored place on the Christmas dinner table. Do you remember Bob Cratchit's Christmas dinner and what a goose there was? Sometimes a whole roast pig with a red apple in its mouth may be the main dish for the Christmas dinner.

Plum pudding with hard sauce or fruit cake frequently displaces pumpkin or mince pie. Ice cream is also a favorite dessert, sometimes frozen in the shape of Christmas trees or other appropriate forms. Candies of all kinds are in high favor, and much is made of them and of fancy cakes and cookies for table decorations.

Candies for Christmas and Other Occasions (Candy Recipes, pages 527–531). Candy seems especially to be associated with Christmas. We can all remember finding candies in our Christmas stockings when we were very young, and candy continues to delight us at all ages. At Christmas we use candy in special ways, for decorations and for gifts. Many people like to make their own candies. Whether we should or should not eat candy, the fact remains that we do. Candy should be eaten at mealtime and counted as part of the day's foods. Between meals, or in excess at any time, it is unwholesome. Why?

Principles of Sugar Cookery

A modern confectionery shop is a dazzling array of marvels made from sugar. The confectioner's wares are the result partly of his own skill and his special equipment, and partly of his use of the few, simple principles of sugar cookery.

Candy Temperature. Success in sugar cookery depends upon a knowledge of the exact temperature required for a given result, and upon an accurate determination of this temperature.

One household test is made by dropping a little of the mixture into ice water. The stages are variously designated as soft ball, firm ball, hard ball, and crack. Another household test is the "thread" test. If a clear sugar solution is dropped from a fork, it will form, at the soft-ball stage, a short thread or a "web" between the tines. A long thread will be formed at the firm-ball stage. At the "crack" stage there will be a long, hard thread. But at the best these tests are inaccurate. For candy-making an accurate candy thermometer is recommended. The same thermometer is useful for jellies, jams, marmalades, and cake frosting.

TEMPERATURES IN CANDY-MAKING

Kind of candy	*Temperature*	*Other household tests*
Fudge, opera creams, panocha, and similar cream candies	234° to 236° F.	Soft ball
Fondant (mints, etc.)	234° to 238° F.	Soft ball or thread
Marshmallows	238° to 240° F.	Soft ball
Caramel mixtures	246° to 252° F.	Firm ball
Taffies	254° to 270° F.	Hard ball
Butterscotch	280° to 300° F.	Crack
Brittles	290° to 310° F.	Hard crack
Boiled frosting		
1 egg white to 1 cup sugar	238° to 242° F.	Soft ball or thread
2 egg whites to 1 cup sugar	244° to 248° F.	Soft ball or long thread
3 egg whites to 1 cup sugar	254° to 260° F.	Firm ball or long thread

Invert Sugar. Sucrose (cane or beet sugar) is a double sugar, and may be converted into two simple sugars, glucose (grape sugar) and fructose (fruit sugar), by cooking with an acid. The process is called "inversion," and the product is often called "invert sugar." Invert sugar is good for use in candy-making, since it does not crystallize or "grain" so easily as sucrose. A little invert sugar in a mixture will prevent the entire mass from graining and thus produce a smooth candy or frosting. Vinegar, lemon juice, and cream of tartar are dilute acids and are sometimes added to hasten the production of invert sugar.

Although invert sugar may be produced by boiling sugar with a dilute acid, it is sometimes included specifically in the recipe. Corn sirup (glucose), which occurs in some candy recipes, is for this purpose.

Crystallization. The size of the crystals is determined by the rate of crystallization. Extremely large crystals, such as those in rock candy, are produced by exceedingly slow crystallization. The creaming of candy is due to the formation of very fine crystals. The graining of candy is due to the formation of coarse crystals.

Crystallization of an entire mass may be brought about by the presence of one crystal; hence the sides of the pan in which candy is cooking must be kept free of crystals. Heat encourages coarse crystals. Stirring or beating also hastens crystallization. A creamy candy should be cooled and then stirred or beaten. Why? A clear candy must not be beaten, and often even the scraping of the pan is disastrous. Why?

Divinity, fudge, fondant, and boiled frosting are examples of confections in which a creamy texture is desired. Three factors are important: (1) The boiling candy must be kept free of crystals. (2) In order to prevent graining owing to large crystals, the candy should be allowed to cool before it is beaten. (3) The candy is creamed by being beaten after it has cooled.

Do's and Don't's in Candy-Making. The following rules will insure successful candy-making:

1. Be sure of good proportions. Use tested recipes.
2. Measure accurately.
3. Cook candy and cake frosting by temperature, using a chemical thermometer or a candy thermometer. Guesswork in this is a form of extravagance. The sugar spoiled by guessing at sugar temperatures would soon pay for a thermometer.
4. While the mixture cooks, use a wet cloth or wet wooden spoon for wiping the sides of the pan. Boil the mixture gently.
5. If a creamy candy is desired, cool the mixture before beating, stirring, or pulling it.
6. For a clear candy, pour the hot mixture without stirring it.
7. All sugar mixtures produce better results if not stirred while cooking. If stirring is necessary, stir only enough to prevent burning.
8. A little corn sirup or an acid will help to produce a creamy smoothness in candy.
9. Pans and surfaces for cooling and molding candy except for fondant should be buttered.
10. Clear weather is the best kind for candy-making. Moisture in the air makes candy sticky, interfering with good results.

Homemade Candies. See recipes, pages 527–531.

Packing a Box of Candy. A box of homemade candy can be rendered attractive by arranging the candies so that there will be a contrast in color, texture, size, shape, and kind.

Dried fruits should be rolled in granulated sugar.

Tiny pieces of candied fruit on top of each piece, in a color to match the coating, make dipped candies attractive.

Caramels look like a professional product if cut in even sizes and wrapped carefully in waxed paper. Devise a way to wrap caramels by studying the way bought caramels are wrapped.

Nuts, salted, sugared, or glacéed, add interest to a box of candy.

Lace paper, waxed paper, clean boxes, and careful wrapping all make their contribution to the attractive appearance of the candy package. Nothing can look more like Christmas than a box of candy beautifully packaged and gaily wrapped. A study of boxes of candy in the shops will yield many other suggestions. Watch the windows of these shops at Christmas and other special occasions.

Buying Candy. Buying candy is important because we buy much more than we make. In addition to the desserts, cakes, pastries, jams and jellies, and the candy that is made and eaten at home, Americans buy each year over sixteen pounds of candy per person, on the average, or about sixty to seventy pounds per family. One third of this is sold in bulk, one third in candy bars, one sixth as penny candy, and the remaining one sixth in boxes; these range from large expensive boxes to the small five- or ten-cent box.

The Federal Government is making an effort to insure that the candy we buy is good. The federal regulations prevail for all candy that is subject to interstate commerce regulations, and are the same as general food regulations. Adulteration and misbranding are forbidden; ingredients must be stated on the label; the net weight must be given; the manufacturer or distributor must give name and address; poisonous coloring is forbidden; the use (but not the kind) of artificial coloring or flavoring must be noted on the label, and the container must be honest and not look as though it contains more than it does. Special regulations that apply now just to candy are the forbidding of packing in it the lead "prizes" that have so often lodged in children's throats; forbidding the use in it of some specific metallic and earthy substances; and limiting in amount materials such as paraffin that are normally used in candy-making, but which have no food value.

Do these federal regulations result in the sale of only wholesome, pure candy? No; such a statement would be an exaggeration, because candy made and sold within one state or city is not subject to these regulations unless the candy factory ships its product into other states. Even pure candy may be contaminated in the stores where it is sold. What are some of the ways in which it may be damaged? Other foods may be cooked, or at least washed before we eat them, but we buy candy ready to eat. For this reason, it is often not wise to buy candy in bulk. Never buy it in a dirty store or from a dirty clerk. Buy candy only when it is sold in a clean store, well wrapped, and fresh. By reading candy labels learn what ingredients it contains.

Cleanliness in the factory where the candy is made is also important. Candy factories should be sanitarily built, well screened, and kept spotlessly clean. Only healthy persons should be employed, and they should be immaculate. Federal and state sanitary officers are working hard to interest candy manufacturers in keeping their factories as clean as you would like to have them.

The Picnic

When the outdoors beckons, nothing is more acceptable than a picnic supper. The possibilities of bacon, eggs, "wieners," sausage and fried apples, and sandwiches need not be elaborated here. Sometimes we take our picnic lunch already prepared, and sometimes we cook it over a campfire.

The automobile and good roads have made picnicking popular. Many people have special picnic equipment and use the picnic as one way of entertaining their friends. Refrigerator baskets, thermos jugs, special dishes and cooking equipment for outdoors are aids to picnickers. Elaborate equipment is, however, not needed. Good food is more important. Have you ever stopped to think that sandwiches are a great deal of trouble? A picnic de luxe can be prepared in less time and at no greater expense than a sandwich supper.

The following picnic menus are suggested as suitable for making a special occasion of the picnic. (You are so familiar with the usual type of picnic that it is not discussed here.) These menus can be prepared and taken from home with little effort if a refrigerator basket, dishes, and a bucket or skillet are available. If a bonfire is not permissible, an outfit that uses solidified alcohol may complete the picnic equipment. To keep the food hot for two or three hours, wrap the vessels while they are very hot with many thicknesses of paper.

MENU NO. 1

Meat Loaf — Barbecue Sauce — Celery
Potato Chips — Rolls — Coffee or Milk
Grapefruit or Cantaloupe or Cake with Whipped Cream
Nuts

Pack in the refrigerator basket first clean ice in the ice container, then the meat loaf, dressed celery, barbecue sauce in a fruit jar, whipped cream in another fruit jar, butter, individual bottles of milk, fruit, and cream for the coffee. Water may be carried in a bottle and poured on the ice in the ice container of the refrigerator basket. Coffee may be carried in a thermos jug or made at the picnic on a campfire. The meat loaf may be sliced and heated with the sauce in a skillet a few minutes before serving. If the evening is cool, a little hot food will be relished.

FIG. 113. GETTING READY FOR A PICNIC

Galloway

FIG. 114. PICNICKING IN YOUR OWN YARD

MENU NO. 2

Broiled or Smothered Chicken — Butter with Lemon Juice
Cheese Straws — Olives — Rolls
Combination Salad
Strawberries and Cream — Coffee or Milk

Take the cooked chicken in a deep pan or bucket in which it may be reheated. Leave the gravy in the same utensil, and in reheating it add butter and a little lemon juice.

Pack in the refrigerator basket a glass jar with a tight top full of strawberries; another jar of whipped cream; a quart glass fruit jar of combination salad (chopped tomato, cucumber, shredded lettuce with French dressing); individual bottles of milk; a bottle of cream for coffee; a bottle of olives. When you arrive at the picnicking place, you have only to reheat the chicken and the supper is ready.

After a picnic be sure that you leave the picnic spot in good condition for the next group of merrymakers. Good citizenship requires this courtesy. Be careful also that there is no spark left in the fire. Disastrous forest fires have been started by a spark carelessly left by thoughtless picnickers.

When We Journey

Let us pretend we are going on a trip to a large city. We have planned the trip for a long time and shall travel well; that is to say, we shall travel in a Pullman car, eat in the dining car, and go to rooms reserved for us at an excellent hotel.

We wear tailored clothes, so chosen that the same ensemble is suitable for travel, shopping, the hotel, and the matinée. In each of our small traveling bags there is either a dark silk dress, rather tailored in design and of the prevailing mode, or a simple long dress with suitable slippers and other accessories. This is for evening wear at dinner and at the theater. Hats and costume accessories have been well chosen.

The Dining Car. After the first few hours of comfortable riding we realize that we are hungry. Soon a waiter in a white coat comes through the car, announcing, "First call to luncheon, dining car forward." After washing our hands and smoothing our hair we go forward to the dining car. The steward, or manager of the dining-car service, seats us at a table for two, and leaves with us a menu card and a card and pencil for writing our order. We note that the prices are higher than those at any local eating place at home, but we observe that our neighbors have generous servings and have ordered only one or two dishes; that the linen, silver, and china are attractive; and that the service is excellent. There is also a club luncheon which is more economical than the à la carte service.

From the bill of fare we quickly select, perhaps, a combination dish that will give us both meat and vegetables, a pot pie, for example, bread and butter, sliced tomatoes, and a glass of milk.

Above the hum of the train the noise of the dishes may be heard occasionally, but there is no loud talking or boisterous conduct. Everyone is quiet, attentive to his own affairs, and considerate of others. Although we do not know any of the other travelers, we feel a friendly air in the dining car, perhaps because the steward has asked us if everything suits our taste and if we have any further wants.

We did not order a dessert because we were not sure that we wanted it. Our meal has satisfied us so well that when the waiter presents the card for us to choose a dessert we tell him that we do not care for anything more. The man across the aisle seems to want dessert, but is undecided what to order. The waiter sees his indecision and suggests that the apple pie is very good, and the order for apple pie and coffee is given.

Our waiter has meanwhile removed all our dishes and placed a finger bowl in front of each of us. He presents the check and we pay him promptly. He returns the change on a small silver tray or a folded napkin. Perhaps we leave one or two coins as a tip for the waiter; in some states, however, tipping is prohibited by law. The waiter thanks us, pulls our chairs out as we rise, and we find our way back to our seats in the Pullman or to the observation car, leaving our places in the diner to other hungry travelers.

Thus far the journey has been delightful and we feel that our vacation is to be a success.

At the Hotel. Hotels are run on either the American or the European plan. An American plan hotel includes meals with the cost of the room. A European plan hotel offers meals, but the guest may eat elsewhere. Most commercial hotels are European plan, resort hotels are often American plan. Our reservation has been made at a large hotel of which we have heard much. Being tired from our journey, we are soon settled in our comfortable room with little idea of the hotel except an impression that the lobby was large, the employees were courteous, and that we were made welcome as guests of the hotel.

Breakfast. The next morning the all-important question is, "Where shall we eat and what shall we eat?"

The morning paper, placed at the door of the room, may have a small colored slip pasted at the top to remind the guest that club breakfasts are served in the coffee shop at reasonable prices. We go to the coffee shop for breakfast. It is a businesslike place with either counter or table service; at the end of the room white-capped cooks are making coffee, toast, or hot cakes in plain view. We may be directed to a table or left to choose one for ourselves. The menu card handed to us is a series of club breakfasts at various prices. A club breakfast, we discover, is a meal with the combination of food designated, and is ordered by number. We order the combination which most resembles the breakfast to which we are accustomed, and tell the waitress our preference in beverages and whether we wish our eggs soft, medium, or hard-cooked and our bacon crisp or medium. We are served quickly and at a reasonable price. The waitress gives us separate checks. We may or may not leave a coin on the table, and pay our own check at the cashier's desk as we go out of the coffee shop.

Luncheon. At noon we return to the hotel and get ready for luncheon. We may eat a business men's lunch in the coffee shop or grill room; the fountain room may tempt us; or we may prefer a near-by tea room. In this hotel the fountain room, a pretty place with shaded lights, attracts us. A waitress in an attractive costume gives us a menu card. With some difficulty, because the list is so tempting, we choose an individual chicken pie, a toasted sandwich, or a delectable salad. The chances are we also order hot chocolate with whipped cream and a hard roll, and an ice for dessert. The tastefully garnished food pleases us immensely.

Our check is larger than at breakfast, but we have had a very satisfactory luncheon in a short interval of time. Perhaps again we leave a coin on the table and pay the cashier as we go out.

Afternoon Tea. In the afternoon we go to the matinée and after the play we may have tea. This time we choose a place that has atmosphere, a tea room. We must not spoil our dinner, but we must have a bite and talk over the play.

The tea room has planned for our needs, for we are given a menu card containing groups of dishes, listed after the plan of the club-breakfast card. We choose Tea No. 2 which consists of toasted English muffins, marmalade, and a pot of orange pekoe tea, or milk. After a very pleasant half hour we return to our hotel to rest.

Dinner. We dress for dinner, but not in formal dinner clothes. This time we choose the main dining room, which is brilliantly lighted. The head waiter, or usher, in full dress, leads us to a table. We notice that in mixed groups the ladies precede the men who accompany them. Waiters pull our chairs out for us and seat us comfortably.

We are given a large card with a smaller one attached. The large card, we soon discover, is the à la carte menu and is a bewildering array of dishes. The smaller card is the table d'hôte menu and simplifies our problem by reducing our range of choice. We must still choose between fruit and shrimp cocktail; consommé and noodle broth; chicken, baked ham, and roast beef; coffee, tea, and milk; and ice cream, French pastry, and other desserts. The dinner is served in formal style, and there is an orchestra, which plays at intervals. At the end of the meal the waiter presents the check, and we pay as we did in the dining car. Since no one is waiting for our table, we linger awhile to chat and to enjoy one more selection from the orchestra.

Throughout the entire day, in the shops, coffee shop, fountain room, tea room, theater, and dining room we have heard no loud voices and have seen only well-mannered people. We like it all, and when our holiday is over we are sorry. There will be other holiday trips now and then, but never one quite like this first one.

CLASS AND HOME PROBLEMS

Throughout the year various occasions for entertaining present themselves. They should be used as opportunities for carrying out class projects. Hospitality is as much a part of homemaking as are the more routine tasks. Each class, throughout the year, can suggest appropriate, interesting, and attractive ways of observing special occasions in the Home Economics Department.

THANKSGIVING DAY

1. Plan a Thanksgiving dinner menu.
2. Plan the table decorations and any other feature that helps make a festive occasion of the day.
3. At home observe the dressing and roasting of a turkey and the making of oyster or chestnut dressing.
4. Make cranberry jelly. (Recipes, pages 391 and 550.)
5. Prepare pumpkin or mince pie. (Find your own recipe.)

CHRISTMAS

1. Make Christmas candies and nuts.
2. Plan a Christmas dinner menu, including favors and decorations. (Study December magazines for suggestions.)
3. Make fruit cake. (Recipe, page 496.)
4. Christmas is a feast day in many lands. Try to find out what the Christmas menu offers in other countries and how the meal is served.
5. Plan a Christmas party.

PUBLIC EATING PLACES

1. Have a question box for receiving unsigned questions involving etiquette at hotels, restaurants, dining cars, tea rooms.
2. Collect sample cards from dining cars, tea rooms, restaurants, hotels. Order mock meals from these cards.

THE PICNIC

1. Plan the following picnic, showing what preparation can be made ahead of time and how the lunch should be packed.

Individual Broiled Fillet Steaks (Bacon Wrapped)

Sliced Tomatoes	Rolls	Milk	Cabbage Slaw
Sweet Pickles	Cantaloupe	Ribbon or Stick Candy	Salted Nuts

2. Estimate the cost and time of preparation for the foregoing picnic menu and compare with the usual type of picnic menu.

3. Show the class various types of picnic equipment: dishes, automobile lunch kit, refrigerator baskets, thermos jugs.

4. Prepare a picnic lunch as a class project.

CANDY

1. Make candies at some special season of the year, as Christmas, Valentine's Day, or Easter. Each student may furnish her own materials or pay a small fee to cover the cost of the materials purchased.

2. Members of the class may learn to make some choice candy outside the class and demonstrate it to the class.

3. Make fondant and fondant variations in class. (Recipes, pages 528–529.)

REFERENCES

Dennison Manufacturing Company, New York, Chicago, Boston, Philadelphia, and Framingham, Massachusetts. Suggestions for decorations and favors on special occasions. Do not use many suggestions for one party! Save the rest for other times.

Current magazines, especially magazines for women.

Games Digest — a magazine on entertainment. 14 E. 62d St., New York.

Van Arsdale, Monroe, and Barber. *Our Candy Recipes*. The Macmillan Company.

Wakefield, Ruth. *Toll House Tried and True Recipes*. M. Barrows and Company.

Wilmot, J. S., and Batjer, M. O. *Food for the Family*. Chapter 34. J. B. Lippincott Company.

Young America's Cook Book. Home Institute, New York Herald Tribune. Charles Scribner's Sons.

Any good Cook Book. See page 387.

CHAPTER THIRTY-ONE

❧ Food for Children

Food Value

Nutritive Value of Foods	*Table* VI, *Appendix*
Nutritive Value in Shares	*Table* VIII, *Appendix*
Vitamins and Minerals	*Tables* IX *and* X, *Appendix*

SUMMARY OF FOOD FACTS

See Chapter 1

DO CHILDREN NEED SPECIAL FOOD? Nobody expects a child to dig a ditch or fell a tree, to run a locomotive or manage a store. Why? These jobs are for adults.

As a child gradually develops into an adult in the world of affairs, there is a gradual change in his physical ability to digest foods. For the first twelve years a child's food should be carefully selected and his eating habits wisely guided. During these early years he is not completely equipped to digest all foods. His digestive system is as young as his brain and his muscles and as incapable of adult performance. When he is seven or eight years old he has only begun to get his permanent equipment for chewing.

A child's food must be carefully selected, for it must contain the materials needed for growth, and these, if the body is to use them properly, must be in a form that is easily digestible. He must also have an abundance of calories to meet his energy requirements.

Eating habits are important. If a child bolts his food before he is twelve, he will probably continue to bolt it. If he develops food prejudices before he is twelve, it is likely that he will continue to hold these prejudices.

The main objectives in feeding children are: (1) to select the foods that will meet their body requirements; (2) to give these foods in simple, easily digested combinations; (3) to teach each child to like a wide variety of suitable foods; (4) to establish good habits of eating.

The Importance of Careful Feeding in Childhood. The following quotations from recognized authorities speak for themselves:

"One year of good feeding at the beginning of life is more important than ten after forty." [1]

"The child's food is the foundation for his future. Health and disease, strength and weakness, usefulness and uselessness may be the result of feeding in childhood.

"The choice of the child's food cannot be left to chance, but must be a matter of thoughtful care from early infancy, if the best growth of body and mind is to be insured." [2]

Foods Each Child Needs Daily. Every child needs, each day:

Foods for growth: complete proteins, minerals, and vitamins.

Foods for energy: easily digested, and non-irritating carbohydrates and fats.

Foods for regulating body processes and for protection against disease: vitamins, water, minerals, and laxative substances.

During the first year the baby should be fed under the direction of a physician, preferably one who is a specialist in child feeding. By the end of six months the baby should double his weight at birth, and by the thirteenth month, triple it. In the first year a child should gain four to eight ounces each week, the greater gains being made in the earlier months.

FIG. 115. SIGNS OF GOOD NUTRITION

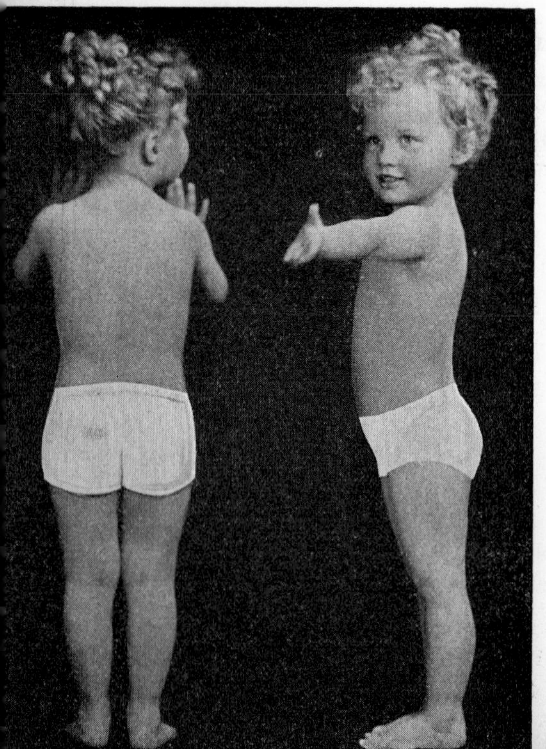

Scrupulous care should be used in handling food for children, especially for babies. The source and grade of the milk should be known. If the source of the milk is in doubt, the milk should be boiled one minute and then cooled immediately. Where the grade of the milk is uncertain, physicians sometimes recommend the use of

[1] Mary S. Rose. *Feeding the Family* (revised ed.), p. 132. Reprinted by permission of The Macmillan Company, publishers.

[2] D. R. Mendenhall. *What to Feed the Children.* University of Wisconsin Extension Circular 166, p. 3.

dried whole milk or irradiated evaporated milk. Mother's milk is preferable to artificial feeding in the first few months.

Feeding the One-Year-Old Infant. By the end of the first year a baby should have daily:

- One quart of milk (boiled).
- Three to four tablespoons of orange juice or tomato juice twice daily.
- Two to three tablespoons of strained green vegetable pulp or juice.
- One half to one raw or cooked egg yolk.
- Two to four tablespoons of cereal, thoroughly cooked and strained.
- A piece of stale bread or crisp zwieback to develop the muscles used in chewing.
- A teaspoon of cod-liver oil in summer, two in winter twice daily.

In order to insure a child's eating these simple foods and continuing to eat what he needs, his appetite must not be perverted by giving him tastes of other foods.

Normal bone growth requires both a right proportion of calcium and phosphorus and the presence of Vitamin D. Vitamin D is found in egg yolk, but halibut-liver oil and cod-liver oil are its richest sources. Rickets seldom occurs in children who are out-of-doors in the sunlight most of their waking time. The direct sunlight seems to make up for an inadequate supply of Vitamin D in food. To insure normal bone development, it is safest to include halibut-liver oil or cod-liver oil in the diet. One teaspoon in summer and two in winter are the recommended amounts of cod-liver oil; less of halibut-liver oil will suffice. A green-leaf vegetable, egg yolk, and play out-of-doors in the sunshine are additional safeguards.

A child arrives very gradually at the accomplishment of eating the foods listed. For a detailed study of the care and feeding of the baby, procure bulletins from the Children's Bureau, United States Department of Labor, and from the Bureau of Human Nutrition and Home Economics, United States Department of Agriculture, Washington, D.C., and from the Bureau of Child Hygiene in your own State Department of Health.

Feeding the Two-Year-Old Toddler. By the time a child is two years old, he should drink all his milk from a cup. No food except water should be given between the regular feeding times. Milk should still be the chief article of food. Cereals may be given unstrained unless they prove too laxative. Dry cooked cereals may be used at times.

Leafy vegetables should have preference, though at this time two vegetables may be given daily. One green vegetable and one root vegetable make a good selection. Spinach, carrots, cabbage, tomatoes, string beans, turnip greens, and tender lettuce are all suitable.

Soups furnish a good method of combining milk and vegetables. Authorities on child feeding sometimes advise the combination of two or three vegetables in one dish with a broth as the foundation. This is a successful method of developing in the child a liking for different flavors.

Small servings of lean meat may be given. Liver once a week.

Fresh fruit juice or pulp should be given daily. Apples, pineapples, oranges, and peaches may be used. Prunes are good, but when they are used, a little raw vegetable should be given. Some uncooked fruits or vegetables are needed daily for Vitamin C. An egg yolk may be given each day or a whole egg every other day. The egg may be raw or soft-cooked. Avoid soft bread. Give hard crackers, stale bread, or zwieback. The child needs the exercise of chewing. No desserts are necessary, and a child of this age is better off without cake or candy. Cod-liver oil should be continued through the second year.

The following articles of food will supply the daily food requirement of pre-school children from two to three years of age:

A quart of milk: The milk may be used as a beverage or in cooking. It may be fresh bottled milk, dried milk (whole), or evaporated milk. If irradiated milk is used it will supply Vitamin D.

Fruits: Fruit should be served at least once a day, preferably twice if it can be afforded. Orange juice, grapefruit juice, or tomato juice daily will furnish the needed Vitamin C. Other fruits, when cooked, may be used, such as apples, pears, bananas, apricots.

Cereal: A well-cooked cereal should be served every day. Preference should be given to whole-grain cereals, or to those to which Vitamin B_1 has been added, but if these needs are met by other foods any well-cooked cereal is acceptable.

Bread: Hard, dry bread, preferably from whole grains, should be included daily for tooth and jaw development.

Vegetables: Two fresh vegetables, green or yellow preferred, should be included every day. Raw vegetables, such as carrots, lettuce, cabbage, should be served frequently. They can be used as sandwich filling. Vegetables should be mild in flavor and well cooked. Potatoes and other cooked vegetables may be served daily. Vegetables are counted on to supply Vitamin C, A, B_1, and G; also minerals and cellulose.

Eggs: One egg daily to insure a plentiful supply of protein, iron, and Vitamin A.

Butter: About a tablespoon daily insures enough Vitamin A.
Meat: One serving of lean meat daily. Liver should be served at least once a week.
Water for regulation of body processes.
Direct sunshine, or *cod-liver oil*, or both, for prevention of rickets, a disease very common among young children. Rickets is an improper calcification of the bones.

Feeding the Pre-School Child (three to seven years). The diet of the child gradually becomes more complex. Combinations of food may be served; also some of the milk may be used with more solid foods: as, for example, top milk or cream with the cereal. Unlimited choice of well-cooked cereals is permissible. Cream soups, milk toast, custards, junket, and other dishes with milk as a foundation may be served.

Fruit, preferably raw, should be used at least once daily. Fresh vegetables are important; they may be enriched with butter or cream sauce. Simple desserts are well liked and are useful additions to the diet. Whole cooked eggs may be used several times each week.

During the fifth or sixth year the quantity of food is gradually increased, but the meals still should consist of milk, cereals, fruits, vegetables, bread, butter, and simple desserts. Richer combinations of food are permissible. Frozen desserts are hailed with much delight and are an acceptable combination of milk with fruit or eggs. Whole raw fruits may be eaten at this time.

Meat now occupies a more important place in the diet. When first introduced into the diet, meat should be given on alternate days with eggs. Easily digested meat is preferable. Meat may be included earlier, but when children eat highly flavored foods they lose their taste for foods of mild flavor. Since the introduction of meat often results in taking less milk, meat should be withheld until the milk habit is so well established that no other food will take its place in the child's diet.

Feeding the School Child. When eight years old, the child is usually in school all day. Since school children may eat one meal away from home, it is wise to teach them what foods they should eat, and why. Children are ambitious to grow to be strong, healthy adults and they can readily be taught to understand the relationship of food to health. The chapter on the school lunch deals with the food of school children. (See Chapter 20.)

The Daily Meals for Children. Young children eat more frequently than older children, but giving them a few fairly substantial meals rather than frequent light meals makes for good digestion.

The smaller children may have their meals at a small table and at different hours from the hours of family meals. Under such a system there is less temptation to give them foods they should not eat; there is more time to teach them to eat properly; and there is more pleasure for the older members of the family. All meals should be regular — by the clock.

All food should be well cooked and pleasingly served. There should be no hurry at mealtime. Children should be taught to eat what is put before them. It is not safe for them to follow their appetites and whims.

Because milk is a bulky food and occupies a large place in each day's meals, it is not advisable to give water at mealtime; give it between meals. Children like sweets, which should be given at the end of a meal if given at all. Food is important for health, but sunshine, a certain amount of outdoor play, and long hours of sleep with plenty of fresh air are also necessary.

Menus for Young Children. The following skeleton menus show how these needed foods can be used in the three meals a day for the young child:[1]

Breakfast	*Dinner*	*Supper*
Fruit	A main dish of eggs, cheese, meat, or fish	A vegetable, creamed, scalloped, or baked
Cooked cereal and Whole-wheat toast	Cooked vegetable	Sandwich or Bread and butter
Milk to drink	Raw green vegetable	Cooked fruit
	Bread and butter	Milk to drink
	Dessert	
	Milk to drink	

The Morning Meal. Breakfasts, important at any age, are most important to young children. The breakfast menu from day to day should be varied. The following are suggested menus:

No. 1	*No. 2*	*No. 3*
Orange juice	Stewed Apricots in Orange Juice	Tomato Juice
Whole-Wheat Cereal with Top Milk	Poached Egg	Whole-Wheat Cereal with Raisins
Buttered Toast	Whole-Wheat Toast	Buttered Toast
Milk	Milk	Milk

[1] Sweeny, Mary E., and Buck, Dorothy Curts, *How to Feed Young Children in the Home.* The Merrill-Palmer School, Detroit.

FIG. 116. LUNCH TIME IN THE NURSERY SCHOOL
Proper equipment is provided and even the small children are encouraged in independence.

The Noon Meal. This should be the heartiest meal in a child's day. Let us take a look at the noon menu in a nursery school where all activities are planned for children from two to five years of age. The following midday menus were selected from a week's dietary for a nursery school, serving meals to children ranging in age from two to four years. The same menu is served to all. Adaptations are made in the size of servings. Notice that these menus can be adapted to use by the whole family.

No. 1

Potato Soufflé	Beets with Lemon Butter
Buttered Spinach	Peanut Butter and Sorghum Sandwiches
Milk	Fruit Cup

No. 2

Minced Chicken	Brown Rice
Buttered Cabbage	Toast
Milk	Orange and Rhubarb Sauce

No. 3

Braised Steak	Broiled Tomatoes
Mashed Potatoes	Carrot Sandwiches
Milk	Apricot Whip

The Evening Meal. The evening meal should be supper when one is very young. An early and simple supper is advisable and promotes quiet sleep. Formerly a supper of cereal and milk was recommended for young children. This type of meal lacked flavor and variety and did not adequately provide for sufficient minerals and vitamins that can be supplied by fruits and vegetables. The following menus include foods which allow for variety and a better balanced diet. These menus, too, can easily be adapted to the entire family.

Buttered Brown Rice
Spinach with Grated Egg Yolk
Bread and Butter
Milk Apple Sauce

Cream of Pea Soup
Prune and Cottage Cheese Salad
Toasted Rolls
Milk Oatmeal Cooky

Creamed Liver Baked Potato
Grated Carrots
Bread and Butter
Milk Baked Apple (¼–½)

Poached Egg on Toast
Buttered Cabbage
Toast
Milk Fruit Gelatin

Supplementary Meals. Orange or tomato juice may be given about nine-thirty in the morning; a glass of milk and a cracker are sometimes given in the afternoon to the young child. These added meals should not interfere with a healthy appetite for regular meals.

Other Suggestions for Planning the Child's Food. Do not give a child tastes of forbidden foods. This practice will pervert his taste and make him dissatisfied with the bland foods he needs.

Give only sound ripe fruit to children. Underripe or overripe fruit is not safe.

Do not give any poorly cooked foods to children.

Avoid in their diet fat meat, such as sausage, ham, or goose.,

Hot soft breads should not be used because they cannot be chewed easily. Crisp breads are preferable.

Tea and coffee should never be given to children.

All rich combinations of food are to be avoided.

One nursery school lists the following foods as being unsatisfactory for the pre-school child:

Berries
Melons
New corn
New potatoes
Cucumbers
Radishes
Green peppers

Fried foods of any kind
Rich foods, such as salad dressing, gravies, fat foods
Pies and pastries
Spiced foods

Chocolate candy
Soft drinks
Iced foods. Ice cream may be served occasionally, but is better slightly melted.

Suggestions for Preparation of Child's Food

Raw vegetables are carefully washed and served grated, or chopped finely, mixed with butter and spread on thin slices of whole-wheat bread. Lettuce, raw carrot, and raw cabbage sandwiches are great favorites with children.

Vegetables are cooked until tender in boiling salted water, or they may be steamed, or baked. Butter and salt are used as seasonings. Occasionally lemon juice is used. Vegetables may also be served creamed or scalloped. Such vegetables as beans and beets are run through a coarse food chopper before serving.

Salmon is served frequently, as the basis of a soufflé, in timbales, creamed, or in a loaf. Liver is combined with cereals in a loaf, creamed or braised and then ground. Chicken is cooked till tender in water and served minced with a little butter for seasoning. Lamb is roasted and cut into small pieces. Beef may be ground and cooked with tomato juice. Some meats may be broiled and cut into small pieces.

A variety of textures should be provided. Often a crisp graham cracker will enable a child to eat baked custard with relish. Carrot strips add interesting texture to a meal. The child enjoys color, and meals should be planned with a view to colors, avoiding white meals.

Children like to eat one food at a time.

Fig. 117. CHILDREN CAN ENJOY MILK BETWEEN MEALS

Salt, butter, a little sugar, occasionally vanilla and lemon juice are the only seasonings used; pepper, paprika and other spices should be avoided.

Favorite desserts are simple cocoa pudding, fruit cup, fruit gelatin, fruit whips, boiled custard, and ice cream.

How Much Food Should a Child Eat at One Serving? No two children have exactly the same food needs. Thus the amount served at any one meal will depend upon the age, size, activity, and appetite of the child. The following amounts of essential or protective foods have been found to be eaten at one meal by the average young child:[1]

Food	2-*Year-Old*	3-*Year-Old*	4-*Year-Old*
Milk	1 cup	1 cup	1 cup
Milk soup	⅓ cup	½ cup	⅔ cup
Egg dish	3 tablespoons	¼ cup	⅓ to ½ cup
Meat —			
Patties	2 tablespoons	¼ cup	¼ cup
Roasts	1 tablespoon*	1½ tablespoons*	2 tablespoons*
Creamed	3 tablespoons	¼ cup	⅓ cup
Vegetables —			
Cooked (milk-flavored)	¼ cup	¼ to ⅓ cup	⅓ to ½ cup
Uncooked (diced)	2 to 3 pieces	2 tablespoons	¼ cup
(strips)	2 strips	4 strips	6 strips
Fruit —			
Uncooked or cooked	⅓ cup	½ cup	⅔ cup
Desserts —			
Whips, custards, blanc mange	⅓ cup	½ cup	⅔ cup

*Approximately.

ESTABLISHING GOOD FOOD HABITS IN CHILDHOOD

1. Children should be taught to like a variety of foods. This will not happen by accident, but will be arrived at by systematic training, as follows:

Accustom a child to new foods one by one.
Start with small amounts of a new food and increase the amount gradually.
Do not try to accustom a child to a second food new in flavor or texture, until he is well accustomed to the first one.
Food must be well prepared if it is to be liked.

2. Meals should be regular — by the clock.

3. The table should be attractive for the toddler. He likes gay dishes and an attractive table as much as we do.

[1] Sweeny, Mary E., and Buck, Dorothy Curts, *How to Feed Young Children in the Home.* The Merrill-Palmer School, Detroit.

Fig. 118. SIMPLE FOODS ARE BEST FOR CHILDREN—A GOOD BETWEEN-MEAL SNACK OF COTTAGE CHEESE AND HOMEMADE BREAD

4. Children are imitators. If they hear older persons say they do not like this or that food, they readily become hard to please too. Always set a good example in your own eating habits, especially where younger children are concerned. A child will usually follow a good example.

5. Even very young children should be taught to feed themselves. A child of fifteen months can, with enough practice and with proper equipment, accomplish this feat.

6. Do not pamper a child's appetite. If he is given what he should have without raising the question as to whether or not he wants it, he will usually accept it without protest.

7. A good appetite is an important asset in proper feeding. Do not blunt the appetite by feeding between meals. A healthy, hungry child will eat well at mealtimes. A temporary loss of appetite, in a child normally hungry at mealtimes, is a warning that something is wrong. Allow the child when tired or upset to miss a meal without taking too much notice of the event. If it is only a temporary upset, it will right itself. If it is a permanent loss of appetite, seek the advice of a physician.

8. To overcome or prevent dawdling, which is a bad food habit occurring commonly among little children, set a time limit for eating. If the food is not eaten in twenty to thirty minutes, remove the plate. The success of this treatment necessitates the removal of any opportunity to secure food other than at mealtimes.

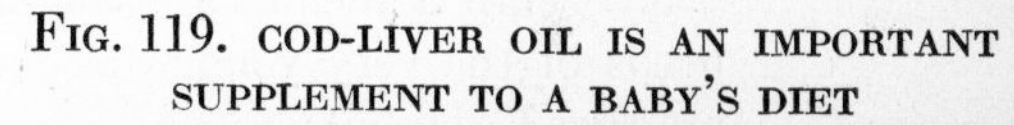

Fig. 119. COD-LIVER OIL IS AN IMPORTANT SUPPLEMENT TO A BABY'S DIET

9. Good food habits may be rewarded by words of praise. Approval of success in eating is more effective than punishment or nagging for failure to eat.

10. Be consistent and firm in feeding children. There should be no differences in authority in deciding questions about children's eating.

11. A sensible, busy housekeeper makes adaptations in the family meals for children instead of providing special menus. The same food served in varying amounts, and with minor adaptations, such as mashing to a pulp, removing the peel and inedible parts, is satisfactory from "toddler" to "teens" with very little extra work for mother.

12. Most of the difficulties in feeding children have small beginnings. Do not make the first mistake by inviting whims and you will save much future trouble.

CLASS PROBLEMS

1. Order bulletins on infant feeding. Study and discuss them in class. Demonstrate the feeding of a child less than six months old.

2. Ask a mother to demonstrate the preparation of a baby's food for one day.

3. Visit a nursery school if possible.

4. If a children's specialist is available, invite him to talk on the importance of right feeding in childhood.

5. Secure a menu card for children from a restaurant where needs of the very young are given special attention. How good are they? Discuss.

From the menu card order a meal for a 2-year-old; a 5-year-old; an 8-year-old.

HOME PROBLEMS

1. Undertake to teach a child good table manners.
2. If you have a younger brother or sister who does not drink milk, try to teach the child to like milk.
3. Prepare suppers for a child for two weeks.
4. Make a study of the food requirements of some child. Plan menus and prepare food for this child for two weeks.

REFERENCES

Bogert, L. Jean. *Nutrition and Physical Fitness.* Chapter XXII. W. B. Saunders Company.

Chaney, Margaret S., and Ahlborn, Margaret. *Nutrition.* Houghton Mifflin Company.

Roberts, Lydia J. *Nutrition Work with Children.* University of Chicago Press.

Rose, Mary Swartz. *Foundations of Nutrition.* Chapters XXIII and XXIV. The Macmillan Company.

Rose, Mary Swartz. *Feeding the Family.* Chapters VII, VIII, IX, X. The Macmillan Company.

Food for Children. United States Department of Agriculture, Farmers' Bulletin 1674.

Good Food Habits for Children. United States Department of Agriculture, Bureau of Human Nutrition and Home Economics, Leaflet 42.

How to Feed Young Children in the Home. The Merrill-Palmer School, Detroit.

Infant Care. United States Department of Labor, Children's Bureau Publication 8.

Menus and Recipes for Lunches at School. United States Department of Agriculture, Miscellaneous Publication 246.

The Child from One to Six. United States Department of Labor, Children's Bureau Publication 30.

Well-Nourished Children. United States Department of Agriculture.

See also Recent Bulletins from the Bureau of Child Hygiene in your own State Department of Health in the State Capitol, and from the State College of Agriculture or State University in your own state.

CHAPTER THIRTY-TWO

❧ Feeding the Sick

GENERAL CONSIDERATIONS. There comes a time in every household when responsibility must be assumed for preparing food for the sick. In cases of serious illness the diet is often of first importance, and the physician prescribes it with as much care as he prescribes the medicine. He expects the housewife or the home nurse to attend to the details of preparing and serving it without any instructions from him. There are many minor cases of illness when the physician is not called or when he does not give specific instructions to the housewife concerning the patient's food. Although she should not presume to prescribe a diet for serious illness, a general understanding of feeding the sick is an asset to any housewife.

Tempting and Appetizing Dishes Are Essential. A sick person seldom wants food even though it is important to his well-being. It is often necessary to give a patient food he does not like. It will be possible sometimes to disguise his food, which may solve the problem. A patient may take an egg in a beverage or a soup and never suspect it. Regard individual preferences so far as circumstances permit. If one notices how the patient receives the tray and what he eats, these preferences can soon be learned.

Do not give the same food twice in succession unless ordered. Variety is more essential in feeding sick people than in feeding well people, and it is much harder to attain, because so many foods are eliminated from a sick person's diet list. Serve small portions and only a few kinds of food at a time. It adds interest to the meal and makes for convenience in eating from a tray if meals are served in courses. Only easily digested foods, prepared in simple combinations, should be served. Tempt the appetite by means of pleasing garnishes and attractive service.

Do not serve very sweet foods. In illness we often dislike the foods that we like best in health. Sweets are a striking example of this. They leave an unpleasant lingering taste and dull the appetite.

Typical Diets for the Sick. The doctor frequently prescribes merely a liquid diet, a soft diet, or a light diet. What does he mean?

Liquid Diet	*Soft Diet*	*Light Diet*
Broths, beef tea Soups, clear and cream Fruit juices — very important Milk and milk drinks Raw eggs Cereal gruels Water ices (strained) (Soft-cooked eggs, sometimes) (Toast dipped in hot milk, sometimes)	Liquid diet and the following foods: Milk toast Soft-cooked eggs Well-cooked, strained cereals Broth with rice Vegetable pulp Custards Cornstarch pudding Junket Frozen desserts (not very sweet) Gelatin — plain	Liquid and soft diets plus an easily digested meat, as: breast of chicken or broiled scraped steak or whitefish Fruits Vegetables Bread or toast Simple desserts

Invalid Cookery. Proper cooking for the sick requires an understanding of the nutritive value of foods and their relative digestibility, but it does not require any unusual skill or technique in cookery. It does require an interest in the patient and careful preparation of the food.

Most of the articles of food listed above have been treated elsewhere in this book. The cream of tomato soup served to the sick person is the same as that served to the well person, perhaps not seasoned as highly. A soft-cooked egg is prepared for the invalid's tray in the same way that it is prepared for the family meal.

For liquid and soft diets, the same food may often be served to the sick member of the family that is served to the others. For example, suppose spinach with egg sauce occurs in the family menu. Before the spinach is seasoned, a small serving for the convalescent may be pressed through a strainer and then reheated with a little salt and perhaps a little butter.

It materially lightens the work in preparing the meals for children, the sick, and the convalescent if the family meals are so planned that the menu contains foods that are easily adapted to these special requirements.

Special Invalid Dishes. If a person is ill for a very few days it makes little difference whether his food meets his energy requirements or not, but in cases of prolonged illness it is highly important that the food approximate the energy requirement of the patient in order to prevent the body tissues from being utilized as fuel, and so wasting away. In fever cases the energy requirement is often higher than the normal energy requirement. Furnishing the proper number of calories in a liquid or soft diet requires much thought and planning.

Clear soups and beef broths have little or no food value in themselves; they are stimulants to appetite. Extra calories can be tucked into broths by the addition of eggs or cereals or milk.

Cereal gruels are easily digested and are not irritating. Their fuel value is not high, but it is higher than that of clear soups, and it may be enriched by the addition of milk or eggs.

Milk is the most important food for invalids. The reasons for this are clear from the discussion of milk in an earlier chapter. Precautions should be taken to have absolutely clean milk. It must be remembered that milk is the most easily contaminated of all foods and that sick people are less resistant to bacteria than well people. If the source of the milk is in doubt, the milk should be boiled.

Modification of Food is Often Necessary. It is easy to modify milk for invalids by combining it with cereal gruels or by making junket dishes.

Buttermilk is sometimes preferred because of its flavor or because it forms no curd in the stomach.

The greatest difficulty encountered may be the invalid's dislike for milk; often this is caused by a lack of variety in the way the milk is served.

Milk may be disguised in a variety of ways. It may be flavored with coffee, tea, cocoa, or some other flavoring that the doctor allows. Malted milk may be used. Milk may be served hot, cold, or frozen.

Dried milk is very useful in feeding sick people who need food, but who will not take much food. For example, if milk and cereals are both on the diet prescribed by the physician, dried milk may be mixed with the cereal and cooked without the patient's detecting it, and the food value of the bowl of cereal may be very greatly increased. Dried milk can also be added to soups and to beverages including fresh milk. One fourth to three eighths of a cup of dried skim milk may be added to a quart of fresh milk without an appreciable change in flavor of the milk. Such an addition makes a significant addition to the food value of the milk for the patient.

Raw eggs are not usually liked, but they can be disguised in milk, broth, cereal gruels, and in fruit juice or water. In these "albumenized" drinks egg white is commonly used and the yolk is omitted. The nutritive value of any drink is improved though not greatly increased by this addition, and the beverage is often soothing to the digestive tract. One egg white adds only about fourteen calories, but one egg yolk adds fifty-six calories.

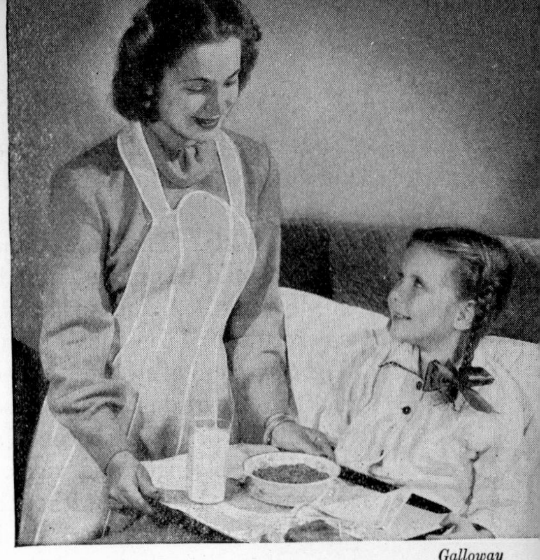

Galloway

FIG. 120. MAKE MEALS ENJOYABLE FOR THE CONVALESCENT

When a patient has fever over a period of time the physician may advise foods which are high in calorie value and yet not taxing to the digestive system. Whole milk, cream, lactic acid milk made from whole milk, egg yolk, lactose added to milk, cereals fortified with dry milk, mashed potatoes are sometimes prescribed.

In some illnesses of short duration, such as indigestion, it may be best not to eat at all. In any case of illness a physician should be consulted and his orders carried out.

The Invalid's Tray. The invalid's tray should be attractive. The prettiest linen in the household stock and the daintiest china, silver, and glassware should be used.

Do not put too many dishes on the tray at one time. It may be best to serve the meal in courses. Serve small portions. Hot foods should be hot and cold foods cold. Do not fill glasses, cups, or bowls very full. A single flower on the tray will be sure to please. Bent glass tubes or straws are useful for drinking beverages.

A special invalid's tray is desirable for continued illness. Two types are available. (1) a table that swings across the bed from a side support; (2) a tray (with end supports) which can be placed across the patient's body without resting on him.

Care of Trays from the Sick-Room. In contagious diseases, even colds, or in illness that has not been diagnosed, scrupulous care should be exercised to prevent spreading of the disease. Burn all left-over foods. Boil the linens. Sterilize the dishes by boiling. Separate utensils should be used for washing dishes from the sick-room.

Special Diets. There are special diets for some diseases. These diseases should be diagnosed and the diet prescribed by a competent physician. A knowledge of foods and cookery insures intelligent execution of the doctor's orders.

The Convalescent's Diet. When the physician gives general instructions on care during convalescence, and dismisses a patient, the responsibility of feeding becomes a major one, for food is the means of regaining strength and vigor. During a continued illness the body may have had to do without many of the needed food nutrients because the patient has been unable to take a sufficient amount or variety of food to insure a balanced diet. The result is that the body loses weight, and becomes generally depleted. During the period of convalescence food becomes even more important than when one is well, for not only must daily body needs be met, but the wasted body tissues must be rebuilt. Also, the normal fatty tissue, which has supplied the body with fuel while sufficient food could not be taken, must be replaced, for fatty tissue not only serves as a reserve supply of fuel for the body, but in normal amounts it is a protective padding to the vital organs of the body.

The greatest lacks in the diet have usually been vitamins and minerals, but proteins and calories are also very important in recovery, for protein is needed in rebuilding body tissue and surplus calories for restoring the useful body fat. Note from the following typical day's menu for a convalescent how these needs are met by simple, easily digested foods:

A DAY'S MENU FOR A CONVALESCENT

Breakfast

Orange Juice
Whole-Wheat Cereal with Top Milk
Buttered Toast Whole Milk

Mid-Morning

Milk with dried milk added
Cracker or Toast

Lunch

Ground Lamb Patty — broiled
Baked Potato Carrots Milk
Toast Lemon Gelatin

Mid-Afternoon

A fruit beverage or milk, with lactose added

Supper

Cream of Pea Soup Crackers
Stewed Apples

Poached Egg on Toast
Milk

If the diet for a long time has been depleted in minerals and vitamins, the doctor may temporarily prescribe concentrates in these foods as a tonic to aid in restoring health. But vitamins should be supplied from the grocery store in foods instead of from the drugstore in "concentrates" unless the latter are prescribed by a physician.

CLASS PROBLEMS

1. Prepare beverages especially suitable for the invalid: albumenized drinks, lactose in drinks, modifications of milk.
2. Set an invalid's tray for different menus. Make special invalid dishes, such as junket, gruels, and custards with lactose.
3. Give a practical review of the simple dishes prepared throughout the course that are suitable for feeding the sick.
4. Set up sample menus for a day's feeding on liquid diet, soft diet, light diet. Estimate the calories in each. Plan family menus that could be used on the same day with a minimum of special preparation for the invalid.
5. Increase the calories in the above menus by the addition of albumen, egg yolk, lactose.
6. Demonstrate methods of handling and sterilizing trays from the sick-room which could be practiced in the average home.

HOME PROBLEM

If there is an invalid in your family, prepare the trays for the evening meal for a period of a week. You must first know the doctor's orders and how they are carried out for the other meals of the day. Why?

REFERENCES

Lanman, Faith R., McKay, Hughina, Zuill, Frances. *The Family's Food*, Chapter XXII. J. B. Lippincott Company.

Pattee, A. F. *Practical Dietetics*. A. F. Pattee, publisher, Mt. Vernon, New York.

Rose, Mary Swartz. *Feeding the Family*, Chapters I, II, XIV, XV. The Macmillan Company.

Consult good Cook Books for preparation of invalid dishes prescribed by physician. See page 387.

CHAPTER THIRTY-THREE

❧ Preserving Food by Drying and Canning

Cook Book References

Timetables for Processing Pages 536, 545, 549

Perishable foods may be kept fresh by cold storage and refrigeration, but even so, they will remain in good condition for relatively short periods of time. The temperature of the refrigerator should be 49 degrees F. and below. No foods that can be kept well in other ways should take up space in the refrigerator except for the purpose of chilling in preparation for eating.

Some foods can be kept for months by the method of cool storage or winter storage. These foods include some fruits, vegetables, grains and grain products, honey and sirups, fats, and eggs. Among fruits and vegetables especially suited to this method are white potatoes, cabbage, onions, carrots, apples, and some varieties of pears. If suitable space is available, winter cool storage is the easiest method of keeping these foods because they require little special treatment before storage. The space used must be one that can be kept cool, slightly damp (except for sweet potatoes, grains, and grain products), protected from rodents, and must be arranged to allow free circulation of air around the stored food. The food should be clean, dry, and entirely sound when stored. Some foods, such as apples, keep better if wrapped in paper.

Foods may be preserved for a considerable length of time by drying, canning, and freezing. The method used should be suited to the food that is to be kept, to the facilities for storing it, and to the future need for it. Most preserved foods are best used within a year of the time when they are preserved, so that a plan covering the family's yearly needs helps to determine how much to preserve, and, to some extent, the method to be used. In deciding what method to use for each food that is to be preserved, advantages and disadvantages of each method should be considered. In this chapter, we will discuss drying and canning.

Drying is the oldest method of keeping food. It is used chiefly with such fruits as apples, peaches, apricots, plums, and figs; and with vegetables that are dry seeds when mature, such as navy beans, soybeans, and black-eyed peas. Meat, some raw vegetables, and some cooked vegetables may be dried also.

Canning can be used with success with a wide variety of foods. Canned food may be kept in exactly the same condition for long periods, and ready or nearly ready for use. In canning, use is made of sterilization by heat and of "natural" preservatives, such as sugar, salt, and spices. Chemical preservatives, such as "canning powders," may be dangerous to health and should never be used in canning foods.

Drying Food

When food is to be dried, it is spread on trays made of heavy screening, protected from insects by mosquito wire, and left in a current of air until most of its water has evaporated. The organisms that cause spoilage are dried, as well as the food; thus they can no longer grow and multiply. If the dried food is tightly covered, it will keep well. The flavor and texture of dried food are quite different from the flavor and texture of fresh food of the same variety.

There are four common methods of drying food. The first is to let the trays on which the food is spread stand in fresh air and sunshine. This method is practicable only in very dry seasons. The second method is to let the food stand in a current of air from an electric fan. A third method is called *solar drying.* The trays are placed in a box having a slanting glass top which concentrates the sun's rays. The fourth method is drying by artificial heat. Several trays are put in a frame that is covered on the sides and screened top and bottom. The frame is placed over a stove or some other source of heat, so that the warm air comes in contact with the food. Not much heat is required, but enough is needed to keep the air in motion.

The foods most commonly dried at home are corn, peas, apples, and peaches. For further information on drying, consult your home demonstration agent or write to the United States Bureau of Human Nutrition and Home Economics, Department of Agriculture, Washington, D.C.

FIG. 121. GRADE A HOME-CANNED FRUITS

CANNING

Canning is a very useful home method of preserving food. It consists of heating the food and sealing it in airtight containers. The preservation is due to three things:

1. Canning destroys chemical agents in the food (enzymes) which are beneficial in causing fruits and vegetables to ripen and meat to become tender, but whose continued action causes over-ripening.

2. Canning destroys microscopic organisms in and on the food which cause food to spoil.

3. Canning prevents organisms from getting into the food after it is heated.

To obtain canned fruit and vegetables of superior quality they should be of first-class quality when canned and the whole process should be carried out in as short a time as possible. "Two hours from garden to can" and "no delays" are two good rules which the home canner should follow.

Methods of Canning. Methods of canning are named according to the main piece of equipment that is used in the process, namely:

1. The boiling-water bath method.
2. The steamer or oven method.
3. The open-kettle method.
4. The pressure-canner method.

The steamer or oven method and the open-kettle method do not give uniformly good results and are not recommended. The boiling-water bath is the method to use for fruits, tomatoes, and any vegetable to which a large amount of vinegar has been added, such as pickled beets. The pressure canner is used with all other vegetables and meats.

There are three forms of organisms in food that need to be destroyed: yeast, mold, and bacteria. The bacteria are the hardest to destroy, so that treatment that kills them will destroy yeast and mold as well. Some forms of bacteria are very resistant to heat and require temperatures higher than the boiling point of water to destroy them. In the steam pressure canner these temperatures can be obtained. Only by the use of the pressure canner for canning non-acid vegetables and meats are they made safe. Therefore the rule is to use the pressure canner always in canning meats and non-acid vegetables. Botulinus poisoning has resulted a number of times from eating home-canned vegetables and meats that have not been heated in the canning process to a temperature high enough to destroy the spore form or "resistant" form of bacteria. This is not a danger with acid foods, such as tomatoes and fruits, partly because acid helps heat to destroy bacteria.

The Boiling-Water Bath. A boiling-water bath canner may be made from a wash boiler, a bucket, or any vessel that has a tight lid, if it is large enough to hold the desired number of cans or jars, and deep enough to permit having them on a rack and covered with one or two inches of water above the tops. A rack, made of heavy wire or wooden slats, is necessary to provide a good circulation of water around the jars or cans, and these containers should have a little space around each for the same purpose.

The Steam Pressure Canner. Steam pressure canners are available in different designs and various sizes. When a homemaker buys a canner, she should seek the advice of an experienced person, such as the county home demonstration

FIG. 122. THESE GIRLS ARE EXAMINING A NEW PRESSURE CANNER

The cover is being lifted in the correct way.

agent. The best pressure canner to use in home canning is made of one piece of heavy cast aluminum. The top is held on tightly. It is fitted with an air outlet called a *pet-cock*, a safety valve, and a pressure gauge.

How to Operate a Pressure Canner. For safe operation of a pressure canner, clean the openings of the pet-cock and the safety valve by drawing a string or a narrow strip of cloth through them. Do this at the beginning of the canning season and often during the season.

An accurate pressure gauge is necessary to get the processing temperatures needed to make the food keep. There are two kinds: a dial gauge and a weighted gauge. A weighted gauge needs only to be thoroughly clean. However, a dial gauge, such as shown in the illustration, should be checked before the canning season, and also during the canning season if the canner is used often. Examine the gauge on the canner you use; if it is a dial gauge, ask your home demonstration agent, dealer, or manufacturer how it can be checked.

If your canner has a dial gauge which is off more than 4 pounds, you had better get a new one. But if the gauge is not more than 4 pounds off, you can correct the inaccuracy. For example, suppose the food you are canning is to be processed at 10 pounds steam pressure:

If the gauge reads high	*If the gauge reads low*
1 pound high — process at 11 pounds	1 pound low — process at 9 pounds
2 pounds high — process at 12 pounds	2 pounds low — process at 8 pounds
3 pounds high — process at 13 pounds	3 pounds low — process at 7 pounds
4 pounds high — process at 14 pounds	4 pounds low — process at 6 pounds

Have your canner thoroughly clean. Wash the canner kettle well if you have not used it for some time. Don't put the cover of the canner in water, but wipe it with a soapy cloth, then with a damp, clean cloth. Dry it well.

After all these things have been done, the canner is ready for use. Let us suppose you have several jars or cans of food ready for processing. Here is the procedure to follow:

1. Have 2 or 3 inches of boiling water in the pressure canner.
2. Place the filled jars or cans in the canner. Allow space around the containers for the circulation of steam.
3. Adjust the top and fasten it securely by tightening alternate

lugs first moderately tight, and then tightening very tight in the same order.

4. Heat first with the pet-cock open so the steam can escape, thus driving out all the air. When the steam has escaped in a straight jet for five minutes, the air has been exhausted and the pet-cock should be closed. Closing the pet-cock will allow the pressure to rise, and with it the temperature will rise, which is the reason steam pressure is effective in canning.

5. Process according to the directions for canning in the Cook Book. Watch the pressure gauge. Just before the pressure reaches the required number of pounds, reduce the heat. Maintain the desired pressure for the exact time required in the table for canning. Count time from the time the pressure reaches the desired pressure, and watch carefully to keep the pressure even. When this is not done, water boils out of glass jars, and the food may be improperly cooked.

6. When the processing is completed, stop the cooking by turning off the heat, or by removing the canner from the heat. Allow canner to cool (not on a cold surface or in a draft) until the gauge registers zero. When using No. 2 tin cans it is possible to begin gradually releasing the pressure from the pet-cock when it has gone down to five pounds. Release the fastenings, and lift the side of the lid away from you first, to avoid steam burns. (See Figure 122.)

Leave glass jars in the canner for one or two minutes, but remove tin cans immediately and plunge into cold water; lift out glass jars carefully, tighten the cover of each, and leave them upright until they have cooled (avoid drafts and cold surfaces for cooling hot jars).

7. If you have a second batch to process, repeat steps 1 to 6. Be sure to re-check the water level in the canner kettle.

8. Wash the pressure canner after it has been used, avoiding the use of abrasives on the surfaces of lid and base that join, leave entire canner including safety valve and pet-cock dry, use a tooth-pick to clean small openings.

Glass Jars. The various types of jars for home use are: (1) the screw-top Mason jar or modified Mason jar, used with a rubber; (2) the glass-top jar with a rubber, sealed with a wire clamp or with a screw-top metal band; (3) the automatic or vacuum-seal jar which has a lacquered top with the sealing material in a groove in the top. A clamp is needed during processing to hold the top on

FIG. 123. SEALING TIN CANS

the vacuum-seal jar. As the jar cools, the sealing material hardens and a vacuum made by condensing steam forms inside the jar; the seal is thereby completed. Types 1 and 2 require a new rubber each time they are used; type 3 requires a new lid each time. All jars should be washed before they are used.

Rubber rings for glass jars should be of good quality. To test, double the ring and press the fold with the fingers. You will find that good rubber will not crack. Or if you stretch it to twice its length, it should return without change of shape.

Tin Cans. Tin cans require the use of a machine that seals the top on the can with an airtight seal. Cans have some advantages over glass jars. They heat quickly and cool quickly, and this prevents overcooking of the food; they do not break unless very roughly handled; more tin cans may be placed in a boiling-water bath and in a pressure canner than glass jars; there is less loss of liquid from cans.

There are three kinds of tin cans available for home canning. One is plain tin. Another has a deep-gold color lining with a bright finish. This lining is called "R-enamel" (or sanitary or standard enamel). The third kind of can has a light gold color lining with a dull finish. This lining is called "C-enamel" or corn enamel. It is important to choose the correct kind of can for each kind of food you preserve. See the tables on pages 536 and 545.

Gaskets of paper or of rubber composition are found under the rim of can lids, and they help make the seal perfect. Paper gaskets must be kept dry; rubber gaskets may be best, after one becomes expert in sealing cans with them. Tin cans should be washed with soap and water before use, but lids can only be wiped out with a damp cloth.

Steps in Canning. Safe canning requires careful attention to every step in the process from the selection of the raw food to the final check-up of the canned products during storage. The following list gives the steps in order:

1. SELECT GOOD MATERIALS. The quality of canned products can be no higher than the quality of the raw food that goes into the can. Use only clean, fresh, sound foods in prime condition, and be sure that the containers in which they are handled are clean. Any unnecessary infection of the raw food increases the difficulty of processing and the liability of spoilage of the canned products.

With fruits and vegetables, grade for size and the same degree of ripeness if a uniform product is desired. Wash thoroughly until every trace of soil is removed. Bacteria that are very dangerous and most difficult to kill may be found in the soil. A wire basket is a help in washing, but should not be loaded too heavily. To avoid bruising, always lift the fruit and vegetables out of the water rather than pour the water off.

2. PREPARE JARS OR CANS. Wash thoroughly and rinse. If glass jars are used, immerse them in a hot-water bath.

3. SIRUP. Make the sirup for fruits in advance so there will be no delay when it is required. Make sirup of sugar by dissolving sugar in cold water by stirring. When ready to use, heat to boiling and use hot.

4. PRECOOKING. Some foods are precooked for a short time before they are packed into the containers. This precooking helps to remove air from the tissues, shrinks the foods, facilitates packing, and speeds up the processing because the foods are already hot when they are placed in the canner.

5. PACKING. When using glass jars, remove one jar at a time from the hot-water bath where it has been held. Keeping the jars hot helps to prevent breakage during packing and processing. If needed, place a new wet rubber ring in position resting flat on the sealing shoulder of the jar.

Pack the containers quickly so that the precooked food remains hot. Use a sufficient proportion of liquid to solids to prevent too dense a pack, and work out the air bubbles with a knife blade.

6. EXHAUSTING AND ADJUSTING COVERS. As each glass jar is packed, carefully wipe off the rubber ring to remove any particles of food, and adjust the cap so that the jar is only partly sealed. Place the jars as finished in the canner or where they will keep hot until processing begins. During the processing, the air in the jars is removed; that is, the jars are *exhausted.*

Tin cans packed with precooked food should be sealed at once, while the food is steaming hot, and placed in the canner. If the food has not been precooked before packing, the cans should be exhausted. This is done by setting them in a pan of hot water and heating until the air is driven out. Seal the cans at once after exhausting.

7. PROCESSING. Process at the temperature and for the time indicated in the tables in the Cook Book.

8. COOLING. Cool glass jars in air but protect them from drafts. After they are cool, check the jars for leakage. Do not attempt to tighten screw caps or screw bands after the jars have cooled. Cool tin cans in cold water, using running water if possible.

9. REPROCESSING. If any containers show signs of leakage, they should be opened immediately, the contents heated and repacked in other containers, and processed again as at first.

10. LABELING. Wipe the containers clean and label with the name, the date, and the lot number, if more than one lot was canned on that day. Glass jars may be labeled with a pencil that writes on glass, or with gummed labels. Use rubber cement to fix paper labels on tin, or if the labels are long enough, put glue along one end, wrap smoothly around the can, and lap the glued end over the other. Tin cans may be marked with a glass pencil, rubber stamp, or canners' ink.

11. CHECKING RESULTS. Hold canned products at room temperature for a week or ten days where they can be examined from time to time to be sure that they are keeping. If any show signs of spoilage, examine all of that lot carefully.

FIG. 124. READY FOR WINTER

12. STORAGE. Store canned foods in a cool, dry place. Protect glass jars from the light so that the food will not fade in color.

Canning Meats and Chicken. Beef, lamb, veal, and chicken may be canned successfully in the home, provided they are processed under steam pressure. They may seem to be all right if canned in other ways, but experience has shown that they may contain dangerous poisons. Pork, except for the cuts listed in the table on canning meats, is usually cured or frozen and not canned.

Meat spoils quickly. Quick work is necessary in preparing meat for canning and in processing meat to prevent spoilage during the canning process.

Examination of Canned Foods Before Use. All foods should be inspected before being prepared for the table. If there is any evidence of spoilage, the food should be discarded and non-acid vegetables and meats should be burned.

Inspect the can or jar before opening. In tin cans both ends should be flat and curved slightly inward. Neither end should bulge or snap back when pressed. All seams should be tight and clean, with no traces of leaks. In glass jars there should be no bulging of the rubber and no signs of leakage.

Never taste to discover spoilage. When spoilage has occurred in non-acid foods there is always a possibility that even a taste may cause serious illness. For this reason it is good practice to boil all canned non-acid vegetables before using them.

When the container is opened there should not be any sudden outburst of air or spurting of liquid. The odor should be characteristic of the product. Any different odor probably indicates spoilage. The inside of tin cans should be smooth and clean or well lacquered and not markedly corroded. Food may be left in a tin can after it is opened, provided it is covered and kept cold just as any other cooked food. Acid foods and tomatoes may dissolve minute quantities of iron from the can and acquire a slightly metallic flavor, but this is harmless. The purple that develops in red fruits and sometimes in peaches and pears canned in tin is merely a change in the color pigments and is also harmless.

The broth over canned meats and chicken may or may not be jellied, depending on the quantity of connective tissue and cartilage in the meat. A liquid broth is no indication of spoilage. The temperature and time recommended for processing meats are greater than for vegetables and should destroy all dangerous bacteria.

Questions and Answers on Canning [1]

Q. Is it safe to process foods in the oven?

A. No, oven canning is dangerous. Jars may seal during processing and explode, wrecking the stove and seriously cutting or burning persons. The temperature of the food in the jars during oven processing does not get high enough to insure destruction of spoilage bacteria in vegetables without exceedingly long processes.

Q. Why is the open-kettle method not recommended for canning fruits and vegetables?

A. In open-kettle canning, food is cooked in an ordinary kettle, then packed into hot sterile jars and sealed without processing. When the food is transferred from kettle to jar, bacteria may get in and cause food to spoil. And for vegetables, the temperatures obtained in open-kettle canning are not high enough to destroy all the spoilage organisms that may be in the food unless it is cooked for an excessively long time.

Q. Must glass jars and lids be sterilized by boiling before canning?

A. No, not when boiling-water bath or pressure-canner method is used. The containers as well as the food are sterilized during processing. But be sure jars and lids are thoroughly clean, and to prevent breakage have jars hot when filling them.

Q. Why is liquid sometimes lost from glass jars during processing?

A. Loss of liquid may be due to cooking food too short a time to drive out the air that's in it before packing it in the jars . . . packing jars too full . . . leaving air bubbles in the jars . . . not keeping pressure steady in a pressure canner . . . lowering pressure too suddenly at the end of the processing period.

Q. Should liquid lost during processing be replaced?

A. No, never open a jar and refill with liquid — this would let in bacteria and you'd need to process again. Loss of liquid does not cause food to spoil, though the food above the liquid may darken.

[1] *Home Canning of Fruits and Vegetables.* AIS-64. United States Department of Agriculture.

Q. What causes cloudy liquid in canned fruits and vegetables?
A. Cloudy liquid may be a sign of spoilage. Or it may be caused by the minerals in hard water, or by starch from overripe vegetables.

Q. How can you tell whether food with cloudy liquid is spoiled?
A. Boil the food and note the odor. Do not taste or use any food having an off odor.

Q. Is it true that ascorbic acid helps keep fruits and vegetables from darkening?
A. The addition of 250 milligrams of ascorbic acid (Vitamin C) to a quart of fruit or vegetable before it is processed retards oxidation, which is one cause of darkening of canned foods.

Q. Is it all right to use preservatives in home canning?
A. Do not use canning powders or other chemical preservatives — some of them may be harmful. Sterilization by heat is safer and more certain.

CLASS PROBLEMS

1. Examine the various types of jars and covers, also tin cans.
2. Examine two types of canners, water bath and pressure.
3. Can in water bath some of the following according to season:

Tomatoes	Peaches	Beets (pickled)
Berries	Rhubarb	Cherries
Plums	Strawberries	

4. Can in the pressure canner some of the following according to season:

Asparagus	Peas
String beans	Spinach or other greens
Beets	Sweet potatoes
Lima or butter beans	Chicken or meat

5. Invite the Home Demonstration Agent to give canning demonstrations, especially meat canning.

HOME PROBLEMS

1. Can twelve jars of fruit or tomatoes at home in the water-bath canner. Label and store the jars.

2. If a pressure canner is available, can a number of jars or cans of various non-acid vegetables, using the hot-pack and cold-pack methods.
3. Make a study of the brands, labels, and contents of the canned goods you use at home.
4. If you have a surplus of vegetables that can be stored, write to the agricultural college in your state for directions for storing these vegetables. Follow the directions. Also consult experienced housewives in your locality.

REFERENCES

Collins, James H. *The Story of Canned Foods.* E. P. Dutton and Company. The history of canning and the canning industry.

Farm and Home Drying of Fruits and Vegetables. United States Department of Agriculture, Farmers' Bulletin 984.

Recent bulletins or circulars from your State Agricultural College or State University.

The following bulletins prepared by the Bureau of Human Nutrition and Home Economics, published by the United States Department of Agriculture:

Home Canning of Fruits and Vegetables. Bulletin AIS-64.
Home Canning of Meat. Bulletin AWI-110.

CHAPTER THIRTY-FOUR

❧ Making Fruit "Preserves" and Freezing Foods

Cook Book References

Jellies, Preserves, and Relishes	*Page* 550
Freezing Foods	*Page* 555

JELLY, PRESERVES, CONSERVES, AND JAMS are very rich sweets. They are of use in making plain food more acceptable. Marmalade with toast is an example. Jelly may be thinly spread on bread for sandwiches in the school lunch. A spoonful of preserves or jam may make a rice pudding or a simple tapioca dessert acceptable. A small spoonful of jelly also makes a plain mold of cooked rice or other cereal into an acceptable dessert for children. Jelly, if tart, may be served with meat. If conserves are used sparingly they give variety to the diet and are not unwholesome. They should not be used in the diets of very young children.

JELLY-MAKING

Selection of the Fruit. Three ingredients are necessary for making good jelly from fruit juices: pectin, acid, and sugar. Pectin is a gum-like carbohydrate substance found in some fruits. It is responsible for the firmness of jelly. The greatest quantity of pectin and acid is found in fruits that are just underripe. The best flavor is furnished by ripe fruit. In selecting fruit for jelly-making, some of the fruit should be underripe to insure the presence of pectin and acid, and some of it should be ripe to insure the best flavor. The fruits containing the most pectin and acid are:

Apples	Currants
Crab apples	Plums
Blackberries	Underripe grapes
Cranberries	

Quince and guava have pectin, but lack acid. Very fine jelly can be made from both these fruits if acid is added. Lemon juice or commercially prepared citric acid may be used to supply acid.

The making of jelly from such fruits as ripe grapes, strawberries, peaches, pears, and cherries is difficult or uncertain because they do not contain the right amount of pectin. Jelly can be made from these fruits by adding pectin extract to the fruit juice.

Preparation of the Fruit. Select a mixture of slightly underripe and ripe fruit and prepare in small quantities of 6 to 8 pounds. Discard damaged parts of the fruit; wash thoroughly; remove the stem and blossom ends; remove caps and stems of berries; peel if there is evidence of spray residue; cut into small uniform pieces, leaving the core.

Extraction of the Juice. Pectin is obtained from fruit juice by boiling. Use the proportions of water to fruit given in the table below unless the fruit seems a little hard and dry, when more water may be needed.

PROPORTIONS OF WATER TO FRUIT AND OF SUGAR TO FRUIT JUICE IN MAKING JELLIES [1]

Kind of Fruit	*Quantity of Water to Each Pound of Prepared Fruit (for Extraction of Juice)*	*Time of Boiling Fruit to Extract Juice*	*Quantity of Sugar to Each Cup of Fruit Juice*
	Cup	*Minutes*	*Cup*
Apples	1	20 to 25	¾
Crab apples	1	20 to 25	1
Blackberries	Firm fruit, ¼	5 to 10	¾ to 1
	Very soft fruit, none	5 to 10	¾ to 1
Black raspberries	Same as blackberries	5 to 10	1
Cranberries	3	5 to 10	¾
Currants	¼ or none	5 to 10	1
Gooseberries	¼	5 to 10	1
Grapes, such as Concord	¼ or none	5 to 10	¾ to 1
Grapes, wild	1	5 to 10	1
Plums, wild goose type	½	15 to 20	¾
Quinces	2	20 to 25	¾
Red raspberries	None	5 to 10	1

Crush berries and soft fruits with a wooden spoon to start the flow of juice; boil in a broad, flat-bottomed kettle, stirring to prevent burning. Start counting time when the fruit begins to boil. Pour the hot fruit and juice into a jelly bag and let the juice drip without pressing the bag until dripping has almost stopped, then

[1] *Homemade Jellies, Jams, and Preserves.* United States Department of Agriculture, Farmers' Bulletin 1800.

press gently; strain the juice again through a bag wrung out in hot water. This juice may be canned without sugar to be used later for making small lots of jelly, if desired. The flavor will be good, but the color may not be quite so good as it is if the jelly is made immediately. If clear jelly is not desired, a wire strainer may be used instead of a jelly bag. The jelly will taste as good, but will not look so pretty as clear jelly.

FIG. 125. THE JELLY TEST

A second extraction may be made by covering the pulp with water, heating to boiling, and heating over hot water for 20 to 25 minutes.

Two tests for the amount of pectin in the juice are in use. A jelmeter is sometimes used. Another test that gives some indication of pectin can be made by pouring an equal amount of denatured alcohol (1 T.) into a sample of the juice (1 T.) *without stirring.* If there is a good amount of pectin, about half of the juice settles in a clear jelly-like mass.

Making the Jelly. Jelly should be made quickly, therefore work with small amounts of juice, not more than six cups at a time. Use a flat-bottomed kettle that permits plenty of room for rapid boiling. Measure the amount of sugar given in the table, preferring ¾ cup instead of one where a choice is given, except when you believe the juice is exceptionally rich in pectin. Combine sugar and fruit juice without preheating. If acid content of juice seems low, use one tablespoon of lemon juice to each cup of liquid, or 1 teaspoon of powdered citric acid to each 6 cups of juice. Heat the juice and sugar quickly to boiling, stirring only until the sugar is dissolved.

Testing the Jelly. Boil rapidly until the jelly stage is reached. The jelly test is the sheeting-off of the mixture from the edge of a large spoon, when the spoon is dipped in the mixture and held up so that the mixture runs off from the side of the spoon. A thermometer is a more reliable way of testing the jelly. Jelly is done when cooked to 222° to 224° F.

FIG. 126. JELLY-MAKING

SCORE CARD FOR JELLY.[1]

Points	Score
1. Package: Glasses of good shape, suitable size, tops clean, tight, and free from tarnish; paraffin layer (if any) smooth, no bubbles or breaks; labels suitable, attractive.....	5
2. Color: Color natural, as determined by the fruit used, no artificial coloring used except for mint jelly. Color deepened by wise use of sugar and other sweetener, not darkened by overcooking..........................	10
3. Clearness: Transparent or translucent, not cloudy nor containing pulpy particles. No bubbles or visible crystals. No mold nor signs of fermentation. No scum or bubbles at top....................................	10
4. Texture (judged after glass is opened): Jelly should hold its shape when turned out on a plate, but should quiver when the plate is moved. Should cut easily with spoon, be tender, yet break with a sharp cleavage line and show sparkling faces. Not sticky, tough, gummy; not brittle; not sirupy; not sugary; no crystals that can be perceived on tongue...	40
5. Flavor: Attractive, pronounced fruity flavor, yet not too sour, nor yet oversweet; not caramelized or scorched.....	35
Total..	100

[1] *Homemade Apple and Citrus Pectin Extracts and Their Use in Jelly-Making.* United States Department of Agriculture, Department Circular 254.

Filling the Jelly Glasses. Sterilize jelly glasses and tops by boiling in clear water. Let the mixture stand in the kettle while the clean jelly glasses are taken from hot water, drained, and placed on a wooden surface or other surface that is not cold; remove scum from the jelly; pour jelly into glasses within one-fourth inch of the top; place tin covers on the glasses and leave them undisturbed while the jelly sets. As soon as it is set, melt paraffin in a small pan or metal teapot kept for the purpose, remove the covers and cover jelly well so that the paraffin sticks to sides of the glass and covers the jelly completely. Wipe the inside of each tin cover and replace; label the jelly and store in a cool, dry, dark place.

Making Preserves and Similar Sweets

Preserves are made from whole small fruits, such as figs, strawberries, kumquats; or from sliced large fruits, such as peaches, pears, quinces. This product is very rich. Three fourths of a pound of sugar to one pound of fruit are the required proportions. The mixture of fruit and sugar should start cooking in a thin sirup if the preserve is to be tender, plump, and light in color. A thick sirup causes the fruit to shrink and makes a tough, dark product. Some hard fruits, such as quince and watermelon rind, require parboiling. Figs should be soaked in soda water. Watermelon rind, if it is to make a clear preserve, is usually soaked in lime water, and alum is added to make it crisp.

Preserves are sometimes partly cooked on one day, allowed to stand overnight in the sirup, and finished the next day. This method makes the pieces more plump. They should be cooked to 222° or 224° F., and then packed in sterilized jars.

Marmalade is of jelly-like consistency. It contains sliced or finely chopped fruit. Citrus fruit marmalade is the kind most commonly used — made of orange, orange and grapefruit, grapefruit, or kumquat. The product is prettier if the rind is sliced almost paper thin. The coarse blade of a food chopper may be used. This is much less trouble, but rind cut that way does not become so clear as rind cut very thin, and the resulting marmalade is not so pleasing in appearance.

Citrus marmalade may be cooked in one day if the fruit has been prepared and has stood for some hours in water, or the process may be carried out on separate days. The three-day process gives a larger yield of marmalade because more pectin is extracted.

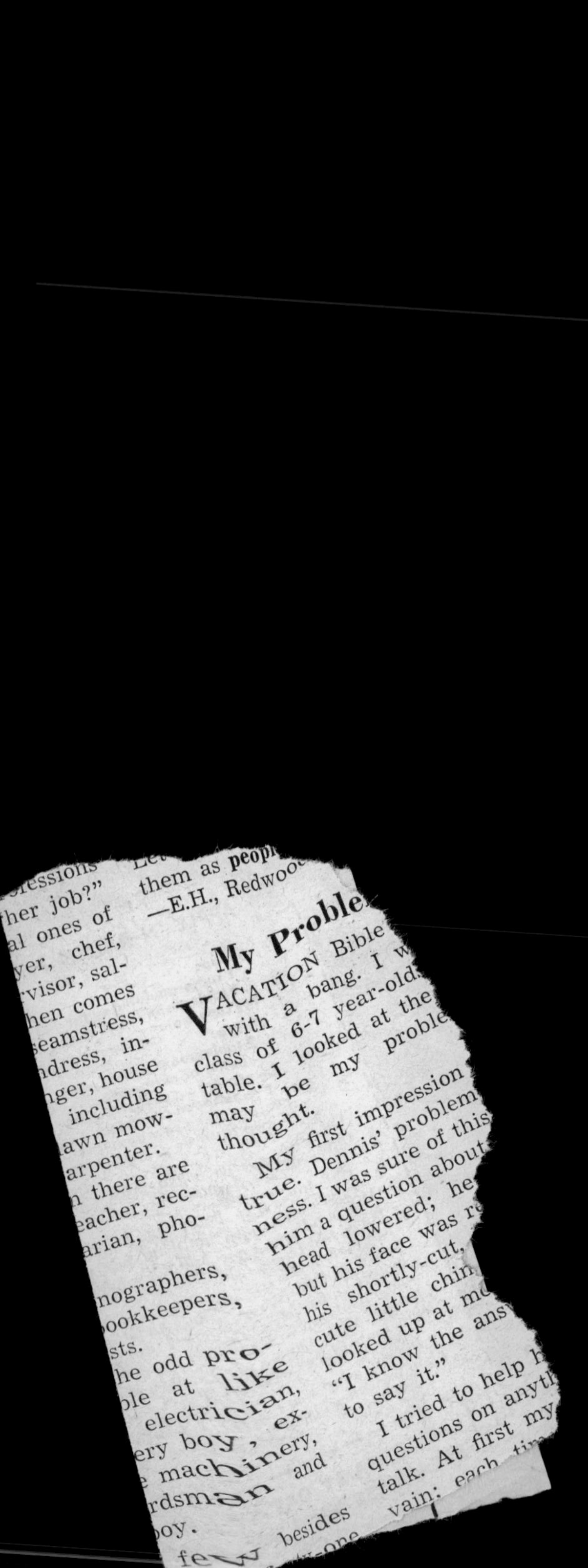

...essions
her job?"
al ones of
yer, chef,
visor, sal-
hen comes
seamstress,
ndress, in-
nger, house
including
awn mow-
arpenter.
n there are
eacher, rec-
arian, pho-
nographers,
ookkeepers,
sts.
he odd pro-
ple at like
electrician,
ery boy, ex-
machinery,
rdsman and
boy.
few besides

them as peopl
—E.H., Redwoo

My Proble

VACATION Bible
with a bang. I w
class of 6-7 year-old
table. I looked at the
may be my proble
thought.

My first impression
true. Dennis' problem
ness. I was sure of this
him a question about
head lowered; he
but his face was r
his shortly-cut,
cute little chin
looked up at m
"I know the ans
to say it."

I tried to help h
questions on anyth
talk. At first my
vain: each ti

Marmalade should be cooked rapidly if a light color and the maximum of flavor are to be obtained. The process is finished at 222° to 224° F. To prevent the fruit from rising to the top of the glasses, cool the mixture slightly, then fill sterilized glasses. Cover the glasses with paraffin as jelly is covered. (See recipes in the Cook Book, page 551.)

Jams are made from fruits containing little or no pectin, such as berries and figs. Jam is better if pectin is present. Three fourths of a pound of sugar to one of the cooked fruit is used. The fruit should be just under ripe unless pectin extract is used, in which case ripe fruit may be used. Why?

Jam should be made in small quantities and cooked rapidly in order to get the best flavor and color. It should be stirred while cooking. The process is finished at 220° to 224° F. (See recipes.)

Fruit butter is made from the pulp of such fruits as plums and apples. Ripe fruit is used. The fruit is cooked and the pulp mashed through a colander or a fruit press. Fruit butter may be made from the pulp left from jelly-making. Add a little fresh juice or a little jelly to this pulp. Less sugar is required for fruit butters than for preserves and jams — not more than a fourth of a pound of sugar to one pound of fruit. Spice is usually added to fruit butter.

Conserves are a mixture of fruits cooked to the consistency of a jam. Raisins and nuts are usually added. Conserves must be cooked rapidly, and stirring will be necessary to prevent burning.

Preservation of Foods by Freezing

The newest method of home food preservation is quick-freezing at low temperatures, either in a home freezer or in a neighborhood freezer-locker plant. Freezing, unlike canning, does not destroy the microorganisms that spoil food. However, it does make them inactive. Zero (0° F.) is the temperature at which frozen foods should be stored for best results. As the temperature rises above zero, the microorganisms that spoil food grow again, causing first loss of quality, and then spoilage. Frozen foods spoil rapidly when thawed; hence, they should be used promptly and should not be refrozen.

Frozen foods, if properly prepared and stored, will maintain their quality for as long as 9 to 12 months. No more than a year's supply of food, therefore, should be frozen in one season.

Steps in freezing food, either commercially or by the family, are:
Selecting the food.
Preparing the food.
Packing it in containers.
Freezing it rapidly.
Storing it at the temperature at which it will keep best.

Selecting Fruits and Vegetables for Freezing

Freezing makes possible garden freshness in foods the year round. If fruits and vegetables are frozen according to instructions, they will be in their natural bright colors, will have a fresh flavor, and will retain most of their vitamin values.

Fruits and vegetables for freezing should be selected when they are at their best. Avoid over-ripe and bruised fruits, and wilted and over-matured vegetables. Food that comes out of the freezer can be no better than the food that was put in it. The sooner fruits and vegetables can be frozen after picking, the better will be the frozen product.

Practically all fruits and vegetables can be frozen. The vegetables that are not recommended for freezing are (1) those with a high starch content, such as potatoes, (2) over-mature peas and beans, and (3) those with a high water content that are to be served raw in salads or as relishes where crispness is desirable, as tomatoes, cucumbers, lettuce, celery, onions, and radishes.

Some varieties of fruits and vegetables freeze better than others. For a list of the varieties in your locality that will give the best quality of frozen product, write your State College of Agriculture.

Preparing Fruits and Vegetables for Freezing

In preparing fruits and vegetables for freezing, first sort them carefully, discarding all over-ripe, under-ripe, bruised, or deteriorating food. Wash the food you select thoroughly in clear water, lifting it out of the wash water so that all dirt will remain behind. Drain the food and dry it immediately with paper or cloth towels. Then prepare the food as for cooking or serving — peeling, trimming, or slicing as usual. (See Tables D and E, pages 558 and 560.)

Special Steps in Preparing Fruits for Freezing. Most fruits have better flavor and texture if sweetened before freezing. Some fruits, such as raspberries, cranberries, and loganberries, are good frozen without sugar. Sweetening may be either with dry sugar or with a sugar sirup. For specific directions for sweetening each fruit, see the Cook Book.

To prevent darkening, fruit (peaches, for example) may be allowed to stand in a solution of citric acid for one or two minutes before packing in sirup or sugar. To make the solution, dissolve ¼ teaspoon of citric acid in 1 quart of water. Citric acid is inexpensive and is available at the drugstore. About a gallon of this citric acid solution is needed for each bushel of fruit. A second way of preventing darkening may be used when the fruit is packed in a sirup. Ascorbic acid (Vitamin C) is added to the sugar sirup, using ¼ teaspoon to 1 cup of sirup. Ascorbic acid can be obtained from the drugstore. It is a little more expensive than citric acid. To keep apples from darkening, slice and immediately scald the slices in steam or boiling water for two minutes or a little less.

Special Steps in Preparing Vegetables for Freezing. Vegetables should be cut into pieces convenient for serving. All vegetables

FIG. 127. A VERY EFFICIENT WAY OF PREPARING A VEGETABLE FOR FREEZING

Notice the basket with scalded and chilled corn on left; the damp cloth and scoop for putting corn into cartons within easy reach; the filling funnel; the tray with labeled cartons set up ready to be filled; and the sealing platform and iron all within reach on the cabinet.

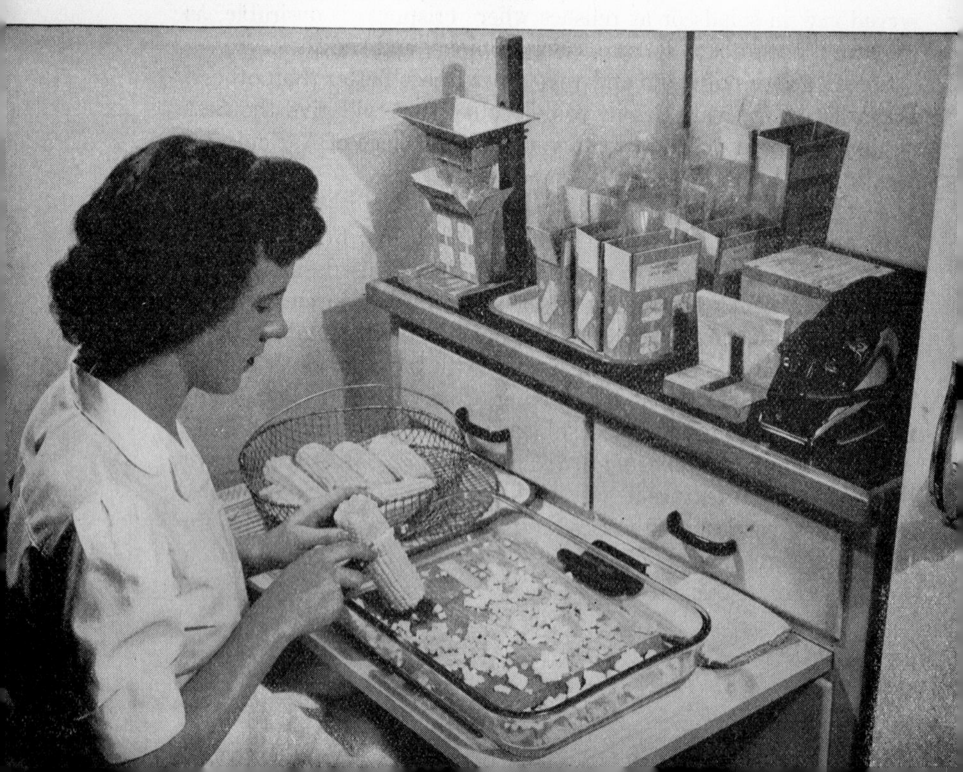

must be blanched before freezing. Blanching or scalding, serves to brighten the color, soften the vegetable, making it easier to pack, and increases the keeping qualities of vegetables by lessening enzyme action. Enzymes are chemical compounds that help in the growth and ripening of vegetables. After a plant reaches maturity, continued enzyme action causes it to lose flavor, color, and vitamins. These changes will continue after freezing if the vegetables are not scalded evenly and long enough.

For scalding or blanching vegetables, use rapidly boiling water. Scalding time should be counted from the time the vegetables are put into the boiling water after the lid is put on the kettle. For each vegetable, follow the directions on specific vegetables given on page 558 of the Cook Book. Broccoli is best scalded in steam.

A fine mesh wire basket, with a lid that fits, to hold the vegetables under the water is best. Small quantities, about 1 pound, should be scalded at a time in order to heat the vegetable evenly. For scalding, the vegetables should be sorted according to size, and pieces of similar size scalded or blanched together for even heating.

After scalding, chill the food immediately in cold water to stop the cooking and to reduce the chance of spoilage through the growth of microorganisms while the food is warm and moist. Plunge the scalded vegetables into enough ice water, or very cold running water to cool them quickly. Test the coolness of the vegetable by biting a piece. When it feels cool to the tongue, remove the water and drain. A good general rule is to chill the vegetable in cold water about the same length of time as was required to scald it.

All vegetables, except green peppers, should be dry packed. A brine solution, using 1 teaspoon of salt to 1 cup of water, is recommended for packing green peppers for freezing.

Packaging

The air in a freezer is very dry; consequently, unless food is properly packaged, moisture will pass from the food to the air, and the food will deteriorate. Food to be frozen should *always* be packed in specially made containers that are moisture- vapor-proof. These are usually plastic-coated boxes and cartons with specially treated linings or covers or both. The most convenient lining is a bag, made of "locker paper" or "freezer paper."

Glass jars are now especially made for freezing. These have wide openings so the frozen food can be removed without thawing. Tin

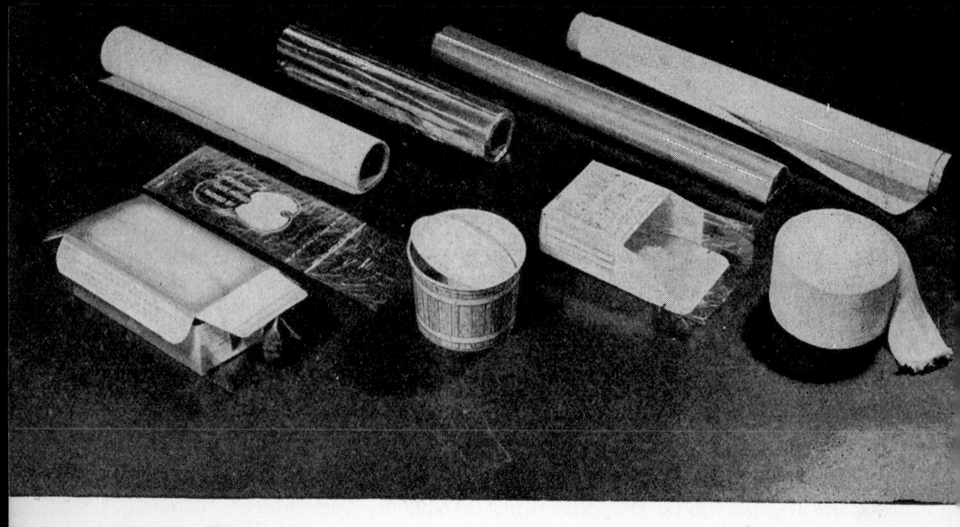

FIG. 128. MOISTURE- AND VAPOR-RESISTANT CONTAINERS FOR FREEZING FOODS, AND HEAT-SEALING SHEETS OF SPECIAL FOIL AND CELLOPHANE

The roll at the right is stockinette, used for wrapping meats.

cans may be used for fruits, but should not be used for vegetables until more research is done on their use.

Rectangular containers pack in the freezer more economically than round ones. Ordinary waxed cups or cartons such as used for cottage cheese and ice cream, should not be used because they cannot be sealed so they are vapor-proof.

Size of Package. Since the entire contents of a package of frozen food should be cooked at one time, it is advisable to select the size of container that best fits the family's requirement. The 1 pound carton is a very usable size package. Small containers have the added advantage of freezing more quickly. The quicker the freezing, the better the quality of the product. Each family should "get a fit" in the size of package for each type of frozen food used.

Filling the Container. Food expands when it freezes, therefore, it is necessary to leave space for expansion in the container. When foods are packed without liquid, allow ½ inch head space at the top of the container, except for loosely packed foods, such as broccoli or cauliflower, which need no head space. For foods packed in liquid, or for crushed fruits, or vegetable purees, leave 1 inch head space.

Sealing and Labeling. After filling a carton or bag, wipe the inside edges clean and dry. Any moisture left on the surfaces to be sealed will prevent a tight seal. Press out all air possible from the top of the package. Fold the surfaces together and press with a warm iron or curling iron. The iron should be at about the temperature for pressing silk. Use only enough heat and pressure to hold the edges tightly together. Over-heating will cause a poor seal.

Every package should be labeled with the following information:

1. Variety of food in the package
2. Date of packing
3. Special details: whether the food is sliced or whole, packed with sugar or without, etc.

Freezing and Storing

Food should be frozen as soon as possible after packaging. As soon as each package is ready, put it in the refrigerator until you have finished the batch and are ready to put it in the freezer.

Freezing Foods. If you have a home freezer, you know that the manufacturer supplies instructions for using it. Here are three general rules:

1. Be sure the temperature is 0° F. or below.
2. For freezing, place the packages against freezing plates or coils. Space them so that air can move between the packages.
3. Allow at least 24 hours for each freezing. If the packages are thick, or heavily wrapped, the freezing period should be longer.

A freezer-locker plant may have a fast freezing room, sometimes called a sharp-freeze room. If such facilities are available, have the food frozen in the fast freezing room.

Storing Frozen Foods. Store frozen foods in the home freezer or the community freezer-locker, where the temperature is 0° F. or lower. Food will deteriorate in palatability, appearance, and in food value if stored above zero (0° F.), even though it remains frozen.

If the electric current is off, or if the freezer fails to operate, *do not open the cabinet needlessly.* Food in a loaded cabinet will stay frozen for two days, even in summer. If the cabinet is not loaded (half full or less), the food may not stay frozen for more than a day.

If there is a stoppage of more than one or two days, locate a freezer-locker plant and arrange to move the food there using an insulated box. Or put dry ice in each compartment. Fifty pounds of dry ice in a 20 cubic foot cabinet should hold the temperature in the cabinet for several days.

An inventory of what is in frozen storage and where and when it is placed in the freezer is recommended. Whenever food is taken from the freezer it should be checked off the list, keeping the inventory up-to-date.

Preparing Meat for Freezing

Select good meat. Freezing will not make good meat out of poor meat. For tender, tasty meat to serve, freeze meat of good quality.

The meat for freezing should be cut and trimmed to the size that is desired for cooking and serving. Steaks and chops should be cut and trimmed to the thickness desired. Ground meat should be shaped as wanted for cooking. In other words, the meat should be prepared so it is ready for cooking, with one exception — *do not season* with any salt before freezing. Salt will make a frozen product of poorer quality.

Place a layer of the moisture- vapor-proof wrapping material between individual steaks, chops, or ground meat patties to keep them from freezing together. Pack together only the amount of meat to be cooked and served for a meal.

Package meat carefully, using special moisture- vapor-proof material prepared for freezing, such as special cellophane or special paper made for freezing. (Do not use ordinary wax paper or wrapping paper.) Use enough wrapping so that the ends can be folded tightly or seal open ends with a heated iron. Then wrap each package in stockinette, cheese cloth, or heavy paper, avoiding excess wrapping because it will delay freezing. Label each package with its contents and the date.

Preparing Poultry for Freezing

Select poultry of good quality. No other poultry is worth space in the freezer. To be sure of good taste and appearance, the chicken should be carefully cleaned, thoroughly drawn, and properly dressed.

Broilers. Cut in half as for broiling. Place a piece of "freezer paper" between the two halves to keep them from freezing together. Wrap giblets separately. Carefully wrap the entire bird in moisture- vapor-proof material and seal tightly, as for meats. Cover with stockinette.

Fryers. Cut the chicken in the pieces desired for frying or for fricassee. Wrap giblets separately. Place the cut pieces in a carton that is properly lined with moisture- vapor-proof paper. To prevent the pieces from freezing together, place "freezer paper" between the pieces. Tightly seal the carton.

Roasters. When preparing the whole chicken, or any other fowl, for roasting, it should be trussed (see pages 476–477) by tying the legs and wings close to the body. Wrap giblets separately in moisture- vapor-proof paper and place inside the chicken. Put the roasting chicken in a cellophane bag, seal tightly, and cover with stockinette, as for meats.

Mark all packages with the contents and the date.

CLASS PROBLEMS

1. Make jelly from fruits containing both acid and pectin. (Recipes, page 550.)
2. Make jellies from fruits containing little pectin by using pectin extract. (Recipes, page 551.) Recipes may also be obtained from distributors of commercial pectin extract.
3. Figure the cost of all jellies made. Score by score card (page 376). Compare in cost and quality with commercial products.
4. Make typical preserve from fruit available in your locality.
5. Make jam from some typical small fruits, such as berries. Experiment with pectin extract in jam-making. Compare costs, quantities, flavor, and quality. (Recipes, page 553.)
6. Suggest menus in which the jelly preserves and conserves that you have made would be delicious.
7. Visit a locker refrigeration plant and a commercial freezing plant, if possible. Observe methods used and discuss costs of freezing and foods frozen most successfully.
8. Prepare for the table one kind of frozen meat, a frozen fruit to be eaten raw, and a frozen vegetable.
9. Explore your community for sources of supplies for packaging and labeling foods for freezing and storing.

HOME PROBLEMS

1. Make jelly at home from plums, cranberries, apples, or some other fruit rich in pectin.
2. Preserve fruits at home by the methods learned at school.
3. If apples or citrus fruits are plentiful, make pectin extracts.

4. Make jellies or jams with commercial or homemade pectin extracts, and with part pineapple juice.
5. Make jelly from dried apples or conserves from dried apricots, prunes, or peaches.

REFERENCES

Homemade Jellies, Jams, and Preserves. Farmers' Bulletin 1800.

Write for bulletins from your State Agricultural College.

Recipes from producers of citrus fruits and dried fruits.

Recipes in bulletins on special fruits, such as strawberries, from the United States Department of Agriculture.

Bulletins from the Agricultural Experiment Station and Agricultural Extension Division of your State College of Agriculture.

Carlton, Harry. *Home Preparation of Fruits and Vegetables for the Freezer-Locker.* University of Tennessee Agricultural Experiment Station, Bulletin 168.

Child, Alice M. *Thawing and Cooking Frozen Meats.* Agricultural Extension Division, Bulletin 189, University of Minnesota.

Diehl, H. C., and Birdseye, M. *Storage of Fruits and Vegetables in Community Freezer-Lockers.* Miscellaneous Publication 47, United States Department of Agriculture.

Winter, J. D., and Noble, I. *Frozen Fruits and Vegetables for Home Use.* Agricultural Extension Division, Bulletin 200, University of Minnesota.

THE Cook Book

UNIT SEVEN

THE COOK BOOK

All recipes included in the Cook Book in this text serve six persons, unless otherwise stated. The small or individual recipes are offered as a convenience for use in the school foods laboratory.

The recipes given in the Cook Book are typical recipes in general use. This Cook Book is a textbook of cookery. No attempt has been made to make it a complete cook book. For students' use, a card catalogue of additional recipes collected by them is recommended.

REFERENCES

The Basic Cook Book. Marjorie Heseltine and Ula M. Dow. Houghton Mifflin Company.

Everybody's Cookbook. Isabel E. Lord. Harcourt, Brace and Company.

Practical Cookery and the Etiquette and Service of the Table. Department of Foods, Kansas State College of Agriculture and Applied Science. Manhattan, Kansas.

Home Institute Cook Book. New York Herald Tribune. Charles Scribner's Sons.

Young America's Cook Book. Home Institute, New York Herald Tribune. Charles Scribner's Sons.

Prudence Penny's Cookbook. Prudence Penny. World Publishing Company.

The Boston Cooking-School Cook Book. Fannie M. Farmer. Little, Brown and Company.

Aunt Sammy's Radio Recipes Revised. Bureau of Human Nutrition and Home Economics, United States Department of Agriculture.

School Lunch Recipes for 100. Bureau of Human Nutrition and Home Economics, United States Department of Agriculture.

The United States Department of Agriculture prepares and publishes many bulletins for the public on food and nutrition. The following list is given to suggest some of the most helpful of these government bulletins. Perhaps some of them are in your school library. If you wish to buy a copy of any bulletin, you may secure it through the Superintendent of Public Documents, Government Printing Office, Washington 25, D.C. Teachers may receive a total of 100 free bulletins (not more than 5 of any one).

AIS- 8 Cooking Dehydrated Vegetables
AIS-21 Food for Two
AIS-22 Making Velva Fruit at Home
AIS-28 Cooking with Dried Eggs
AIS-39 Foods — Enriched, Restored, Fortified
AIS-42 Root Vegetables in Everyday Meals
AIS-43 Green Vegetables in Everyday Meals
AIS-48 Home Freezing of Fruits and Vegetables
AIS-53 National Food Guide
AIS-58 Sweet Potato Recipes
AIS-59 Food for the Family with Young Children
AIS-64 Home Canning of Fruits and Vegetables
AIS-68 Peanut and Peanut Butter Recipes
AIS-69 Money-saving Main Dishes
AIS-71 Food for Families with School Children
AWI- 1 Food for Growth
AWI- 2 Vitamins from Farm to You
AWI- 16 Cheese in Your Meals
AWI- 59 Oven Drying
AWI- 73 Cooking with Soya Flour and Grits
AWI- 85 Potatoes in Popular Ways
AWI- 89 Egg Dishes for Any Meal
AWI-103 Pickle and Relish Recipes
AWI-104 Tomatoes on Your Table
AWI-107 Eat a Good Breakfast
AWI-110 Home Canning of Meat
F-1705 Milk for the Family
F-1775 Homemade Bread, Cake, and Pastry
F-1800 Homemade Jellies, Jams, and Preserves
F-1888 Poultry Cooking
F-1908 Meat for Thrifty Meals
L-113 Honey and Some of Its Uses
L-213 Sour Cream — How to Prepare and Use It at Home

Measuring

The pictures (page 27) show you how to measure accurately.

Abbreviations that you will constantly use are:

tsp. or t. = teaspoon
Tb. or T. = tablespoon
c. = cup
qt. = quart
gal. = gallon
lb. = pound

Some measures you will need to learn are:

3 t. = 1 T.
16 T. = 1 c.
(4 T. = ¼ c.; 8 T. = ½ c.)
2 c. = 1 pt.
2 pt. = 1 qt.
4 qt. = 1 gal.

Fruit

See Chapter 4

Some Ways of Serving Fresh Fruit

A sharp paring knife is a first aid for preparing fruit. A stainless steel blade is best for fruit because the acids of the fruit stain the ordinary steel blade.

Fresh ripe fruit will spoil easily. It should not be bruised in handling. Fruit keeps best if washed just before serving. Thin-skinned ripe fruits, such as peaches, plums, grapes, berries, will keep best in a cold, dry place. Place in a covered container in the refrigerator. Special containers for refrigerating fruits and vegetables have holes for ventilation, which aids in keeping them fresh. A banana is ripe for eating if all green has disappeared from the blossom end. Prepare immediately before serving. If berries are to be kept overnight, remove imperfect ones, but do not wash or hull.

Sectioning Orange or Grapefruit

With a sharp knife, begin at stem end and cut off skin as in paring an apple, taking care to leave pulp exposed. Save all of juice. Cut into center on each side of the membrane that separates the sections, and remove each section whole. Squeeze out any juice left in refuse part of orange. Fruit is prepared in this way for salad, for gelatin dishes, or arranged on a fruit plate for breakfast.

Orange or Grapefruit Served in the Skin

Cut fruit in halves crosswise; remove center and seeds by cutting them out with scissors or a sharp knife. With a small sharp knife or a grapefruit knife, loosen each section from the membrane around it. To do this, begin at center between the pulp of the section and the membrane surrounding

Fig. 129. SECTIONING GRAPEFRUIT

it; follow the membrane around the section toward the rind and back to the center.

Fresh Pineapple

Cut off both ends of the pineapple. Cut in slices. Pare and remove "eyes" with a sharp-pointed knife. Cut small wedge-shaped pieces from core of each slice, or cut the core from the center of whole slices. Serve pineapple for breakfast ice cold and sprinkled with powdered sugar. Serve it ice cold with French dressing or whipped cream mayonnaise for salad.

Grapefruit Juice Cocktail

2 c. fresh grapefruit juice, or unsweetened canned juice
1½ T. white or light brown sugar
¼ t. lemon juice or 1 T. orange juice
Finely crushed ice

Dissolve sugar in fruit juices; add crushed ice about five minutes before serving; or add crushed ice to each glass before pouring the cocktail. Serve in small beverage glasses as the first course of luncheon or dinner. This is a pleasing beverage to serve in the living room before dinner.

Orange Juice Cocktail

2 c. orange juice ½ c. sugar 2 T. lemon juice Ginger ale (iced)

Mix sugar, orange juice, and lemon juice and freeze to a mush. When ready to serve, half-fill fruit juice glasses with frozen mixture. Open a bottle of ginger ale and pour over the frozen fruit juice, filling the glasses. Serve immediately as the first course for luncheon or dinner. It may be served in the living room.

Baked Apples

6 apples
1 t. lemon juice, if desired
⅓ to ½ c. granulated sugar; or half brown and half granulated sugar

Wash and core the apples. Cover the bottom of a pan or baking dish about one fourth inch with water. Put in apples, pour the sugar into the cavities and add a few drops of lemon juice if desired. Bake in a moderate oven (325°–350° F.) until soft, or about 30 minutes.

If a quantity of sirup is left after the apples are cooked, remove them from the pan, cook this sirup until thick and pour over the apples.

Small recipe: 1 *apple, few drops of lemon juice,* 1 *T. sugar.*

Baked Apple with Raisins

Use recipe for baked apples.

Mix 2 T. of raisins with the sugar before filling cavities. A few broken nut meats may be sprinkled over the apples when served.

Baked Bananas

6 bananas 2 T. lemon juice 2 T. melted butter ⅓ c. sugar

Peel bananas, scrape off stringy fibers, cut in half lengthwise. Place in a baking dish or shallow pan. Mix butter, sugar, and lemon juice. Baste bananas with the mixture. Bake slowly for about 20 to 25 minutes, basting as the bananas cook.

Small recipe: 1 banana, 1 t. lemon juice, 1 t. melted butter, 2 t. sugar.

Cranberry Sauce

4 c. cranberries 2 c. sugar 1 c. water

Pick over and wash the cranberries. Cook cranberries, water, and sugar in a covered saucepan until the skins burst; this requires only about ten to fifteen minutes. Skim if necessary, and cool. Overcooked cranberries are bitter.

Small recipe: ½ c. cranberries, ¼ c. sugar, ⅓ c. water.

Apple Sauce[1]

Wash, remove stem and blossom ends with a sharp knife, pare, quarter, and core the apples; or, if the sauce is to be put through a colander, leave the skins on. Cook the apples until soft in a covered pan, using just enough water to keep them from scorching. If the skins have been left on, put the sauce through a colander. Sweeten to taste; add a few grains of salt.

Flavor may be varied by adding lemon juice or spices, such as cinnamon, nutmeg, or cloves. Nutmeg should be used only in apple sauce which is to be eaten at once, for it is likely to make the flavor bitter on standing. (See pictures on pp. 22 and 23.)

Small recipe: 1 tart apple, 1 T. water, 1 t. lemon juice, 1 T. sugar (or to taste), spice if desired.

Candied Apples

1 lb. apples 2 c. sugar 1 c. water

Prepare whole crab apples, or halves or quarters of apples, or

---

[1] Courtesy of Bureau of Human Nutrition and Home Economics, United States Department of Agriculture.

apple balls. Cook the fruit in a sirup made in the proportion of 2 c. (1 lb.) sugar to 1 c. water. Add red coloring, if red apples are desired. Cook slowly until apples have transparent appearance of all preserved fruit.

Spiced Apples

1 lb. apples (pared and cut)	1 c. water
2–4 T. lemon juice or mild vinegar	4 whole cloves
2 c. sugar	Stick cinnamon (1 inch)

If red color is desired, use ½ c. small red cinnamon candies in place of the spices.

Pare and slice apples in quarters. If crab apples are used, pare only. Make a sirup of all ingredients (except apples). Cook apples in the sirup, slowly, until they have the transparent appearance of preserved fruit. Spiced apples are an attractive and inexpensive accompaniment for meat or heavy salads.

Fried Apples

4 apples	½ to ⅔ c. sugar	2 T. butter or bacon fat

Wash apples, cut in halves, and in half-inch wedge-shaped slices. Heat butter in frying pan; add apples; cover and cook slowly for 5 to 10 minutes. Add sugar, and cook until soft and transparent, stirring only occasionally. Serve hot. Fried apples with crisp bacon is a favorite dish for breakfast or luncheon.

Dried Fruits

The usual way of cooking dried fruits (except apples) is to soak them and then cook them in the same water either over the direct heat, or in the double boiler. Dried apples take up water more readily than other dried fruits. Soaking darkens them.

Prunes, Stewed or Steamed

Wash prunes, or soak 15 minutes and wash. Soak 2 hours or more in cold water to cover them. Cook slowly in the same water with 1 or 2 slices of lemon over the direct heat or in the double boiler until tender. If sugar is added, use about one fourth cup per pound of prunes; add just before removing from the heat

Steamed Raisins

Wash raisins thoroughly. Put in top part of double boiler without extra water. Cook until swelled and tender.

For **Dried Fruit with Cereals,** *see pages* 400, 401.

Spiced Prunes

½ lb. large prunes   2 sticks cinnamon   6 whole cloves

Wash and soak as for stewed prunes. Add spices and cook slowly in small amount of water until tender. Cool; remove stones; stuff centers of half of prunes with remaining ones. Serve hot or cold as a relish and garnish for dinner meats. Steam over boiling water for 20 minutes before serving if desired hot.

Fruit Cocktail

See **Fruit Desserts,** *pages* 240, 241.

For other fruit recipes, see also **Beverages, Desserts, Salads,** *and* **Canning and Preserving.**

Beverages

See Chapter 7

Hot Chocolate or Cocoa

½ c. water   4 c. (1 qt.) milk
3 T. powdered cocoa or   3 T. sugar
1 sq. (1 oz.) chocolate   Few grains salt

Cook water and cocoa or chocolate (finely cut) in the top part of the double boiler, directly over the fire until smooth (about five minutes). Place over boiling water in double boiler, add milk, sugar, and salt, and cook until smooth. Beat with a rotary beater just before serving in order to break the film that forms when milk is heated. Cocoa and chocolate may be made directly over the fire. In this case heat almost to boiling, stirring constantly, but do not boil. Serve with whipped cream if desired. Vanilla is a desirable addition to chocolate.

Small recipe: cocoa 2½ t., 1 T. sugar, ¾ c. milk, ¼ c. water, pinch of salt, few drops vanilla.

Chocolate: ¼ oz. chocolate or cocoa, 1 T. sugar, ½ c. milk, ¼ c. water.

Spiced Rich Cocoa

1 tall can evaporated milk   ⅛ t. cinnamon   3 c. hot water
½ t. vanilla extract   ½ t. almond extract   ¼ c. sugar   5 T. cocoa

Mix cocoa, sugar, cinnamon, and water. Boil 3 to 5 minutes.

Add milk. Heat almost to boiling, add vanilla and almond extract. Beat with rotary egg beater and serve.

Note: Mexican chocolate may be used instead of cocoa. This is sold in cake form and is already sweetened and spiced. Mexican chocolate is sold in some places in the Southwest and makes a delicious spiced chocolate drink.

Chocolate Sirup

4 sq. chocolate	1/8 t. salt	1 c. sugar
1 c. hot water	1 t. vanilla	

Melt chocolate over hot water. Add water, sugar, and salt. Boil 5 minutes. Remove from stove, add vanilla and cool. Chocolate sirup may be made in quantity and stored in the refrigerator.

Rich Chocolate

1/3 c. whipped cream   1/2 c. chocolate sirup   3 c. milk

Scald milk, add chocolate sirup. Serve with whipped cream.

Iced Chocolate

Use two tablespoons of chocolate sirup for each cup of milk. Pour over cracked ice just before serving.

Percolated Coffee

8 T. (1/2 c.) ground coffee   4 c. boiling water

Put water in the lower part of percolator and coffee in upper part. Heat and allow to percolate for 5 to 8 minutes, as desired. Remove grounds from the percolator and keep the coffee hot until served.

The coffee grounds themselves act as a strainer and keep the beverage clear, so that the egg used for boiled coffee is not needed here. If percolated too long, the coffee will become bitter with tannin and the coffee flavor will be destroyed.

Small recipe: 2 T. ground coffee, 1 c. boiling water.

Drip Coffee

2 T. pulverized coffee   1 c. water

Put coffee in the coffeepot strainer, and pour over it 1/3 c. of boiling water. In about 3 minutes after placing the pot in a pan of boiling water, pour over the second third of the cup of boiling water, and 3 minutes later, the remaining third. Serve.

This coffee has less of the tannin flavor and more of its own than either boiled or percolated coffee has.

Vacuum-Method Coffee

2 T. finely ground coffee — 1 c. water

Use a glass coffee maker. Put coffee in top part and water in bottom; when the water boils, it will go into the upper part of the coffee maker. Turn off heat and allow coffee to drip back into lower part of coffee maker. Remove the upper bowl of the coffee maker and serve from the lower bowl.

Boiled Coffee

8 T. (½ c.) ground coffee	2 t. egg white
½ c. cold water	4 c. boiling water

Use coffeepot preferably of enamel ware or enamel pan with lid. Mix ¼ c. cold water and egg white with ground coffee; add boiling water and boil 3 to 5 minutes or allow to steep 5 to 7 minutes without boiling. Remove from fire. Settle by adding ¼ c. cold water and allowing to stand 3 minutes. Serve immediately, or strain from grounds and keep hot and covered until served.

Small recipe: 2 T. coffee, 2 T. cold water, ½ t. egg white, 1 c. boiling water.

Coffee with Milk (Café au Lait)

3 T. coffee — 1 c. water — 1 c. hot milk

Make coffee by any method with the coffee and water. After removing the liquid from the grounds, add the hot milk to the liquid coffee. Add whipped cream if desired.

Iced Coffee

4 T. coffee — 1 c. water

Make coffee by any method. Pour hot coffee over cracked ice in tall glasses. Serve plain or with cream and sugar. If preferred, whipped cream may be used.

Hot Tea

1 c. freshly boiling water — 1 t. tea

Pour boiling water over tea leaves and allow to steep for 1 to 3 minutes. Strain and serve. The use of a tea ball is more convenient, since the tea will not have to be strained. For stronger tea, use more tea rather than steeping longer. Longer steeping makes bitter tea.

To have good tea: Buy good tea; keep in a covered tin box; use china or earthenware teapot; use fresh water; steep one to three minutes.

Serve tea with lemon or cream. If lemon is used, it may be cut in thin slices or in wedge-shaped pieces.

Afternoon tea. For afternoon tea, one of the following may be served instead of lemon: one or two cloves per cup; candied cherries or ginger; sliced orange; rock candy or peppermint sticks.

Milk Shakes or Eggnogs

4 c. (1 qt.) milk   2 to 4 eggs   4 to 6 T. sugar   cracked ice

For flavoring use one of the following:

2 t. vanilla and 1/8 t. nutmeg   1/2 c. chocolate sirup (see page 394)
4 T. orange juice

Stir together 1/2 c. of the milk, a small amount of cracked ice, the eggs, and the sugar until thoroughly mixed. Do not beat. Add remaining milk, more cracked ice, and flavoring. Beat with rotary beater and serve.

Small recipe: 1 c. milk, 1/2 t. vanilla, or 1 T. orange juice or other flavoring, dash of nutmeg, 1 to 1 1/2 T. sugar.

Lemonade

3 1/3 c. cold water
2/3 c. lemon juice
2/3 to 1 c. sugar

Orangeade

3 c. cold water
1 1/2 c. orange juice
2 to 3 T. lemon juice
3/4 c. sugar
Sprigs of mint if desired

Make a sirup of the sugar and 1/3 the water. Cool and add remaining water and fruit juice. Serve with generous quantities of crushed ice.

For *Pineapple Beverage*, add 2/3 c. shredded pineapple to lemonade.

For *Lemon Whey*, use the whey from freshly soured milk in place of water in making lemonade. This is a refreshing cold beverage.

For *Ginger Ale Cup*, use equal parts of lemonade and ginger ale. Combine just before serving.

Fruit Punch

(Serves about 25 people)

1 qt. cold water or tea
1 No. 2 can shredded pineapple
2 c. sugar
1 c. lemon juice
1 pt. any fruit juice in season
1 qt. water, or carbonated water, or ginger ale

Make a sirup of 1 qt. water (or tea) and sugar. Cool, and allow the rind of 4 lemons to stand in the sirup for several hours. Add lemon juice and fruit. Add iced water or carbonated water or ginger ale just before serving. Serve in a punch bowl with ice cubes or a small block of ice (or with a quart brick of hard-frozen lemon or mint sherbet), or in tall glasses filled at least one third full of crushed ice, and with slices of orange. Orange juice may be substituted for the pineapple (1½ c. orange juice for 1 can pineapple).

Small recipe: one fourth of given amounts. Serves 6.

Oriental Punch

(Inexpensive; 20 servings)

2 c. tea infusion
2 c. water
4 c. sugar
12 whole cloves
1 T. chopped crystallized ginger
2 to 3 one-inch pieces of stick cinnamon
4 c. orange juice
2 c. lemon juice
2 T. grated orange rind
3 to 4 drops oil of peppermint
Mint leaves

Tie spices in a piece of cheesecloth. Cook sugar, water, and spices together for 10 minutes. Cool. Add fruit juice, tea infusion, and a few sprigs of mint. Just before serving, add peppermint oil. Color the punch green if so desired. Serve as for fruit punch.

Small recipe: ½ c. tea, ½ c. water, 1 c. sugar, 3 whole cloves, 1 t. chopped crystallized ginger, 1 c. orange juice, ½ c. lemon juice, ½ T grated orange rind, one drop oil of peppermint, mint leaves. Serves 5 or 6.

Mint Punch

1 c. sugar
2 c. water
1 c. crushed mint leaves
Juice of 6 lemons
Ginger ale

Make a sirup of the sugar and water. Add crushed mint leaves to the hot sugar sirup and let stand until cool. Strain. Add the juice of six lemons.

Use ⅓ glass of this mint sirup, add crushed ice and fill the glass with ginger ale. Stir well and serve immediately. Carbonated or plain water may be used instead of ginger ale. A sprig of fresh mint in each glass is attractive.

Cereal Gruels. (*See page* 401.)

Beef Tea. (*See page* 423.)

Egg yolks may be added to soups, cocoa, milk, and fruit drinks. Each egg yolk yields approximately 50 calories.

Egg white may be added to water or fruit drinks. Each egg white yields about 14 to 17 calories.

Cereals

See Chapter 6

Timetable for Cooking Cereals

KIND AND AMOUNT	SALT	WATER	DOUBLE BOILER	PRESSURE CANNER	PERSONS SERVED
Cream of Wheat, 1 c.	1½ t.	4 c.	40 min.	10 min. at 15 lb.	8 to 10
Corn meal, 1 c.	1½ t.	4 c.	3½ hr.	25 min. at 15 lb.	8 to 10
Rice, 1 c.	1 t.	3 c.	40 min.	15 min. at 10 lb.	6 to 8
Hominy (coarse), 1 c.	1 t.	5 c.	3 hr.	25 min. at 15 lb.	10 to 12
Hominy (fine), 1 c.	1½ t.	4 c.	2 hr.	25 min. at 15 lb.	8 to 10
Rolled oats, 1 c.	1 t.	2½ c.	1 hr.	10 min. at 15 lb.	5 to 8
Cracked wheat, 1 c.	1 t.	4 c.	4–6 hr.	60 min. at 15 lb.	8 to 10

Cooking Cereals in Double Boiler

Have the required amount of water salted and boiling in the top part of the double boiler over direct heat. Add the cereal slowly so that boiling will not stop. Boil cereal and water for five minutes. Place over boiling water in lower part of double boiler. Keep the lower part one third to one fourth full of boiling water.

Cooking Cereals with Milk

Substitute half milk and half water for all water, or substitute all milk for all water. Heat the milk in the top part of the double boiler; add salt; add cereal and stir. Place over boiling water in double boiler; increase the time of cooking by one third.

Cooking Cereals in Thrift Cooker on an Electric Stove

Have required amount of water, salted and boiling. Add cereal slowly so as not to stop the boiling. Boil 5 minutes. Turn current on low, cover, and continue cooking the required time. (See above, Timetable for Cooking Cereals, in double boiler.)

Cooking Cereals in Pressure Canner

Reduce the amount of water about ⅓ c. for each 3 c. of water used. Have water salted and boiling in a pan that will fit in pressure canner. Add cereal as for cooking in double boiler, and allow to boil for 5 minutes. Prepare the pressure canner by pouring in one pint to one quart of water and putting the rack in place. Place vessel containing cereal in canner and close canner except for pet-cock. Heat until a straight stream of steam comes through pet-cock; close pet-cock; cook for required length of time at required pressure. (See above, Timetable for Cooking Cereals, in pressure canner.)

Rice

Blue Rose rice is the type most used. Ask your grocer what type of rice he handles. Brown rice has a tough outer coat and will require a longer cooking time. It does not become sticky as does white rice.

For variation in cooking time of different varieties of rice, see United States Department of Agriculture, Leaflet 112.

Boiled Rice[1]

1 c. rice   2 qts. boiling water   2 t. salt

Wash the rice in hot water; drain. Add rice gradually to rapidly boiling salted water. Reduce heat, so rice boils gently. Cook uncovered until grains are tender, about 25 minutes. Drain at once in a colander or sieve and pour hot water through rice to remove starch. Cover with cloth and set over hot water; place in a warm oven to plump rice grains.

Brown Rice

Cook in same way as boiled rice except after rice has boiled gently for 30 minutes, cover and simmer until rice is thoroughly cooked and water is absorbed.

Soft Rice

If a soft, moist cooked rice is desired, as for croquettes, patties, or rice ring, cook rice in a double boiler, fireless cooker, or waterless cooker. Use about 3 cups of water to 1 of rice, and cook until the rice is tender. Do not rinse with hot water.

Creamy Rice

1 c. rice   1 c. milk
2 c. hot water   1½ t. salt

Follow directions for cooking rice; but cook in a double boiler. Do not drain or rinse.

Steamed Whole Wheat

1 c. wheat grains   2 c. water   1 t. salt

Mix whole-wheat grains, water, to which the salt has been added. Cook in pressure canner at 10 pounds pressure for one hour.

[1] Adapted from *Cooking American Varieties of Rice*, United States Department of Agriculture, Leaflet 112.

Whole Wheat in Milk[1]

1 c. whole-wheat cereal	1 tall can evaporated milk (1⅔ cups)
½ t. salt	2½ cups boiling water

Mix cereal, salt, and milk. Add boiling water and boil until thickened, about 15 minutes, stirring constantly. Or, when cereal comes to a boil, set over boiling water and cook 25 to 30 minutes. Serve hot with additional diluted evaporated milk. Use brown or granulated sugar, if desired. Yield: 6 servings.

Quick-Cooking Cereals

The market now offers some cereals for which the cooking process has been materially shortened by partially cooking them in the process of manufacturing. The instructions for cooking these cereals is found on the package. In general, they are cooked a short time (3 to 10 minutes) in boiling water or milk over direct heat. These preparations differ in flavor from those that are cooked longer, because long cooking develops the flavor in cereals. These quick-cooking cereals compare favorably in wholesomeness with other cereals.

Cereals in Mold

Rice and cream of wheat and other well-liked cereals make attractive cold simple desserts for children.

Pour the hot cereal into small smooth molds; custard cups may be used. Let it cool and stiffen. When ready to use, loosen edges with a knife and turn the cold shape into a small dish. Take out a teaspoon of cereal from the top and put in its place a teaspoon of jelly or fruit sauce.

Macaroni and Spaghetti

2 c. macaroni or spaghetti broken in small pieces
2 qt. boiling water
2 t. salt

Cook the macaroni or spaghetti in boiling water until tender. Drain. *See* **Macaroni and Cheese,** *page* 442.

Cereal with Dried Fruit

Dried fruits are used with cereal for breakfast occasionally and for simple desserts.

[1] Courtesy of Evaporated Milk Association.

For one cup of cereal use one-half pound of dried fruit cut in small pieces. The fruit may be cooked with the cereal (stirred in when the cereal is cooking over hot water) or stirred into the cooked cereal.

If fruit is cooked with it, the cereal is somewhat darkened and sweetened and is flavored throughout with the fruit flavor. Dried figs, raisins, or dates are most often used.

Serve this cereal hot with milk or thin cream for breakfast. Mold it and serve cold with thin or whipped cream for a simple dessert. For dessert, nuts may be added just before molding. Use ¾ to 1 c. broken nut meats to each cup of cereal.

Fried Mush

Mold the cereal to be fried in a thin layer in a shallow pan. Cut in 2½ to 3-inch squares. Cook in small amount of fat until golden brown on one side; turn and brown on the other side. Serve hot with sirup or with jelly.

Cereal Gruels (one serving)

⅞ c. water
1 T. cereal: rice, barley, oatmeal
2 T. whole milk
Dash of salt

Heat milk and water to boiling, add cereal and allow to boil 25 to 30 minutes. Strain, add salt, and serve.

Left-Over Cereals

Left-over cereals may be used in griddlecakes, waffles, or muffins; left-over rice may also be used in soups, puddings, croquettes, and stuffed vegetables.

Toast and Quick Breads

See Chapters 7 and 19

Toast

Toast is used for breakfast; as an accompaniment with soups, salads, and creamed vegetables; and for tea.

Bread for toasting should be a day or more old. Cut in slices from ½ to ¼ inch thick, according to preference; remove crusts if desired. Toast should be evenly browned. Toast will have a crisp surface but a soft interior if made rapidly. If crisp, dry toast is desired, it should be made in a slow or moderate oven. Toast made of whole-wheat, nut, and raisin bread is delicious. Serve toast hot. It may be buttered at the table, or buttered just before serving and left in the oven a few minutes.

Toast Accompaniments: marmalade, jelly, or other sweets.

Croutons and Toast Sticks

Use thick slices (half-inch) of whole-wheat or white bread cut in three-fourths-inch strips, or in half-inch squares, or in other shapes and small sizes. Butter the pieces lightly before toasting and sprinkle after toasting with a tiny bit of paprika. Croutons and toast sticks are served with soups.

Melba Toast

Cut bread in ⅛-inch slices. Arrange on a baking sheet. Bake in a slow oven until the bread is dry and an even golden color. Turn once during baking.

Cinnamon Toast

Butter thin half slices of whole-wheat or of plain bread and toast. Spread with a mixture of ½ c. sugar and 1 T. cinnamon, using ¾ T. of mixture to each half slice. Heat in a hot oven for 1 to 2 minutes and serve immediately.

Milk Toast

Butter thick slices (three eighths to one-half inch) of whole-wheat or plain toast and place in cereal bowls. Pour over them hot milk, using about 1 c. milk for each two slices of toast. Sprinkle with salt and serve immediately.

French Toast

1 egg ⅛ t. salt 4 T. milk (or water) Slices of bread a day or more old

Beat egg with milk (or water); dip into it slices of bread three-eighths inch thick. Cook in a small amount of fat in a hot frying pan. Cook brown on both sides. Serve immediately, lightly dusted with powdered sugar. Serve jelly or sirup with French toast. Raisin bread and whole-wheat bread make good French toast.

Leavening Agents for Quick Breads

Using Baking Powder

Three general types of baking powder are available:

1. Tartrate baking powder. 2. Phosphate baking powder. 3. Sodium-aluminum sulphate baking powder (S.A.S.)

Look on the label to see what kind of baking powder is to be used. The tartrate and phosphate baking powders are known as *quick-acting* because they release their carbon dioxide in the cold mixture. Baking powder containing sodium-aluminum sulphate is known as a *slow-acting* or *double-acting* baking powder, since part of the carbon dioxide is released while the mixture is cold and the other part is released after the mixture is placed in the oven.

General Proportions for Baking Powders and Soda

1½–2 t. of tartrate or phosphate baking powder to 1 c. flour.

1–1½ t. of sodium-aluminum sulphate (S.A.S.) baking powder to 1 c. flour.

The recipes in this book use the proportion of approximately 1½ t. to 2 t. of baking powder to 1 c. flour. This will be a safe proportion to use for either type of baking powder. It must be remembered that the proportion of eggs, of fat, and of sugar will affect the amount of baking powder required. (See page 84.)

When sour milk or cream is used, soda is used as a leaven. The amount of soda used varies with the acidity of the milk.

¼ t. soda with 1 c. slightly sour milk.
½ t. soda with 1 c. average sour milk.

Mixtures containing brown sugar, molasses, or fruit juices also use soda as part of the leaven.

Changing Sweet-Milk Recipes to Sour-Milk

In most cases both soda and baking powder should be used as leavens when a sweet-milk recipe is changed to a sour-milk recipe.

For practical purposes in changing a sweet-milk recipe to a recipe calling for average sour milk, use ½ t. soda and reduce the baking powder by approximately 1½ t. to each cup of milk.

Soda should always be sifted with the dry ingredients.

For examples see recipes for sour-milk waffles and griddlecakes, pages 405, 406.

Table of Temperatures and Time for Baking Flour Mixtures[1]

Food	Baking Temperatures (Degrees Fahr.)	Baking Time (Minutes)
Baking-powder biscuits	450–460	12 to 15
Bread	350–400	45 to 60
Butter cakes (loaf)	325–360	40 to 60
Butter cakes (layer)	365–380	20 to 30
Cake, angel	300–360	50 to 60
Cake, fruit	275–325	3–4 hours
Cake, sponge (loaf)	300–350	40 to 60
Cookies (thin, rolled)	380–390	10 to 12
Cookies, molasses drop	350–375	18 to 20
Cream puffs	300–350	45 to 60
Meringues	250–300	40 to 60
Muffins (baking-powder)	400–425	20 to 25
Pie crust (large pies)	400–500	20 to 40
Popovers	350–450	45 to 50
Rolls	400–425	20 to 25

Flour in all mixtures is measured after sifting.

"The size of the pan is a factor influencing time and temperature of baking any mixture. A small amount of the same mixture may be cooked for a shorter time at somewhat higher temperature. For example, rolls and a loaf of bread may be made of exactly the same mixture, but the baking time for the loaf of bread is longer and the temperature is lower than for rolls."

Popovers

1 c. sifted flour	2 eggs	1 c. milk
⅓ t. salt	1 T. melted butter	

Mix and sift flour and salt, add milk gradually to make a smooth batter. Add eggs well beaten, and beat mixture well with rotary egg beater. Beat in melted butter. Half fill hissing hot greased pans or cups. Place in hot oven (450° F.). After 15 minutes, begin decreasing heat and finish at the end of 40 minutes with a moderate oven (350° F.). Popovers should be well puffed, well browned, and fairly dry on inside of shell. Serve very hot for breakfast, and butter them as soon as they come to the table.

Small recipe: ½ c. flour, ⅙ t. salt, 1 *egg, ½ c. milk,* 1½ *t. (or ½ T.) melted fat.*

[1] Used through the courtesy of New York State College of Home Economics at Cornell University. Adapted for use here.

Waffles, Sweet-Milk

2 c. soft-wheat flour (sifted)	1½ c. milk
2 t. baking powder	2 eggs
½ t. salt	3 T. melted fat

(If desired, 1½ T. sugar or maple sirup.)

Mix and sift dry ingredients; add egg yolks, milk, and melted fat which have been thoroughly mixed; and fold in stiffly beaten egg whites. Pour onto the center of a hot and well-greased waffle iron from a pitcher or cup, allowing about one-third cup of mixture for one waffle. Bake until evenly browned and crisp. Serve with butter or melted butter and sugar or sirup. If not cooked on an electric iron, the waffle iron should be turned once during each cooking and reheated between times.

For heating the iron, especially a new iron, follow explicitly the directions that come with the iron. Bake waffle until it stops steaming. Do not open iron while waffle is cooking. Electric irons should be used without greasing after the first time.

Small recipe: ⅔ c. flour, ⅔ t. baking powder, ⅙ t. salt, ⅜ c. milk, 2 t. fat, 1 egg (1 t. sugar if desired).

Waffles, Sour-Milk

2 c. flour	½ t. baking powder		¾ t. soda
1½ c. buttermilk (or sour cream)	1 t. salt	2 eggs	3 T. fat

Mix and sift dry ingredients. Separate eggs. Mix well milk, egg yolks, and melted fat, then add dry ingredients and beat smooth. Fold in well-beaten egg whites.

Small recipe: ⅔ c. flour, ½ c. buttermilk, ¼ t. soda, 1 T. fat, 1 egg, ¼ t. baking powder, ⅓ t. salt.

Pecan Waffles

Add 1 c. chopped pecans to the waffle batter before baking.

Corn-Meal Waffles

Substitute 1 cup fine white corn meal for 1 cup of the flour in sour-milk waffles.

Rice or Hominy Waffles

2 c. cooked rice or hominy grits	1 c. flour	1 T. butter
3 eggs	2 c. milk	3 t. baking powder

Mix as for waffles, adding the cooked cereal to the milk and egg yolk mixture.

Griddlecakes, Sweet-Milk

3 c. flour
4 t. baking powder
1 t. salt
¼ c. sugar
2 c. milk
1 egg
2 T. melted fat

Mix and sift dry ingredients; add egg and milk mixed together; add melted fat. Stir mixture until smooth. Have griddle well greased and hot. Drop batter on griddle by spoonfuls, allowing for spreading. When puffed and bubbles have broken on top, it should be evenly browned on the under side, and is ready to be turned with a spatula.

Small recipe: ½ c. flour, 1 t. baking powder, ⅙ t. salt, ⅓ c. milk, 1 t. fat, 2 T. beaten whole egg.

Griddlecakes, Sour-Milk

2½ c. flour
1 t. salt
1 t. soda
2 c. sour milk
1 egg
1½ T. melted fat
1½ t. baking powder

Mix and cook as for Sweet-Milk Griddlecakes.

Small recipe: ½ t. sugar, ⅙ t. salt, ⅙ t. soda, ½ t. baking powder, ⅓ c. sour milk, ⅜ c. flour, ½ T. fat, ½ egg.

Maple Sirup

1 c. brown sugar
½ c. water
¾ c. maple sugar

Mix and heat until sugar is dissolved. Serve hot or cold.

Sugar Sirup

½ c. water
1 c. brown sugar
1 t. butter

Mix and heat ingredients until sugar is dissolved. Serve hot.

French Pancakes with Fruit Sauce

⅔ c. flour
1 T. corn meal
¼ t. salt
1 egg
1 c. milk
1 T. white or brown sugar

Mix dry ingredients, add milk and egg unbeaten; beat with a rotary beater until thoroughly mixed; drop spoonfuls on a lightly oiled griddle and cook until light brown on each side. These should be very thin. Roll and serve immediately, with hot fruit sauce.

Fruit Sauce

1 c. orange juice	¼ c. banana pulp
1 T. lemon juice	2 T. white or brown sugar
2 T. butter	¼ stick cinnamon

Sections of 2 large or 3 small oranges

Heat all materials except orange sections for 5 minutes, without allowing to boil; add orange sections and remove cinnamon and pour around hot French pancakes.

Score Card for Muffins [1]

Do not write in this book

STANDARD PRODUCT — 100 POINTS		
External Characteristics		**30**
Shape: symmetrical, well-rounded top, free from peaks or knobs	10	
Crust: tender, thin with rough surface, uniform browning	10	
Volume: light in weight in proportion to size	10	
Internal Characteristics		**40**
Texture: medium fine, moist tender crumb	20	
Grain, round even cells free from tunnels	10	
Color: characteristic of kind of muffin	10	
Flavor		**30**
Blended flavor of well-baked products	30	
Total	100	**100**

Muffins (standard recipe)

2 c. flour	2 T. sugar
3 t. baking powder	1 c. milk
1 egg	2 T. melted fat

½ t. salt

Mix and sift dry ingredients; add milk, egg, and melted fat; mix quickly until all ingredients are moistened. Do not beat or over-

[1] Adapted from Farmers' Bulletin 1775, *Homemade Bread, Cake, Pastry*, United States Department of Agriculture.

mix. Fill buttered muffin tins half to two thirds full. Bake in hot oven (400° to 425° F.) for 20 to 25 minutes.

Small recipe: ½ c. flour, ¼ c. milk, 1 t. baking powder, 1 T. beaten egg, ½ T. sugar, ½ T. melted fat, pinch of salt.

Graham Muffins

1½ c. coarse unsifted graham flour or 2 c. finely ground
3 t. baking powder
1 T. sugar
½ t. salt
1 egg
1 c. milk
1 T. melted fat

Mix all dry ingredients well, but do not sift. Proceed as for plain muffins.

Berry Muffins

2 c. flour
¾ c. milk
1 egg
3 t. baking powder
½ to ⅓ c. sugar
½ t. salt
¼ c. melted butter
1 c. berries

Berries suggested for use: huckleberries, blueberries, cranberries cut in quarters. If sour berries, use ⅓ c. sugar.

Mix and sift dry ingredients, reserving 2 T. flour for dredging the berries. Beat egg slightly, add milk and gradually the dry ingredients. Add melted fat. Fold in berries well coated with flour. Pour into greased muffin tins and bake in moderately hot oven (400° F.) for about 30 minutes, or until brown. Serve at once.

Bran Muffins

1 c. flour
1 c. bran flakes
3 t. baking powder
¼ t. salt
2 T. sugar
1 egg
¾ c. milk
3 T. fat

Mix all dry ingredients. Do not sift. Proceed as for muffins. Fill tins ⅔ full. Bake 25 minutes at 450 degrees F.

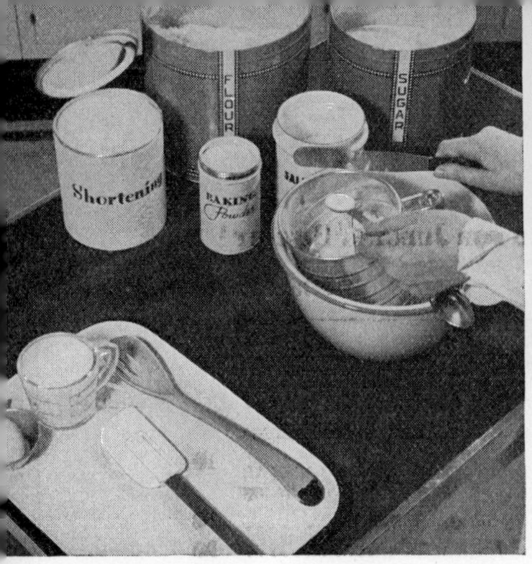

Measuring dry ingredients

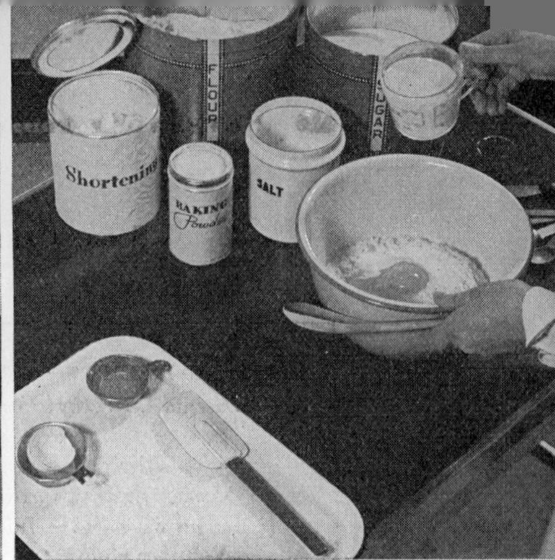

Adding egg and liquid

Stirring slightly

Putting in pans

FIG. 130. STEPS IN MAKING MUFFINS

Score Card for Judging Biscuit[1]

Do not write in this book

STANDARD PRODUCT — 100 POINTS		
External Characteristics		**30**
Shape: cylindrical, uniform, free from bulges on sides or top	10	
Crust: uniform browning, free from yellow or brown spots — fairly smooth, tender	10	
Volume: almost twice volume of unbaked	10	
Internal Characteristics		**40**
Texture: medium fine, tender crumb	20	
Grain: flaky, peeling off in thin strips with fine even cells	10	
Color: creamy white, free from brown or yellow spots	10	
Flavor		**30**
Blended flavor of well-baked ingredients, free from individual flavors of fat, baking powder or salt	30	
Total	100	**100**

Baking-Powder Biscuit, Sweet-Milk

2 c. flour	3 or 4 T. fat
3 t. baking powder	⅔ c. milk
1 t. salt	

Mix and sift dry ingredients. Cut fat into mixture, using two knives. Add milk gradually to make soft dough. Toss on floured board, knead gently, and roll lightly to one-fourth-inch or one-half-inch thickness. Cut with biscuit cutter first dipped in flour. Bake on unbuttered pan in hot oven (450° F.) 12 to 15 minutes.

Small recipe: ½ c. flour, ¾ t. baking powder, ¼ t. salt, ¾ to 1 T. fat, 3 T. milk (approximately.)

[1] *Homemade Bread, Cake, Pastry.* Farmers' Bulletin 1775, United States Department of Agriculture.

Baking-Powder Biscuit, Sour-Milk

2 c. flour	1/4 t. soda	2 t. baking powder
3 T. fat	2/3 c. buttermilk	1 t. salt

Combine ingredients and bake as Baking-Powder Biscuit, Sweet-Milk.

Shortcake

2 c. flour	2/3 to 3/4 c. milk
1 T. sugar	1/2 t. salt
3 t. baking powder	4 T. butter or other fat

Mix and roll out as for biscuits. For individual shortcakes, cut round with large biscuit cutter and place two together, one on top of the other, before baking. For larger cakes, cut two large squares, placing one on top of the other for baking. Bake in a hot oven (425° to 450° F.) until delicately browned. Split and fill with crushed fruit, or whole berries or sliced fruit (strawberries, raspberries, fresh cherries, sliced peaches, orange slices), slightly sweetened, preferably with powdered sugar. Put top crust on and cover with fruit. Serve with plain cream or cover with whipped cream and serve.

Crust for Meat or Chicken Pie

Use ingredients and mix as for shortcake. Pat or roll the dough to three-eighths-inch thickness. Place materials for pie in baking dish, cover with crust and bake in a moderately hot oven (400° to 425° F.) for 15 to 18 minutes. The sides of the dish may be lined with crust if desired. The top crust may be made of circles cut with doughnut cutter; these indicate individual servings.

Cinnamon Rolls

Biscuit Dough	*Additional Ingredients*
2 c. flour	1/2 c. sugar
3 t. baking powder	1 or 2 T. cinnamon
3 or 4 T. fat	raisins if desired
1 t. salt	
2/3 c. milk	

Mix biscuit dough and roll out one-fourth-inch thick; spread or dot with butter; sprinkle with a mixture of sugar and cinnamon. Dot the dough with raisins if desired. Make a roll of the dough; cut across the roll in slices; place with cut side up on greased pan and bake in hot oven (425° to 450° F.).

Dumplings for Meat or Chicken Stew

¾ c. flour (sifted) 1 t. baking powder ⅓ c. milk ½ t. salt 1 egg

Mix and sift dry ingredients. Beat egg, add to milk and mix with dry ingredients. Drop by spoonfuls on top of meat or chicken stew. Cover well and cook 15 to 20 minutes without removing the cover.

Apple Dumplings

2 c. flour	3 t. baking powder	4 T. butter or other fat
1 T. sugar	⅔ to ¾ c. milk	½ t. salt
	6 small apples	

Make a biscuit dough and roll very thin (about one-eighth-inch thick). Pare and core apples; fill center with sugar in which a little nutmeg is mixed. Brown sugar or cinnamon may also be used. Cut the dough in strips and wrap around the apples. Dot the dumplings with butter; bake in moderately hot oven (400° F.) for 30 minutes.

Meat Turnovers

2 c. flour 2 T. fat 3 t. baking powder ½ t. salt ⅔ c. milk

Mix as for biscuit. Roll dough one-eighth-inch thick. Cut in circles with a saucer and paring knife. Moisten edges slightly with egg white. Place meat mixture (see below) in center of one side and double other side over to make a semicircle. Pinch edges together with a fork or fingers and prick top. Bake in a moderately hot oven (400° F.) for 20 minutes. Tops of baked turnovers should be brushed with milk or egg when half done. Serve with brown sauce (page 437). For filling for turnovers use any kind of chopped cooked meat, season with salt, pepper, and chopped parsley.

Spoon Bread (sour-milk)

1 c. corn meal	½ t. salt	¾ to 1 t. soda
2 c. buttermilk	1 t. baking powder	1½ T. butter
	2 eggs	

Beat eggs well, add milk, sift in meal, baking powder, and salt; add soda, mixed with a tablespoon of water. Heat butter in a baking pan, taking care to butter the pan well with it. Pour butter into the batter, then turn mixture into the pan, and bake in a moderately hot oven (400° F.) for 30 to 45 minutes. Serve from the dish in which baked. *Note:* Sweet milk may be used, in which case omit soda.

Small recipe: ¼ c. corn meal, ½ c. buttermilk, ⅛ t. salt, ¼ t. soda, 2 t. butter, 2 T. beaten egg.

Spoon Bread (evaporated milk)

2 c. boiling water
1 t. salt
¾ c. corn meal
3 T. butter or 2 T. bacon fat
2 eggs
⅔ c. evaporated milk
1 t. baking powder

Add meal to briskly boiling water. Boil until just thickened, stirring frequently. Add butter. Beat egg yolks, add milk and stir into meal. Fold in stiffly beaten egg whites and baking powder. Turn into a buttered baking dish or small individual casseroles. Bake at 375° F. until brown, about 40 minutes.

Boston Brown Bread[1]

1 c. corn meal and 1 c. rye meal, or
2 c. corn meal
1 c. graham flour
1 t. salt
¾ c. molasses
2 c. sour milk, and 1½ t. soda, or
2 c. sweet milk, ¼ t. soda, and
4 t. baking powder

Mix the dry ingredients and add the molasses and the milk. Beat the mixture thoroughly, and pour into greased molds until they are about three fourths full. Cover loosely to keep out the moisture, and steam for 2 hours. If steamed in one mold, allow 3 hours. Remove the covers and bake the bread in a moderate oven for about 10 minutes to dry it off. If the bread seems likely to crumble, loop a string around the loaf and cut slices by pulling the ends of the string.

This mixture will fill about 4 one-pound baking-powder tins.

Small recipe: ¼ c. corn meal and ¼ c. rye meal, or ½ c. corn meal, ½ c. graham flour, ¼ t. salt, 3 T. molasses, ½ c. sour milk, and ½ t. soda, or ½ c. sweet milk and 1 t. baking powder.

Nut Bread[1]

2½ c. sifted flour
2 T. sugar
3 t. baking powder
1 t. salt
2 eggs
1 c. milk
1 c. chopped nuts
4 T. melted fat
½ t. cinnamon

[1] Courtesy of Bureau of Human Nutrition and Home Economics, United States Department of Agriculture.

FIG. 131. DOUGHNUTS IN THE MAKING

Sift together the dry ingredients. Beat the eggs, add the milk, and add to the first mixture. Stir in the chopped nuts and the fat. Let the dough stand in a well-greased bread pan for 20 minutes. Bake in a moderate oven (350° F.) for about 1 hour.

Doughnuts

1½ c. flour	1 egg
¼ t. salt	⅓ c. sugar
1½ t. baking powder	2 T. milk
1 t. flavoring	2 T. fat

Cream fat, sugar, and egg together. Add flavoring and salt. Stir this into flour and baking powder sifted together. Add milk, if necessary, to make a dough. Roll the dough one-fourth-inch thick, cut, fry in deep fat (see pages 447, 448), and drain on brown paper. Dust with powdered sugar.

Small recipe: ½ c. flour, pinch of salt, ½ t. baking powder, ½ t. vanilla, ⅓ egg, 1½ T. sugar, 2 t. milk, 2 t. fat.

Southern Corn-meal Muffins or Corn-meal Sticks

2 eggs	1 t. salt	2 c. thick buttermilk or clabber
2 c. fine white corn meal	1 t. soda	

Beat eggs into milk. Sift together dry ingredients and beat thoroughly into the milk. Bake as soon as mixed, in a hot oven in hot, well-greased muffin or bread-stick pans.

To be successful with corn-meal batter breads the pans must be well greased and the oven hot. Muffin pans made of iron are best for corn bread. Ten minutes before filling, the pans should be placed on top of range or stove to heat. Put 1 t. of lard in each ring and allow to heat smoking hot. Fill each ring half full of batter. Bake brown in a hot oven.

Small recipe: ½ egg, ½ c. fine white corn meal, ¼ t. salt, ½ c. thick buttermilk or clabber, ¼ t. soda.

Southern Corn Dodgers or Corn Pone

4 c. fine white corn meal	2 c. buttermilk	1 T. lard	½ t. salt

Mix salt with meal and rub in lard. Add milk. Shape into small oblong cakes or pones with the hands and bake on a greased griddle in a hot oven.

Orange Bread[1]

4 c. flour	1 c. milk
4 t. baking powder	2 eggs
1 t. salt	1 c. candied orange peel
⅓ c. sugar	⅓ c. sirup from peel or
¼ c. shortening	1 c. orange marmalade

Sift flour and measure. Sift again with baking powder, salt, and sugar. Cut shortening into flour mixture. Add milk to well-beaten eggs and mix thoroughly with flour mixture. Stir in orange peel and sirup. Bake in a moderate oven 50 minutes. This recipe makes 2 medium-sized loaves.

Serve plain with butter for afternoon tea or with cheese filling for delicious sandwiches.

Orange Marmalade Rolls[1]

2½ c. bread flour, ½ t. salt, 3½ t. baking powder, 1 egg,
2 T. shortening, 2 T. sugar, milk, orange marmalade

Sift flour, salt, baking powder, and sugar together. Work in butter with the fingertips, keeping the mixture coarse. Beat egg very lightly in a cup and fill cup with milk. Moisten first mixture with the egg and milk and pat to one-fourth-inch thickness on floured board. Cut into thick biscuit rounds, put a teaspoon of marmalade on each, fold over, and place folded side down on well-greased baking pan. Brush with milk and dust with granulated sugar. Bake in a quick oven (400° F.) for 20 minutes.

Eggs

See Chapter 8

To Break an Egg: Hold the egg in the left hand and with a knife strike a sharp blow in the middle of it. Insert the two thumbs in the crack and break the shell by pulling it apart.

To Separate White from Yolk: Slip the egg from one half shell to the other, catching the yolk, but allowing the white to slip into a dish or cup.

[1] Courtesy of Agricultural Extension Service, State of Florida.

It is safer to break each egg separately into a dish or cup, to make sure of its freshness.

For uses of eggs in cooking, and preservation of eggs, see Chapter 8.

"The secret of success in cooking eggs and dishes in which eggs predominate is to cook slowly, at moderate, even heat." [1]

Soft-Cooked Eggs

1. Put eggs into cold water and bring to boiling point. Serve immediately.
2. Pour boiling water over eggs, cover, let stand 5 to 7 minutes.
3. Put eggs into top part of double boiler. Pour boiling water over them and into lower part of double boiler. Keep covered 5 minutes.

Hard-Cooked Eggs

Use method No. 3 above. Keep the vessel on the fire for 30 minutes. The eggs will be firm, but not as tough as when boiled.

Creamed Eggs

3 hard-cooked eggs — 6 slices toast
1½ c. white sauce No. 2 (*page* 436)

Slice hard-cooked eggs into white sauce. 1 to 2 t. chopped parsley may be added. Season to taste; serve on toast.

Small recipe: hard-cooked egg, 2 slices toast, ¾ c. white sauce No. 2 (page 436).

Eggs à la Goldenrod

3 hard-cooked eggs — 1½ c. white sauce No. 2 (*page* 436) — 6 slices of toast

Separate the whites of the hard-cooked eggs from the yolks. Chop the whites; add them to the white sauce; season with salt and pepper; pour over the toast. Put yolks through strainer or potato ricer and decorate the covered toast with it.

Scalloped Eggs

3 hard-cooked eggs
2 c. white sauce, No. 2 (*page* 436)
½ c. bread crumbs — 1 T. butter
¾ c. cooked material if desired: ground ham, flaked fish, crabmeat, or chopped chicken

Arrange alternate layers of sliced eggs and other cooked material in a buttered baking dish. Pour white sauce over the mixture; cover with bread crumbs, dot with butter, and brown in a mod-

[1] *Eggs At Any Meal.* United States Department of Agriculture, Leaflet 39.

erate oven. Serve in the baking dish as a main dish for luncheon or supper.

Small recipe: 1 *hard-cooked egg,* ½ *c. white sauce No.* 2 (*page* 436), 2 *T. bread crumbs,* 1 *t. butter, and* 2 *T. chopped meat or fish if desired.*

Poached Eggs

Grease the bottom of a shallow pan. Add enough boiling salted water (1 t. salt to 1 qt. water) to cover the eggs. Slip eggs, one at a time, into pan; cover; move to the back of stove or turn flame very low to prevent boiling. Cook 3 to 10 minutes, according to degree of firmness desired.

Serve on buttered toast; season with salt and tiny dots of butter. Use very small sprigs of parsley for garnish. A pretty variation is obtained by cutting the toast round and using greased muffin rings to hold the eggs in shape.

For *Eggs Poached in Milk,* use milk in the pan instead of water. Pour the milk over the toast before serving the eggs on toast.

Eggs in Molds (Coddled or Baked)

Butter individual molds or cups, which may then be sprinkled with chopped parsley. Slip an egg into each cup; sprinkle with salt; add a few drops of cream. Set molds in vessels of hot water and cook on top of stove or in a slow oven until eggs can be turned out. Serve on toast with or without sauce.

White sauce No. 2 or tomato sauce may be used. Eggs may be cooked together in a deep plate and served without being removed from the plate.

Scrambled Eggs

4 eggs	½ t. salt; pepper to taste
⅓ c. milk	1 t. butter or margarine

Beat eggs until mixed; add seasonings and milk. Heat omelet pan with butter in it; add eggs, and cook until creamy, scraping from the bottom of pan as the mixture cooks. Serve on thin toast.

Scrambled Eggs with Cheese: Add ½ c. grated cheese when eggs begin to thicken.

Swiss Eggs

6 eggs	1 c. tomatoes	½ c. grated cheese
1 small chopped onion	1 T. fat	½ t. salt

Beat the eggs together until well mixed; cook small chopped

onion and tomatoes with fat before eggs are added. Add eggs, cook slowly, and stir; add ½ c. grated cheese as the eggs begin to thicken.

Small recipe: 1 *egg,* ½ *slice onion,* 2 *T. tomato,* ½ *t. fat,* 1 *T. cheese. Season to taste.*

Fried Eggs

Heat frying pan with enough butter or bacon fat to cover well the bottom of the pan. Slip eggs into pan one at a time; season with salt. If desired turned, use a spatula or cake-turner. Cook slowly to desired firmness.

General Rules for Omelets

1. Select large eggs. Allow 1 egg to each person and 1 T. liquid to each egg.
2. Have omelet pan smooth. If it is not perfectly smooth, clean with salt by heating salt in pan and rubbing with paper.
3. An inexperienced cook should never use more than three eggs for an omelet. A large omelet is hard to handle. It is difficult to find a pan large enough to make a puffy omelet for more than four people. If more than four persons are to be served, it is best for even an experienced cook to make more than one omelet.

Omelets are of two kinds — puffy or plain, and creamy or French.

Plain Omelet (or Puffy Omelet)

Large		*Small*
3	eggs	1
3 T.	water, milk or white sauce	1 T.
¼ t.	salt	pinch
to taste	pepper	dash
1 t.	butter	½ t.

Method of Mixing: Separate yolks from whites. Add salt to the whites. Beat yolks until thick and lemon-colored; add seasoning (except salt) and hot water. Heat omelet pan and butter lightly bottom and sides. Beat whites stiff but not dry; cut and fold into them the yolk mixture. Turn into pan; spread evenly. Cook slowly 2 or 3 minutes on top of stove until well puffed and brown on bottom. Place in a moderate oven (350° F.) to brown

FIG. 132. TURNING AN OMELET FROM A PAN

top. An omelet is done if it does not cling to the fingers when touched.

To serve an omelet, crease through the center, fold over with a spatula, and roll it from the pan to a hot platter. Serve at once.

Note: If ½ c. white sauce No. 3 is added to the large recipe (yolk mixture), it gives a larger creamy omelet with more body. Some cooks add baking powder to an omelet to hold it more firm — ½ t. to each egg.

Variations in Omelets

Chopped cooked bacon, meat, or ham, parsley, or bread crumbs may be folded into the mixture before it is cooked, or sauce or creamed vegetable or meat may be served around it.

For *Cheese Omelet*, use plain omelet recipe adding 1 T. grated cheese for each egg. Sprinkle grated cheese over omelet just before serving. Cheese may also be folded in just before cooking.

For *Jelly Omelet*, use plain omelet recipe; omit pepper and add 1 t. sugar for each egg. Before folding omelet spread with jelly, jam, or marmalade. Fold, turn, and sprinkle with powdered sugar.

For *Bacon Omelet*, use plain omelet recipe. Fold into the uncooked mixture crisp bacon broken in pieces. Garnish with whole slices of broiled bacon.

For *Orange Omelet*, substitute orange juice with 1 t. lemon juice for the liquid in the plain omelet. Add 1 T. of powdered sugar to the yolk mixture. Cook as plain omelet.

Shred 2 oranges and place slices of shredded orange well sprinkled with powdered sugar over half the omelet. Turn the omelet out of pan. Garnish with other part of orange. Sprinkle with powdered sugar and serve at once.

French or Creamy Omelet

6 eggs	½ t. salt	1 T. butter
6 T. milk or water	Pepper	

Beat eggs just enough to mix whites and yolks. Add liquid and seasonings. Turn into hot omelet pan in which butter has been melted. Cook over a slow fire. As mixture cooks, lift from the pan by sticking the spatula under the omelet. Cook to a creamy consistency. Place over hotter flame to brown quickly on bottom. Loosen from pan and roll onto a hot platter. Serve at once.

Small recipe: 1 *egg,* 1 *T. liquid,* ½ *t. butter, a pinch of salt, and a dash of pepper.*

For *Spanish Omelet*, serve French Omelet with Tomato Sauce and cooked vegetables (as desired).

Tomato Sauce

1 c. unstrained tomatoes	2 T. flour	2 T. butter	¼ t. salt

Melt the fat, remove from flame, stir in flour until smooth, add tomatoes and cook in top of double boiler. Add cooked vegetables as desired. Suggestions: peas, mushrooms, finely chopped green pepper, onions, chopped olives. Pour around the omelet.

Soufflés. (*See* **Main Dish for Luncheon or Supper,** *page* 441.)

Stuffed Eggs. (*See* **Salads,** *page* 485.)

Soups

Cream Soups

Cream soups and vegetable soups are usually served for luncheon; clear soups are served for dinner.

General Proportions: Cream soups are made of milk, vegetable pulp, thickened and seasoned, 1 c. cooked vegetable or vegetable pulp to 2 c. white sauce No. 1. A quart of soup is six servings.

Proportions for White Sauce No. 1

1 c. milk	1 T. flour	1 T. butter	¼ t. salt

For method of combining white sauce, see page 437.

Seasoning Cream Soups: The usual seasonings are: 1 t. salt for each 2 c. of soup; 2 t. chopped parsley for each pint, both for flavoring and for garnishing such soups as cream of celery or potato; two or three drops of onion juice or ¼ t. finely chopped onion with each pint; ⅛ t. pepper with a pint of cream of corn soup; an extra tablespoon of butter in any soup; sugar (1 T. to 1 pt. soup) with cream of pea or cream of corn.

For *Cream Soups Made with Strained Vegetable Pulp:* use tomato, pea, potato, spinach, or bean.

For *Cream Soups Made with Cut Vegetables or Vegetable Pieces:* use celery, mushroom, corn, or asparagus.

Combination of Cream Soups: have vegetable or vegetable pulp and white sauce hot. Combine just before serving. Soups made with strained vegetable pulp are improved by beating.

Serving Cream Soups: Serve hot in cream soup cups or bowls. Serve as accompaniments crisp crackers, croutons, or toast. (See page 402 for Croutons.)

Small recipe for cream soup: ½ c. white sauce, ¼ c. strained vegetable pulp, season to taste.

Cream of Tomato Soup

2 c. canned tomatoes or tomato juice		2 or 3 drops onion juice
⅓ c. butter		1 t. salt
⅓ c. flour	4 c. milk	White pepper to taste

Simmer tomatoes and press through a sieve. Make a white sauce of other ingredients. Add the hot tomato pulp to the white sauce. Season to taste. Serve immediately after combining.

Small recipe: ½ c. tomatoes, 1 T. butter, 1 T. flour, ¼ t. salt, 1 c. milk, other seasonings to taste.

Cream of Pea Soup

1 No. 2 can peas	2 T. butter
2 T. sugar	2 T. flour
2 c. liquid	1 t. salt
2 c. milk	Pepper to taste

1 slice onion

Measure liquid from the can and add enough water to make 2 cups. Add sugar and peas and cook until the peas are soft (about 20 minutes). Rub peas through a sieve. Reheat this mixture and add to a white sauce made of the other ingredients. Season to taste. The onion should be scalded in the milk and removed before soup is served.

Small recipe: ½ c. peas, 1 t. sugar, ½ c. liquid, ½ c. milk, ¼ slice onion, ½ T. butter, ½ T. flour, ¼ t. salt, dash of pepper.

Corn Soup[1]

2 c. canned crushed corn	1 T. flour
1 c. water	4 T. butter
1 qt. milk	Salt to taste
1 onion, cut in half	Pepper

Combine the corn and the water, cook for 10 minutes, and stir constantly to keep from sticking to the pan. Press the corn through a strainer. Heat the milk and the onion in the double boiler and thicken with the flour and fat, which have been well blended. Add the corn pulp, salt, and pepper. Heat, remove the onion, and serve. Buttered popcorn makes an interesting substitute for croutons to serve with corn soup.

Small recipe: ¼ c. canned corn, 2 T. water, ½ c. milk, small slice onion, 1 t. flour, ½ T. butter, seasonings to taste.

Potato Soup[1]

2 c. diced raw potato	4 T. butter
1 qt. boiling water	1 T. flour
1 pt. milk	1 t. salt
1 onion	Pepper

2 T. finely chopped parsley

Cook the potato in the boiling water until soft, drain off and keep 1 pint of the potato water, and rice the potato. Heat the milk in a double boiler with the onion. Cook the parsley in the

[1] Courtesy of Bureau of Human Nutrition and Home Economics, United States Department of Agriculture.

fat, add the flour, stir until well blended, combine with the milk and potato, stir until smooth, cook for 2 or 3 minutes, and add the salt and pepper. Remove the onion before serving.

Small recipe: ½ c. diced potatoes, 1 c. boiling water, ½ c. milk, slice of onion, 1 t. chopped parsley, 1 T. butter, 1 t. flour, salt and pepper to taste.

Oyster Stew

1 qt. hot milk or cream	1 t. salt
1 pt. oysters	½ t. pepper
4 T. (¼ c.) butter	Oyster crackers to serve with stew

Look over oysters carefully to remove any pieces of shell. Wash oysters and drain. Heat milk (in double boiler). Add oysters to hot milk and heat until they are plump and their edges curl. Add butter, salt, and pepper and serve immediately.

Clear Soups (Stock Soups)

Beef Tea is beef juice extracted from beef by heating. It is prepared only for invalids.

Meat Stock is made from meat and vegetables, seasoned to taste, and served without meat or vegetables. Brown stock is made from meat, part of which has been browned. White stock is made from meat that has not been browned.

Bouillon is made from lean beef delicately seasoned, and is served clear.

Consommé may be made from two or three kinds of meat, is lightly seasoned, and is cleared before serving.

To Clear Soup: Remove the fat from cold soup stock, heat the stock slightly and season it. Allow ½ to 1 egg white and 1 eggshell for each quart and mix thoroughly while soup is only warm. Let simmer 15 minutes or boil 5 minutes. Set aside to cool for 15 minutes, then strain through a double thickness of cheesecloth.

Beef Tea

Cut up 2 lb. lean beef into half-inch cubes and put it in glass fruit jar. Cover jar and place in a pan of hot water. Let stand for about three hours, or until meat has lost its red color. Pour juice from meat. This juice will keep on ice for 12 to 24 hours. It needs little seasoning and should be served hot.

Brown Soup Stock, or Bouillon

4 lb. shin of beef (⅔ meat and ⅓ bone)	¼ c. diced celery
2 qt. water	3 or 4 celery tops
¼ c. diced carrots	1 small sprig parsley
¼ c. diced turnips	2 T. chopped onion
	2 pepper corns

2 t. salt

Cut meat into 1-inch cubes. Cook one third of meat in a hot greased frying pan until well browned. Soak all meat and bone in cold water for 30 minutes; heat and simmer for 4 hours. Add vegetables, and cook 1 hour. Strain and add water to bring quantity to two quarts. Clear to make bouillon.

White Soup Stock, or Bouillon: Use veal instead of beef. Prepare as brown soup stock without browning the meat. Clear to make bouillon.

Consommé: Use half beef and half veal knuckle or chicken and veal. Cook as for brown soup stock. Strain, cool, and clear. A few pieces of diced vegetable or a little cooked rice may be served in consommé; consommé is served in bouillon or coffee cups. In hot weather consommé or bouillon may be served cold (jellied) with a slice of lemon.

Noodle Soup, or Soup with Rice or Barley

To soup stock, brown or white, or to chicken broth add cooked noodles, boiled rice, boiled barley, or boiled macaroni cut in 1-inch pieces. Use 1 cup of the material preferred to each quart of soup.

Emergency Bouillon, or Consommé

3 bouillon cubes	Vegetables as for brown soup stock or
2 qt. water	Tomato catsup (to taste) for tomato bouillon

Cook vegetables in water for 1 hour; add bouillon cubes; add salt if necessary; strain and serve.

Vegetable Soups with Meat Stock[1]

1 large soup bone, cracked	1 c. finely diced carrots
3 qt. cold water	1 c. finely diced turnips
4 T. fat	2 c. finely diced potatoes
1 green pepper, chopped	2 c. tomato juice and pulp
1 c. chopped onion	3 t. salt, or to taste
1½ c. chopped celery and leaves if desired	¼ t. pepper

[1] Courtesy of Bureau of Human Nutrition and Home Economics, United States Department of Agriculture.

Wash the soup bone and be careful to remove all small loose pieces of bone. Put the bone in a large kettle, cover with the cold water, and simmer for 2 hours. Remove the bone from the broth. Cook all the vegetables, except the tomatoes, in the fat in a skillet for about 10 minutes, stirring frequently. Add the vegetables, tomato, salt, and pepper to the broth, and simmer until the vegetables are tender but not broken. Serve the meat with the soup or save it for hash or croquettes.

This makes a rather large quantity of soup, but it is equally good reheated and served another day.

Vegetables

See Chapters 16 and 26

The method of cooking vegetables should be such as to preserve the maximum of food value.

Time Chart for Cooking Fresh and Dried Vegetables

Vegetables are considered sufficiently cooked when they are tender; overcooked when they are soft and flabby. The time varies with the age of the vegetable, the amount cooked, the amount of liquid used, and other factors.

VEGETABLE	METHOD OF PREPARATION	BOILING	STEAMING	BAKING
Artichokes	Whole	20–40 min.		
Asparagus	Tied in bundles	15–20	15–30 min.	
Beans, string	Cut crosswise	20–30	25–30	
Beans, Lima, dried	Soaked 4 hours	2–3 hrs.		6–8 hrs.
Beans, Lima, fresh	Shelled		20–25	30 min.
Beans, Navy, dried	Soaked 4 hours	2–3 hrs.		6–8 hrs.
Beets, young	Whole	35–45 min.	45–60	45–60 min.
Beets, mature	Whole	60–90	60–120	
Beet greens		15–25		
Broccoli	Cut in strips	20–25	25–30	
Brussels sprouts	Whole	15–20	20–25	
Cabbage	Quartered	10–15	15	
Cabbage	Shredded	5–10	10–12	
Carrots	Quartered or sliced	15–20	20–25	

VEGETABLE	METHOD OF PREPARATION	BOILING	STEAMING	BAKING
Cauliflower	Separated in flowerlets	10–15	15–18	
Cauliflower	Whole	20–30	25–30	
Celery	Cut in 1½″ pieces	10–30	25–30	
Chard, Swiss	No water added	10–15	18–20	
Collards		15–20	30	
Corn on cob	Whole ears	6–15	10–12	
Eggplant	Diced	10–15	15	25
Kale		15–25		
Kohlrabi	Pared, sliced	30	25–35	
Okra	Whole	10–20	20	
Onions	Small, whole	30–40	35	50
Parsnips	Whole	20–30	30–40	½ to ¾ hr.
Peas, green	Shelled	10–25	25–30	
Peas, dried	Soaked 4 hours	2–3 hrs.		6–8 hrs.
Potatoes, white	Medium whole	20–40	25–30	40–60 min.
Potatoes, sweet	Medium whole	20–40	25–30	40–60
Spinach	No water added	8–10	10–15	
Squash, Hubbard	Cut in 2″ pieces	20–25	25–30	¾–1 hr.
Squash, summer	Cut in thin slices	15	10–15	
Tomatoes	Quartered	5–20	10–15	
Turnips, white	Cut in 1″ cubes	15–25	20–25	
Turnips, yellow	Cut in 1″ cubes	20–30	25–30	
Turnip greens	Boiled (*Note:* Southern method requires longer cooking)	20–30		

Cooking Time for Frozen Vegetables[1]

Dry-pack vegetables are considered best when plunged into boiling water while frozen, but may be allowed to thaw first. It is possible to cook brine packs by plunging the frozen mass into boiling water; or they may be thawed and drained, the brine heated to the boiling point, and the vegetables added. Only enough water should be used to prevent burning, and the residue should be served with the vegetables.

Cooking times are shorter for frozen than for fresh vegetables by approximately one half, starting from the time the thawed mass resumes boiling.

[1] *Freezing and Storage of Foods in Freezing Cabinets and Lockers.* Bulletin No. 690, New York State Agricultural Experiment Station.

VEGETABLE	METHOD OF COOKING	TIME OF COOKING IN MINUTES
Asparagus	Boiling	5–8
Beans, green shell	Boiling	20–25
Beans, Lima	Boiling	16–20
Beans, snap	Boiling	12–15
	Steaming	12–15
Broccoli	Boiling	5–7
Beets, young whole	Boiling	18–20
Beets, cooked, and sliced before freezing	Boiling	Heated to proper temperature for serving
Beet greens	Boiling	10–12
Brussels sprouts	Boiling	2–3
Carrots	Boiling	5–10
Cauliflower	Boiling	5–8
Sweet corn, cut	Boiling	3–4
	Steaming	5
Sweet corn, on cob	Boiling	3
	Steaming	5
Kale	Boiling	20–25
Kohlrabi	Boiling	8–10
Mushrooms	Sauté	15–20
Mustard, curly	Boiling	12–15
Peas	Boiling	6–8
	Steaming	6–8
Rhubarb	Stewing	10–12
Spinach	Boiling	4–6
Squash, summer	Boiling	10–12
Squash, winter	Steaming in double boiler	Heated to proper temperature for serving
Swiss chard	Boiling	8–10
Turnips	Boiling	12–15
Turnip greens	Boiling	15–20

Preparation of Vegetables

Most vegetables are washed thoroughly (scrubbed if very dirty) and cooked in their skins; or pared or peeled and cooked.

String Beans are cooked whole or in 2-inch pieces after the ends and strings have been removed.

Lima Beans (butterbeans) and peas are washed and then shelled for cooking.

Beets are washed and then boiled or baked in their skins, with 2 inches of top and the root left on to prevent loss of color or "bleeding." When beets are almost tender, dip them in cold water and then break the skin with the fingers and slip it off.

Cabbage is washed, poor outer leaves discarded, inspected for insects, and sliced, shredded, or cut in wedge-shaped pieces. It may be freshened for 15 to 30 minutes in cold water before slicing.

Cauliflower has leaves and stalk removed. Wash, soak head down in cold salted water for 30 minutes. Cook whole with head up, in uncovered vessel.

Carrots are scrubbed, the skin scraped off, and cooked whole, diced, or sliced crosswise or lengthwise. Old carrots are peeled to remove the tough skin.

Celery should be scrubbed under running water with a brush.

Celery Prepared for the Table, Club Style: Wash and scrub each bunch. Cut the stalks in quarters lengthwise and serve on crushed ice or very cold. The tough outer stalks must be removed.

Green Corn: Remove the silk with the point of a sharp knife. The husk may be used as a cover during roasting.

Eggplant is washed and left whole for baking; it is pared, cut across in half-inch slices and soaked in salted water (2 T. to 1 qt.) for frying. Often it is also pressed by having a weight placed on the raw slices which have been sprinkled with salt.

Greens are washed by dipping up and down in three or four fresh waters, or cleansed leaf by leaf under running water.

Lettuce (for leaf lettuce, see *Greens*). To wash head lettuce, cut off stem end and cut stem out of head for about three fourths inch to 1 inch deep. Let water run into the hole, turn the head upside down and drain; repeat the process four or five times.

Parsnips and Turnips are pared and sliced or diced.

Peppers are cut open at stem end (around the stem), or are cut in halves, and seeds removed.

Potatoes are scrubbed and boiled either in skins or in pieces after paring. They are baked in their skins to retain steam, which helps to make them "mealy." Pare potatoes as thinly as possible.

Spinach. See *Greens.*

Tomatoes are peeled for salad and for broiling, sometimes for frying or stewing. To peel a ripe tomato (1) either rub it all over with the back of a knife; (2) or dip it in boiling water for a half minute and then in cold water; (3) or hold on a fork over a gas flame until the skin splits. Slit the skin at blossom end and peel toward stem end. Cut out the stem.

Common Methods of Cooking Vegetables

Boiled: Cook until tender in a small amount of boiling salted water (1 t. salt to 1 pt. water). The water should be boiling when the vegetable is added. Lower the heat when the water boils after the vegetable is in it. Cook in a tightly covered pan. Young tender vegetables should be cooked a very short time. Strong vegetables, as cabbage, cauliflower, and onions, may be made milder by cooking in an uncovered vessel. Season boiled vegetables with salt, pepper, and butter. See Time Chart for Cooking Vegetables, pages 425–426, and Preparation of Vegetables for Cooking, pages 427–428.

Steamed: Vegetables are prepared for steaming as for boiling, but are placed in a very small amount of boiling water and cooked in the steam. The process saves more of the valuable minerals and vitamins. A thrift cooker (on an electric range) is good for steaming.

Baked: Wash and place vegetable, usually whole, in a pan or on the rack in a moderate oven (350°–400° F.). Cook until tender.

Creamed: Cooked vegetables, whole or in pieces, may be served in white sauce. (See page 436.) White sauce Number 1 (thin) is used for starchy vegetables, as potatoes. White sauce Number 2 (medium) is used for carrots, peas, turnips, string beans, onions, cabbage, chard, salsify, asparagus, celery, cauliflower.

Scalloped Vegetables: Vegetables are placed in a buttered baking dish, with white sauce or milk (except tomatoes), covered with buttered bread crumbs and baked in a moderate oven (about 375° F.) until heated through and the crumbs browned.

Au Gratin: Prepare cooked vegetables as for scalloping; cover with buttered crumbs and brown. Cheese may be added to the white sauce or may be sprinkled over the top of the vegetable.

Stuffed Vegetables (except tomatoes) are usually boiled, steamed, or baked until tender, then stuffed, usually covered with buttered bread crumbs, and baked. Scoop out the center of the vegetable and mix this pulp with seasonings and with bread crumbs, cooked rice, or chopped meat. Put mixture in shell and bake until browned.

Fried: Potatoes, onions, and eggplant may be sliced thin and fried in deep fat. See General Rules for Deep-Fat Frying, page 447.

Glazed Vegetables: Carrots, sweet potatoes, squash, and onions are first boiled whole for about half the length of time required to make them tender, then sliced and either (1) cooked in sirup until partially transparent and tender, or (2) placed in buttered pan, covered with sugar or a heavy sirup, and baked. Use a sirup made in proportions of 2 c. sugar to 1 c. water.

Broccoli[1]

Trim off and discard the leaves and tough lower portion of the stalks of broccoli. Thoroughly wash the remaining center stalks with flower heads attached, and cut lengthwise into strips. Drop into salted boiling water. Cook in uncovered kettle for 15 to 25 minutes. As soon as the broccoli is tender, and while the color is still fresh green, drain, season with salt and pepper to taste, and add melted butter or other fat, or serve with Hollandaise sauce. (See recipe, page 438.)

Boiled Cabbage

Wash and chop or shred young cabbage and cook in boiling salted water until barely tender, 8 to 10 minutes. Drain off the water, season with salt, pepper, and melted butter.

Scalloped Cabbage

Put alternate layers of boiled cabbage cut in pieces, and of cracker or bread crumbs in a buttered baking dish. Pour over the contents of dish enough milk, seasoned with salt and pepper, to moisten crumbs. Cover with buttered crumbs and bake until brown in moderate oven and serve in the baking dish. An interesting variation is made by alternating sliced tart apples with the cabbage.

Cauliflower au Gratin

1 medium-sized cauliflower	½ c. grated cheese
1 c. white sauce (medium)	½ c. buttered bread crumbs

Salt and paprika

Place the whole boiled cauliflower, head up, in a buttered baking dish. Add the cheese to the white sauce and season to taste with salt and paprika. (A well-mashed pimiento may be added if desired.) Pour this sauce over the cauliflower, cover with buttered crumbs, and brown in a moderate oven (350° to 400° F.) from 15 to 20 minutes.

[1] Courtesy of Bureau of Human Nutrition and Home Economics, United States Department of Agriculture.

Corn Pudding

2 c. corn pulp	1½ T. sugar
2 eggs	½ t. salt
2 c. milk	2 T. butter

Beat eggs, add salt, sugar, milk, melted butter, and corn pulp. Bake in buttered dish in a slow to moderate oven (325°) until firm (30 to 35 minutes).

If corn pudding is cooked too rapidly, it will become watery.

Small recipe: ½ c. corn pulp, ½ c. milk, 1 t. sugar, 2 T. egg, a pinch of salt. Bake in ramekins or in custard cups until firm in slow oven.

Baked Cucumbers[1]

4 large cucumbers	1 c. bread crumbs
2 T. chopped onion	1 c. tomato pulp
2 T. chopped parsley	1 t. salt
4 T. butter or other fat	Pepper

Wash and pare the cucumbers and cut them in half lengthwise. Scoop out as much of the seed portion as possible without breaking the fleshy part, parboil the cucumber shells in lightly salted water for 10 minutes, and drain. Meanwhile cook the onion and parsley in the fat, add the other ingredients and the cucumber pulp, and cook this mixture for 5 minutes. Fill shells with the hot stuffing, place in a shallow baking dish, add a little water to keep them from sticking; bake in a moderate oven for 15 minutes, or until the stuffing has browned on top. Serve in the baking dish.

Scalloped Eggplant[1]

1 large eggplant	Pepper
2 T. butter or other fat	1 c. buttered bread crumbs
1 green pepper, chopped	1 qt. canned or chopped raw tomatoes
1 small onion, chopped	
2 t. salt	

Pare eggplant and cut into small pieces. Melt fat in a skillet, add the green pepper and onion, and cook for a few minutes. Add the tomatoes, eggplant, seasonings, cook for 10 minutes. Place in a shallow greased baking dish. Cover with buttered crumbs. Bake in a moderate oven for 15 minutes, until the crumbs are browned.

[1] Courtesy of Bureau of Human Nutrition and Home Economics, United States Department of Agriculture.

Turnip or Mustard Greens (Southern style)

Select young tender turnip or mustard greens. Wash carefully. Place in a covered kettle with no water except what is on the well-washed greens. Brown in a skillet 3 or 4 thick (½-inch) slices of salt pork. Add salt pork to greens and cook until the greens are tender. The time will vary according to the age of the greens. Young tender greens will cook in 25–30 minutes. *Note:* If greens are older, they will be tough and will require more water for the longer cooking. Add water as needed during the cooking.

Stuffed Onions[1]

5 large mild onions
3 T. butter or other fat
½ c. chopped celery
2 c. bread crumbs
1 t. salt
Pepper
2 T. chopped parsley

Skin the onions, cut in half crosswise, simmer in salted water until almost tender, and drain. Remove the centers without disturbing the outer layers and chop fine. Melt 2 T. of the fat in a skillet, add the chopped onion, celery, parsley, and cook for a few minutes. Push the vegetable to one side, melt the remaining fat and add to it the bread crumbs, salt, and pepper, then combine with the vegetables. Fill the onion shells with the stuffing, cover, and bake in a moderate oven for about 30 minutes, or until the onions are tender. Remove the cover from the baking dish during the last of the cooking so that the onions will brown on top.

Stuffed Peppers

4 medium-sized green peppers
⅔ c. ground ham or other meat
1 c. soft bread crumbs
1 T. butter
1 T. minced onion
Salt and pepper to taste
Tomato juice or meat stock to moisten
½ c. buttered bread crumbs

Cut the tops from the peppers and remove seeds. Drop into boiling salted water. Allow peppers to stand in hot water (below the boiling point) for 10 minutes. Remove, drain, and stuff. Cover with buttered crumbs and bake in moderate oven (350° F.) until tender (15 to 20 minutes).

To make the stuffing, melt butter, add onion, and cook slightly. Mix bread crumbs and meat and add to onion and butter. Moisten with tomato juice or meat stock, season to taste. Fill peppers.

[1] Courtesy of Bureau of Human Nutrition and Home Economics, United States Department of Agriculture.

Baked Potatoes[1]

Select good baking potatoes of uniform size and shape, scrub thoroughly, and bake in a moderately hot oven (375° F) for 45 to 60 minutes, or until soft when pressed. Take the potatoes from the oven at once, work gently with the fingers to loosen the skin, make a short gash to allow the steam to escape, season with butter, salt, and a dash of paprika, and serve at once.

Stuffed Baked Potato

Cut baked potatoes in half (as soon as taken from the oven). Remove the inside, mash, season with salt, pepper, and butter. Add enough hot milk to make the consistency of mashed potatoes. Beat smooth and light. Refill the skins, dot with butter or brush with melted butter. Bake until brown (8 to 10 minutes) in a hot oven (400° F.).

Variations in Baked Stuffed Potatoes

1. To the mashed potatoes before the skins are filled add beaten egg white (1 egg white to 3 or 4 medium-sized potatoes).
2. Grated cheese (½ c. to 3 or 4 medium-sized potatoes). Mix cheese with the potato, reserving a small amount to sprinkle on the top of the potato after stuffing.
3. Chopped parsley — sprinkle top of stuffed potatoes.

Fried Potatoes

Slice potatoes one half inch thick and cut the slices in half-inch strips for French fried potatoes; slice in very thin crosswise slices for potato chips; or slice with special cutters for waffle potatoes. Soak sliced potatoes for 5 minutes in cold water. Dry between towels and fry a few slices at a time. Fry in deep fat and drain on brown paper (see Deep-Fat Frying, page 447); sprinkle with salt, and serve hot. Sweet potato chips are very good. Potatoes may also be sautéed; cook them in a skillet in a small amount of hot fat.

Hashed Brown Potatoes

4 medium-sized cooked potatoes, chopped fine — 1 t. salt
1½ T. flour — 2 T. milk — 2 T. fat — Pepper to taste

Heat fat in frying pan. Stir flour, pepper, and salt into potato and press it down firmly into pan; add milk. Brown the potato

[1] Courtesy of Bureau of Human Nutrition and Home Economics, United States Department of Agriculture.

slowly, allowing 30 minutes for cooking. Turn it out as an omelet is turned, and serve hot.

Scalloped Potatoes (raw)

Pare and slice potatoes thin. Put in buttered baking dish, sprinkling each layer very lightly with flour, salt, and pepper, and butter. Pour over the potatoes just enough milk to be seen through the top layer. Bake in a moderate oven (350° to 400° F.) until potatoes are tender (about 1 hour).

Scalloped Potatoes (cooked)

Cut boiled potatoes into slices one-quarter-inch thick. Arrange in layers in a buttered baking dish. Cover with a thin white sauce (No. 1), then with buttered crumbs and cook until brown.

Sweet Potatoes (Southern style)

Pare and cut sweet potatoes into strips as for French fried potatoes. Place layer in baking dish. Put over them 2 T. sugar, 2 T. butter, and sprinkle with cinnamon. Repeat in layers. Bake about 2 hours in a moderate (375° F.) oven. If they are drying instead of cooking, add a little water. Baste occasionally with melted butter.

Candied Sweet Potatoes

Boil 6 medium-sized sweet potatoes until almost tender, peel, cut in halves lengthwise, or slice, place in baking dish and finish in any of the following ways:

1. Sprinkle with 1 c. brown sugar and grated orange rind. Dot with ¼ c. butter. Add ½ c. water. Bake about an hour in a slow oven.
2. Cook together 1 c. of brown sugar and ½ c. water for 5 minutes. Add 1 T. butter. Sprinkle potatoes with cinnamon. Pour the sauce over the potatoes and cook until well browned.
3. Spread 1 c. of honey over the potatoes. Bake until brown.
4. Cover potatoes with a sauce made of 1 c. maple sugar, ½ c. water, and 4 T. butter. Brown in oven.
5. Make thick sirup of ½ c. Karo, ½ c. sugar, and ¼ c. water. Pour over potatoes. Brown in oven.

Sweet Potato Puffs (croquettes)

Mash desired number of boiled sweet potatoes. Season with salt and melted butter (add 1 egg to 2 c. potatoes if desired). Shape in balls and roll in flour, finely sifted bread crumbs, or finely rolled corn flakes. Brown in deep fat. Serve as a vegetable.

Chopped nuts may be added to the mixture.

Spinach

Pick over spinach and discard wilted leaves. Cut off stem ends. Wash in several waters to remove grit. If young and tender, spinach may be cooked in the water that clings to the leaves. Heat slowly, stirring frequently, until well cooked down and tender (10 to 15 minutes). Chop fine, season with pepper, salt, and butter. If desired add lemon juice or vinegar. Serve garnished with slices of hard-cooked egg.

Note: Older spinach will require the addition of a small quantity of water. Cook until tender (about 20 minutes), drain, chop, and season.

Broiled Tomatoes[1]

Wash tomatoes, remove the stem ends, cut in half, put in a greased shallow baking dish, add salt, pepper, and melted butter or other fat to season, and place under the flame of a broiling oven, far enough from the heat to allow the tomatoes to cook before browning. Broil for 10 to 20 minutes, or until tender and lightly browned. Serve hot garnished with parsley on crisp buttered toast. If overcooked, tomatoes will be watery and lose their shape.

Sautéed Tomatoes

6–8 firm tomatoes (underripe)	Finely sifted dry bread crumbs
1 egg	Salt and pepper
1 T. cold water	1 T. chopped parsley

Wash tomatoes, remove stem ends, cut into ½-inch slices. Beat egg slightly, add water. Mix seasonings with crumbs. Dip tomato in egg, roll in crumbs, and brown in a small amount of fat (sauté) in a skillet.

Scalloped Tomatoes

2 lb. fresh tomatoes or 1 No. 2 can of tomatoes	½ bay leaf	2 t. salt
2 c. fresh bread crumbs (fresh bread crumbled or cut in half-inch cubes)	2 whole cloves	⅛ t. pepper
	2 T. sugar	2 to 3 T. fat

Peel fresh tomatoes, cut in pieces and cook until soft. Add seasoning to canned or cooked tomatoes and boil for five minutes.

[1] Courtesy of Bureau of Human Nutrition and Home Economics, United States Department of Agriculture.

Remove bay leaf and cloves. Put alternate layers of bread crumbs and tomatoes in buttered baking dish; pour over it the melted butter and cook in moderate oven about 10 to 15 minutes.

Mashed Turnips

Pare turnips and slice. Cook in uncovered vessel in boiling salted water until tender. Drain, mash, season with cream or butter, salt if needed, and pepper. A small amount of sugar may be added if desired.

Fried Carrots and Apples[1]

6 medium-sized carrots 6 tart apples 2 T. fat 1 T. sugar ¼ t. salt

Scrape the carrots and cut them lengthwise into thin slices. Pare the apples or leave the skin on, as preferred, core, and cut into slices about one fourth inch thick. Place a single layer of the apples and the carrots in a large skillet with the fat, cover tightly, and cook until well browned, turn, and brown the other side. Just before the cooking is finished, sprinkle with the sugar and salt. Serve on a hot platter, first a layer of carrots, then a layer of apples, so the two can be lifted together.

Dried Vegetables

Pick over and wash dried vegetables. Cover well with cold water and soak for several hours. Boil as for fresh vegetables.

Sauces

PROPORTIONS FOR WHITE SAUCES

White Sauce	*Liquid*	*Thickening Material*	*Fat*	*Seasoning*	*Use*
No. 1 Thin	1 c. milk	1 T. flour	1 T.	½ t. salt	Cream soups
No. 2 Medium	1 c. milk	2 T. flour	1½ T.	½ t. salt	Creamed or scalloped dishes or gravy
No. 3	1 c. milk	3 T. flour	2 T.	1 t. salt	Soufflés
No. 4 Thick	1 c. milk	4 T. flour	2½ T.	1 t. salt	Croquettes

To give the sauce a good flavor, use either butter or margarine.

[1] Courtesy of Bureau of Human Nutrition and Home Economics, United States Department of Agriculture.

Methods of Combining White Sauces

Method 1. Melt fat in a frying pan or in the top part of a double boiler; remove from heat and stir flour in to make a smooth paste. Add one third of the hot milk and stir until the mixture is smooth. Add the remainder of the liquid and salt, and cook until smooth and thick. The process takes about 10 to 15 minutes over direct heat, and about 25 to 30 minutes in a double boiler.

Method 2. Mix flour with ¼ c. of liquid and stir until smooth. Add the remainder of the liquid and cook in double boiler or over direct heat, stirring constantly until it thickens. Add fat and salt.

General Proportions for Gravies

Liquid	*Fat*	*Flour*
1 c. water	2 T. butter or drippings	2 T. white flour
stock		or
milk		2½ T. browned flour
tomatoes		
or a mixture of these		

These ingredients may be combined in either of two ways to make a suitable mixture. The flour may be added to the melted fat, or the flour may be mixed with a little of the cold liquid and added to the hot mixture.

Barbecue Sauce for Meats. (*See page* 481.)

Tartar Sauce. (*See* **Salad Dressings,** *pages* 488–489.)

Brown Sauce

2 T. fat	2 T. chopped parsley	½ t. salt
¼ c. flour	2 c. water or stock	⅛ t. pepper

Brown the flour by stirring over a hot fire in a dry skillet. Add to melted butter. Add stock and seasonings, and cook until thick. Add 1 t. of Worcestershire sauce if desired. Strain if not smooth.

Mushroom Sauce

1 c. white sauce No. 2 or brown sauce	¾ c. sliced mushrooms
Few drops onion juice	1 T. fat

Cook mushrooms in fat 5 minutes; add sauce and onion juice, heat one minute. Serve with meats, broiled steaks, or meat loaf.

Cheese Sauce

In 1 c. white sauce No. 2, melt ½ c. grated cheese. Serve hot.

Tomato Sauce

1 c. canned tomatoes	1 sprig parsley
½ c. water	1 T. chopped onion
Dash of cloves	1 T. butter
Dash of allspice	2 T. flour
1 piece bay leaf	¼ t. salt
Few drops of thyme	Dash of pepper

Put tomatoes and all of seasoning, except onion, into a pan and boil 2 or 3 minutes. Melt butter and brown onion in it. Add flour and gradually the hot tomatoes. Return to fire and heat. Strain and serve.

For a less highly seasoned sauce, modify by omissions to suit the taste.

Hollandaise Sauce[1]

½ c. butter	2 T. lemon juice	Dash of cayenne
4 egg yolks	¼ t. salt	¼ c. boiling water

Divide the butter into three portions. Beat the egg yolks and lemon juice together, add one piece of butter, and cook in a double boiler, stirring constantly until the mixture begins to thicken. Remove from the stove, add a second piece of butter, and stir rapidly. Then add the remaining butter, and continue to stir until the mixture is completely blended. Add the salt, cayenne, and boiling water. Return to the double boiler, and stir until the sauce thickens.

Mock Hollandaise Sauce

1 c. hot white sauce No. 2 (page 436)	2 egg yolks
1 T. lemon juice or vinegar	2 T. butter

When white sauce is cooked, remove from heat and beat in lemon juice gradually, then egg yolks and butter. Cook slightly to thicken yolks. Beat well and serve immediately. Serve with vegetables, such as boiled cauliflower or asparagus, or with fish.

Egg Sauce for Fish or Vegetables

1 c. white sauce No. 2 (page 436)	2 T. lemon juice if desired
2 sliced hard-cooked eggs	1 t. parsley if desired

When white sauce is cooked, remove from fire and beat in lemon juice (if used) gradually; add eggs and parsley. Eggs may be mashed to a paste and mixed with sauce.

[1] *Aunt Sammy's Radio Recipes Revised.* Bureau of Human Nutrition and Home Economics, United States Department of Agriculture.

Maître d'Hôtel Butter

4 T. butter
1 T. lemon juice
2 t. chopped parsley
¼ t. salt
⅛ t. paprika

Cream butter with a wooden spoon, and cream in lemon juice, parsley, and seasonings. Form into small balls and serve with fish or meats.

Drawn Butter Sauce

4 T. butter
1½ T. lemon juice
¼ t. salt

Heat, mix well, and serve hot with vegetables or meats.

Mint Sauce for Lamb

1 c. hot vinegar
¼ c. sugar
8 sprigs mint, finely minced

Pour vinegar over sugar and mint. Let stand 30 minutes to 1 hour. Strain and serve.

Cucumber Sauce for Fish

1 medium cucumber
2 T. mild vinegar
½ t. salt, or to taste
⅛ t. white pepper

Pare and grate or chop cucumber; mix with seasonings.

Lemon Sauce

1 T. cornstarch, or 1½ T. flour
½ c. sugar
2 T. butter
1 c. boiling water
Grated rind of 1 lemon
3 T. lemon juice

Mix cornstarch and sugar with 3 T. cold water and stir into hot water in double boiler. Cook until thick (20 to 30 min.). Add grated lemon rind and juice, and cook 5 to 10 minutes.

Small recipe: ½ T. cornstarch (or 2½ t. flour), 1 T. cold water, ¼ c. sugar, 1 T. butter, ½ c. boiling water, 1½ T. lemon juice, grated rind of ½ lemon.

Hard Sauce

⅓ c. butter
flavor to taste
1 c. powdered sugar

Cream butter; add sugar gradually. Suggested flavoring ½ t. vanilla or ½ t. lemon extract.

Custard Sauce

See Soft Custard, page 515, for proportions and method of making. Flavor with vanilla.

Chocolate Sauce

1 oz. chocolate or 3 T. powdered cocoa	1 c. sugar
½ c. water	½ t. vanilla
1 T. butter	⅛ t. salt

Cook chocolate or cocoa with the water until smooth; add butter, sugar, and salt, and heat until sugar is dissolved. Add vanilla and serve. Use for ice cream or puddings.

Caramel Sauce

1¼ c. sugar   1 c. hot water   1 T. butter

Caramelize ¼ c. sugar by heating until melted and a light brown. Add water to dissolve sugar. Add the remaining sugar and butter, and heat until sugar is dissolved.

Strawberry Sauce

1 pt. berries   ½ c. sugar   1 t. lemon juice

Crush berries, add sugar and lemon juice, and stir until sugar is dissolved.

Butterscotch Sauce

½ c. granulated sugar	4 T. butter	1 c. hot water
¾ c. brown sugar	⅛ t. salt	

Caramelize 1 T. of granulated sugar by heating until melted and a light brown. Add water to dissolve sugar; add brown sugar, remaining granulated sugar, butter, and salt, and heat until sugar is dissolved. This sauce may be thickened with ½ T. cornstarch, mixed with a little cold water.

Foamy Sauce

½ c. butter	1 egg
1 c. powdered sugar	2 t. vanilla, or 3 T. orange juice

Melt butter over hot water and add sugar; add beaten egg and beat the mixture with rotary beater. Cool slightly and add vanilla. Serve with steamed puddings or cake puddings.

Butter Balls

Cream butter, and measure in ½ T. lots. Make into rough balls, using spatula. Drop into ice water. Scald and then chill the butter paddles. Shape balls with paddles. If a mold is used instead of paddles, treat it in the same way. When balls are finished, drop into ice water or place on crushed ice.

Whipped Cream

Chill cream. Put into a deep bowl or glass jar and whip with rotary beater until stiff. Thick cream is required for whipping.

Main Dish for Luncheon or Supper

See Chapter 17

Soufflés

Soufflés may be made with cheese, vegetable pulp, ground meat, or flaked fish. A soufflé is an excellent main hot dish for luncheon, supper, or dinner.

A soufflé is made by binding one of these materials together with bread crumbs or white sauce, with egg yolk, and leavening it with well-beaten egg whites. A soufflé that contains bread crumbs holds up better than one made with white sauce alone.

A soufflé requires slow cooking. Cook in a very moderate oven (300° F.), for an hour or longer is best, though satisfactory results may be obtained at 350° for less time. A soufflé should be served immediately when taken from the oven. A slowly cooked soufflé will shrink some, but it will not collapse like one that is cooked too rapidly for the center to be set.

Cheese Soufflé

1 c. chopped or ¾ c. grated cheese
2 T. butter
3 T. flour
1 c. milk
3 eggs
½ t. salt
Dash of cayenne or paprika
White pepper to taste

Make a white sauce of flour, butter, seasoning, and milk. Add cheese and cook until the cheese melts. Add egg yolks and stir well. Cool. When ready to bake, beat the whites until stiff and fold into the cheese mixture. Pour into a well-buttered baking dish (½ to ⅔ full) and bake in a slow to moderate oven until firm and brown. It will require 30 to 45 minutes at 350° or 60 minutes at 300° F. Serve at once in its baking dish.

Small recipe: ¼ c. cheese, ⅔ T. butter, 1 T. flour, ¼ c. milk, 1 egg, salt and pepper.

Salmon Soufflé

4 eggs	1 T. butter or other fat	Paprika to taste
1½ c. milk	1 No. 2 can salmon (2 c.)	Tabasco if desired
1 c. fine dry bread crumbs	1 t. salt	

Heat the milk, bread crumbs, and fat in a double boiler. Flake the salmon and season with lemon juice. Put into the hot mixture, add egg yolks, and cook thick. Season to taste. Beat egg whites stiff, fold in the hot (or cool) mixture, pour into a greased baking dish and bake in a moderate oven (350° F.) for 45 minutes, or in a very moderate oven (300° F.) for one hour. Serve immediately in the dish in which baked.

The cheese and salmon in the above recipes may be exchanged. One of these recipes illustrates a soufflé made with white sauce; the other, a soufflé made with bread crumbs.

Omelets (pages 418–420)

Spanish Omelet is especially good for luncheon and for supper.

For other luncheon dishes made with eggs, see recipes in section on Eggs, pages 415–418.

Welsh Rabbit[1]

1 pint milk	½ t. salt	Onion juice
4 T. melted butter or other fat	½ lb. cheese, shaved thin	Soy sauce
4 T. flour	Tabasco sauce	1 egg

Heat the milk in a double boiler. Mix the melted fat, flour, and salt, and stir into them a small quantity of the heated milk. Add this to the remainder of the milk, stir until thickened, add the cheese and a few drops of each of the seasonings, and beat lightly until the cheese has melted. Pour a little of the cheese mixture into the well-beaten egg, then add this to the rabbit, and cook for 2 or 3 minutes longer. Serve on thin crisp toast or crackers.

Macaroni or Spaghetti and Cheese

1 c. macaroni or spaghetti broken in pieces	2 T. butter
1 c. to 1½ c. grated cheese	2 T. flour
1 c. milk	1 t. salt
	¼ t. paprika or ⅛ t. white pepper

Cook macaroni or spaghetti. See directions on page 400. Put

[1] *Aunt Sammy's Radio Recipes Revised.* Bureau of Human Nutrition and Home Economics, United States Department of Agriculture.

a layer of boiled macaroni into a buttered baking dish. Sprinkle with grated cheese or cover with cheese sliced thin. Repeat. Pour over this a white sauce made of the milk, flour, butter, and seasonings. Bake in a moderate oven (350° F.) until brown.

Small recipe: ¼ c. macaroni or spaghetti broken in pieces, ¼ c. grated cheese, ½ T. flour, ¼ t. salt, ¼ c. milk, dash of white pepper or paprika.

Rice and Cheese

Substitute rice for macaroni in the preceding recipe.

Vegetable Dishes

Stuffed vegetables are stuffed either with meat or with bread crumbs and vegetable pulp. Creamed, au gratin, scalloped or baked vegetables are good hot dishes for luncheon or supper. (See Vegetable Recipes, pages 430–436.)

Creamed Dishes

1½ c. diced material ½ c. white sauce No. 2

Creamed dishes of vegetables, cooked meat, fish, hard-cooked eggs, or sweetbreads are good luncheon dishes. Serve on toast or in toast cases. See directions for toast cases on page 444.

Creamed Sweetbreads

Wash in cold water, allow to stand in cold salted water one hour. Drain. Parboil (slowly) about 20 minutes or until firm in salted water containing a small amount (1 t.) of vinegar. Drain and plunge into cold water. Remove membranes. Sweetbreads are always parboiled in this way for cooking.

Separate into sections, and peel off as much of membrane as possible. Cut into ½-inch cubes. Reheat in 1 cup of white sauce No. 2. Season to taste. A small amount of cooked green pepper may be added. Serve on toast, or in timbale cases or toast cases.

Chicken à la King

1½ c. cooked chicken cut in cubes
1½ c. white sauce No. 2 (page 436)
1 minced green pepper or pimiento
3 chopped mushrooms
Salt and pepper to taste

Add chicken and other material to white sauce and heat for 10 minutes. Serve on toast, in toast cases, or in timbale cases. Garnish with parsley.

Service of Creamed Dishes

Creamed dishes may be served on toast, in toast cases, or in timbale cases.

Toast Cases: Cut stale bread in 2½-inch cubes. Trim off all crust. Hollow out center, leaving sides of box half an inch thick. Toast in a hot oven until delicately browned but not dried; or fry in deep fat and drain on brown paper. Fill cases with creamed vegetables, creamed eggs, creamed meats or shellfish.

Timbale Cases:

¾ c. flour
½ c. milk
¼ t. salt
1 egg slightly beaten
1 T. melted fat or oil

Mix egg and milk and add gradually to flour; add salt and melted fat and beat only until smooth. Dip timbale iron, previously heated in hot fat, about two thirds into a cup of batter. Lift iron, inverting to prevent batter from dripping, immerse it in deep, hot fat and fry until the batter is brown. The mixture will slip from iron before iron is lifted from batter if the fat is either too hot or too cold. Test the fat first by frying a small case. Wipe fat from iron before putting into the batter. If the case rises above top of iron, it was dipped too deep in the batter.

Drain timbale cases on brown or unglazed paper. Just before serving, fill three fourths full of creamed mixture of vegetables or meats. Makes 25 to 30 timbale cases.

American Chop Suey

2 medium onions sliced thin
1 c. celery, sliced
½ c. sliced mushrooms if desired
½ medium green pepper, shredded
½ lb. pork or chicken, cut small
¼ c. rice
1 c. stock
1½ t. salt

Brown meat and onions together slightly in frying pan, using 1 to 2 T. fat with the chicken. Add pepper, sliced mushrooms, and celery; add rice, salt, and stock, and cook for 10 minutes. Place in baking dish and cook in moderate oven (350° to 375° F.) for one hour. Serve hot.

Italian Baked Rice

3 c. cooked rice
½ c. grated cheese
¼ c. chopped pimiento
1½ c. tomato juice
2 t. salt
⅛ t. pepper

Mix ingredients thoroughly and pour into a baking dish. Cover the top of the dish with the pulp left from straining the tomatoes. Bake for 30 minutes in a moderate oven 375° F. and serve hot.

Small recipe: ½ c. cooked rice, 1 T. grated cheese, ½ T. chopped pimiento, ¼ c. tomato juice, ⅓ t. salt.

For **Meat Pie.** (*See page* 474.)

Baked Beans

2 c. dried beans
1 qt. water
⅛ lb. fat salt pork
2 t. salt
¼ c. molasses
½ c. hot water
¼ t. mustard

Soak beans overnight in cold water to cover; drain and add 1 qt. cold water. Heat and allow to simmer two hours, or until skins are tender and loose. (Instead of simmering process, beans may be cooked in pressure cooker at 20 lb. for 20 minutes.) Add salt, mustard, and molasses to beans, pour into greased bean pot or baking dish with a lid; press sliced pork in at top and pour boiling water over it. Cover and bake slowly at 250 to 300 degrees F. for 3 to 5 hours. (If a quick cooking is desired, cook in a pressure canner 30 minutes at 10 lb., then in a moderate oven for 30 minutes to 1 hour.)

Meat or Salmon Loaf

3 c. ground meat or salmon
(meat may be cooked or uncooked)
1 or 2 eggs
1 T. chopped parsley
1 slice onion, finely minced
1 c. bread crumbs
1 c. milk
1 t. salt
¼ t. pepper
2 slices bacon, chopped fine, or
2 T. butter

Mix thoroughly; press into a greased bread pan. Bake in moderate oven (350° F.) for 30 to 40 minutes. Serve salmon loaf with 1 c. white sauce No. 2 containing chopped parsley or chopped hard-cooked egg. Serve meat loaf with or without tomato sauce.

Jellied Turkey or Chicken Loaf

2 c. diced turkey or chicken
2¼ T. powdered gelatin
3½ c. turkey or chicken stock
1 c. mayonnaise
1 t. onion juice
½ t. lemon juice
2 c. diced celery or chopped cabbage
3 hard-cooked eggs, sliced
1 t. salt
2 t. pimiento

Soften gelatin in a little of the cold turkey or chicken stock and dissolve in the remainder that has been heated. Chill in the refrigerator. When it begins to thicken, stir in mayonnaise and add other ingredients that have also been chilled. Place in a loaf pan and return to refrigerator to chill and stiffen. Unmold and garnish with parsley or watercress.

Chilled Corned-Beef Loaf

1 T. powdered gelatin	1 T. grated onion
½ c. cold water	¼ t. paprika
1¾ c. boiling water	1 t. dry mustard
1 T. lemon juice	3 c. corned beef, flaked or chopped fine

Soften gelatin in cold water and dissolve in boiling water. Add paprika and mustard. Chill in refrigerator. When slightly thickened, fold in corned beef with onion and lemon juice. Turn into refrigerator tray and allow to stand in refrigerator, but not in ice compartment, for two hours. Unmold and serve on large plate for main meat of a summer dinner. Mark in squares with dots of cream cheese softened with milk, or cut in squares before serving.

Oyster Loaf

Cut top from a loaf of bread. Pull out middle and toast the loaf and its top in oven. Pour melted butter over the inner surfaces and return to oven to brown. Fill toasted loaf with layers of fried oysters, olives, sliced pickles, and celery. Season the layers with catsup. Replace top. Serve hot and whole, and slice into 1½ to 2-inch slices for individual servings.

Fish Chowder

1 lb. fish	1 t. salt
3 c. hot fish stock or hot water	Dash of pepper
1 c. hot milk	½ T. flour
⅛ lb. salt pork, diced	1½ c. diced potatoes

2 slices onion

Use a fish that has white flesh. Wrap fish in cheesecloth and cook it 20 minutes in boiling salted water (1 t. salt to 1 qt. water). Remove from water and save water for fish stock; after removing bones and skin, cut fish in small pieces. In kettle to be used for chowder, fry salt pork for 3 to 5 minutes with onions. Sprinkle fish with salt, pepper, and flour and mix fish and diced potatoes; place in chowder kettle and pour over it the fish stock. Cook slowly, without stirring, for 40 minutes. Add hot milk just before serving, and serve hot, in soup plates, with crisp crackers.

Chicken Gumbo

- 1½ lb. chicken meat
- Bacon fat
- Flour
- 1 slice onion
- 1½ c. okra (or canned corn)
- 2 T. finely chopped red or green pepper
- ½ c. strained tomato
- ¼ t. salt
- ¼ c. rice

Cut chicken in small pieces; cook in water to cover until almost tender. Remove chicken from broth and save broth. Roll chicken in flour and brown with finely chopped onion in bacon fat. Add okra, finely chopped pepper, tomato, salt, and rice. Add broth, with hot water, if necessary, to make 2¼ cups. Boil 25 minutes, or until both chicken and rice are tender.

General Rules for Deep-Fat Frying

The fat used for cooking may be olive oil, cotton-seed oil, peanut oil, hydrogenated fats, beef drippings, lard, corn oil, or a mixture of several fats.

To keep the food from absorbing fat, cover it with crumbs and egg, or mix egg with it.

Place the articles to be cooked in a bath of hot fat deep enough to float them. The kettle should be of iron; a frying basket may be used. The kettle should be only two thirds full, in order to avoid spattering fat.

Foods already cooked or needing little cooking require a higher temperature than batters. The temperature of the fat for frying oysters, croquettes, fish balls, and other food already cooked may be tested by browning a cube of bread in forty seconds. When the bread browns in sixty seconds the fat is the right temperature for all batters.

All the articles cooked must be drained on brown unglazed paper.

Only small quantities may be fried at a time. When one quantity has been taken out, the fat must be reheated and tested before a second lot is added.

In the absence of a frying basket, a wire spoon or strainer may be used to remove the food from the fat.

Fat which has been used for frying should be cooled and clarified by cooking slowly a few slices of raw potato in it for ten

FIG. 133. DEEP-FAT FRYING

1 Equipment | 2. Cutting out cutlets
3. Frying cutlets | 4. Finished cutlets

minutes, then strained through several thicknesses of muslin, and covered when cold. Fat may be used several times for frying and then made into soap.

Since fish imparts a flavor to fat, separate fat should be kept for cooking fish, or fat in which fish is cooked should be clarified with great care as soon as it has been used.

Temperatures for Fried Foods [1]

Cooked foods (croquettes, etc.)	375°–385° F.
Uncooked foods (doughnuts, fish, fritters)	365°–375° F.
Uncooked foods containing large amounts of water (potatoes, onions)	380°–395° F.

[1] Heseltine, Marjorie, and Dow, Ula M., *The Basic Cook Book.* Houghton Mifflin Company.

Croquettes (1 dozen)

Croquettes consist of ground meat well seasoned, mixed with a stiff white sauce. When cold it should be stiff enough to shape.

STEPS IN MAKING CROQUETTES

I. Meat Mixture	*II. White Sauce Mixture*
3½ c. chopped chicken or other meat	2 c. milk or cream
1 T. chopped parsley	¼ c. butter
Few drops onion juice	½ c. flour
Lemon juice	1½ t. salt
	½ t. white pepper
	1 t. celery salt
	Dash of cayenne

Make white sauce, add meat. Taste to see if well seasoned. Spread on a plate to cool. Shape into cones or cylinders using one rounding tablespoon of the mixture for each croquette. Roll in crumbs, dip in egg, roll again in crumbs. Fry in deep fat and drain on brown paper.

Small recipe (two croquettes):

Meat mixture: ⅓ c. meat, 3 drops onion juice, ½ t. chopped parsley, ½ t. lemon juice.

White sauce mixture: ¼ c. milk, 1 t. butter, 1 T. flour, ⅛ t. salt, dash of pepper, celery salt, cayenne to taste.

Fritters I (sliced fruit)

1 c. flour	1 T. butter	¼ t. salt	
⅓ c. milk	1 t. baking powder	1 T. sugar	2 eggs

Mix and sift dry ingredients. Beat yolks and add to them the milk. Stir the liquid into dry ingredients, and stir in the melted butter. Fold in beaten whites. Fry at 365 to 370 degrees F.

Slices of any fruit may be stirred into this batter and fried immediately in deep fat. Pineapple or bananas are most frequently used. Serve with lemon sauce.

Small recipe: ½ c. flour, ⅛ t. salt, 2 T. milk, 1 egg, ½ T. butter, ½ t. baking powder, ½ T. sugar.

Fritters II (fruit or vegetable pulp)[1]

1 c. sifted flour	1 T. sugar	½ T. fat
1½ t. baking powder	1 egg, beaten	½ c. fruit or vegetable pulp
½ t. salt	½ c. milk	

Mix as for Fritters I.

[1] *Homemade Bread, Cake, and Pastry.* Farmers' Bulletin 1775, United States Department of Agriculture.

Small recipe: ¼ c. flour, ½ t. baking powder (scant), pinch of salt, 1 T. beaten egg, 1 t. sugar, 2 T. milk, ½ t. fat, 2 T. fruit or vegetable pulp.

Cherry Jam Fritters[1]

12 slices of bread	¼ c. cold water	1 T. lemon juice
1 egg	Cherry jam	3 T. butter

Cut the slices of bread about one-fourth inch thick and then cut these in rounds, using a cooky or biscuit cutter. Spread the rounds of bread with the cherry jam and cover them with another round, as in a sandwich. Beat the egg until it is light, add the lemon juice and cold water, and continue to beat until the ingredients are well mixed. Dip each sandwich into the egg mixture quickly and brown in a frying pan, using the butter as the fat.

Scalloped Oysters

1 pt. oysters	1½ c. cracker crumbs	Salt
6 T. top milk	½ c. melted butter	Pepper

Remove any pieces of shell from oysters. Wash oysters in cold water. Add cracker crumbs to melted butter, mix well. Cover the bottom of a buttered baking dish with a thin layer of crumbs. Add a layer of oysters, season with salt and pepper and add one half the milk. Repeat and cover top with remaining crumbs. Bake 30 to 45 minutes in moderately hot oven, 425° to 450° F. Never use more than two layers of oysters in scalloped oysters. If three layers are used, the middle layer will be underdone when the other layers are cooked.

Small recipe: ¼ c. oysters, ¼ c. cracker crumbs, 1 T. milk, 1 T. butter, salt and pepper.

Oyster Stew (*see page* 423).

Oysters in Ramekins (8 servings)

4 hard-cooked eggs	½ c. cream or milk
2 raw eggs	2 T. butter
2 doz. oysters	Salt, pepper, parsley, cracker crumbs

Melt butter in double boiler, add milk. When milk is scalded add oysters (washed, drained, and chopped). Season, add beaten egg, and cracker crumbs to thicken. Cook thick, remove from fire, add chopped hard-cooked eggs. Fill ramekins or individual dishes

[1] Courtesy of College of Home Economics, Cornell University

with this mixture. Cover with buttered crumbs and brown in oven.

Small recipe: ½ hard-cooked egg, 2 T. raw egg, 3 oysters, 2 T. milk, 1 t. butter, cracker crumbs, salt and pepper.

Fried Oysters

1½ pt. oysters   2 eggs   4 T. water
2 to 3 c. dry bread crumbs or corn meal   Kettle of deep fat

Wash and drain oysters. They may be marinated for 20 minutes in French dressing (¼ t. salt, ⅛ t. pepper, 1 T. lemon juice, 2 T. salad oil, well blended). Roll in fine crumbs, or white corn meal, or in a mixture of white corn meal and flour sifted together and salted. Dip in egg mixed with water and in crumbs again. Fry in deep fat 1 minute and drain on brown paper. The mixture of corn meal and crumbs gives a good flavor and a crisp texture. See General Directions for Deep-Fat Frying, page 447.

Shrimp may be fried in the same way.

Club Sandwich

3 slices of toast for each sandwich   2 or 3 slices of crisp bacon
Lettuce   Sliced tomato
Sliced chicken breast (or turkey)   Sliced onion or sweet pickle (if desired)
Butter and salad dressing as desired

Toast 3 slices of bread, butter, cover one slice with crisp bacon and lettuce, add salad dressing if desired. Cover with a second slice of toast. Butter or spread with salad dressing. Cover with lettuce leaf, sliced chicken, turkey, or other cold meat, add sliced sweet pickle. Cover with a buttered piece of toast.

Garnish with olives or pickles. Cut in triangles and serve while toast is hot.

For a small club sandwich omit one slice of toast. Ham is sometimes substituted for bacon.

Toasted Sandwiches

It is better to toast the whole sandwich than to make toast separately for sandwiches except when filling contains large quantity of mayonnaise. An electric grill for toasting the sandwich on both sides at the same time is available. The results are excellent. Some sandwiches that are improved by toasting are:

American Cheese: Thin slices of cheese between thin slices of bread; ¼ lb. cheese makes about 5 or 6 sandwiches.

Combination Sandwiches: ⅔ c. deviled ham, ⅓ c. sour cream, 1 T. lemon juice.

Open Sandwiches

To make an open sandwich, use a foundation of one slice of toast. Place on the toast a generous serving of sandwich filling. Garnish attractively with toast points (small triangles of bread toasted), with olives or small pickles, and with lettuce or parsley. Cold sliced chicken, lettuce, tomato, and Thousand Island dressing make a good open sandwich.

Yeast Bread, Rolls, and Sandwiches

See Chapter 19

Plain Yeast Bread

Proportions for Each Loaf:

1 c. hot liquid: all milk, or ½ milk and ½ water.

Yeast: 6-hour process, ¼ package fast-rising or ¼ cake compressed; overnight process, ⅛ package fast-rising, or ⅛ cake compressed, or ½ cake dry; 3-hour process, 1 to 2 packages fast-rising or 1 to 2 cakes compressed.

3 to 4 c. flour (enough to make a light dough that can be handled on a bread board with very little flour).

1 T. sugar   1½ t. salt   1 T. fat

Procedure. There are two processes of making bread: (1) the straight-dough method, and (2) the sponge method. The only essential difference between the two methods is that in the straight-dough method all the flour is used at the start and a dough is made at once, and in the sponge method only enough flour is used at first to make a stiff batter, and the remainder is added after the batter has been allowed to rise.

Straight-Dough Method

1. Scald liquid
2. Add shortening, sugar, salt to half of hot liquid
3. Cool to 95° F. or below
4. Add yeast mixed with remaining liquid which was cooled before being mixed with the yeast
5. Add flour to make a soft dough (all the flour required except that for use on the bread board)
6. Knead dough until smooth
7. First rising. Set in greased bowl to rise until double its bulk
8. Knead or punch down
9. Second rising (same as first)
10. Knead and shape
11. Allow to rise in greased pans
12. Bake
13. Remove from pans

Sponge Method (preferable for old-fashioned dried yeast)

1. Scald liquid
2. Add sugar, shortening, salt to half of hot milk liquid
3. Cool to 95° F. or below
4. Add yeast mixed with remaining liquid which was cooled before being mixed with the yeast
5. Add enough flour to make a medium batter
6. Beat batter smooth
7. Allow sponge to rise to double its bulk
8. Add sponge to rest of flour and make into a dough, kneading until smooth and elastic
9. Allow dough to rise until double its bulk, in warm place, in covered, greased bowl
10. Knead and shape
11. Allow to rise in greased pans
12. Bake
13. Remove from pans

Score Card for Yeast Bread [1]

STANDARD PRODUCT — 100 POINTS		
External Characteristics		30
Shape, well proportioned, evenly rounded top	10	
Crust, uniform browning except slightly darker on top, about 1/8 of an inch, deep crisp, tender, smooth, free from cracks and bulges	10	
Volume, light in weight in proportion to size	10	
Internal Characteristics		40
Texture, tender elastic crumb, free from dryness or doughiness	20	
Grain, fine cells elongated upward, evenly distributed, cell walls thin	10	
Color, characteristic of ingredients used, free from dark streaks	10	
Flavor		30
A blend of well-baked ingredients, free from undesirable flavor from bacterial action (sourness) or yeast or other ingredients	30	

Reasons for the Various Procedures

1. The milk is scalded to kill any undesirable bacteria and to melt the fat and dissolve readily the sugar and salt.

2. The liquid is cooled before the yeast is added because high temperature kills yeast plants.

[1] *Homemade Bread, Cake, and Pastry.* Farmers' Bulletin 1775, United States Department of Agriculture.

3. The dough is kneaded to develop the gluten. Bread may be kneaded by a bread mixer or may be turned out onto a clean floured board and worked quickly with the palms of the hands. It is easy to demonstrate kneading, but difficult to describe it adequately. Watch an expert kneader and then try to imitate the action. Perhaps the picture will help (Fig. 134).

4. The bread may rise either once or twice. A finer texture is produced by the double rising, but the double process is not necessary.

5. Pans are greased to prevent the dough from sticking. Butter should not be used because it burns easily. The rising of the dough in the pans should be carried on at room temperature or slightly above. Why? The length of time for rising varies with the amount and vitality of the yeast and with the strength of the gluten. A good rule is to allow the mass each time to double its bulk. Test it by touching the dough lightly with the finger. If slight depression remains on the surface, the dough has risen enough.

6. Bread should be started baking in a hot oven from 400° to 415° F., according to the size of the loaf. A good-sized loaf will require about an hour for baking, but a smaller loaf less time (50 minutes). After the first 20 minutes the temperature should be reduced. At the last a slow oven may be used.

7. If the bread is ready to leave the oven, it will give a hollow sound when rapped lightly with the knuckles. After removing from the oven, place it to cool, uncovered, on cake racks. Store it in a ventilated and very clean bread box.

Yeast Breads from Soft-Wheat Flour. Recipes and directions for yeast breads are on the basis of bread flour (hard wheat), but soft-wheat (pastry) flour which is used widely in the South for quick breads may also be used for yeast breads with special handling. It requires less moisture than hard-wheat flour to make a dough of the same consistency when soft-wheat flour is used.

During the rising the dough becomes softer. Doughs made from soft-wheat flour rise more quickly than doughs made from hard-wheat flour because they offer less resistance to gas bubbles.

A better quality bread is secured by using a large proportion of yeast and sugar to hasten the fermentation.

Soft-wheat flour doughs will not stand much handling. They can be lightly folded together instead of kneaded on a board. Soft-wheat flour doughs do not require a second rising in the bowl.

FIG. 134. STEPS IN MAKING YEAST BREAD

1. Kneading
2. Testing risen bread with thumb
3. Cutting down risen dough
4. Pan with loaf before rising and after rising.

They reach their limit of stretching power when they have doubled their original volume and should be checked by punching down before this point is reached. Long rising periods will produce overstretching cells which may collapse and give an uneven texture. As the dough rises quickly in the oven, the rolls made from this type of flour may be placed in the oven, before they have risen double in volume.

Brown Nut Bread

1 package yeast	1 c. nuts (broken or chopped)
1 c. milk	½ c. whole-wheat flour
1 T. molasses	2½ to 3½ c. white flour
1 t. salt	

Make by the sponge method; add nut meats to the scalded milk.

White Nut Bread

1 package yeast	2 T. butter
1 c. milk	1 egg white
1 T. sugar	¾ c. chopped nuts
3 c. white flour (approximately)	⅔ t. salt

Add nuts to scalded milk. Mix by the sponge method. Fold beaten egg whites into sponge. Proceed as for making bread.

Oatmeal Bread[1]

1½ c. rolled oats	2 T. sugar
4½ c. all-purpose flour	1 T. fat
1¾ c. milk	2 t. salt
½–1 package yeast	

Mix rolled oats with the white flour and proceed as for white bread. This will make 2 loaves.

Raised Doughnuts

1 package yeast	¾ c. sugar
1 c. milk	1 egg
1½ t. salt	¾ t. grated nutmeg and cinnamon
2 T. butter or other fat	3½ to 4 c. flour

Scald and cool milk. Mix yeast with milk. Add a little of the sugar. Add flour enough to make a stiff batter. Allow this to rise to double its bulk. Add melted fat, sugar, eggs well beaten, nutmeg, and flour enough to make a stiff dough. Knead, roll to one fourth inch, cut with a floured doughnut cutter. Allow to stand on floured board until the doughnuts rise (1 hour), turn over and allow to finish rising. Fry in deep fat. (See General Rules for Deep-Fat Frying, page 447.) Dust with granulated sugar.

Rolls

The ingredients listed for one loaf of bread will make a dough yielding 24 rolls. Use white, graham, or whole-wheat flour.

[1] *Homemade Bread, Cake, and Pastry.* Farmers' Bulletin 1775.

Mix as for bread, but let rise and knead three times instead of twice. One tablespoon of butter may be added if desired, when kneaded the third time. When the sponge is made for sweet rolls, 1 to 2 eggs and 2 to 3 T. sugar may also be added. The dough may be made into a great variety of rolls.

Shaping: From a rolled "stick" or from balls make PLAIN ROLLS, setting them in the pan far enough apart to bake separately, or placed against one another; CLOVER-LEAF ROLLS (3 tiny balls in a greased individual muffin tin); BREAD STICKS in a bread-stick pan.

Baking: Rolls are allowed to rise after they are shaped until their size is doubled; they are then baked in a hot oven until light and delicately browned. Bake 10 to 15 minutes at 425 degrees F. Rolls are attractive if the surface is buttered very lightly before they are served.

Parker House Rolls[1]

1 c. milk
1 package yeast
1 T. sugar
1½ t. salt
1½ T. butter or other fat
About 3¼ c. sifted hard-wheat flour, or
4 c. sifted soft-wheat flour

The straight dough method is used. Allow the dough to rise the first time as for loaf bread. It may be permitted to rise again before it is rolled or the second rising may be omitted. Roll the dough out thin and cut with a biscuit cutter. Brush the top with melted fat, crease through the center with the handle of a table knife, fold over and press down. (See Fig. 135.) Brush the top with melted fat if a soft crust is desired. When rolls have doubled in bulk, bake in hot oven 425 degrees F. for 10 to 15 minutes; yield — 16–24 rolls.

Small recipe: ⅓ c. milk, ⅓ package yeast, 1 *t. sugar,* ½ *t. salt,* ½ *T. butter or other fat. About* 1 *c. flour (hard-wheat) or* 1⅓ *c. (soft-wheat).*

Cinnamon Rolls

Roll Parker House roll dough one fourth inch thick. Sprinkle with sugar and cinnamon (4 parts sugar to 1 part cinnamon), dot with butter. Roll the dough, then slice the roll into half-inch slices and place slices in baking sheet to rise.

[1] *Homemade Bread, Cake, and Pastry.* Farmers' Bulletin 1775.

FIG. 135. PARKER HOUSE ROLLS

1. Rolling dough
2. Cutting out rolls
3. Folding rolls
4. Dropping melted butter on top of each roll

Candied Cinnamon Rolls

Grease the pan; sprinkle with a shallow layer of granulated and brown sugar mixed in equal proportions. Dot with bits of butter. Sprinkle with a few drops of water. Shape rolls and place in the pan close together. Bake in a hot oven. When well browned, turn out, bottom side up.

For **Toast,** *see* **Quick Breads,** *page* 401

Refrigerator Rolls[1]

1 package yeast	About 8 cups sifted all-purpose flour
¼ c. lukewarm water	2 t. salt
⅝ c. fat	½ c. sugar
2 cups scalded milk	

Soften the yeast in lukewarm water, add the fat and sugar to the hot milk, cool and combine with yeast and water. Stir in sifted flour and salt until the dough is stiff enough to turn out on board. Follow straight dough method. After second rising, cut off as much as needed, shape as desired, let rise until double, bake at 400 degrees F. for 15 to 20 minutes. Grease remaining dough and place in a refrigerator. Will keep about a week; yields 32–48 rolls.

Sandwiches

Bread for sandwiches should be 24 hours old and cut in thin, even slices. Cream the butter. If fancy shapes are desired, shape slices before spreading with creamed butter. The following mixtures are recommended for filling:

With white or brown bread (the following amounts make about 6 whole sandwiches):

1. *Olives* or *celery* chopped fine and mixed with salad dressing, ¾ c. dressing to ½ c. olives; ½ c. dressing to ½ c. chopped celery.
2. *Sliced tomatoes* and *mayonnaise*, ½ lb. tomatoes, sliced thin (slice from blossom end to stem end), ½ c. mayonnaise. Lettuce may be used.
3. *Chopped celery* and *chopped crisp bacon* with mayonnaise, ¼ c. celery and ¼ c. bacon to 1 c. mayonnaise.
4. *Chopped green pepper* and *chopped crisp bacon* with mayonnaise, ¼ c. green pepper, ¼ c. bacon, to 1 c. mayonnaise.
5. *Cream cheese* or *cottage cheese* mixed with any of the following (½ c. cheese to ½ c. other material with 3 or 4 T. milk or cream to soften): nuts; olives; olives and nuts; raisins; drained shredded pineapple; dates; figs and nuts; marmalade or jelly. If raisins, dates, or figs are used, add a few drops of lemon juice.
6. *Butter* (⅜ c.) and *chopped peanuts* or *peanut butter* (½ c.) and a little cream, creamed together.
7. *Dates* (¾ c.) and *preserved ginger* (¼ c.) chopped and blended, using cream cheese or salad dressing.

[1] *Homemade Bread, Cake, and Pastry.* Farmers' Bulletin 1775, United States Department of Agriculture.

8. *Chicken, ham,* or *other meat* (½ c.), cooked and chopped, with chopped celery (2 T.), olives (2 T.), one hard-cooked egg, and ½ c. mayonnaise.

9. *Raisins* (⅓ c.), *dates* (¼ c.), and *nuts* (½ c.), few drops of lemon juice.

10. *Jelly:* 1 glass jelly beaten with 1 unbeaten egg white makes 12 to 16 whole sandwiches.

With Nut Bread. Good fillings are: creamed butter; lettuce and mayonnaise; and cream cheese.

Rolls. Flat rolls, either finger or round shaped, are used for sandwiches. They are hollowed out and filled with almost any filling. Suggested fillings: chicken or meat salad; tuna fish; broiled steak (picnics). Hamburg steak patties may be made into sandwiches with sliced tomatoes, thinly sliced pickles, and dressing; 1 lb. ground steak for 8 to 10 patties and 1 lb. tomatoes for 12.

Open Orange Sandwiches

½ c. butter
½ c. grated orange rind or more if desired
¼ t. salt
A small quantity of orange or lemon juice

Cream the butter, add the grated rind of the orange and the juice, a little at a time. Add the salt. Spread on slices of thin sandwich bread and serve as an open sandwich. The slices may be cut diagonally or in fancy shapes. Especially attractive for color scheme in serving tea.

Homemade Peanut Butter

2 c. roasted peanuts
1 T. oil
⅔ t. salt

Cover the peanuts with boiling water for ½ minute; drain. Run through food chopper twice, using finest plate and screwing it up tight. Add oil and salt. Mix well. Keep in tightly closed glass jars.

Sandwiches for Very Young Children

Fill bread-and-butter sandwiches with raw vegetables finely chopped (chopped cabbage, grated carrots, chopped celery, lettuce, watercress, parsley, spinach, thin slice of peeled tomato, or sliced apple are suitable). Use irradiated evaporated milk instead of salad dressing.

Meat

See Chapter 24

General Rules for Meat Cookery

Meat should be weighed, trimmed, and either wiped with a damp cloth or washed in running water before it is cooked.

Tender Meat Cookery. Tender cuts may be baked or roasted, broiled or pan-broiled. Large pieces of 3½ lb. or more are baked or roasted and those from 1 to 3 inches thick are usually broiled.

Tender Cuts Suitable for Roasting:

Rib roasts and the whole tenderloin of beef and rump "pot roast."

Leg, shoulder, and stuffed breast of lamb.

Shoulder, leg, loin, and stuffed breast of veal.

Loin, spareribs, ham, and shoulder of fresh pork.

Ham of cured pork.

Tender Cuts Suitable for Broiling:

Steaks of beef from the hindquarter, such as sirloin, T-bone or porterhouse, tenderloin or fillet, and ground beef patties.

Lamb chops, either loin or rib, and lamb patties.

Veal chops.

Ham and bacon.

Roasting Meat

Wipe with a damp cloth or wash under running water.

Rub lightly with salt and pepper (white pepper is preferable).

Place in shallow pan or on rack in shallow pan.

Bake at a constant temperature of 300 or 350 degrees F., without adding water and without a cover, for the length of time given in the recipes or until a meat thermometer shows the desired temperature. (In roasting poultry cover for the last 30 minutes.)

Cooking Roast in Thrift Cooker (Electric Range)

Prepare by wiping with damp cloth or washing under running water and rubbing with salt and pepper. Heat skillet and sear roast on all sides. Place in thrift cooker, add 1 c. water, heat until steam appears; turn heat to low and cook 2½ to 4 hours.

Time for cooking: Pork — 30 minutes per pound.
Beef — 45 minutes per pound.

Broiled Meat

Method for Oven Broiling:

Wipe with a damp cloth or wash under running water.

Trim off superfluous fat.

Preheat broiler to 450 to 500 degrees F.

Place meat on rack with drip pan below, with surface of the meat 2 or 3 inches below heat (consult table for distance below heat for cut you are broiling); be sure to leave the oven door open.

Broil on one side about half of the time given in the table, or until brown; turn and finish broiling.

Season with salt and pepper; dot with small pieces of butter; place on a hot platter; garnish and serve.

Method for Pan-Broiling:

Wipe with a damp cloth or wash under running water.

Trim off superfluous fat.

Heat pan but do not grease. Salt may be sprinkled in it.

Place meat in pan and sear on one side; turn and cook about half of the time given in the table, or until brown; turn again and finish cooking the side that was seared at first; season the side up with salt and pepper; turn and re-heat about 30 seconds, seasoning side up. When turning the meat, avoid spearing it with a fork. Place in hot platter; dot with butter or pour over melted butter; garnish and serve.

TABLE FOR BROILING AND PAN-BROILING

MEAT	TOTAL TIME AT 450 TO 500 DEGREES, IN MINUTES		DISTANCE BELOW HEAT	ACCOMPANIMENTS
Beef:				
1 in. thick	Rare to medium	7 to 10	2 in.	Butter
	Well done	15 to 20	3 in.	Maître d'hôtel butter
1½ in. thick	Rare to medium	10 to 15	2 in.	Mushroom sauce
	Well done	18 to 20	3 in.	Broiled mushrooms
2 in. thick	Rare to medium	16 to 25	2 in.	Broiled tomatoes
	Well done	30 to 35	3 in.	Lemon as garnish
				Parsley as garnish
Beef or lamb patties	Well done	20 to 30	3 in.	Broiled onions
				See also lamb and beef
Bacon, thin	Crisp	3 to 6	3 in.	Broiled pineapple
Lamb chops,	Medium	10 to 12	2 in.	Butter
rib or loin, 1 in. thick	Well done	25 to 30	3 in.	Parsley
Pork chops, ½ in. thick	Well done	18 to 25	3 in.	Apple rings
				Spiced stuffed prunes
Veal chops, ½ in. thick	Well done	10 to 12	3 in.	Broiled mushrooms
				Tart jelly

1. Open pan with rack, and no water

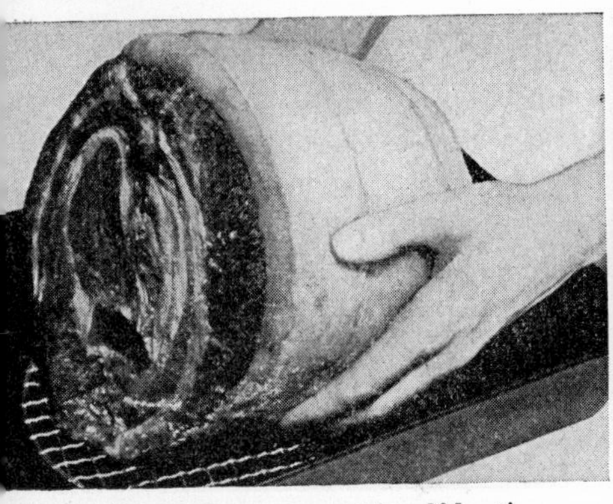

2. Placed fat side up, a roast is self-basting

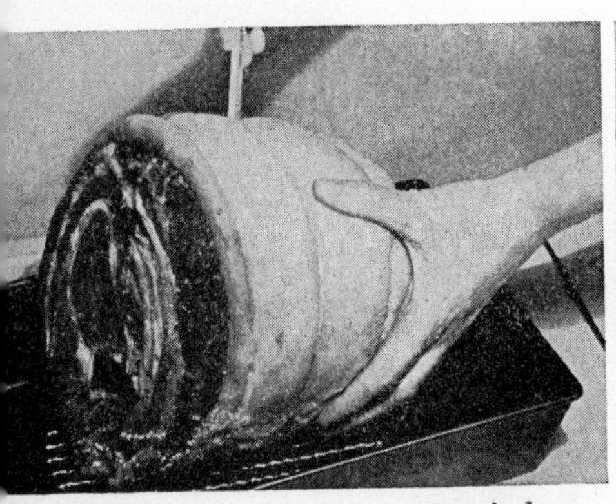

A thermometer to tell when the roast is done

4. Brown lightly in a hot oven (450° to 500°F.) then lower the heat and finish slowly

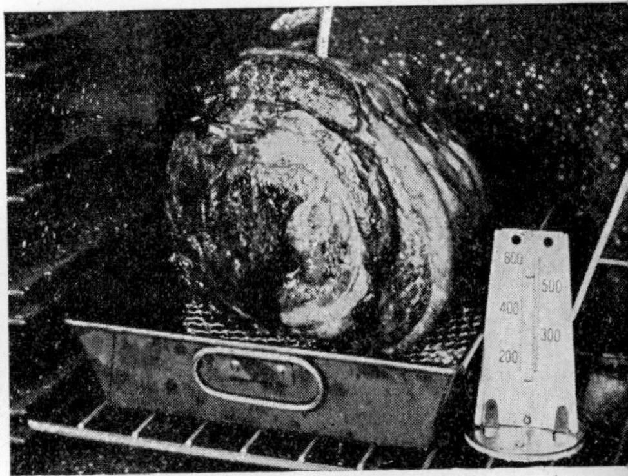

5. Or roast at moderate heat (about 350°F.) for the entire time

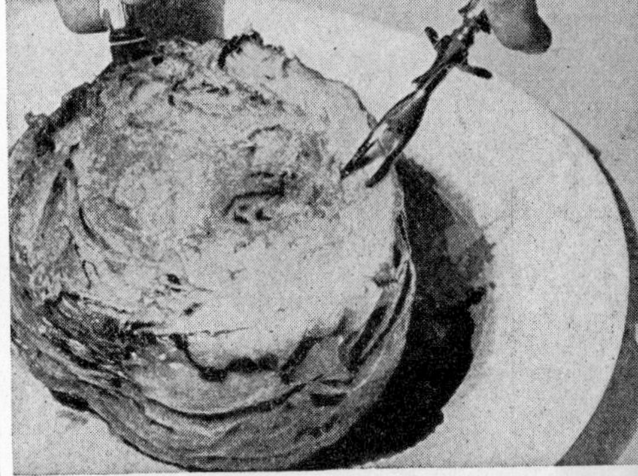

6. Plump, brown, juicy, evenly cooked

FIG. 136. ROASTING A TENDER CUT OF BEEF

The easy, modern way to cook any tender roast of beef, lamb, or pork, with a good covering of fat.

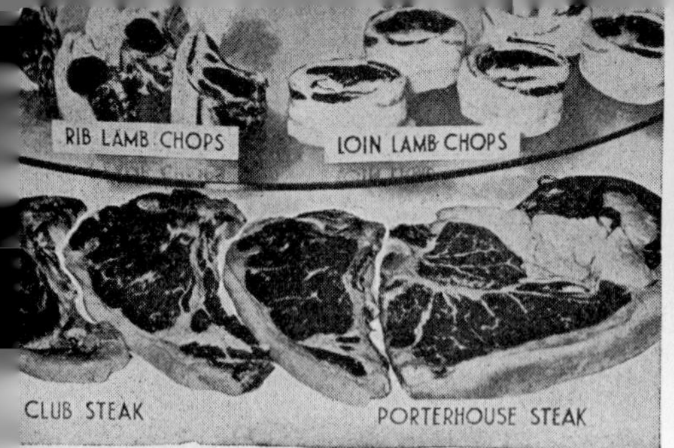

1. For broiling, select tender cuts with plenty of fat

4. For pan-broiling, use a hot skillet

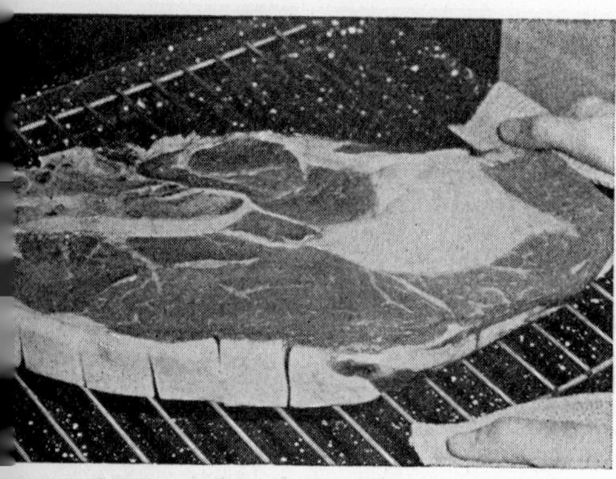

2. Start a steak or chops in a hot broiler

5. No water and no lid, because steam draw the juices out of meat

3. Brown quickly on both sides, then finish slowly

6. Season steak or chops after broiling

FIG. 137. BROILING TENDER STEAKS AND CHOPS

Whether broiling by direct heat or pan-broiling, sear quickly and then finish at moderate heat.

Broiled Hamburg Steak on Onion Rings[1]

2 c. ground lean raw beef	1 T. chopped parsley
¼ c. ground suet	3 T. butter
1 c. soft fine bread crumbs	2 t. onion juice
7 strips bacon	½ t. salt
7 slices Spanish onion (½ inch thick)	⅛ t. pepper
	1 T. water

Lay the slices of onion in a buttered shallow baking dish. Pour over them 2 T. of melted butter, sprinkle with salt and pepper, add the water, cover closely, and bake in a moderate oven (350° F.) for 30 minutes, or until tender. In the meantime, cook the chopped parsley in 1 T. of butter and combine with the beef, suet, crumbs, and seasonings. Knead until thoroughly mixed. Mold into seven flat cakes and wrap each with a slice of bacon. Place each cake on an onion slice in the baking dish, and broil under direct heat for five minutes on each side. Baste occasionally with the drippings. Serve at once from the baking dish.

If it is not convenient to broil the meat cakes by direct heat, pan-broil them in a hot skillet, and serve on the onion slices.

Breaded Veal Chops

Select loin chops, or cut a steak from the round into individual pieces. Remove any extra fat and dip the meat in crumbs, egg, and crumbs again (or use a mixture of corn meal and crumbs); cook 25 to 30 minutes in a small amount of fat in a frying pan, browning first on one side, then turning, seasoning with salt and pepper, and browning on the other.

Baked Ham Slice

A center slice of ham at least one inch thick	1 t. mustard
3 T. sugar	Milk

Trim off the rind of a thick slice of ham. Place in a baking dish. Mix mustard and sugar (either brown or white sugar) and spread on the ham. Pour in enough milk to come almost to the top of the slice of ham. Bake uncovered in a moderately slow oven until tender (an hour and a half to two hours).

Serve with sliced pineapple sautéed in butter.

[1] *Cooking Beef According to the Cut.* United States Department of Agriculture, Leaflet 17. Courtesy of Bureau of Human Nutrition and Home Economics.

Cooking Tenderized Ham

Tenderized ham requires less cooking than other ham. Note special directions for length of cooking time as given by the manufacturer for any given brand of tenderized ham.

Baked Ham[1]

Wash and scrape the ham thoroughly and soak it overnight in a large pan with cold water to cover. In the morning wipe the ham dry. Make a small incision through the rind with a sharp knife or a steel skewer, cut short gashes around it with scissors, and insert a roast-meat thermometer through the opening so that its bulb reaches the center of the fleshiest portion of the ham. Place the ham, rind side up, on a rack in an open pan. Do not add water and do not cover. Bake the ham in a slow oven (260° F.) until the thermometer in the meat registers 170 degrees F. Between 25 and 30 minutes per pound will probably be required to bake a whole ham. For half hams, proportionately more time per pound is necessary. Shank ends usually require from 40 to 45 minutes per pound, and butts from 45 to 55 minutes per pound to bake when the oven temperature is 260 degrees F. When the ham is done, remove the rind.

Make a paste of 2 cups of brown sugar and 3 cups of fine soft bread crumbs, 1 teaspoon of prepared mustard, and cider or vinegar enough to moisten the mixture. Spread the paste over the fat covering of the baked ham and stick long-stemmed cloves into the surface. Bake the coated ham for 10 minutes in a hot oven (500° F.).

Boiled Ham[1]

Wash and scrape the ham thoroughly, and place it, rind side up, on a rack in a ham boiler or a large kettle, and add water to cover. Partly cover the kettle with a lid. Cook the ham at simmering temperature, just below boiling, and keep it well covered with water. If desired, add two or three bay leaves, several stalks of celery, a carrot, an onion, and one-half cup of vinegar. A roast-meat thermometer can be used to tell when the ham is done. Insert it as directed for baked ham and let it remain in the meat during the cooking. Cook until the thermometer registers 170 degrees F. If a thermometer is not used, cook the ham for 25 to

[1] *Cooking Cured Pork.* Leaflet No. 81, United States Department of Agriculture.

30 minutes per pound, or until the meat is tender. If possible let the ham cool in the broth. Remove the rind, sprinkle the fat surface with brown sugar, stud with cloves, and brown in a hot oven (about 500° F.), or coat the ham as directed for baked ham.

Ham Cooked Under Steam Pressure[1]

Wash and scrape the ham thoroughly. Into a large pressure canner pour enough water to cover the bottom; usually 1 quart is sufficient. Put the ham, rind side up, on a rack that is high enough to hold the meat completely out of the water. Clamp the lid on the canner securely, and heat, with the pet-cock open, until steam has escaped for 7 minutes. Close the pet-cock and cook at 10 pounds pressure, allowing about 3 hours for a 12-pound ham. When the time is up let the pressure fall to zero before opening the pet-cock and then take off the lid. Remove the rind from the ham, coat with a brown-sugar mixture, and brown in a hot oven.

Stuffed Pork Rib Chops with Apples[2]

6 rib pork chops, 1½ in. thick	¼ t. salt
1 c. fine dry bread crumbs	⅛ t. savory seasoning
¼ c. chopped celery	Dash of pepper
1 T. butter	⅛ t. celery seed
1 T. minced onion	3 tart red apples

1 T. chopped parsley

For the stuffing cook the celery, onion, and parsley in the butter for a few minutes, add the bread crumbs and seasonings, and stir until well mixed. Wipe the chops with a damp cloth. Cut a pocket in each chop. Sprinkle the chops with salt and pepper and rub lightly with flour. Sear the chops in a heavy hot skillet, turning the fat edges down at first and then browning both sides. Then fill each chop with stuffing and skewer the edges together with toothpicks. Lay the stuffed chops on a rack in a baking dish or pan with cover. On the top of each chop place, cut side down, one half of an apple which has been cored but not pared. Cover closely and bake in a moderate oven (350° to 375° F.) for about 45 minutes, or until the meat is tender. Lift the chops and apples together from the baking dish onto a hot platter and remove the toothpick skewers. Garnish with parsley and serve at once.

[1] *Cooking Cured Pork.* Leaflet No. 81, United States Department of Agriculture.

[2] *Pork in Preferred Ways.* Leaflet No. 45, United States Department of Agriculture.

Roast Leg of Lamb[1]

Select a leg of lamb, preferably cut so as to include some of the loin. Wipe the meat with a damp cloth, sprinkle with salt and pepper, and rub well with flour. Lay the roast, skin side down, on a rack in an open pan without water. Insert a meat thermometer so that the bulb reaches the center of the thick round of the leg. If the fat covering is very thin, lay several strips of bacon on top. Sear for 30 minutes in a hot oven (about 480° F.); or if bacon has been added, for a shorter time so as to avoid overbrowning. When the roast is seared and lightly browned, reduce the oven temperature rapidly to 300° F. and continue the cooking at this temperature without water and without a cover. By this method basting is generally not necessary. If one desires the meat to be slightly underdone, remove the leg from the oven when the meat thermometer registers 175° or at 182° F., for well-done lamb.

The length of time required to roast a leg of lamb depends chiefly on the size of the leg and the temperature of the oven. A leg weighing 5 pounds will probably require from two and one half to three hours, including searing, and a 7-pound leg from three to three and one half hours, to cook to the well-done stage at the oven temperature given.

Braised Beef, Veal, or Lamb with Browned Potatoes[2]

Select a piece of beef, veal, or lamb weighing 3 to 5 pounds. Use chuck, rump, or round, or a very lean rib roast of beef; any cut of veal; or very lean lamb leg or shoulder.

Sprinkle the meat with salt, pepper, and flour. Brown on all sides in fat as for a pot roast; or, if this is not convenient, omit the browning, and lay pieces of suet, salt pork, or bacon over the top of the meat. Then put the meat on a rack in a roasting pan, cover closely to hold in steam, and cook in a moderately hot oven (about 375° F.) until tender. This will probably take from 1½ to 2½ hours, depending on the size and tenderness of the cut. About 45 minutes before the meat is done, put pared raw potatoes into the pan around the meat. Turn the potatoes in the drippings and sprinkle with salt. Cover the pan again and cook until meat and potatoes are tender. Remove the lid to allow them to brown before serving. Make gravy of the drippings.

[1] *Lamb As You Like It.* Leaflet No. 28, U.S. Department of Agriculture.

[2] Courtesy of Bureau of Human Nutrition and Home Economics, United States Department of Agriculture.

Broiled Lamb Chops

Whether single or double, from loin, ribs, or shoulder, have lamb chops cut in uniform thickness and the fell removed. Double loin chops may be boned, rolled, and wrapped in sliced bacon. Rib chops are often "Frenched" by trimming the rib ends bare. All lamb chops are best broiled either by direct heat or in a heavy uncovered skillet.

To broil by direct heat, lay the chops on a cold greased rack and place over live coals or under an electric grill or the flame of a gas oven.

If a gas oven is used, have the chops 3 inches below a moderate flame. Sear them on both sides. Place double rib chops fat side up at first so that they will also sear along that edge. After searing, lower the flame and finish the cooking at reduced temperature. Turn the chops occasionally, but do not prick the brown crust. If more convenient, after searing double chops (1½ to 2 inches thick) under the flame transfer the broiler to a moderately hot oven (375° to 400° F.) to finish the cooking.

To pan-broil, lay the chops in a heavy, sizzling hot skillet, sear quickly on both sides, and also turn thick chops on edge so as to brown the fat. Then reduce the heat, turn the chops frequently, and finish the cooking at low temperature. Do not add water or cover the skillet. From time to time pour off excess fat so that the chops broil, not fry. If preferred, with very thick chops, after searing, slip a rack under them in the skillet, and finish the cooking in a moderately hot oven (375° to 400° F.).

Lamb on Skewers or "Shish Kabobs"

Shish kabobs are usually made of lamb shoulder. Remove all the bones, cut the pieces of lean meat about 1½ inches square and 1 inch thick from the well-fleshed parts of the shoulder. Put 4 or 5 pieces on a skewer with alternate small squares of bacon. A medium-sized lamb shoulder will provide enough meat for about seven skewers. Lay the kabobs in a dripping pan and broil 12 to 15 minutes, turning frequently for uniform cooking. When the meat is done, season with salt and pepper and serve at once on skewers.

Note: The bones and parts of the shoulder not suitable for kabobs can be used for making a broth or stew.

1. Pound in flour and seasoning

2. Brown in beef fat to give rich flavor

. Add tomatoes or water, cover, and finish slowly

FIG. 138. BRAISING SWISS STEAK

1. Spread with stuffing and roll from the sid

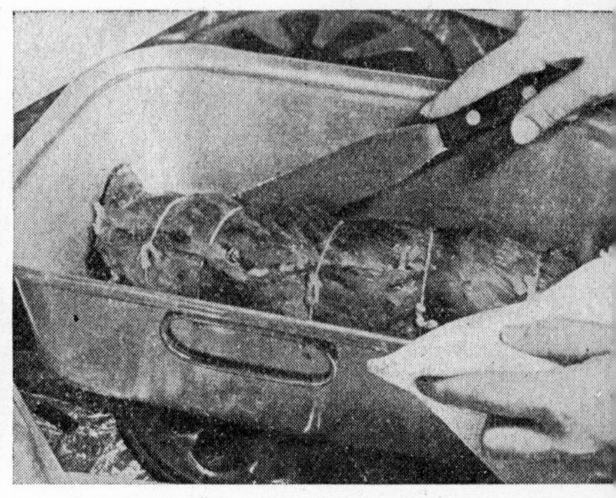

2. After browning, cover, and finish in a moderate oven (350° F.)

3. Stuffed flank steak with potatoes

FIG. 139. BRAISING STUFFED FLANK STE

Many a low-cost cut may be turned into such braised dishes as a casserole or brown stew.

Tough Meat Cookery

For soups from tough meat, see Clear or Stock Soups, page 423.

In the cookery of tough meat such as chuck, brisket, plate, rump, round, and flank, special means are employed for making the meat tender, as:

Pounding or grinding.

Long cooking at a low temperature, often with moist heat.

The use of acid in cooking, as Spanish steak.

Swiss Steak

1½ lb. round of beef about 1 inch thick

Flour   Bacon fat   1 t. salt   ⅛ t. pepper

Pound flour, salt, and pepper into both sides of steak with the edge of a saucer. Sauté steak in bacon fat until brown. Cover with water or meat stock; cover the pan; let simmer on top of stove or in oven for one hour or until meat is tender.

Creole Spanish Steak

1½ lb. round of beef about 1 in. thick	2 slices onion
2 T. bacon fat	½ t. salt
2 c. cooked or canned tomatoes	⅛ t. pepper
3 whole cloves	⅛ bay leaf

Sear steak in pan greased with bacon fat. Pour tomatoes over it and add water to cover; add spices, and cook on stove or in oven 1 hour.

Pot Roast of Beef

Cuts of beef suitable for pot-roasting are chuck ribs, cross arm, clod, round, and rump. Select a piece from 4 to 6 pounds in weight. Wipe with a damp cloth. Rub the meat with salt and pepper. Brown the meat on all sides in a heavy kettle, using about 3 T. of beef fat. Slip a low rack under the meat, add one-half cup of water, cover tightly, and simmer until tender. The time required for cooking cannot be definitely stated, but it will probably be about three hours. Turn the roast occasionally. When the meat is done, remove from the kettle, skim off the excess fat from the liquid, and measure the remainder. For each cup of gravy desired, measure 2 T. of fat and return to the kettle, add 1½ to 2 T. of flour and stir until well blended and slightly browned. Then add 1 c. of the meat stock or of cold water and stir until smooth.

Season the gravy with salt, pepper, and chopped parsley. Serve on a hot platter with buttered carrots and stuffed onions.

If desired, any of the following vegetables may be cooked in the pot with the roast: carrots, celery, onions, potatoes, tomatoes, and turnips. Add the vegetables during the last hour of cooking the meat if they are to be served whole or in quarters. If preferred, they may be cooked longer and mashed and served as purée in the gravy.

Pot roast may be cooked in a thrift cooker of an electric range.

Beef Croquettes[1]

2 c. ground lean cooked beef	Tabasco sauce, as desired
1 c. mashed potato	Salt
3 T. gravy or stock	Pepper
1 T. onion juice	Dry grated sifted bread crumbs
1 T. chopped parsley	1 egg beaten up with 1 T. water
1 T. butter	Fat for deep frying

Cook the parsley in the butter, and mix with the meat, potato gravy, and other seasonings thoroughly. Mold into croquette shapes. Dip into the egg mixture, roll in the bread crumbs, and let stand an hour or longer to dry the coating. Heat the fat in a deep vessel to 350 degrees F. or until a cube of bread browns in 40 seconds. Place two or three croquettes at a time in a frying basket and lower slowly into the hot fat for two minutes or until they are a golden brown. Remove the croquettes and drain on a sheet of paper. Serve hot with parsley garnish and tomato sauce.

To make softer croquettes, omit the mashed potato, and either increase the quantity of gravy to three-fourths cup, or use three-fourths cup of white sauce. To prepare gravy or white sauce thick enough to act as a binder for a croquette mixture, blend 3 tablespoons flour with 1 tablespoon butter, add three-fourths cup meat stock or milk, and cook in a double boiler, stirring until smooth. Mix the gravy or sauce with the meat and seasonings.

Meat and Vegetable Stew

1 lb. beef or veal, cut in 1-inch cubes	3 to 4 T. flour	1 t. salt
3 or 4 potatoes, diced	3 slices onion	¼ t. pepper
¾ c. diced carrots	½ c. diced turnip	Bacon fat

Roll the meat in flour and brown in bacon fat; cover with water

[1] *Cooking Beef According to Cut.* Leaflet No. 17, United States Department of Agriculture.

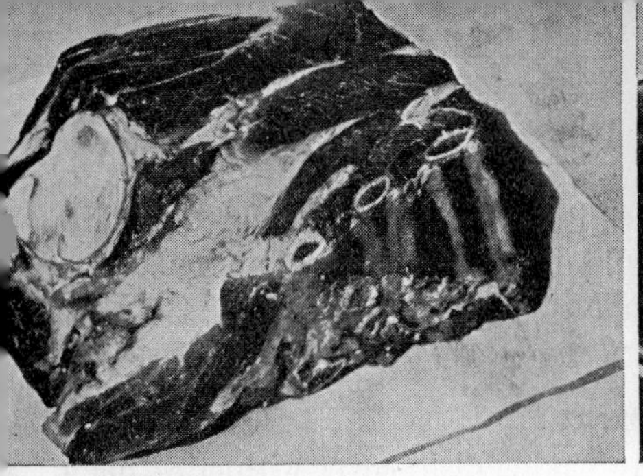

1. For a pot roast, select beef chuck, rump, or round

2. Use a pot with close-fitting lid and a rack

3. Brown in beef fat to give rich flavor

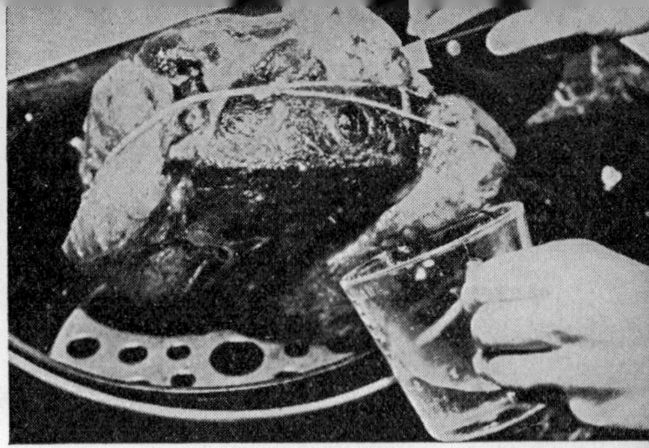

4. Add a little water — about one-half cup

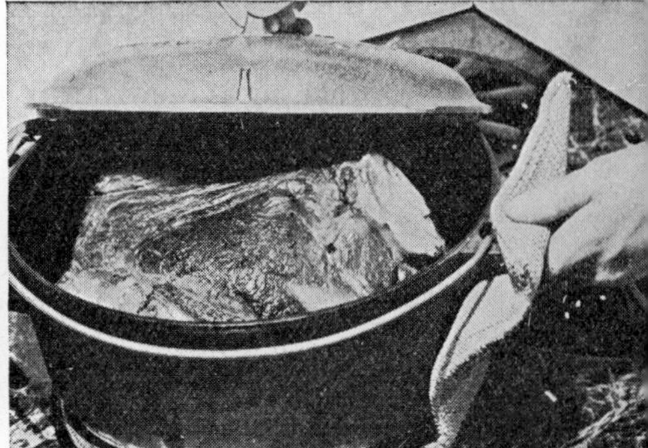

5. Cover and cook slowly until tender all through

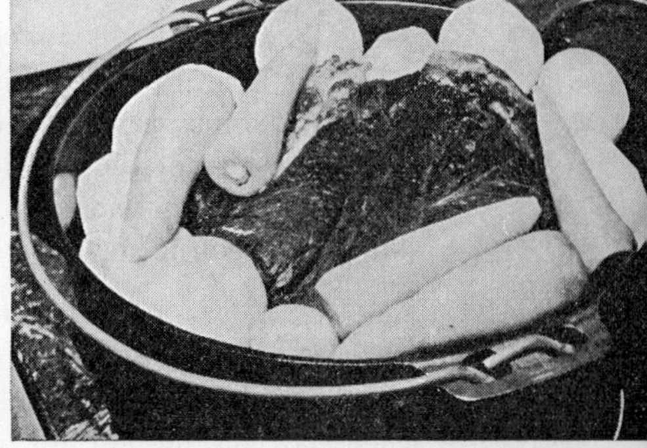

6. Add vegetables during the last hour

FIG. 140. POT-ROASTING A LESS TENDER CUT

Long, slow cooking with a lid to hold in the steam is the way to make tough meat tender.

and boil 1 to 2 hours, or until it is almost tender; add vegetables and seasonings and cook until vegetables and meat are tender.

Small recipe: 1/8 pound beef, 1/2 potato, 1 carrot, 1/2 slice onion, 1 slice turnip, 1/2 T. flour, bacon fat, seasonings to taste.

Meat Pie

Make meat stew; pour into baking dish; cover with crust made of biscuit dough (see page 411) or cover with crust of mashed potatoes into which 1 egg white or 1 whole egg has been beaten. Bake in hot oven until crust is brown (450° F.) for 15 minutes.

Meat and Dumplings

Make meat stew. Mix dumplings (see page 412). Drop by spoonfuls on top of stew. Cover kettle tightly and cook dumplings 15 to 20 minutes.

Meat Turnovers (*see page* 412)

Casserole or Italian Hash

1/4 lb. macaroni (about 2 c.)	3/4 c. grated cheese
2 c. chopped cooked meat	1 c. tomato or brown sauce

Cook macaroni in boiling salted water until tender. Drain off the water. Butter a casserole or baking dish. Put macaroni in dish, pushing it to the sides. Fill center with chopped meat. Sprinkle with grated cheese. Pour over the whole a highly seasoned tomato or brown sauce. Brown in oven.

Liver and Bacon

Calf or lamb liver sliced in half-inch slices is preferable. Beef or pork liver may also be used. Trim outer skin and blood vessels. Scald liver to clot the blood; let stand a few minutes. Mix salt, pepper, and flour and coat each slice with the mixture. Cook slowly in bacon fat or other fat. Serve with broiled bacon.

Liver and Onions

Prepare liver as described above. Brown sliced onions in bacon fat, then add liver and cook. If gravy is desired, remove liver when cooked, and add hot water or milk to the hot fat and cook until it is thick.

Broiled Bacon

Use thinly sliced bacon from which the rind has been removed. Place the strips close together for cooking, because bacon shrinks.

1. *Pan-broiled:* Place bacon in hot omelet pan or skillet and cook to the desired brownness over a moderate fire. Turn meat as it broils, and as the fat accumulates, pour it off. Drain broiled bacon on brown paper.

2. *Cooked in the oven:* Place bacon in shallow pan and cook in oven to desired brownness. Remove from the fat and drain on brown paper.

3. *Cooked on broiler:* Place the bacon on the wire broiler in the dripping pan. Broil under the flame or in the oven to the desired degree of brownness. Turn the meat to prevent its burning.

Poultry and Fish

See Chapter 25

Preparation of Poultry for Cooking

Removal of Feathers. Chickens are scalded for picking, but ducks, turkeys, and geese are picked dry. Remove the pin feathers by pressing with a knife. Ducks may be skinned instead of picked. Wild ducks and sage chickens are often skinned before they are cooked. The hairs are singed over a low flame — a low gas flame or the flame from burning paper. Wash thoroughly.

The Drawing or Cleaning of Fowl. The removal of the entrails and vital organs of a fowl is called drawing. The method to be used will depend upon the size of the bird and the manner in which it is to be cooked. The feet and neck are cut off first and the oil sack is always removed from the end of the back. Slit the skin at the back of the neck from the base toward the head, and pull it loose from neck and crop. Cut off the neck at its base and pull out the crop and windpipe, cutting them off as far down as possible.

FOR BROILING: Very young chickens are split open down the side of the back with scissors or a sharp knife; the contents of the cavity are removed. Save the giblets — the heart, liver, and gizzard. The chicken is flattened for cooking, with the tip of each wing folded between the wing and the body. Wash thoroughly in cold water.

FOR FRYING: The drumsticks, second joints, and wings are removed first. The carcass is then split on each side of the back where the thighs are removed. Loosen and pull out the entrails; save the giblets. The wishbone is cut out next and the shoulder separated from the breast; the breast is usually cut into two pieces. Wash in cold water.

FOR BAKING OR ROASTING: The incision may be made either under one leg or between the legs from the vent toward the breastbone. Loosen the entrails well, and pull them out gently. Save the giblets. Wash thoroughly in cold water.

GIBLETS: The liver, gizzard, and heart are termed giblets and are considered choice. Remove the green gall bladder whole from the liver because, if its contents come in contact with the meat, it gives it a bitter flavor. To clean the gizzard, remove all fat, then cut through thick outer muscle and turn the gizzard inside out, discarding the inner sack. To clean the heart, remove the fat and cut arteries and veins from it. Wash thoroughly.

Trussing. A bird is trussed for baking or roasting in order that the legs and wings may be held in place during cooking. Metal skewers are sometimes used, but are not necessary. They shorten the time of cooking slightly by making it easier for the heat to penetrate the bird.

If stuffing or dressing is used, fill the cavity loosely, thus allowing space for swelling. Sew up the cavity. Fold the tip of each wing under the wing joint, or cut off the tip and fasten the wing flat with skewers. Pull the legs down to the tail and tie them with a cord. Tie the wings down (allowing no strings to cross the breast) and pull back the skin of the neck and either sew it to the back or fasten it there with toothpicks.

Methods of Cooking Chicken

Young chickens are broiled and slightly larger chickens are either smothered or fried (see Table of Weights in Chapter 25). When they reach the dressed weight of 3½ pounds they are usually baked or roasted, boiled for salad or croquettes, stewed with dumplings or used in chicken pie. For roasting it is sometimes advisable to simmer the fowl for 2 to 4 hours before roasting. When this is done, the fowl should be first trussed, but not stuffed. Stuff after simmering and before roasting.

Giblets may be cooked with the chicken in any of the above ways, but are often, except when frying chicken, cooked separately in boiling water for 30 to 50 minutes.

ood propor-
ions for stuf-
ng are: to
very 2 quarts
crumbs from
read 2–3 days
ld . . .

. . . a pint or more of mixed celery, parsley, onion sautéed in ¾ cup of fat, with seasonings to taste.

2. Fill with stuffing but do not pack, finish with a crust of bread, and . . .

3. . . . tuck the legs under the band of skin, and . . .

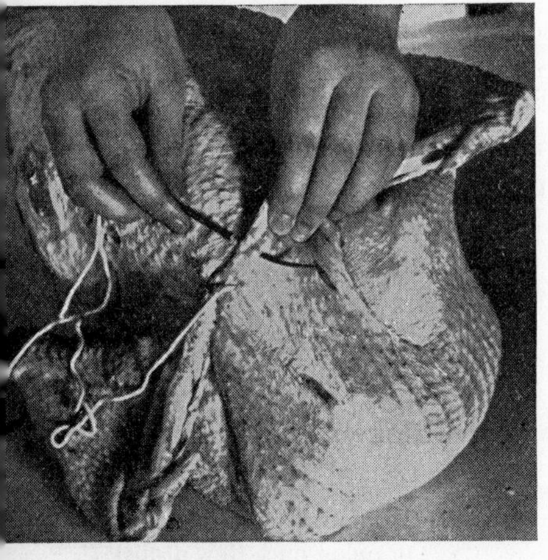

4. . . . after stuffing the neck, draw the skin back, and stitch or skewer in place . . .

5. . . . then brush with melted fat, add salt, sprinkle lightly with flour . . . and the bird is ready for the oven.

FIG. 141. STUFFING AND TRUSSING

Broiled Chicken

Clean and draw for broiling according to directions. Rub surface with salt and pepper and brush with either melted butter or chicken fat. Broil over hot coals, under direct gas flame, or in electric broiler, or in an oven at 350 degrees F. It will take 30 to 40 minutes in the broiler or about 45 minutes in an oven. Brush again with fat every 15 minutes. Cook for the first 10 or 15 minutes with skin side down, and rest of time skin side up. Broiled chicken is also delicious if 1 T. lemon juice is stirred into each half cup of basting liquid.

Fried Chicken

Prepare chicken according to directions for frying on page 447. Coat with flour seasoned with salt and pepper. Fry in hot fat ½ to ¾ inch deep in iron skillet. Keep covered. Brown well. The use of bacon fat for frying gives a good flavor.

Chicken may also be cooked in deep fat. Use temperatures for uncooked foods.

Baked or Roast Chicken or Other Fowl

Clean, draw, and truss according to directions for baking. Rub skin with melted fat and flour that has been well seasoned with salt and pepper. Place in a roasting pan that has a cover (which may be used late in the baking). Bake at 350 degrees F., allowing 30 minutes per pound for small birds (3½ to 4 lb.) and 20 to 25 minutes for those weighing 4 to 6 pounds and 18 to 20 minutes per pound for all larger birds. Cover small and medium-sized birds the last 30 minutes of cooking in order to make the skin tender; cover large birds for the last 45 minutes. Remove skewers, cord, and thread before serving.

Dressing or Stuffing for Chicken and Turkey

For a three-pound bird:

2 c. stale bread (yeast bread or corn bread, or both)
½ c. melted butter
Dash of powdered sage
1 T. minced onion (if desired) or onion juice (few drops)
½ t. salt (to taste)
⅛ t. pepper

Season to taste with salt, pepper, and sage if desired. Mix well. Add the melted butter. Moisten with water or milk. Chopped parsley and celery may be added if a more savory dressing is desired.

For *roast duck*, add 2 T. (currant) jelly to this stuffing.

I. In shallow fat

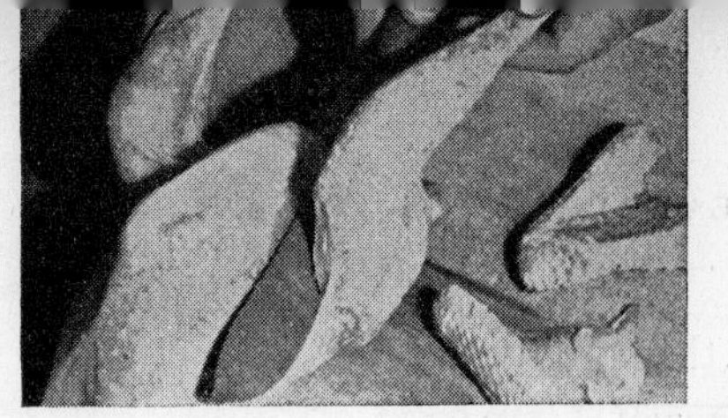

1. Cut up a young frying chicken . . .

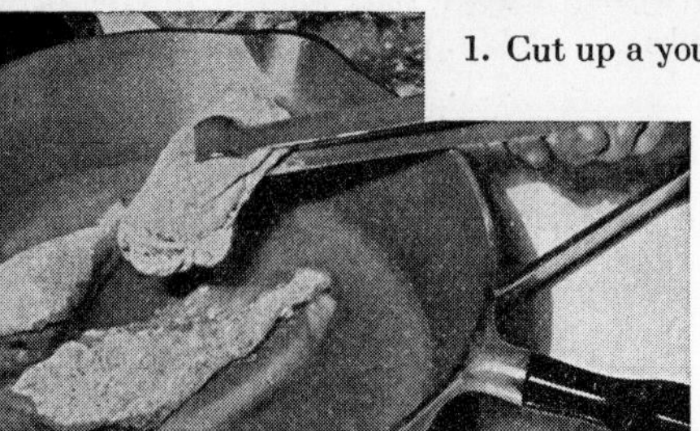

. . . salt, flour, and place the pieces in a skillet with plenty of hot, but not smoking, fat . . .

3. . . . cover, turn when brown, and cook with moderate heat for 20 to 25 minutes for the thick pieces.

II. In deep fat

1. Quarter the chicken, dip into thin batter, and . . .

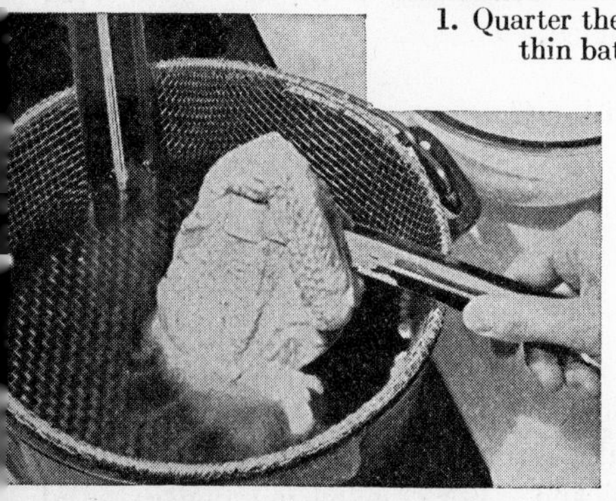

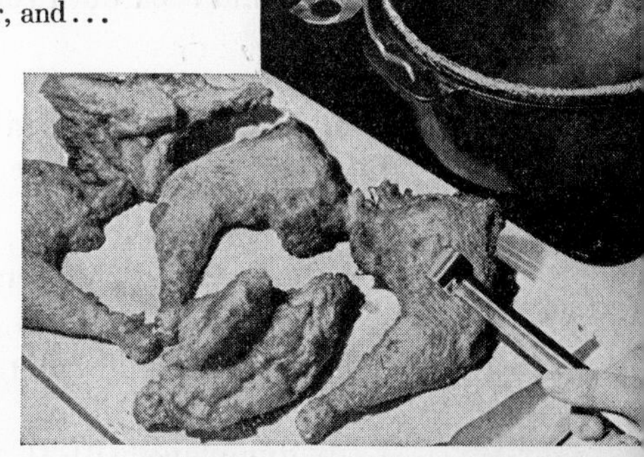

. . . have the fat heated to 350° F. when the chicken goes in, and fry at 300° to 325° for 10 to 15 minutes.

3. Crisp brown on the outside, thoroughly cooked inside, drain on absorbent paper, and keep hot until ready to serve.

Fig. 142. TO FRY CHICKEN
I. IN SHALLOW FAT
II. IN DEEP FAT

Oyster Stuffing or Dressing

For a three-pound bird:

1 c. crumbs of stale bread	1½ t. salt
1 c. cracker or corn bread crumbs	¼ t. pepper
⅛ c. melted butter	2 T. water or oyster liquor
1 c. (½ pt.) oysters	Parsley (if desired)

Apple Stuffing[1]

¼ c. diced salt pork	5 tart apples diced
½ c. chopped celery	½ c. sugar
½ c. chopped onion	1 c. fine dry bread crumbs
¼ c. chopped parsley	¾ t. salt

Pepper

Fry the salt pork until crisp, and remove the pieces from skillet. Cook the celery, onion, and parsley in the fat for a few minutes and remove them. Put diced apples in skillet, sprinkle with sugar, cover, and cook until tender. Remove the lid and continue to cook until the juice evaporates and pieces of apple are candied. Mix with the apples the bread crumbs, crisp salt pork, cooked vegetables, salt, and pepper. Use stuffing while hot.

Milk Gravy for Poultry

Pour off most of fat from pan in which roast, broiled, or fried chicken has been cooked. Add white flour (2 T. or ⅛ c. for each cup of gravy desired) and stir until browned. Add ½ to ¾ c. milk and stir until it thickens; add remaining milk, or liquor from giblets, and cook until thickened.

Giblet Gravy

Add chopped cooked giblets and hard-cooked egg to milk gravy. Stock in which giblets were cooked may be used in place of part of the milk.

Stewed Chicken for Pie or with Dumplings

Cover chicken with boiling water and let simmer until tender. Thicken broth with white flour. Add 2 t. salt and ¼ t. pepper for each 3 lb. chicken. Make dumplings (see recipe, page 412). Cook dumplings with the chicken. For chicken pie, place stewed chicken in a baking dish and cover with crust (see recipe, page 411). Cook 20 to 30 minutes.

[1] Courtesy of Agricultural Extension Service, State of Washington.

Barbecued Chicken

Prepare chicken according to directions for broiling. Broil in covered pan or over direct fire until tender, basting every 3 to 5 minutes with barbecue sauce. To baste when broiling, wrap a newly cut stick or a long-handled fork with cheesecloth, dip in sauce and rub over chicken. Keep sauce hot so that the butter will stay melted.

Barbecue Sauce

¼ lb. butter
½ c. catsup
1 T. Worcestershire sauce
3 T. vinegar or lemon juice
½ c. water

Melt butter and mix well with other ingredients. Use for basting broiled chicken or meat, or heat slices of meat loaf in it.

Preparation of Fish for Cooking

For **Shellfish,** *see pages* 450–451

Fish cooks more quickly than meat. The protein in it is coagulated by heat and hardened by high heat, as is the protein of meat. When fish is cooked, the connective tissue is partly dissolved and the fish is flaky — that is, it flakes apart when lifted with a fork.

One third to one half pound of fresh fish will serve one person.

If the scales have not been removed, remove them by immersing the fish in water and repeatedly drawing the back of a knife from the tail toward the head. The scaling is done while the fish is held under the water to prevent scattering of the fish scales.

To Clean a Fish: Hold the fish in the left hand, backbone against your hand, and the tail toward your elbow. With a sharp knife slit the fish from the small vent near the tail to the gills under the head. Cut the gills loose where attached to head and to body. Beginning at tail end of cavity, and using a small sharp knife, lift out entrails and gills with one motion. Make sure that the backbone is clean. Wash cavity with cold water. The head is usually cut off just above the gills; if left on, the eyes are removed.

Broiled Trout, or Other Small Fish

Wash and clean fish. Rub with a small amount of fat and dip in a mixture of crumbs or of flour and white corn meal, seasoned with 1 t. salt and ¼ t. pepper to each cup. Broil for 25 to 30 minutes in a hot greased pan, or on a hot greased grill over hot coals, or in an oven. Let the fish brown on both sides. Cover to keep from drying, and baste occasionally with melted fat.

Boiled Fish

A large piece of fish is used for boiling. Wrap in cheesecloth and simmer in hot water, until it flakes apart (about 30 minutes), adding ½ t. salt and 1 t. vinegar or lemon juice for each quart of water. Remove skin and bones and use boiled fish for creamed dishes, for scalloped fish, for fish hash, and for salads.

Creamed Fish: 1 c. boiled or canned fish, 1 c. white sauce No. 2, 1 T. chopped green or red pepper (or 2 T. catsup). Serve on toast or in toast cases.

Scalloped Fish: Make creamed fish; put in a large baking dish or in individual baking dishes; cover with buttered crumbs and bake until crumbs are brown. Garnish with parsley or slices of hard-cooked egg.

Fish Hash: 1½ c. boiled or canned fish, 1½ c. hot mashed potato, a few drops onion juice (or 1 T. finely minced onion), 1 t. salt, and ⅛ t. white pepper. Beat together with a fork, spread in well-greased pan and cook until well browned on bottom. The hash may be stirred and then browned again.

Fried Fish

Prepare small fish as for broiling. Roll in seasoned corn meal, or in corn meal and crumbs, or in egg and flour. Drop into hot fat and cook about 3 to 5 minutes, or until brown.

Codfish Balls

1 c. salt cod	2½ c. diced potatoes	1 egg
½ T. butter	⅛ t. pepper	Parsley (if desired)

Wash and soak fish in cold water. Divide it into small pieces and cook with potatoes in boiling water until potatoes are soft. Drain. Mash potatoes well. Add butter, beaten egg, and seasonings. Add salt if needed. Slip by tablespoons into kettle of hot fat. Fry brown. Garnish with parsley and serve for breakfast or luncheon. (See General Rules for Deep-Fat Frying, page 447.)

Small recipe: ¼ c. fish, ⅔ c. potatoes, 1 T. egg, ½ t. butter, dash of pepper.

FIG. 143. PUTTING FISH IN OVEN TO BAKE

Baked Fish

Clean and prepare fish for stuffing. Stuff, sew up with tailor's stitch. Rub thoroughly with salt and pepper. Cut gashes in both sides 2 inches apart and fill with thin slices of bacon or salt pork. Lay thin slices of salt pork on back and head. Lay in a pan on top of folds of cheesecloth. Dredge with flour. Bake at 370° F. 12 to 15 minutes to each pound, basting frequently.

Dressing or Stuffing for Baked Fish

1 c. cracker crumbs or dry bread crumbs	1/8 t. pepper	1 T. chopped pickle
1/4 t. salt	1/4 c. melted butter	1 t. chopped onion
	1 t. chopped parsley	1 T. lemon juice

Mix dry ingredients and add melted butter and lemon juice to make them stick together. If crumbs are too dry to stick together, increase butter or moisten with hot water. Pimientos may be chopped and added to the stuffing.

For **Salmon Loaf,** *see page* 445

FIG. 144. BAKED FISH READY TO SERVE

Salads, Salad Dressings, and Salad Accompaniments

See Chapters 18 and 26

A salad is made of a body, a salad green, and a dressing. In a green salad the body and green are of the same material. The green is usually lettuce. The body may be of one or more of a wide variety of foods mixed with a small amount of salad dressing and arranged in a small mound on lettuce or other salad green. A bit of decoration is attractive, such as a tiny leaf of lettuce, a ring or two of stuffed olive, or a small piece of vegetable cut in a fancy shape.

Salad must always be cold, and uncooked vegetables must be crisp. Place the body of the salad as closely together as possible to avoid a scattered appearance. Cut pieces should be small enough to be eaten without further cutting; it should be possible to do any necessary cutting with a fork. Salads must be dainty.

Amounts and ingredients may be varied according to preference. For small recipes, use one fourth or one sixth of given amounts.

Meat Salads

1. *Chicken, Fish, Turkey, or Veal:* 2 c. diced meat; 1 c. sliced celery; ¼ c. chopped olives; 1 c. to 1½ c. salad dressing. Cucumber may be used instead of celery and hard-cooked egg in place of olives.

2. *Meat or Chicken:* 2 c. ground meat; 1 c. celery; 2 hard-cooked eggs, sliced or diced; 1¼ c. mayonnaise.

3. *Flaked Fish:* 2¼ c. flaked fish (boiled or canned fish, tuna fish, salmon, or crab flakes); 1 c. sliced celery; 2 T. chopped green pepper; 1½ c. salad dressing.

4. *Shrimp:* 2 No. 2 cans shrimp; 1½ c. sliced celery; 1 c. to 1½ c. mayonnaise. Clean the shrimp by cutting out the line of black that is on the outside edge of each one. Use the point of a sharp knife.

Cheese and Egg Salads

1. *Cream Cheese or Cottage Cheese:* 1½ c. cheese; 2 to 4 T. cream; ½ c. broken nut meats or chopped olives; 1 c. mayonnaise or cooked dressing.

2. *Cream Cheese or Cottage Cheese Balls:* Soften 1½ c. cream

cheese with mayonnaise or cooked dressing. Form into balls and roll them in ¼ c. finely chopped nuts or 3 T. chopped parsley. Serve 3 or 4 balls for each salad.

3. *Prunes or Pineapple with Cottage Cheese:* Soften ½ to ¾ c. cheese with mayonnaise or cooked dressing; make small balls to stuff pitted, cooked, or canned prunes; make large balls for the center of pineapple slices. Use 1 slice pineapple, or 3 prunes for each serving.

4. *Stuffed Eggs:* 4 hard-cooked eggs cut in half; yolks mashed with ½ t. lemon juice or vinegar, ¼ t. mustard, ½ t. salt, ⅛ t. cayenne, 1½ T. melted butter; whites refilled with yolk mixture.

5. *Egg:* 6 hard-cooked eggs, quartered lengthwise; 1 c. chopped celery; 1 T. chopped pimiento; 1 c. mayonnaise. Arrange the eggs yolk up; mix celery and mayonnaise and pile the mixture in the center; decorate the salad with pimiento.

Vegetable Salads

1. *Tomato and Lettuce:* 6 medium-sized tomatoes (2 lb.); 1 head or 1 bunch lettuce; ¾ c. mayonnaise. Peel tomatoes, cut in quarters from blossom almost through stem end. Lay each tomato on a leaf of lettuce and put 1 T. mayonnaise in the center of it. Chopped celery, diced cucumber, or diced pineapple (½ c. of any one) may be mixed with the mayonnaise and piled in the center.

2. *Stuffed Tomatoes:* 6 medium-sized tomatoes (2 lb.); 1 c. diced chicken, veal, or cucumber, or chicken and celery mixed; 1 c. dressing. Peel tomatoes; cut stems out and hollow each tomato. Remove water from tomato by sprinkling inside of shell with salt and placing it hollow down, on a plate for 30 minutes to 1 hour. Mix solid part of pulp with meat or cucumber, and with dressing; fill tomatoes and serve ice-cold on lettuce.

3. *Cabbage:* ½ lb. cabbage; 4 medium-sized oranges; 1¼ c. mayonnaise or cooked dressing. Section oranges (see page 389) and shred cabbage.

4. *Asparagus:* 1 square can asparagus (will serve 6 persons); ¾ c. mayonnaise; strips of green or red pepper. Pile stalks together on a lettuce leaf; place garnish in a narrow band; add 2 T. mayonnaise.

5. *Carrot:* ¾ lb. raw carrots grated; 1 c. ground celery; 1 c. mayonnaise or cooked dressing, or ½ c. French dressing. Beat

ingredients together with a fork and pile salad in a small mound on lettuce.

6. *Potato Salad:* 1½ lb. potatoes, cooked and diced; 3 sliced hard-cooked eggs; 3 drops onion juice; 3 chopped small sweet pickles; 6 stuffed olives; 1¼ c. mayonnaise or cooked dressing. Garnish with long slices of hard-cooked egg, slices of iced cucumber, or olives.

7. *Combination Salad:* ½ c. diced cooked carrot; ¼ c. peas or string beans; 1 c. shredded cabbage or lettuce; 24 stalks cooked asparagus or strips cooked celery; ¾ c. French dressing or mayonnaise or Spanish dressing. Mix together all except asparagus; pile on lettuce around asparagus.

8. *Cole Slaw:* 3 c. shredded cabbage; dressing made of 1 t. salt, ½ t. mustard, dash of cayenne, 1 T. sugar, 1 egg, ½ c. hot milk, 1 T. butter, ½ c. hot vinegar. Make dressing by mixing seasonings and unbeaten egg; add hot milk and butter and stir and cook until the dressing thickens; remove from heat and beat in vinegar. Pour dressing over cabbage; serve cold.

9. *Green Salads:* Green salads are made of lettuce, romaine, endive, watercress, and other greens. Lettuce may be shredded and served with French dressing; or head lettuce may be cut in wedge-shaped slices and served with Spanish dressing or Thousand Island dressing. Romaine is usually served with French dressing made with lemon or orange juice, or with Roquefort dressing. Any green salads may be served with French dressing.

Fruit Salads

Beat whipped cream into mayonnaise or cooked dressing for fruit salads.

1. *Grapefruit, or Orange, or Orange and Grapefruit:* 3 grapefruit, or 4 medium oranges, or 2 oranges and 2 grapefruit; ½ c. French dressing. Section fruit, pile on lettuce, and just before serving pour over it French dressing or add mayonnaise.

2. *Waldorf or Apple Salad:* 3 medium apples (1 lb.) cut in small pieces; 1 c. sliced celery; 1 c. broken nut meats — English walnuts, pecans, peanuts, or Brazil nuts; 1 c. mayonnaise. The walnut meats will darken if combined and allowed to stand.

3. *Pear and Cherry:* 6 halves pear, fresh or canned; 24 canned red cherries; 24 blanched almonds (or ¼ c. cheese and ¼ c. raisins made into balls); ½ c. French dressing. Stone cherries and put an

almond into each cavity. Arrange four cherries on a lettuce leaf with each half pear; pour French dressing over them.

4. *Canned Apricot:* 1 No. 2 can apricots; 1/8 lb. marshmallows cut in quarters; 1 c. whipped cream seasoned with salt and paprika. Mix lightly and serve on lettuce.

5. *Frozen Fruit Salad:* 1 tall No. 2 can sliced fruit, peaches, pears, or mixed fruit, and 1 c. whipped cream mayonnaise. Freeze fruit in the can with 1 part salt to 3 of ice; pack it, if it is to be kept after freezing, with 1 part salt to 4 parts ice to prevent its freezing too hard. Cut can on side near top; slip mixture out, slice, and serve on lettuce with mayonnaise. This salad is pretty on glass plates.

6. *Apple Salad:*[1] Select medium-sized, firm, tart apples, pare, and core. Cook in a covered pan in sirup made in the proportion of 2 c. water and 1 c. sugar. Use enough sirup to cover the apples. Red cinnamon candies added to the sirup give the apples an attractive rose color. After cooking, drain the apples, chill, and fill with cottage or cream cheese which has been mixed with salt, paprika, and a little finely chopped green pepper. Or form the cheese into balls, roll in ground nuts, and place beside the apples. Serve on lettuce with mayonnaise or French dressing.

7. Combine diced apples with seedless grapes, malagas, or tokays, which have been halved and seeded. Serve on lettuce with mayonnaise or French dressing.

Gelatin Salads

To 2 c. fruit juice, or thin vegetable pulp, use 1 T. granulated gelatin. Add a little cold liquid to gelatin and allow to stand for 5 minutes or until it swells; add remaining liquid hot, and stir until gelatin is dissolved. Chill until gelatin has stiffened.

To unmold gelatin salad set mold in warm water for a few seconds, loosen edge with knife.

Perfection Fruit Salad

2 grapefruit and 2 oranges in sections
2 T. sugar and 1 T. lemon juice in 1 c. gelatin
made from water, fruit juice, and 3/4 T. gelatin

Fill small molds with sections of fruit and pour the gelatin over it. Chill until gelatin stiffens.

[1] Courtesy of Bureau of Human Nutrition and Home Economics, United States Department of Agriculture.

Fruit Salad (to serve 30)

4 envelopes gelatin
3 c. cold water
7 c. boiling water
10 apples
6 sectioned oranges
2½ c. sugar
2 envelopes citric acid [1]
3 c. pecans or blanched almonds
1 large can pimiento
3 cans sliced pineapple

Follow general rules for making gelatin. Fill molds with mixed chopped fruits. Put in gelatin. Chill until the gelatin has stiffened.

Perfection Vegetable Salad

Gelatin made of ½ c. cold water, 1½ T. granulated gelatin, 1 c. boiling water, ⅓ c. sugar and ½ c. strained lemon juice Cool and add ¾ c. minced celery, 1 T. mild vinegar, ¾ c. minced cabbage, and 3 T. chopped green pepper

Stir occasionally before gelatin stiffens, so that vegetables will be well distributed.

Tomato Jelly for Salad

¼ c. cold water
1 slice onion
1 t. sugar
1½ T. gelatin
1 peppercorn
1 t. salt
2 c. strained tomato
1 whole clove

Soak the gelatin in cold water. Heat tomato, onion, and seasonings together for 3 minutes; strain, and add gelatin with cold water. Stir until gelatin is dissolved. Pour into 6 individual molds.

French Dressing

4 T. salad oil
½ t. sugar
1½ to 2 T. lemon juice or mild vinegar
⅛ t. pepper
⅛ t. paprika
½ t. salt

Mix vinegar and dry ingredients and add salad oil; add a small piece of ice, and beat with a silver fork or shake in a covered jar until it is thick and creamy. Serve immediately or reshake just before serving.

Spanish Dressing: Add 2 T. catsup to French dressing.

Roquefort Dressing: Cream 2 T. Roquefort cheese into French dressing.

Mayonnaise Made with Whole Egg

1 egg
1 t. salt
¼ t. mustard
¼ T. sugar
1 c. to 1¼ c. salad oil
2 T. lemon juice or vinegar (or lime or orange juice)
1 T. hot water (omit if desired)

[1] Substitute ½ c. lemon juice, reducing liquid by ½ c.

Break egg into bowl and beat well; add seasoning and lemon juice, and beat with a fork. Add 1 or 2 t. oil and beat well. Add ¼ c. oil and beat with rotary egg beater until thick. Add a second ¼ c. oil and beat until thick. Add remaining oil in same manner, adding 1 T. boiling water when all of oil has been added.

For mayonnaise made with egg yolk, use 1 yolk instead of 1 egg. Add oil, a few drops at a time at first, then in larger amounts, and continue as for mayonnaise made with whole egg.

Thousand Island Dressing: To 1 c. mayonnaise or cooked dressing add 2 T. chili sauce, 2 T. finely chopped sweet pickle, 2 T. chopped olives, and 2 T. chopped pimiento. One tablespoon of finely chopped green pepper may be added, if desired. Use this dressing for head lettuce salad or for open sandwiches. The flavors will be well blended if it is mixed and allowed to stand for 2 hours before use.

Tartar Sauce: To 1 c. mayonnaise, add 2 or 3 T. capers, 2 T. finely chopped sweet pickles, and 2 drops onion juice if desired.

Cooked Salad Dressing

½ t. mustard	1 T. sugar	1 c. milk
½ t. salt	2 egg yolks or 1 whole egg	¼ c. mild vinegar
¼ t. paprika	1 T. butter	1½ T. flour

Mix dry ingredients, and add egg and milk. Cook over hot water. (Add butter.) Add vinegar slowly. Stir until smooth.

Cream Dressing: 1 c. of whipped cream (sweet or sour cream) may be added to cooked salad dressing when cold. 2 T. peanut butter may also be added.

Cheese Straws

1 c. crumbs from fresh bread	½ t. salt	Dash of cayenne
⅔ c. flour	1 c. grated cheese	2 T. milk
1 T. butter	⅛ t. white pepper	

Mix crumbs, cheese, flour, melted butter, and seasonings. Add milk if needed. Roll or pat one-fourth-inch thick; cut into strips, one-fourth-inch wide and about 4 inches long. Bake until brown in a moderate oven (375° F.). Serve with salad.

Small recipe: ¼ c. fresh crumbs, ⅙ c. flour, 1 t. butter, pinch of salt, ¼ c. grated cheese, dash of pepper and dash of cayenne, 1 t. water.

Cheese Balls

1½ c. grated cheese	Few grains cayenne
1 T. flour	3 egg whites
¼ t. salt	¾ c. fine cracker crumbs

Mix cheese with flour, salt, and cayenne. Beat whites until stiff and add flour. Shape in small balls; roll in crumbs, fry in deep fat, and drain on brown paper. Excellent served with fruit or vegetable salad. Serve immediately after cooking.

Stuffed Celery

12 small pieces celery	8 to 10 stuffed olives (chopped)
¾ c. cream or cottage cheese	or 2 T. chopped pimiento
2 to 3 T. milk or cream	¼ t. salt

Soften cheese with milk or cream, add olives or pimiento and salt. Fill the rounded side of celery with mixture. Serve cold with green salad or fruit salad.

Cottage Cheese (Using a Little Sour Milk)

1 gal. sweet skim milk	⅛ junket tablet	1 t. salt
¾ c. clean, sour milk	4 T. cold water	

Stir sour milk into sweet skim milk; place vessel in hot water and raise temperature to almost lukewarm (75° F.). Remove and set where it is to remain until clabbered. Dissolve junket tablet in water and stir it in. Cover the vessel with cloth and leave at about 75 degrees F. for 12 to 16 hours, or until there is a slight whey on top. Drain through cotton cloth (not cheesecloth). When well drained, work in salt. (This recipe makes about 1½ pounds of cheese.)

Small recipe: 2 *c. sweet skim milk,* 1½ *T. clean sour milk,* ⅛ *junket tablet,* ½ *T. cold water,* ⅛ *t. salt.*

Cottage Cheese (Using Freshly Soured Milk)

1 gal. fresh clabber	1 t. salt

Heat clabber slightly over hot water until almost lukewarm (75° F.). Let stand for about 1 hour. Drain curd on a cotton cloth; work in salt; add ¼ c. thin cream. (This recipe makes about 1½ pounds of cheese.)

Small recipe: 1 *pint milk.*

Cottage cheese is used in salads and sandwiches or eaten with sugar and a little cream, or with salt and pepper.

Cakes and Cookies

See Chapters 20, 21, 27, 29

Also see material on Baking Powders, page 403

SCORE CARD FOR CAKES CONTAINING FAT [1]

STANDARD PRODUCT — 100 POINTS		
External Characteristics		30
Shape, symmetrical, slightly rounded top, free from cracks or peaks	10	
Surface		
Unfrosted, smooth, uniform light brown except where ingredients darken the color	10	
Frosted		
Consistency — characteristic of kind, creamy, moist, free from stickiness, crystals, or crustiness		
Flavor — characteristic of kind, delicate and pleasing in combination with cake		
Distribution, style and color, suitable to kind of cake and frosting		
Volume — light in weight in proportion to size	10	
Internal Characteristics		40
Texture — tender, moist crumb, velvety feel to the tongue	20	
Grain, fine, round, evenly distributed cells with thin cell walls, free from tunnels	10	
Color, uniform, characteristic of cake	10	
Flavor		30
Blended flavor of ingredients, free from undesirable flavor from fat, leavening, flavoring, or other ingredients	30	
Total	100	100

Methods of Mixing Butter Cakes

There are two methods of mixing butter cakes: (1) the *muffin*, or *quick method*, and (2) the *cake method*. These are given in the recipes which follow.

[1] *Homemade Bread, Cake and Pastry*. Farmers' Bulletin 1775.

The Baking of Butter Cakes

Cake pans should be greased or the bottom lined with heavy waxed paper and should be filled two thirds full, the batter being spread a little to the sides to prevent the cakes rounding in the center.

The baking of a cake can be checked by dividing the required baking time into fourths:

First quarter — Cake should begin to rise (bubbles).
Second quarter — Cake should continue to rise and form a crust.
Third quarter — Cake should finish rising and begin to brown.
Fourth quarter — Cake should finish browning and shrink from sides of pan.

If the oven is too quick and cannot be regulated, place a pan of hot water above the cake and another below it. If no oven thermometer is available, watch the division of time very carefully and reduce the oven temperature if the cake is cooking too quickly.

Be careful not to move the cake during the rising period, second and third quarters. Why? If the oven does not cook evenly, the cake may be moved in the first and fourth quarters.

Time and Temperature Required for Cake-Baking

Sponge cakes	Loaf cake	Cup cakes	Layer cakes	Pound cake
275° to 325° F.	325° to 350° F.	350° to 375° F.	365° to 400° F.	300° to 325° F.
40 min. to 1 hr.	40 min. to 1 hr.	15 to 25 min.	20 to 30 min.	1 hr. or longer

The temperature for cake-baking may be even throughout, or it may be a rising temperature. It is safest not to allow the temperature to reach the highest point given.

Cakes are done when they shrink from the sides of a pan, are delicately browned, and spring back into place when touched gently with the finger.

To Remove Butter Cakes from the Pan: Remove the cake from the oven and let stand in pan on a rack 5 to 10 minutes. Loosen edges with a sharp knife, invert the pan, and let the cake slip out on a wire cake rack under which paper has been spread to catch crumbs. Allow cake to cool on rack.

Plain Cake (Quick Muffin Method)[1]

3 c. flour (soft wheat)	1 c. sugar	1 c. milk
4 t. baking powder	1 egg, beaten	½ to 1 t. flavoring
¼ to ½ t. salt	¼ c. fat, melted	

[1] *Homemade Bread, Cake, and Pastry.* Farmers' Bulletin 1775.

1. Sift dry ingredients together.
2. Combine beaten egg, milk, melted fat and flavoring.
3. Add the dry ingredients all at once; stir until the mixture is smooth.
4. Pour into greased pan, filling about two thirds full.
5. Thin loaf: bake in moderate oven (365° F.) 25 minutes.

Cup cakes: bake in a moderately hot oven (375° F.) for 20 minutes.

This cake can be quickly made, the flavor will be good, the texture somewhat coarse. The keeping qualities will be poor, but the cake will be delicious served hot with a sauce.

Small recipe: 1 *c. flour,* 1⅓ *t. baking powder,* ⅙ *t. salt,* ⅓ *c. sugar,* 1⅓ *T. beaten egg,* 1⅓ *T. melted fat,* ⅓ *c. milk,* ⅓ *t. vanilla.*

Foundation Cake (Cake Method)[1]

¼ c. fat	2–3 eggs	¼ to ½ t. salt
¼ to 1 t. flavoring	3 c. soft-wheat flour	1 c. milk
1¼ c. sugar	3½ t. baking powder	

1. Cream fat until soft; add flavoring and gradually add the finely granulated sugar, stirring until the mixture is light and fluffy.
2. Continue creaming and add egg yolks one at a time.
3. Add flour sifted with the baking powder and salt and milk alternately, a little at a time. Add the flour first and last. Beat in the dry ingredients and stir in the milk.
4. Fold in the beaten egg whites which are stiff enough to hold their peaks, but are still moist and shiny in appearance.
5. Pour batter into a lightly greased pan.
6. For a layer cake bake in a moderate oven (365° F.) for 25 minutes.

For a loaf cake, bake in a moderate oven (325° F.) for 40 to 45 minutes.

Small recipe: 1⅓ *T. fat,* ⅓ *t. flavoring,* ½ *c. sugar,* 1 *egg,* 1 *c. flour,* 1⅓ *t. baking powder,* ⅙ *t. salt,* ⅓ *c. milk.*

Spice Cake

Moisten 1 t. cinnamon and ½ t. cloves with ½ T. hot water and mix with the creamed butter and sugar.

[1] *Homemade Bread, Cake, and Pastry.* Farmers' Bulletin 1775.

Rich Cake[1]

1 c. fat	4 eggs	¼ to ½ t. salt
½ to 1 t. flavoring	3 c. soft-wheat flour	1 c. milk
2 c. sugar	2½ t. baking powder	

Follow directions for Foundation Cake.

White Cake[1]

¼ c. fat	4–6 egg whites	2½ t. baking powder
¼ to 1 t. flavoring	3 c. soft-wheat flour	1 c. milk
1¼ c. sugar	¼ to ½ t. salt	

Follow directions for Foundation Cake. Egg whites are folded in after flour is mixed.

Yellow Cake (from Foundation Recipe)[1]

¼ c. fat	4–6 egg yolks	¼ to ½ t. salt
¼ to 1 t. flavoring	3 c. soft-wheat flour	1 c. milk
1¼ c. sugar	4½ t. baking powder	

Follow directions for Foundation Cake. Egg yolks are beaten till thick and mixed with creamed butter and sugar. Bake in a loaf pan in a moderate oven 40 minutes at 350 degrees F.

Rich Chocolate Cake[1]

⅞ c. fat	4 eggs	¼ to ½ t. salt
½ to 1 t. flavoring	2⅞ c. soft-wheat flour	1 c. milk
2 c. sugar	2½ t. baking powder	

2 ounces (2 sq.) chocolate, melted, unsweetened

Follow recipe for Foundation Cake. Melt chocolate over warm, not boiling water; add just before egg whites are folded into batter.

Devil's Food Cake[1]

⅜ c. fat	2⅞ c. sifted soft-wheat flour
¼ to 1 t. flavoring	½ t. soda
1¼ c. sugar	2 t. baking powder
2 to 3 eggs	¼ to ½ t. salt
2 ounces (2 sq.) chocolate melted, unsweetened	1 c. sour milk

Follow directions for Foundation Cake. Melt chocolate over warm water, not boiling water; add just before egg whites are folded into batter.

[1] *Homemade Bread, Cake, and Pastry.* Farmers' Bulletin 1775.

FIG. 145. CREAMING FAT AND SUGAR

FIG. 146. ADDING EGGS

FIG. 147. ADDING FLOUR AND LIQUID

FIG. 148. FOLDING IN EGGS

FIG. 149. SPREADING EVENLY IN PAN

FIG. 150. TURNING OUT CAKE

Apple Sauce Cake[1]

½ c. fat
1 c. unsweetened thick apple sauce
1 t. soda
1 c. chopped raisins
⅛ t. nutmeg
1 c. sugar 1 egg
2½ c. soft-wheat flour
½ t. cinnamon
½ t. cloves
½ t. salt

Cream butter and sugar. Add whole beaten egg. Add apple sauce. Sift dry ingredients. Mix raisins with ½ c. flour. Add remaining ingredients and beat until smooth. Bake in a loaf at 325 degrees F. for one hour.

Fruit Cake (Dark)

(Ingredients for small recipe given in parentheses)

1 lb. butter (½ c.)
1 lb. brown sugar (⅔ c.)
1 lb. flour (1 c.)
9 eggs (2)
2 t. cinnamon (¼ t.)
½ t. cloves (⅛ t.)
1 t. mace (¼ t.)
2 T. milk (2 t.)
4 T. lemon juice (1 T.)
2 lbs. raisins (¾ lb.)
2 lb. currants (½ lb.)
½ lb. citron (⅛ lb.)
1 lb. candied cherries (5 oz.)
1 lb. shelled almonds, blanched (¼ lb.)
1 lb. shelled pecans (¼ lb.)
1 T. vanilla (2 t.)
½ lb. candied orange peel (⅛ lb.)
1 t. soda (¼ t.)

Candied pineapple may be substituted for orange peel.

Blanch almonds and heat them in a moderate oven until a delicate brown. Cut fruit and nuts into small pieces. Melt butter and add sugar; mix together until thoroughly blended. Add well-beaten eggs. Dredge mixed fruit with half of flour. Sift together remaining flour, soda, spices, and salt. To the cake batter add dry ingredients and milk alternately. Add nuts and fruit. Mix thoroughly. Line pans with waxed paper and fill three fourths full of cake mixture. Bake for 4 hours in a very slow oven (300° F. or below).

Instead of baking in the oven, cook in pressure cooker. Cover the pans with 3 thicknesses of waxed paper tied in place to keep the tops of the cakes dry. Cook in steam pressure cooker at 10 lb. for 45 minutes, then at 15 lb. for 30 minutes. When done remove the paper covers. Put cakes in a slow oven for 12 minutes to dry them.

Small recipe: 2 lbs. fruit cake. Use quantities given in parentheses.

[1] *Homemade Bread, Cake, and Pastry.* Farmers' Bulletin 1775.

White Fruit Cake

For Batter	*Fruits*
½ c. butter	¾ lb. citron chopped fine
1½ c. sugar	1 lb. blanched almonds
½ c. milk	¼ lb. red cherries
2½ c. flour	2 pkg. dried coconut
1½ t. baking powder	1 slice candied pineapple
½ t. cream of tartar	1 lb. white raisins

Follow directions for Fruit Cake (dark).

Cup Cakes

Use one half of any butter- or sponge-cake mixture; fill muffin tins (greased for butter cake, ungreased for sponge cake) two thirds full of mixture. Bake about 20 to 25 minutes in moderate oven (350° to 375° F.) for butter cake, or in moderately slow oven (325° to 350° F.) for sponge cake.

Orange Dessert Cake[1]

1½ c. sugar	½ c. butter
1 c. sour milk	1 t. soda dissolved in the milk
2 eggs, beaten light	2 c. flour (soft wheat)
¼ t. salt	1 c. raisins 1 orange

Grate orange peel slightly. Partially squeeze juice from oranges, add ½ c. sugar, mix and let stand. Cut center core and seeds from the oranges. Grind remaining orange rind and pulp with 1 c. raisins. Cream fat and sugar. Add beaten eggs, sifted flour, salt, and soda, add alternately with the liquid. Add last the orange and raisin mixture.

Pour into an 8 × 8 × 2-inch pan and bake about 45 minutes. While still hot cover with orange juice and sugar mixture and let stand in the pan until juice is absorbed. Do not dissolve sugar entirely. Let it glaze top of cake.

Apple Upside-Down Cake[2]

¼ c. butter or other fat	½ c. sugar 1 egg
1 t. vanilla	½ c. milk ¼ t. salt
1½ c. sifted soft-wheat flour	2 to 4 firm-fleshed apples
2 t. cinnamon mixed with ¼ c. sugar	2 t. baking powder

Cream the fat, add the sugar, well-beaten egg, and vanilla. Sift the flour, baking powder and salt together and add alternately

[1] Courtesy of Agricultural Extension Service, State of Florida.

[2] Courtesy of Bureau of Human Nutrition and Home Economics, United States Department of Agriculture.

with the milk to the first mixture. Spread a thick coating of fat on the bottom and sides of a glass baking dish or a very heavy pan. Pare, quarter, and slice the apples thin, spread in an overlapping layer on the bottom of the baking dish, and sprinkle with the cinnamon and sugar. Pour the cake mixture over the apples. The batter is rather thick and may need to be smoothed on top with a knife. Bake in a very moderate oven (300° to 325° F.) for 45 minutes. Loosen the sides of the cake, turn it out carefully, upside down, and the top will be covered with a neat layer of transparent apples. Serve hot with hard sauce or whipped cream.

Uncooked Frosting

5 or 6 T. liquid — 3 T. butter — Flavoring as desired
A sufficient amount of sifted powdered sugar to make frosting thick enough to spread on the cake (about 3 c.)

Cream the butter, add sugar and liquid gradually, stirring until soft and creamy. Flavor and use at once.

Small recipe: ½ c. powdered sugar (approximate), 1 T. liquid, ½ T. butter, flavoring extract.

Uncooked Chocolate Butter Frosting

1½ squares chocolate
1 egg yolk
⅓ c. cream
1 t. melted butter
Powdered sugar
½ t. vanilla
Pinch of salt

Melt chocolate (over water). Heat cream and add to chocolate. Also add salt, egg yolk, and melted butter. Mix well. Add powdered sugar until the mixture is thick enough to spread. Add flavoring and spread.

Orange Butter Frosting[1]

3 t. grated orange rind
4 T. orange juice
3 T. butter
3 c. sifted confectioners' sugar
½ t. grated lemon rind
2 t. lemon juice
1 egg yolk, unbeaten
⅛ t. salt

Add orange and lemon rind to fruit juice and let stand 10 minutes; strain if desired. Cream butter, add egg yolk and salt, and mix well. Add part of sugar gradually, blending after each addition. Add remaining sugar, alternately with fruit juice, until of right consistency to spread. Beat after each addition until smooth. Makes enough frosting to cover tops and sides of two

[1] Courtesy of Agricultural Extension Service, State of Florida.

9-inch layers, or top and sides, of 8 × 8 × 2-inch cake (generously), or about 3 dozen medium cup cakes.

Boiled White Frosting

1 c. sugar
⅓ c. water
⅛ t. cream of tartar
Few grains salt
1 egg white, beaten stiff but not dry
1 t. lemon juice or 2 t. vanilla

Dissolve sugar in water and cook with cream of tartar and salt to soft-ball stage. (See pages 330, 331 for temperature of soft-ball stage (238°–242° F.) and for precautions in sugar cookery.) Add sirup to egg white, beating constantly. Beat in flavoring, and beat until thick enough to spread.

Boiled-Chocolate Frosting

1 c. sugar
⅛ t. cream of tartar
⅓ c. water
Few grains salt
1 egg white
1½ squares melted chocolate
1 t. melted butter

Boil together sugar, water, cream of tartar, and salt to soft-ball stage (238° F.). Melt chocolate over hot water and add to it the butter. Beat egg white stiff but not dry. Add sirup to beaten egg white, then add melted chocolate and flavoring. Beat until thick enough to spread without running off.

Fondant Icing

For recipe see Fondant, page 528.

For use in frosting cakes, melt fondant over hot water (in double boiler). Flavor and color as desired. If the melted fondant is too stiff to use, add a few drops of boiling water. Small cakes, or loaf cake cut into small shapes, may be frosted with fondant by dropping whole into melted fondant in the same way that nuts are dipped in fondant.

Caramel Frosting

1 c. brown sugar ½ c. granulated sugar 1 c. cream 1 T. butter

Boil to soft-ball stage (238° F.). Cool, and beat until thick enough to spread.

Lady Baltimore Filling

Use boiled white frosting. When cool, add 1 c. chopped seeded raisins, 1 c. chopped figs, 2 c. chopped nuts, and ½ t. lemon juice. Use as filling for white cake. The cake may be frosted with a plain boiled frosting.

Score Card for Cakes Without Fat (Sponge)[1]

STANDARD PRODUCT — 100 POINTS		
External Characteristics		30
Shape, symmetrical, level top	10	
Surface	10	
Unfrosted, smooth, uniform, light brown		
Frosted		
Consistency — characteristic of kind, creamy, moist, free from stickiness, crystals, or crustiness		
Flavor — characteristic of kind, delicate and pleasing in combination with cake		
Distribution, style and color, suitable to kind of cake and frosting		
Volume — light in weight in proportion to size	10	
Internal Characteristics		40
Texture — tender, feathery, resilient crumb	20	
Grain — fine, round, evenly distributed cells with thin cell walls, free from tunnels	10	
Color — Uniform, characteristic of cake	10	
Flavor		30
Delicate, free from excessive flavor of egg, flavoring, or acid	30	
Total	100	100

Plain Sponge Cake[1]

1 c. sifted soft-wheat flour	1 c. sugar	1 t. lemon rind, grated
1 c. eggs (4–5)	2 T. lemon juice	½ t. salt

1. Sift flour three times after measuring.
2. Beat the egg yolks until thick and lemon colored (rotary egg beater can be used).
3. Gradually add half the sugar, beating thoroughly, and then the lemon juice and rind. Beat until thick.
4. Beat the egg whites and salt until they start to peak, but will still flow.
5. Fold in the remainder of the sugar into the egg whites to make a meringue.
6. Fold the egg yolk mixture into the egg white meringue carefully.
7. Fold in the flour gently.

[1] *Homemade Bread, Cake, and Pastry.* Farmers' Bulletin 1775.

8. Pour batter as soon as it is mixed into an ungreased baking pan.
9. A large or medium-sized sponge cake should be baked in a slow oven (325° F.) for about 1 hour.

Small recipe: 1 *egg*, ¼ *c. sugar*, ¼ *c. flour*, 1 *t. lemon juice, a little grated lemon rind.*

Small cakes in muffin pans or jelly cake tins may be cooked about 30 to 40 minutes. The greatest danger to sponge cake is having too hot an oven, which makes the cake rise too quickly and then fall.

Invert the pan on a cake rack. When it is cold, loosen edge with sharp knife; the cake will loosen itself from the pan by its own weight.

The cake is done when it shrinks from the sides of the pan, and when the portion near the center of the crust springs back on being touched lightly with the finger.

Angel Food Cake[1]

1 c. sifted soft-wheat flour	½ t. salt
1 to 1¼ c. sugar	¾ t. cream of tartar
1 c. egg whites (8–10)	1 t. flavoring (¾ t. vanilla, ¼ t. almond extract)

1. Sift flour and half of sugar together three or four times.
2. Beat the egg whites until frothy; sprinkle salt and cream of tartar over top, and beat until egg foam starts to peak, but is not dry.
3. Fold in other half of sugar to form a meringue.
4. Fold in the flour sugar mixture gradually and gently.
5. Add flavoring when mixture is partly blended.
   (A gentle folding motion should be used in mixing; stirring tends to release the air depended on for leavening.)
6. Place in an ungreased pan; a tube pan is best.
7. A large cake will require about 1 hour in a moderately slow oven at 325° F.

If a crisp crust is desired, sprinkle the top with a little sifted powdered sugar before baking.

Small recipe: ¼ *c. sifted soft-wheat flour*, ¼ *c. sugar*, ¼ *c. egg whites* (2–3), ⅛ *t. salt*, ¼ *t. cream of tartar*, ¼ *t. flavoring.*

Filled Angel Food Cake

In recipe for angel food cake, increase sugar to 1½ c. and flour to 1 c., and add ½ c. chopped nuts and ½ c. candied cherries and pineapple. This makes good angel food squares for parties.

[1] *Homemade Bread, Cake, and Pastry.* Farmers' Bulletin 1775.

Oatmeal Cookies

½ c. fat	⅓ c. sour milk	⅛ t. salt	½ t. soda
1 c. sugar	1½ c. rolled oats	½ t. cinnamon	½ t. baking powder
1 egg	1½ c. flour	1 c. chopped raisins or nuts	

Cream butter, add sugar, and well-beaten egg and milk. Flour raisins and nuts with a small amount of the flour. Sift the remaining flour with the salt, cinnamon, soda, and baking powder. Add oatmeal. Add gradually to butter mixture, add nuts and raisins. Drop by spoonfuls in greased pans or baking sheets. Bake in moderate oven (350° to 375° F.) for 15 to 20 minutes.

Small recipe: 1 T. fat, 2 T. sugar, 1 T. (¼) egg, ½ T. sour milk, 3 T. rolled oats, 3 T. flour, ⅛ t. soda, speck of cinnamon, 2 T. raisins.

Peanut Cookies

⅛ c. butter	1 egg	1 c. flour
½ c. sugar	1 t. vanilla	1 t. baking powder
¼ t. salt	2 T. milk	¾ c. chopped peanuts

Cream butter, add sugar and well-beaten egg. Stir in milk and vanilla, and add remaining dry ingredients well sifted together. Stir in peanuts last. Drop by teaspoonfuls on buttered sheet. Bake in moderate oven (350° to 375° F.) for about 8 to 12 minutes. Remove from pan with a knife, while hot.

Small recipe: ½ T. butter, 2 T. sugar, pinch of salt, 1 T. egg, ¼ t. vanilla, ½ T. milk, ¼ c. flour, ½ t. baking powder, 3 T. chopped peanuts.

Chocolate Cookies

Add 2 sq. (2 oz.) melted chocolate to peanut cooky recipe and decrease flour 2 T. Any other nut may be used.

Small recipe· Add ½ sq. chocolate to small recipe for peanut cookies.

Toll House Chocolate Cookies[1]

½ c. fat	½ t. salt
½ c. brown sugar	¼ c. chopped nuts
¼ c. granulated sugar	1 7-oz. bar semi-sweet chocolate
2 eggs, well beaten	½ t. vanilla
½ t. soda	1⅛ c. flour, sifted

1. Cream fat and sugar; add beaten eggs and beat well until thick.
2. Sift remaining dry ingredients and stir into mixture.

[1] Ruth Wakefield, *Toll House Recipes*. By permission of M. Barrows & Co.

3. Add chopped nuts, and chocolate which has been cut into pieces the size of a pea.
4. Add vanilla.
5. Drop by half teaspoons on a greased cooky sheet; bake 10–12 minutes in 375° F. oven. This recipe makes around 50 small cookies.

Ginger Snaps

½ c. fat | ½ c. molasses | ½ t. soda | ¼ t. cinnamon
½ c. sugar | ¼ c. water | ½ to 1 t. ginger | About 2¼ c. flour

Mix like other cookies or butter cakes, adding enough flour to make a stiff dough. Roll thin on a slightly floured board, cut with cooky cutter; place on greased pans and bake in moderately hot oven (400° F.) for about 10 minutes.

Vanilla Wafers

⅔ c. butter | 1 egg | 1¼ c. flour | ¼ t. salt
½ c. sugar | 2 T. milk | 1 t. baking powder | 2 t. vanilla

Mix as for peanut cookies; drop by half teaspoons on a lightly greased baking sheet, allowing room to spread. Bake in a moderate oven (350° F.) for about 10 minutes, or until the edges are brown.

Tea Cakes (Plain Cookies)

1½ c. flour | 1½ t. baking powder | ¼ c. butter | 3 T. milk
¼ t. salt | 1 egg | ½ c. sugar | ½ t. flavoring

Cream butter, add sugar and well-beaten egg. Add salt and flavoring. Sift flour and baking powder together and add them to the mixture a little at a time, alternating with the milk until all are in. Roll ⅛-inch thick; cut into cakes and bake in moderate oven (350° F.).

Brownies

½ c. flour
1 c. sugar, light brown or granulated
¼ c. melted fat
1 egg
¾ t. vanilla
2 sq. chocolate, melted
½ c. broken walnut or pecan meats

Combine ingredients in order given and mix well. Spread in well-greased, shallow pan and bake in slow oven (300°–350° F.) 30 to 40 minutes. Remove from oven and mark off in squares while warm. Cool in pan.

Small recipe: 2 T. flour, ¼ c. sugar, 1 T. melted fat, 1 T. egg, ¼ t. vanilla, ½ sq. melted chocolate, 2 T. nut meats.

Crisps

1 c. butter	2 c. sugar
Grated rind and juice of 1 lemon	3 eggs (2 eggs and 1 yolk)
	Flour to knead

Cream butter, add sugar gradually, then the rind of one lemon and juice, then yolks well beaten, then beaten whites; add flour enough to knead. Roll as thin as possible. Brush with egg whites, dust with granulated sugar before baking. These cakes may be decorated with cherries, almonds, citron, etc., cut in small pieces.

Rolled Wafers

1/4 c. butter		7/8 c. flour
1/2 c. sugar (powdered)	1/4 c. milk	1/2 t. flavoring

Cream butter and sugar together. Add milk gradually, then flour and flavoring. Spread very thinly with spatula on bottom of slightly greased square pans. Crease in squares, and bake in slow oven (300° to 350° F.) until delicately brown. Cut squares. Remove from pans, turn over so the glazed side will be outside, and roll cornerwise while hot. If squares become too brittle to roll, put in oven to soften.

Marguerites

1 c. sugar	4 marshmallows	2 T. shredded coconut	1 c. nuts
1/2 c. water	2 egg whites	1/4 t. vanilla	Saltines

Boil sugar and water until sirup will spin a long thread when dropped from the tines of a fork. Remove from fire. Add marshmallows cut in pieces. Do not stir. Pour into stiffly beaten egg whites, beat until stiff. Add coconut, nuts, and vanilla. Pile on crackers and bake in slow oven (325° to 350° F.) until delicately browned.

Kisses

1/2 c. egg white (about 4 whites)	1/2 t. vanilla
	1/8 t. cream of tartar
1 c. powdered sugar	1 c. chopped nuts
1/8 t. salt	

Add salt and cream of tartar to egg white and beat very stiff. Beat in 1/4 c. powdered sugar and fold in remaining sugar, nuts, and vanilla. Drop by teaspoonfuls on ungreased paper on a pan, dust with powdered sugar, and bake in a slow oven (275° F.) about 50 minutes, increasing the heat at last to brown slightly.

Icebox Cookies

1½ c. shortening	½ t. soda
1 c. brown sugar	1 t. salt
⅓ c. white sugar	2 t. cinnamon
3 eggs.	4 c. flour

2 t. baking powder

Cream shortening, add sugar, and beat well. Add eggs one at a time and beat again. Sift remaining dry ingredients and add to first mixture. This dough may be divided, adding melted chocolate and vanilla to one portion, grated coconut to another portion, nuts and raisins or chopped dates to another portion. These portions may be made into sausage-like rolls, wrapped in waxed paper and placed in the refrigerator overnight or until wanted.

Before baking, slice very thin. Bake in a hot oven on a baking sheet.

Small recipe: ½ c. fat, ⅓ c. brown sugar, 1⅔ T. white sugar, 1 egg, pinch of soda, ⅔ t. baking powder, ⅓ t. salt, ⅔ t. cinnamon, 1⅓ c. flour.

Pastry

See Chapter 21

Score Card for Pies [1]

STANDARD PRODUCT — 100 POINTS		
External Characteristics		30
Shape — regular, free from bulges on top	10	
Surface	20	
Crust — uniform browning		
No meringue — smooth, free from cracks		
Meringue — slightly browned, adhering to crust, light and moist in appearance around edge of pie		
Internal Characteristics		40
Crust	20	
Texture, tender, but free from tendency to crumble, crisp on the bottom as well as along edges		
Grain — flaky, slightly rough, almost blistered appearance		
Filling	20	
Fruit — well cooked, neither too dry nor too juicy		
Custard — tender and quivery, keeps angles when cut and does not weep on standing		
Cream, smooth, stiff enough to prevent running when cut, free from pastiness or rubberiness		
Flavor		30
Crust — rich, blended flavor of ingredients		
Filling — characteristic of kind, free from excessive sweetness or flavor of uncooked starch	30	
Total	100	100

Kinds of Pies

Pies are difficult to classify according to the filling, but we may group them according to the crust.

1. *One-Crust Pies for Which the Crust is Baked Separately.* Lemon, chocolate, cream, and various fruit pies for which the

[1] *Homemade Bread, Cake, and Pastry.* Farmers' Bulletin 1775.

fruit is cooked first and served in the pie crust, with whipped cream, are types of one-crust pies. Apple sauce and banana custard, also, are used as fillings for one-crust pies.

Tarts are individual pies of this type. They are frequently filled with jelly or preserves, as cherry tarts.

2. *One-Crust Pies with the Filling and the Crust Baked Together.* Custard, pumpkin, and molasses pies are examples.

3. *Two-Crust Pies (crust and filling cooked together) with Latticed or Crossbarred Tops, or with Solid Tops.* Openings must always be made in the top crust of two-crust pies in order to allow the steam to escape as the pie cooks. Fruit pies are examples of two-crust pies.

Plain Pastry (Two Crusts)

1½ c. flour	1 t. salt
5 to 6 T. fat	2½ T. cold water (variable)

Use no water if a liquid fat is used.

Small recipe for 5-inch pie plate: ½ c. flour, 1½ to 2 T. fat, ¼ t. salt, 1 T. water or less.

Cut fat into flour with two knives, or rub it in with the tips of the fingers, for a flaky crust. Stir in only enough water to hold the dough together. Knead very lightly to mix well. The pastry may be chilled on ice before it is rolled. Rub just enough flour on bread board to keep pastry from sticking. Roll lightly with the rolling pin to about one-eighth-inch thickness.

Two-Crust Pie. Place rolled dough in pan, press it down carefully, and trim edge with a knife. Place filling in pie, heaping very slightly toward center. Form the second crust of strips, or of rolled dough in which a few cuts have been made in order to allow the steam to escape. Moisten edge of lower crust; place top crust in position, and press the two together with fingers or fork.

One-Crust Pie. To make a well-shaped crust there must be no bubbles between pastry and pan. The edge of the crust must also be fastened to the pie tin by pinching with the fingers or by marking with fork or pastry wheel. Prick dough very thoroughly with a fork to avoid air bubbles. Bake crust in hot oven (about 450° F.) until delicate brown. Remove from oven, cool, and fill. Crust may be baked on the outside of pie tin instead of inside.

Crumb Pie Crust

Zwieback: Grind or roll finely 1 pkg. zwieback. Reserve 1 cup. Add to the remaining crumbs 1/4 c. sugar and 1/4 lb. butter melted. Line a pie tin with this mixture. Use any cream pie filling. Cover with meringue. Sprinkle reserved crumbs over top of meringue. Brown at 325° F. Chill thoroughly before serving.

Graham Cracker:

(*a*) 1 1/2 c. graham cracker crumbs mixed with 1/2 c. powdered sugar and 1/4 lb. butter. Pat mixture into pie tin in shape of crust.

(*b*) Roll enough graham crackers to make 1 1/2 c. Mix with 1/3 c. condensed milk. Line buttered pie tin, packing mixture well.

One-Crust Apple Pie

Fill a baked pie crust with apple sauce. Flavor the sauce with a few drops of lemon juice and a dash of nutmeg. Spread about three-fourths inch thick, cover with stiff whipped cream sweetened to taste.

Two-Crust Apple Pie

2 c. pared and sliced apples (about 4 apples)	2 T. butter
Dough for 2 pie crusts	3/4 c. sugar
1 t. cinnamon or nutmeg	

Cut out stem and blossom ends. Pare, core, quarter apples and slice thin. Line pie tin with pastry; pile in slices, rounding slightly toward the center, and sprinkle with sugar. Dot with butter and sprinkle with cinnamon or nutmeg. Cover with pastry according to general directions. Bake 10 minutes in hot oven (400° to 425° F.); reduce temperature and finish baking 25 minutes in moderate oven (350° F.).

Small recipe: 2 apples (1 c.), 1 T. butter, 3/8 c. sugar, 1/2 t. cinnamon or nutmeg, dough for one pie crust.

Peach, Apple, or Berry Cobbler

Pastry for 1 crust	1 1/2 c. sugar
Pastry strips or whipped cream	2 1/2 to 3 c. fruit

Line a deep (about 2-inch) pie tin with pastry prepared and cooked according to directions for one crust. Fill with cooked,

FIG. 151. CUTTING IN THE FAT

FIG. 152. MAKING THE PASTRY DOUGH

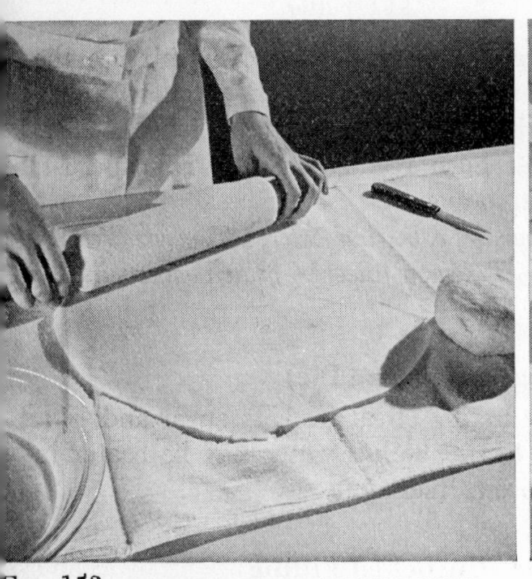

FIG. 153. ROLLING OUT PASTRY DOUGH

FIG. 154. FITTING THE PASTRY

FIG. 155. THE FINISHING TOUCHES

FIG. 156. PASTRY READY TO EAT

sweetened, pared, and sliced apples or peaches, or with well-sugared berries. Cover with pastry strips and bake in a moderately hot oven (375° to 400° F.) until pastry is cooked. If whipped cream is used, heat filled pie for 5 minutes in a moderate oven (about 350° F.); cool; cover with whipped cream, and serve.

Small recipe: pastry for ½ pie crust, ¾ c. sugar, 1½ c. fruit.

Lemon Pie (Cooked Filling)

¾ c. sugar	2 egg yolks
¾ c. boiling water	3 T. lemon juice
2 T. cornstarch	1 grated lemon rind
2 T. flour	1 t. butter

Mix cornstarch, sugar, and flour and pour over mixture the boiling water. Stir constantly. Cook until thick. Add egg yolks, butter, lemon juice, and rind. Cook until egg thickens. Stir constantly, as mixture will burn readily. Fill a baked crust, cover with meringue, brown in oven.

Small recipe: ⅜ c. sugar, ⅜ c. boiling water, 1 T. cornstarch, 1 T. flour, 1 egg yolk, 1½ T. lemon juice, ½ grated lemon rind. ½ t. butter.

Meringue (for One Pie)

Beat two egg whites until stiff. Beat in 3 T. sugar and ½ t. vanilla or lemon juice. ½ to 1 T. boiling water may be beaten in last. Spread on pie and brown meringue.

Lemon Pie (Uncooked Filling)

(1 pie crust)

1⅓ c. condensed milk (sweetened)	2 egg yolks
½ c. lemon juice (2 to 3 lemons)	½ T. grated lemon rind

Stir egg yolks into milk; add lemon juice and rind; pour into crust. Cover with meringue and brown meringue in oven.

Chocolate Pie

3 egg yolks	1 T. cornstarch
1 oz. chocolate	1 c. boiling water
1 c. sugar	1 t. vanilla

Mix cornstarch and sugar, and add boiling water. Cook until thick; add chocolate (finely cut), egg yolks, and cook in double boiler until thick. Flavor, pour into baked crust, cover with meringue and brown.

Small recipe: 1 egg yolk, ⅓ oz. chocolate, ⅓ c. sugar, 1 t. cornstarch, ⅓ c. boiling water, ⅓ t. vanilla.

Tarts

Tarts are made from plain pastry. All scraps of pastry dough may be utilized for making tarts. Bake crusts on bottom of muffin pans. Fill with any pie filling; cover with meringue.

Fresh fruit, chopped and sweetened, or jam or jelly makes an excellent filling for tarts. Cover with whipped cream.

Cream Puffs

(Recipe for 12 puffs)

1½ c. flour	1 c. hot water
½ c. butter	4 or 5 eggs
3 c. filling	

Add butter to boiling hot water. When melted, add flour all at once. Mix thoroughly and cook over direct heat for 5 minutes. Cool for 5 minutes and then beat unbeaten eggs in, one at a time. Drop by tablespoonfuls on buttered baking sheet, allowing 2 to 3 inches between puffs for expansion. Bake in moderately hot oven (450° F.) for 15 minutes; reduce temperature to 325–350° and bake 20 to 30 minutes longer. Cool; split open and fill with sweetened whipped cream, sweetened whipped cream flavored with cocoa (1 T. to 1 c. cream), or cream filling.

Small recipe: ⅓ c. flour, 2 T. butter, ¼ c. hot water, 1 egg.

Cream Filling for Cream Puffs

⅓ c. flour	2 eggs
2 c. milk	⅞ c. sugar
1 T. butter	⅛ t. salt

Make cream sauce of flour and milk in double boiler (cooking 15 minutes). Add eggs, sugar, and butter after creaming together; cook until eggs thicken; cool and add flavoring.

Chocolate Cream Filling. Add 1 sq. (1 oz.) melted chocolate to cream filling before adding eggs.

Small recipe: 2 T. flour, ½ c. milk, ½ egg, 3 T. sugar, ½ t. butter.

Puddings, Custards, and Fruit Desserts

See Chapters 21 and 27

See pages 439–440, sauces for desserts.

Steamed Plum Pudding

½ lb. seeded raisins
½ lb. currants
⅛ lb. candied orange peel
1 oz. citron or candied pineapple
¾ c. finely chopped suet
⅛ t. allspice
⅛ t. grated nutmeg
½ c. flour
1¼ c. stale bread crumbs
4 eggs
⅝ c. light brown sugar
2 t. cinnamon
½ c. jelly (apple or currant) or ½ c. water

Wash and dry currants and raisins; cut citron and orange peel fine. Mix dry ingredients; mix liquid ingredients; combine liquid and dry ingredients. Fill greased molds two thirds full and steam 4 hours. Steam again 1 to 2 hours immediately before using. Serve hot with hard sauce or whipped cream.

Small recipe: 2 oz. seeded raisins, 2 oz. currants, ½ oz. candied orange peel, ¼ oz. candied citron, 3 T. chopped suet, pinch of allspice, nutmeg, 2 T. flour, ¼ c. stale bread crumbs, 1 egg, 2½ T. light brown sugar, ½ t. cinnamon, 2 T. jelly or water.

Steamed Fig Pudding

Omit fruit in plum pudding and add a half-pound of finely chopped figs and 1 finely chopped sour apple. Steam four hours and serve with lemon sauce, hard sauce, or foamy sauce.

Blanc-Mange (Cornstarch Pudding)

3 c. milk
4½ T. cornstarch
1 t. flavoring
½ t. salt
¾ c. sugar

Mix cornstarch and sugar; add milk and mix thoroughly. Cook in double boiler, stirring frequently until well thickened (about 20 minutes). Add flavoring and salt and serve with custard, chocolate, or caramel sauce (pages 439–440).

Chocolate Blanc-Mange

Melt 1 sq. (1 oz.) chocolate and stir in ½ c. milk. Mix remaining milk with cornstarch and sugar; heat; after cooking about 20 minutes, stir in chocolate and milk. Or stir in ½ c. cocoa when blancmange is almost cooked. Serve with thin or whipped cream.

Junket

1 junket tablet	3 c. milk	¾ t. vanilla
1 T. cold water	¼ c. sugar	⅛ t. salt

Mash the junket tablet with a spoon and dissolve it in cold water. Heat milk to lukewarm (80° to 85° F.); add other ingredients and junket tablet dissolved. Pour quickly into dishes in which it is to be served. Leave in a warm place until firm; chill; serve.

Caramelized sugar (dissolved in a little water) or cocoa (1½ T.), mixed with the sugar, may be used in place of vanilla.

Small recipe: ¼ junket tablet, 1 t. cold water, ¾ c. milk, few drops of vanilla, pinch of salt.

Tapioca Custard

3½ T. minute tapioca	2 eggs
2 c. hot milk	⅛ t. salt
1 t. vanilla	⅓ c. sugar

Cook tapioca and milk in double boiler until tapioca is transparent (15 to 20 minutes); stir in gradually egg yolks, mixed with salt and sugar. Cook 15 minutes or until thickened. Cool for a few minutes and fold in flavoring and stiffly beaten egg whites. Serve with custard sauce, thin or whipped cream, crushed fruit, or cooked apples.

Fruit Tapioca

Substitute water for milk in above recipe, omit eggs, and add 1 c. sliced fruit — as apples or peaches. Fruit may be added after the first five minutes of cooking and the fruit tapioca baked in a moderate oven for 30 minutes.

Rice Pudding (Cooked Rice)

2 c. milk or milk and cream	⅓ c. sugar
¾ c. cooked rice	4 eggs
2 T. butter	½ c. seeded raisins

1 stick cinnamon

Scald milk with cinnamon. Remove cinnamon. Add butter and sugar. Add to slightly beaten eggs, mix well, add rice and raisins. Bake in a buttered baking dish in slow oven (300° F.) for 45 minutes or until brown.

Baked Creamy Rice Pudding[1] (Uncooked Rice)

3 T. uncooked rice	⅓ c. sugar	½ t. salt
1 qt. milk	½ t. nutmeg	½ c. raisins

Mix and bake 2½ to 3 hours at 250–300° F. Stir gently with a fork three or four times during first hour. The delicious flavor is due to the long, slow cooking.

Cocoa Rice Pudding

Part I	*Part II*
1 c. rice	1 c. milk
3 c. water	3 T. cocoa
	⅓ c. sugar

Bake part one until water is almost evaporated. Stir in part two, and bake 15 minutes longer. Serve either hot or cold with thin or whipped cream.

Rich Chocolate Bread Pudding

2 c. milk	⅛ t. salt
2 eggs	1 c. bread crumbs
2 T. melted butter	1 t. vanilla
½ to ⅔ c. sugar	1 sq. (1 oz.) chocolate or 3 T. cocoa

Beat egg yolks with butter and sugar; add crumbs, salt, and milk. Cook in double boiler until thick. Add cocoa or melted chocolate. Beat about 1 minute with rotary beater; fold in vanilla and egg whites beaten stiff. Bake in moderate oven until firm (when a knife will come out clean). Serve with whipped cream, hard sauce, or lemon sauce.

Lemon Bread Pudding

Omit chocolate and substitute grated rind and juice of 1 lemon.

Brown Betty (Scalloped Apples)

1 lb. apples (3 apples) pared and sliced	¼ c. sugar (light brown)
1¼ c. stale bread cubes	¼ t. grated nutmeg (if desired)
¼ c. butter, melted	Grated rind and juice of ½ lemon

Stir butter into cubes of bread; cover bottom of buttered baking dish with bread, and spread over it half the apples, sugar, and seasonings; repeat, covering with a light layer of bread. Bake 30 to 40 minutes in a moderate oven (325° F.). Serve with hard sauce or thin cream.

[1] *Cooking American Varieties of Rice.* United States Department of Agriculture, Leaflet 112.

Apple Crumble

3 or 4 apples
½ c. brown sugar
Whipped cream
6 T. butter
⅓ c. graham cracker crumbs
or macaroon crumbs

Pare and slice apples and place in buttered baking dish. Mix sugar, melted butter, and crumbs, and pour over apples. Bake 20 to 30 minutes, or until apples are cooked, at 400° F. Serve in glass dishes with a little whipped cream on each.

Boiled or Soft Custard

2 egg yolks or 1 whole egg
1 c. milk
2 T. sugar
Pinch of salt
¼ t. vanilla

Beat egg slightly, add other ingredients (except vanilla). Cook mixture in double boiler with water below boiling point and stir constantly until the custard coats a spoon. Wooden spoon recommended. Cool, add vanilla (and nutmeg if desired). Serve cold (with whipped cream if desired).

Caution: Do not overcook custard or it will lump or "curdle." Lumpy custard should be beaten well with a rotary egg beater.

Small recipe: 1 *egg yolk,* ½ *c. milk,* 1 *T. sugar, pinch of salt, and few drops of vanilla.*

Floating Island: Make boiled custard (3 c. for 6 people) with egg yolks. Beat the whites until stiff and drop by spoonfuls into a pan of hot water. Bake until firm and slightly brown. Place on custard in serving dish with a wire whisk. Chill floating island and serve cold.

Orange Custard

Pour boiled custard (above) over four or five sections of sectioned orange in a custard cup or an individual baking dish. (For additional orange flavor add grated orange rind when making the custard.) Cover with meringue (page 510) flavored with lemon juice. Bake in slow oven until meringue is delicately browned. Serve immediately.

Baked Custard

Use ingredients for boiled custard. Butter custard cups slightly. Pour custard into cups. Cook in slow oven. As an additional precaution, set cups in a pan of hot water. Custard is done when firm in the center. Test by sticking the point of a knife in the center. If custard is done, it will not stick to the knife.

Caramel Custard· Omit flavoring and sugar from baked custard. Add for each cup of milk used 2 T. caramel sauce.

To make caramel sauce, caramelize sugar, add a little hot water to dissolve caramel.

Chocolate Custard: Use ½ sq. chocolate or 1½ T. cocoa for each cup of liquid. Add chocolate or cocoa to a little (⅓ to ½ c.) hot milk and stir until smooth. Mix with remaining milk (hot) and combine according to general directions.

Fruit Desserts

Uncooked Fruit Whip

Two stiffly beaten egg whites or ½ c. heavy cream, whipped, 1 c. fruit pulp, ¼ to ½ c. sugar, 2 t. lemon juice. Mix all ingredients carefully to retain lightness. Grated raw apple, apricot pulp, grated apple and pineapple mixed, crushed banana, berries, or sectioned oranges make excellent whips.

Pile whip lightly in individual dishes and serve cold.

Baked Prune Whip

1 c. dried prunes	1 T. lemon juice	½ c. sugar
Whites of 3 eggs	2 c. cold water	⅛ t. salt

Wash prunes carefully. Soak 10 to 12 hours or overnight in 2 c. cold water. Cook in the same water till tender. Remove stones and rub pulp through strainer. Add sugar and reheat. This mixture should be the consistency of marmalade. Add salt to whites of eggs and beat till stiff. Add cold prune mixture gradually; add lemon juice. Pile lightly in buttered baking dish and bake 30 minutes, or until firm, in a slow oven.

Apple Dumplings

Pare and core tart cooking apples. Roll out plain pastry dough (page 507) or shortcake dough (page 411) into a thin sheet. Cut in strips wide enough to cover the sides but not the tops or bottoms of the apples. Roll the dough about the apples, making a tight seam by moistening the edge of the dough and pressing together. Place apples in a greased pan so they do not touch. Fill centers with a mixture of sugar, cinnamon, nutmeg, and pinch of salt. Raisins or nut meats may be added if desired. Dot with butter and bake in a moderate oven (300° to 375° F.) for 30 minutes or until brown. Baste with the sirup as the dumplings cook.

If brown crusty dumplings are desired, cook in muffin pans.

Serve hot with hard sauce.

Fruit Roll

3 c. berries or sliced fruit	2 T. butter
1½ c. sugar	Spices if desired

Roll shortcake dough (page 411) or plain pastry dough (page 507) into a thin sheet. Cover with sugar, dot well with butter, cover with fruit. Roll the dough (as for cinnamon rolls). Stick the edge of the dough together by moistening edge and pressing. Lay the roll in buttered pan, prick the top with a fork, dot with butter, and sprinkle with a little sugar. Bake until brown (about 30 minutes) in a moderate oven (350° to 375° F.). Baste occasionally with the sirup. Serve hot with the sirup that cooks out, or with hard sauce.

Shortcakes

Shortcakes are made with rich biscuit dough, with pastry squares, with sponge cake, or with butter cake, according to preference. Strawberries, fresh cherries, sectioned orange, huckleberries, prunes, blackberries, and raspberries are favorites for shortcake. Sweeten the fruit slightly before using it and crush part or all of it as desired. See variations for biscuit (pages 410–411), plain pastry (page 507), sponge cake (page 500), and one-egg cake (pages 492–493) for the foundation of shortcake. Do not combine fruit with shortcake more than 20 to 30 minutes before serving.

Fruit Tapioca. *(See page* 513.)

Fruit Cup

Cut the fruit into half-inch pieces. Amounts and ingredients have endless possibilities of variation. A larger serving of fruit cup should be used for dessert than the serving used as a cocktail. Serve fruit cup very cold. Use in it the juice from sectioned oranges or grapefruit. The following are favorite suggestions:

Sections of grapefruit or orange, sweetened to taste.

Grapes (¾ lb. white), pineapple (4 slices), lemon juice (1 t.), almonds (¼ lb. blanched), sugar if necessary; ⅛ lb. marshmallows may be added, if the fruit cup is used as a dessert.

Orange (4 or 5 medium), mint (3 sprigs fresh, finely minced), sugar (2 to 4 T.). One T. lemon juice or 4 T. grapefruit juice may be added.

Orange (4 medium), coconut (½ to ¾ c. fresh shredded), lemon juice (1 T.), sugar (2 to 4 T.).

Grapefruit (2 medium), pear (1 fresh), orange (2 medium). Add 1 T. lemon juice if desired. Add 1 drop of oil of peppermint if desired.

Grapefruit (3 medium), orange (3 medium), sugar if needed. Add grated rind of 1 orange if desired.

Apricot (6 to 8 halves, fresh or canned), pineapple (4 slices), pear (2 fresh or 4 canned halves), lemon juice (1 t. to 1 T.).

Ambrosia

1 doz. large sweet oranges
½ c. sugar (or to taste)
1 c. grated fresh coconut
½ c. grated pineapple (canned)

Section the oranges (page 389). Save all orange juice. Cut each orange section in two or three pieces. Mix orange, pineapple, and three fourths of the coconut. Add sugar to taste. Let stand in the refrigerator for several hours. Serve in low sherbet glasses, sprinkling remainder of the grated coconut on the top of each serving.

Ambrosia means "food for the gods." This is a dessert that was especially popular for Thanksgiving or Christmas dinner before frozen desserts were invented. It is still a superior dessert when accompanied by fruit cake.

Old-Fashioned Grated Sweet Potato Pudding

Grate 4 large raw peeled sweet potatoes. Have beaten in a separate bowl:

2 whole eggs
1 c. molasses
½ c. milk
½ c. melted butter
Dash of salt

Stir into this the grated potato, put into buttered pan, and bake in moderate oven two hours or more. The pudding should be almost caramelized. Serve with whipped cream or lemon sauce. Spices may be added. Makes 12 servings.

Sweet Potato Tarts

1 c. Karo
2 eggs
¼ c. brown sugar
1 c. halved pecans
1 c. mashed (cooked) sweet potato

Beat eggs well. Add sugar, sirup, potatoes, and pecans. Fill individual unbaked pastry shells two thirds full and cook at 400° F. for ten minutes, reduce heat to 375° F. and bake until firm. Serve topped with whipped cream. Will make 16 small tarts.

Gelatin Desserts

See Chapter 21

General Rules for Making Gelatin Dishes

1. Soak gelatin in a small amount of cold water for 5 minutes or until it swells. Use an amount of gelatin that will give a proportion of 2 or 3 T. gelatin to 1 qt. total liquid in the final product.
2. Dissolve gelatin in hot liquid.
3. Add sugar and fruit or vegetable juice. Strain if clear jelly is desired.
4. Have molds clean. It is not necessary to rinse in cold water.
5. Pour gelatin into molds if plain jelly is to be made. If a sponge-type jelly is desired, let stand until partially thickened and beat until foamy, like beaten egg white, then pour into molds.
6. Chill. If chilling is to be hurried, surround the gelatin with crushed ice.
7. To unmold the gelatin, dip mold in lukewarm water and loosen upper edge with a sharp knife. Invert on the dish on which it is to be served. If it does not unmold readily, shake mold gently to loosen gelatin.

Lemon Jelly

2 T. granulated gelatin
½ c. cold water
1 c. sugar
½ c. lemon juice
2½ c. boiling water

Soak gelatin in cold water; dissolve in hot water, add sugar and lemon juice; pour into molds and chill. See general rules above.

Small recipe: 1 *t. gelatin,* 2 *T. cold water,* ½ *c. boiling water,* 2 *T. sugar,* 1 *T. lemon juice.*

Orange Jelly

2 T. gelatin
1 c. orange juice
1½ c. water
½ c. lemon juice
1 c. sugar

Orange or Lemon Mint Jelly: Add to either orange jelly or lemon jelly while hot 8 sprigs of mint finely chopped and 1 drop of oil of peppermint.

Fruit Jellies

Use 1½ c. small or chopped fruit with lemon or orange jelly. Allow jelly to become partially set, then add fruit, arranging as desired.

Sponges

Mix plain gelatin of any desired flavor; let stand until partly thickened; beat with rotary beater until foamy. Fold in 1 beaten egg white for each cup of liquid used; 2 c. liquid will make enough gelatin sponge for 6. Lemon sponge is often called snow pudding and is served with custard sauce (¼ c. sauce per person).

Orange Charlotte

1½ T. gelatin	⅓ c. cold water
⅓ c. boiling water	1 c. sugar
3 T. lemon juice	1 c. orange juice and pulp
3 egg whites	2 c. cream, whipped stiff

Soak gelatin in cold water, dissolve in boiling water. Strain and add sugar, lemon juice, orange juice, and pulp. Chill in pan of ice water; when quite thick beat with wire spoon or whisk until frothy, then add whites beaten stiff and fold in the cream. Line a mold with sections of oranges (see page 389), or fold sections into mixture. Turn into molds. Spread evenly and chill.

Spanish Cream

2 T. granulated gelatin	3 eggs	¼ t. salt
3 c. milk	½ c. sugar	1 t. vanilla

Soak gelatin in ⅓ c. cold milk. Scald the rest of the milk and dissolve gelatin. Add egg yolks, sugar, and salt. Return to double boiler and cook as for boiled custard (page 515). Add vanilla; cool. Beat egg whites, fold into the custard mixture, turn into gelatin molds and chill. Serve with whipped cream if desired.

Strawberry Icebox Cake[1]

1 T. gelatin	1 T. lemon juice
¼ c. cold water	1 c. cream, whipped
½ c. boiling water	¼ t. salt
1¼ c. sugar	Sponge cake
1 qt. strawberries, crushed	

Soak the gelatin in the cold water for 5 minutes. Add the boiling water and sugar; stir until gelatin and sugar are dissolved. Mash the berries, add the lemon juice, combine with the gelatin mixture, and chill. When partially set, fold in whipped cream, to which the salt has been added. Chill again, then spread between layers of sponge cake and keep in a refrigerator several hours or overnight before serving.

[1] Courtesy of Bureau of Human Nutrition and Home Economics, United States Department of Agriculture.

Frozen Desserts

See Chapter 21

Mixtures Frozen While Stirring

Freezing:

1. Use crushed or finely chopped ice with rock salt.
2. Prepare freezer container by scalding and chilling. Pour in mixture to be frozen, allowing a space of about one third or one fourth of can for expansion of mixture when it freezes. Put can in place in bucket before adding ice.
3. Proportion of ice and salt:

   For mixtures to be stirred while freezing, use 1 part salt to 6 or 8 parts ice.
   For packing mixtures that are frozen, use 1 part salt to 4 parts ice.

4. Put in ice and salt so that the packing comes above the level of the mixture to be frozen; see that the upper drain for salt water is open and is 1 or 2 inches below the top of the ice-cream container. Rapid freezing improves the texture. If a motor is available for turning the freezer, freeze rapidly; if the crank must be turned by hand, it is better to turn it steadily and slowly rather than rapidly for a while and then stop for an intermission.
5. When mixture is frozen, remove ice and salt from top of can; uncover; remove and scrape dasher; stir cream down into can; place clean paper or paraffin paper over hole and plug with a cork; invert a cup over the cork; drain off water and repack cream with ice and salt. Make sure that the proportion of salt to ice is not more than 1 to 4, otherwise cream will freeze too hard. Cover freezer with burlap or newspapers.

A tightly covered tin can and a wooden pail may be substituted for an ice-cream freezer; a wooden spoon or spatula should be used to scrape the mixture from the sides and bottom of the can as it freezes.

Preparation of Mixture to be Frozen: In preparing frozen fruit or water ice, the sugar and water should be made into a sirup. In preparing ice cream with fruit, let the sugar and crushed fruit stand 1 hour in a cool place, or until the sugar is dissolved, then add the cream and freeze the mixture; or freeze the fruit mixture to a mush, add the cream, and finish the freezing; in preparing ice creams without fruit, dissolve the sugar in the liquid, cool, add the flavoring, and freeze.

Fruit juice is used for water ice. For frozen fruit the fruit is pressed through a colander or cut in small pieces. Either juice or crushed fruit may be used for ice cream; if fruit is very seedy, only the juice should be used.

Amounts for Frozen Mixtures: One pint of frozen mixture serves 3 or 4 persons, but a pint of liquid will make about 1½ pints of frozen mixture and will serve 4 or 5 persons. When beaten cream is used, the mixture does not swell as much during freezing as when unbeaten cream is used.

Plain or Philadelphia Ice Cream

1 qt. thin cream (or cream and milk) ¾ c. sugar
3 t. vanilla

Dissolve sugar in cream, add flavoring, and freeze.

Frozen Custard

2 c. milk	1 t. vanilla
2 eggs	Pinch of salt
½ c. sugar	1 c. cream (either thin or thick)

Make a boiled custard of the milk, egg yolks, sugar, and salt. (See Custards, page 515.) Cool. Fold in well-beaten egg whites, add vanilla and cream, and freeze.

Uncooked custard may be used instead of cooked custard.

Peppermint Ice Cream

1½ c. milk	¼ lb. of peppermint
½ c. thick cream	stick candy

Heat the milk and candy (in double boiler) until the candy is dissolved. Cool and freeze to a mush. Add whipped cream and finish freezing.

Chocolate Ice Cream

1 qt. thin cream (or cream and milk)	1 T. vanilla
1 c. sugar	Pinch of salt
1½ oz. chocolate or ¼ c. cocoa	⅓ c. hot water

Melt the chocolate, add sugar and hot water and cook until smooth. Add to the cream, flavor, and freeze.

Note: Custard may be used instead of thin cream.

Lemon Ice Cream

1 qt. thin cream (or cream and milk)	3 T. lemon juice
⅔ c. sugar	Grated rind of 1 to 2 lemons

Dissolve the sugar in the cream, chill. Immediately before freezing, add lemon juice and lemon rind.

Orange Ice Cream

1 qt. thin cream	4 T. orange juice	2 T. lemon juice
⅔ c. sugar	Grated rind of 1 orange	

Dissolve sugar in cream. Chill. Immediately before freezing, add fruit juice and orange rind.

Caramel Ice Cream

1 qt. thin cream (or cream and milk)	2 t. vanilla	1⅓ c. sugar
	2 eggs	
2 c. milk	⅛ t. salt	

Caramelize half the sugar. Add to this two or three tablespoons of boiling water and cook until all the caramel is dissolved. Make a custard of the milk, eggs, and sugar. (See directions for custards on page 515.) Cool, add caramel, cream, and vanilla. Freeze.

Strawberry Ice Cream

3 c. thin cream (or milk and cream)	1 c. sugar
1 qt. strawberries	¼ t. salt

Wash and hull berries; crush and mix with sugar; let stand 1 hour or shorten the process by heating the berries with the sugar. Mash through a strainer. Freeze cream to a mush, add strawberries, and finish freezing.

Raspberry Ice Cream

1 qt. raspberries	4 T. lemon juice
½ c. water	3 c. thin cream
1 c. sugar	¼ t. salt

Follow directions for Strawberry Ice Cream. Add lemon juice and water to crushed fruit.

Apricot or Peach Ice Cream

2 c. thin cream	1 c. sugar
2 c. apricot or peach pulp (fresh or canned)	4 c. water

Make a sirup of sugar and water. If canned fruit is used, the fruit juice may be substituted for the water. Add fruit pulp. Freeze to a mush. Add cream and finish freezing. To make a richer dessert whipped cream may be added instead of the thin cream.

Cherry Ice Cream[1]

1 pt. canned sour pitted cherries
2 c. sugar
¼ t. salt
3 pts. thin cream
⅛ t. grated lemon rind

Chop the cherries very fine. Scald the cream in a double boiler, add the sugar, and stir until it is dissolved. Cook the mixture, add the other ingredients, including the cherry juice, and freeze. If fresh-cooked cherries or cherries canned with the pits are used, a flavor resembling maraschino cherries may be obtained if eight to twelve pits are cracked in a tightly tied muslin bag and cooked with the mixture. This recipe makes about two quarts of ice cream.

Water Ices

2½ c. liquid, 1 c. sugar, 1 to 2 T. lemon juice when desired. Fruit juices or fruit pulp are used for water ices. If fruit pulp is used, press fruit through a fruit press or strainer.

Cranberry Ice. Use 1½ c. cranberry juice and 1 c. water with 1 c. sugar.

Lemon Ice. 1¾ c. water, ¾ c. lemon juice (3 lemons), 1⅛ c. sugar.

Mint Ice. 2¼ c. water, 1 c. sugar, ¼ c. lemon juice, 8 sprigs mint, chopped fine. Combine and let stand 1 hour before freezing. Strain and freeze.

Orange Ice. 1 c. water, 1½ c. orange juice (4 or 5 oranges), 1 T. lemon juice, 1 c. sugar.

Pineapple Ice. 1½ c. water, 1¼ c. shredded pineapple, 1 T. lemon juice, 1 c. sugar.

Raspberry or Strawberry Ice. 1 c. water, 1½ c. crushed strawberries or raspberries (about 1 qt.), 2 T. lemon juice, 1 c. sugar.

Sherbets

Add 2 stiffly beaten egg whites to any water ice when half frozen or frozen to a mush, and finish the freezing.

Milk Sherbet. Substitute milk for water in lemon ice or orange ice. Dissolve sugar in milk; add lemon juice just before freezing.

[1] Courtesy of College of Home Economics, Cornell University.

Frappés

Freeze to a mush any desired beverage, such as grapejuice, lemonade, orangeade, cocoa. Serve in small frappé glasses.

Mint frappé adds a refreshing flavor to ginger ale or lemonade.

Ice Creams Frozen Without Stirring

The mechanical refrigerator offers a convenient and easy means of providing frozen desserts. For freezing without stirring a rich mixture must be used and the ingredients carefully combined. The texture of such desserts is not so velvety as are those frozen with stirring, but they have a flaky, crystalline texture which is pleasing.

See discussion of general principles of freezing without stirring, page 301.

Plain Mousse[1]

1 c. thick or heavy cream
1 c. rich milk or thin cream
1 t. gelatin
6 T. sugar
2 egg whites
Pinch of salt
½ t. vanilla

Soak the gelatin until soft in a little of the milk or thin cream. Heat the remainder of the milk or thin cream, and pour over the gelatin. Add the sugar, stir until dissolved, and put the mixture aside to chill. Whip the thick cream. When the mixture containing the gelatin has thickened slightly, beat it to incorporate air. Add the vanilla, and fold in the whipped cream and the well-beaten egg whites. The egg whites reduce richness, increase volume, and improve texture. These proportions will make over 4 cups before freezing; or, if the egg whites are not used, about 3 cups.

Substitutes for Gelatin as the Thickening. Use recipe for plain mousse here with variations as follows:

Moisten 1 tablespoon of flour with a little of the milk or thin cream, add to the remainder, heat to boiling, cool, and combine with the whipped cream and other ingredients.

Or prepare a custard from the cup of rich milk, two egg yolks, and the sugar. Cool, beat, and add to the other ingredients as described.

[1] United States Department of Agriculture, Leaflet 49. Courtesy of Bureau of Human Nutrition and Home Economics.

Or use 1 cup of evaporated milk instead of the rich milk or thin cream. Heat first in top of double boiler. Chocolate or any of the more decided flavors will cover the evaporated-milk flavor.

Or add one-fourth-cup of marshmallows cut in small pieces to the milk or thin cream, and follow the usual method.

Mousse of Various Flavors[1]

Use recipe for plain mousse here with variations as follows:

Coffee: Substitute ½ c. strong coffee for ½ c. of the thin cream.

Peppermint: Use ¼ pound of peppermint stick candy instead of the sugar.

Peanut brittle: Use ¼ pound of peanut brittle finely ground instead of the sugar.

Burnt almond: Melt 8 t. of sugar carefully and stir in ½ c. of chopped almonds. Heat until the almonds are browned. Crush and add to the cream. Flavor with vanilla and a few drops of almond extract.

Chocolate: Add one or two squares of unsweetened chocolate to the milk or thin cream in place of the other thickening agents suggested. Add 8 to 12 tablespoons of sugar, depending upon the quantity of chocolate used. Cook until smooth. This requires a lower temperature to freeze than the other mixtures, especially when the larger proportions of sugar and chocolate are used, but makes a very rich and palatable dessert.

Grated or shaved chocolate may be used to flavor these desserts without affecting the freezing time. The marshmallow mixture is especially good with ⅛ pound of shaved sweet or bitter chocolate added.

Strawberry Mousse[1]

1 c. thick cream, whipped
1 c. crushed strawberries
2 egg whites, well beaten
Pinch of salt
½ c. sugar

Combine the sugar and crushed fruit and stir until the sugar is dissolved. Fold the sweetened fruit into the whipped cream. Fold in the beaten egg whites to which the salt has been added. Pour into the tray or mold for freezing.

Canned or frozen fruit pulp or bottled fruit juice may be used.

[1] United States Department of Agriculture, Leaflet 49. Courtesy of Bureau of Human Nutrition and Home Economics.

Heat the juice and thicken by adding 1 t. of gelatin, softened in 2 T. cold water. Cool, and beat in air before adding to the whipped cream.

Peach or Apricot Mousse. Substitute 1 cup of fruit pulp for berries. To prevent darkening, sprinkle fruit with sugar before sieving.

Candies

See Chapter 30

Chocolate Fudge

2 c. granulated sugar	2 T. corn sirup
3 to 4 T. cocoa or 1 sq. chocolate	1 T. butter
½ c. cream	1 t. vanilla
½ c. milk	½ to 1 c. nut meats (if desired)
Few grains of salt	

Combine sugar, cocoa or chocolate, cream, milk, sirup, and salt in a deep pan and heat. Stir until sugar is completely dissolved and the mixture boils. Boil until the test for soft-ball stage is given when a little of the mixture is tested in cold water. Remove from the fire and add butter and vanilla. Cool until only warm, beat until thick and creamy. Add nuts, if used, and pour into a buttered pan. Mark in squares.

Double Fudge

Cook the following two mixtures separately, one ten minutes ahead of the other, as fudge is cooked. After beating the first mixture until creamy, pour into a greased pan, spreading it one third to one half inch thick. When the second mixture is creamy, pour it on top of the first.

Chocolate Mixture	*Panocha Mixture*
1 lb. (2 c.) sugar	1 lb. (2¼ c.) brown sugar
1 sq. (1 oz.) chocolate	½ c. water
⅔ c. water	3 T. butter or ⅓ c. cream
4 T. butter or ½ c. cream	1 c. broken walnut meats
½ t. vanilla	½ t. vanilla

Divinity Fudge

2 lb. granulated sugar	Pinch of salt
1 c. Karo sirup	4 egg whites
1 T. vinegar	½ lb. walnut meats
1 c. water	1 T. vanilla

Cook sugar, sirup, water, vinegar, and salt to 262° F. Beat slowly into well-beaten egg whites. Add walnuts and vanilla. When it begins to thicken, drop by the spoonful on heavy waxed paper. Pack fudge in airtight tin boxes or cans.

Panocha

Use the ingredients and amounts in panocha mixture of double fudge and use the fudge method of cooking.

Raisin Fudge

Add 1½ c. chopped seeded raisins to panocha, omitting nuts.

Fondant

2 lb. (4 c.) granulated sugar	Cold water to dissolve sugar (about 1½ c.)
¼ t. cream of tartar	

Mix ingredients, heat, and stir until sugar is dissolved. Allow to boil gently after sugar is dissolved, cooking to soft-ball stage (236° to 238° F.), and washing down sides of pan occasionally with wet cloth swab. Pour on a platter without scraping the pan, and cool until hand can be held on bottom of platter. Beat the mixture until it "sugars," and knead for a few minutes, or until creamy. It becomes more creamy still if allowed to stand 20 to 24 hours in a covered jar before it is used.

Fudge can be beaten at a higher temperature than fondant because it contains butter and other materials which prevent rapid crystallization.

Peppermint Creams

Melt about 1 c. fondant in the top of a double boiler; flavor with 2 drops of oil of peppermint, and stir until creamy. Drop from the tip of teaspoon or from pastry bag in small patties on heavy waxed paper.

Tutti-Frutti

Knead 1 c. to 1½ c. fondant and flavor with ½ t. almond extract; knead into it a mixture of chopped candied cherries, citron, candied pineapple, currants, and sliced blanched almonds. Shape into a flat cake and allow to stiffen. Cut into oblong or square pieces.

Orange-Peel Creams

Knead 1 c. ground candied orange peel into 1 c. fondant and add 1 T. orange juice or ½ t. orange flavoring. Shape into a long stick about 1 inch thick and cut it into pieces one-half-inch thick.

Fondant Roll

Knead two pieces of fondant, flavoring and coloring as desired (one green flavored with peppermint, and the other vanilla, or one chocolate and the other vanilla). Roll into very thin pieces between layers of heavy waxed paper. The pieces should not be more than 2½ to 3 inches wide, but may be as long as desired. Remove waxed paper, place one piece on top of the other, and roll into a long stick. Cut the stick across into half-inch pieces.

Stuffed Dates or Prunes

Wash and dry the fruit. The prunes should be steamed for 20 minutes before used. Stone fruit and place in each cavity a nut and a small lump of fondant kneaded and flavored with vanilla. Roll stuffed fruits in granulated sugar.

Centers Dipped in Fondant

Melt fondant in top of double boiler. Flavor and color as desired (delicate colors are usually preferred). Dip centers (nuts, raisins, Parisian sweets, etc.) into fondant on a fork, a candy dipping fork, or a toothpick. Place on heavy waxed paper to harden. Decorate if desired, with the tiniest possible pieces of candied fruit or nuts.

Fondant Candies Dipped in Chocolate

Melt dipping chocolate very slowly over hot, but not boiling, water (120° F.). Beat chocolate until creamy; keep warm; drop fondant centers in and dip them out with a fork; place on heavy waxed paper. Let harden in a cool, very dry place.

Choice Caramels

1 lb. (2 c.) sugar	¼ lb. (½ c.) butter
1 lb. (¾ c.) glucose (corn sirup)	1 pt. thick cream

Put sugar, glucose, butter, and half of cream over the fire and stir until the mass boils thoroughly. Then stir in, so gradually as not to stop the boiling, a second cup of cream. Put the sugar thermometer in, and let the mixture go on boiling, stirring it every 3 or 4 minutes, until the thermometer registers 250 degrees F. Then stir in 1 t. vanilla, and turn the candy into well-buttered pans, to the depth of three fourths of an inch. When the candy is nearly cold, cut it into cubes and roll the cubes in waxed paper. If a thermometer is not available, boil the mass to a fairly firm hard ball. In summer or rainy weather the caramels will hold their shape better if boiled from 2 to 4 degrees higher.

Peanut Candy

1 c. shelled and chopped peanuts	2 c. sugar

Put sugar into a smooth frying pan and stir with bowl of the spoon until it melts, keeping the spoon flat. Remove immediately from the fire and stir in the nuts. When it begins to stiffen, pour on an oiled surface and cut into squares.

Butterscotch

2 c. sugar	2 T. vinegar	½ c. brown sugar
1 c. butter	¼ c. boiling water	⅛ t. salt

Boil ingredients together to hard-crack stage (290° F.). Turn into greased pans. Mark candy into squares when partly cold.

Candied Orange Peel or Grapefruit Peel

Cut peel of two oranges or of one grapefruit into narrow strips. Cook in boiling water until tender or until white is partly clear. Dissolve 1 c. of sugar in ½ c. of water and boil to thread stage. Add peel, and simmer 20 to 25 minutes, stirring.

Salted Almonds

Blanche almonds by pouring boiling water over them, and let stand until skins loosen. Pour cold water over them. Skin, dry them between towels. Brown in enough hot oil to float the nuts (¼ to 1 c. in small pan). Drain on brown paper. Sprinkle with salt.

Salted Pecans

Heat 1 c. pecan meats with 1 T. butter in the oven in a pan. Stir to keep from burning. Salt, and drain on brown paper.

Canning

See Chapter 33

Fruits, Tomatoes, and Pickled Vegetables

Fruits, tomatoes, and pickled vegetables may be safely processed in a boiling-water bath at 212° F. Special directions and processing times are given in Table A, pages 536 to 539. The *hot-pack method* is illustrated by peaches and the *cold-pack method* is illustrated by tomatoes.

Fruit may be canned sweetened or unsweetened. For most fruit, make a sugar sirup. For very juicy fruit, use sugar without added liquid.

To make sugar sirup: Boil sugar and water or fruit juice 5 minutes. Remove scum. Use the following proportions according to the kind of sirup you want:

Sirup	*Sugar*	*Water or Juice*
Thin	1 c.	3 c.
Medium	1 c.	2 c.
Heavy	1 c.	1 c.

To make fruit juice: Crush thoroughly ripe, juicy fruit, and bring to a boil over low heat. Strain through jelly bag or other cloth.

To sweeten very juicy fruit: Add dry sugar to raw fruit — about ½ cup to a quart. Bring to a boil over low heat. Pack the fruit in the juice that cooks out.

To can without sugar: Heat fruit in its own juice, in extracted juice, or in water. Process according to directions for peaches given on pages 532–533. To sweeten these fruits before serving, drain the liquid, add sugar to it and heat for a few minutes; pour over the fruit, and let stand for several hours.

Canning Peaches: Hot-Pack Method [1]

Any fruit may be canned in the following way. Peaches are used as an example of the steps in canning fruits by the hot-pack method for boiling-water bath. Each step is illustrated by the picture of the same number on the next page (Figure 157).

1. Choose peaches that are sound, ripe, firm. Wash fruit well. Work with only enough for one canner load at a time. Lift out of water. Don't bruise.

2. Dip peaches in boiling water just long enough to loosen skins. Then dip quickly into cold water. Use a wire basket or cheesecloth to hold the fruit.

3. Remove skins; halve and pit fruit. To keep peaches from turning dark, drop into water containing 2 tablespoons each of salt and vinegar to the gallon. Drain just before heating.

Put peaches in boiling sugar sirup. Heat fruit through but don't cook until soft.

4. Meantime, heat clean jars and lids in water. Remove from water and put hot, wet rubber ring on jar. Pack peaches loosely. Leave ½-inch space at top of jar.

Cover peaches with cooking liquid, still leaving the ½-inch space at top of jar. It usually takes about ¾ to 1 cup of liquid to each quart jar.

5. Remove air bubbles by working the blade of a table knife down sides of jar. Add more liquid if needed to cover fruit, but be sure to have a ½-inch space at top of jar.

6. Wipe jar rim and rubber ring with a clean, damp cloth to remove food that might keep the jar from sealing. Put on lid.

Push long wire bail over lid into the groove at the center. Leave the short wire up. Put jars into canner as soon as they are filled. If a screw top jar is used, screw the top in place and then loosen the top by turning back ¼ inch.

7. When all jars are in the canner, see that water comes over tops. Cover canner. When water boils, count time — 20 minutes for quarts and pints of peaches, at sea level. (For higher altitudes, see page 536.)

8. When time is up, take out jars. Quickly push the short wire down to complete seal, or tighten the screw-top if this type of jar is used. Cool jars top side up, on thick cloth or paper. Keep jars away from drafts, but don't cover.

[1] From *Home Canning of Fruits and Vegetables*, AIS–64. Prepared by the Bureau of Human Nutrition and Home Economics.

Fig. 157. CANNING PEACHES: HOT PACK

FIG. 158. CANNING TOMATOES: COLD PACK

Canning Tomatoes: Cold-Pack Method [1]

1. Inspect every tomato. Use only ripe, firm ones. Tomatoes with spoiled spots that need trimming may give a canned product poor flavor and appearance. Wash tomatoes thoroughly. Take care not to bruise. Prepare only enough for one canner load.

2. Put tomatoes in a wire basket or thin cloth. Dip into boiling water about ½ minute, covering pan. Then dip into cold water.

3. Cut out stem ends and peel tomatoes. Cut or leave whole. While doing so, have clean jars and caps heating in water.

4. When ready to pack, take one jar at a time from hot water. Place hot, wet rubber ring on shoulder of jar. Pack tomatoes into jars, pressing down enough to fill spaces. Fill jars to ½ inch of top. Add salt — ½ teaspoon to a pint jar; 1 teaspoon to a quart.

[1] From *Home Canning of Fruits and Vegetables*, AIS–64. Prepared by the Bureau of Human Nutrition and Home Economics.

5. Remove air bubbles by working the blade of a table knife down sides of jar. Press tomatoes down with a spoon. Add more tomato if needed to fill jar again to ½ inch of top. Wipe jar rim and rubber ring with a clean, damp cloth. Food on the sealing surface may prevent an airtight seal. Screw cap down tight; then turn back ¼ inch.

6. Place filled jars in canner containing hot, but not boiling water. Add boiling water if needed to bring to 1 or 2 inches over jar tops. Be careful not to pour water directly on jars.

7. Put cover on canner. When water boils, begin to count time. At sea level, process pint jars of tomatoes 35 minutes; quart jars, 45 minutes. (For higher altitudes, see page 536.) When time is up, remove jars from canner. Complete seal by screwing the cap on tight. Cool top side up on rack or on thick cloth or paper, away from drafts.

8. Next day, test for leaks. Wipe jars with a damp cloth. Label jars and store in a cool, dry place.

TABLE A

PROCESSING TIMES FOR CANNING FRUITS, TOMATOES, AND PICKLED VEGETABLES IN BOILING WATER BATH (212° F.)[1]

(*See also Chapter 33*)

The processing times in this table apply to places at an altitude of less than 1000 feet. At altitudes above 1000 feet you must increase the time for processing foods in the boiling water bath because the boiling temperature will be less than 212° F. For each 1000 feet above sea level add 1 minute to the processing time if the time called for is 20 minutes or less; add 2 minutes for each 1000 feet altitude if the processing time is more than 20 minutes.

PRODUCT	IN GLASS		IN TIN		
Preparation and Packing	*Pints*	*Quarts*	*Type of Can*	*No. 2*	*No. 2½*
APPLES Pare and core apples, cut in pieces. To keep fruit from darkening, drop it into water containing 2 T. each of salt and vinegar per gallon. Drain, then boil 5 minutes in thin sirup or water. Pack hot fruit to ½ inch of top. Cover with hot sirup or water.	**15 min.**	**15 min.**	Plain tin	**10 min.**	**10 min.**
APPLESAUCE Make applesauce, sweetened or unsweetened. Heat through, stirring to keep it from sticking to pan. Pack hot to ¼ inch of top.	**10 min.**	**10 min.**	Plain tin	**10 min.**	**15 min.**
APRICOTS Follow method for peaches. Peeling may be omitted.	**20 min.**	**20 min.**	Plain tin	**25 min.**	**35 min.**
BEETS, PICKLED Cut off beet tops, leaving 1 inch of stem. Also leave root. Wash beets, cover with boiling water, and cook until tender. Remove skins and slice beets. For sirup, use 2 c. vinegar (or 1½ c. vinegar and ½ c. water) to 2 c. sugar. Heat to boiling. Pack hot beets to ½ inch of top. Cover with boiling pickling sirup. Add ½ t. salt to pints; 1 t. to quarts.	**30 min.**	**30 min.**			

[1] *Home Canning of Fruits and Vegetables* — AWI–93 and AIS–64. Courtesy of the Bureau of Human Nutrition and Home Economics.

TABLE A (*continued*)

PRODUCT *Preparation and Packing*	IN GLASS		IN TIN		
	Pints	*Quarts*	*Type of Can*	*No. 2*	*No. 2½*
BERRIES, EXCEPT STRAWBERRIES *Hot Pack.* (For firm berries.) Wash berries and drain well. Add ½ c. sugar to each quart fruit. Cover pan and bring to boil, shaking pan to keep berries from sticking. Pack hot to ½ inch of top.	**15 min.**	**15 min.**	R-enamel	**15 min.**	**20 min.**
Cold Pack. (For red raspberries and other soft berries.) Wash berries and drain well. Fill jars to ½ inch of top. Shake while filling for a full pack. Cover with boiling sirup, leaving ½-inch space at top.	**20 min.**	**20 min.**	R-enamel	**15 min.**	**20 min.**
CHERRIES Follow method for firm berries, adding a little water when heating unpitted cherries to keep them from sticking to the pan.	**15 min.**	**15 min.**	R-enamel	**15 min.**	**20 min.**
FRUIT JUICES Wash fruit, remove pits, if desired, and crush fruit. Heat to simmering. Strain through cloth bag. Add sugar, if desired — ½ to 1 c. to 1 gallon juice. Fill hot to top. Process in water bath with water gently boiling.	**20 min.**	**20 min.**	R-enamel	**20 min.**	**20 min.**
FRUIT PUREES Use sound, ripe fruit. Wash; remove pits, if desired. Cut large fruit in pieces. Simmer until soft, adding a little water if needed to keep fruit from sticking. Put through a strainer or food mill. Add sugar to taste. Heat again to simmering. Pack hot to ¼ inch of top.	**20 min.**	**20 min.**	R-enamel	**20 min.**	**20 min.**

TABLE A (*continued*)

PRODUCT *Preparation and Packing*	IN GLASS *Pints*	 *Quarts*	IN TIN *Type of Can*	 *No. 2*	 *No. $2\frac{1}{2}$*
PEACHES Wash peaches. Dip in boiling water, then quickly in cold water. Remove skins, cut peaches in halves, remove pits. Slice if desired. To prevent darkening during preparation, drop fruit into water containing 2 T. each of salt and vinegar per gallon. Drain just before heating or packing cold.					
Hot Pack. Heat peaches through in hot sirup. If fruit is very juicy you may heat it with sugar, adding no liquid. Pack hot fruit to ½ inch of top. Cover with boiling liquid.	20 min.	20 min.	Plain tin	25 min.	35 min.
Cold Pack. Prepare peaches as directed above. Pack raw fruit to ½ inch of top. Cover with boiling sirup.	25 min.	35 min.	Plain tin	25 min.	35 min.
PEARS Wash pears. Peel, cut in halves, and core.					
Hot Pack. Proceed as with peaches.	20 min.	20 min.	Plain tin	25 min.	35 min.
Cold Pack. Proceed as with peaches.	25 min.	35 min.	Plain tin	25 min.	35 min.
PLUMS Wash plums. To can whole, prick skins. Freestone varieties may be halved and pitted. Heat to boiling in sirup or juice. If fruit is very juicy you may heat it with sugar, adding no liquid. Pack hot fruit to ½ inch of top. Cover with boiling liquid.	15 min.	15 min.	R-enamel	15 min.	20 min.
RHUBARB Wash rhubarb and cut into ½-inch pieces. Add ½ c. sugar to each quart rhubarb and let stand to draw out juice. Bring to boiling. Pack hot to ½ inch of top.	10 min.	10 min.	R-enamel	10 min.	10 min.

TABLE A (*continued*)

PRODUCT *Preparation and Packing*	IN GLASS *Pints*	 *Quarts*	IN TIN *Type of Can*	 *No. 2*	 *No. 2½*
SAUERKRAUT Heat well-fermented sauerkraut to simmering. Do not boil. Pack hot kraut to ½ inch of top. Cover with hot juice.	**25 min.**	**30 min.**	R-enamel	**15 min.**	**20 min.**
STRAWBERRIES Wash and stem berries. Add ½ c. sugar to each quart of fruit. Bring slowly to a boil, shaking pan to keep fruit from sticking. Remove from stove and let stand overnight. Bring quickly to boil. Pack hot to ½ inch of top.	**15 min.**	**15 min.**	R-enamel	**10 min.**	**15 min.**
TOMATOES Use only perfect, ripe tomatoes. To loosen skins, dip into boiling water for about ½ minute; then dip quickly into cold water. Cut out stem ends and peel tomatoes.					
Hot Pack. Quarter peeled tomatoes. Bring to boil, stirring often. Pack hot to ½ inch of top. Add ½ t. salt to pints; 1 t. to quarts.	**10 min.**	**10 min.**			
Cold Pack. Leave tomatoes whole or cut in halves or quarters. Pack tomatoes to ½ inch of top, pressing gently to fill spaces. Add no water. Add ½ t. salt to pints; 1 t. to quarts.	**35 min.**	**45 min.**	Plain tin	**45 min.**	**55 min.**
TOMATO JUICE Use ripe, juicy tomatoes. Wash, remove stem ends, cut into pieces. Simmer until softened, stirring often. Put through strainer. Add 1 t. salt to each quart juice. Reheat at once just to boiling. Pack boiling hot juice to ¼ inch of top.	**15 min.**	**15 min.**	Plain tin	**15 min.**	**15 min.**

Canning Vegetables in a Pressure Canner

All non-acid vegetables should be canned under pressure. They may be canned either in glass jars or in tin. For specific processing instructions, see directions for each vegetable to be canned in Table B, pages 545 to 548. To describe in detail the pressure canning process, the canning of beans is given step by step as an illustration of how to can in glass, and the canning of corn is given as an illustration of how to can in tin.

If you live more than 2000 feet above sea level it takes more than 10 pounds pressure to reach 240° F. You need to increase pressure by 1 pound for each 2000 feet altitude. A weighted gauge may need to be corrected for altitude by the manufacturer.

Canning Beans: In Glass [1]

1. Select beans fresh from the garden — young, tender, firm, and crisp. Wash beans in several waters, until every trace of sand and grit is gone. Lift them out of the water each time, so dirt that has been washed off will not be drained back over them. Trim and cut beans. Prepare only enough for one canner load at a time. Cover beans with boiling water and boil 5 minutes. Meantime, heat clean jars with water.

2. Pack hot beans loosely to ½ inch of top. Cover with hot cooking liquid, leaving ½-inch space at top of jar. Add salt — 1 teaspoon to a quart; ½ teaspoon to a pint.

Remove air bubbles by working the blade of a table knife down the sides of the jar. Add more liquid if needed to fill jar to ½ inch of top.

3. Wipe jar rim clean, so no speck of food will keep the lid from making an airtight seal with the jar. Place clean, hot metal lid on jar so that sealing compound is next to the glass. Screw metal band on firmly.

4. Have 2 or 3 inches of boiling water in the pressure canner. Place filled jars in canner.

5. Fasten canner cover tight. Let steam escape for at least 10 minutes. Then close pet cock (or put the weight on the gauge). Let pressure rise to 10 pounds.

Process quarts of beans 25 minutes, pints 20, at sea level. Regulate heat to keep pressure steady. When time is up, slide canner from heat.

[1] *Home Canning of Fruits and Vegetables* — AIS–64. Courtesy of the Bureau of Human Nutrition and Home Economics.

6. When pressure falls to zero, wait a minute or two, no longer. Then slowly open pet cock, or take off weighted gauge. Unfasten cover. Tilt far side up, away from your face. Be careful not to disturb closures as you take jars from canner. Grasp the glass shoulder, not the metal band. This closure is a self-sealing type, so don't tighten it further. Let jars cool on rack or thick cloth, out of drafts. Next day take off screw bands, if you can without forcing. Covering for a moment with a hot, damp cloth may help loosen band.

FIG. 159. CANNING BEANS: IN GLASS

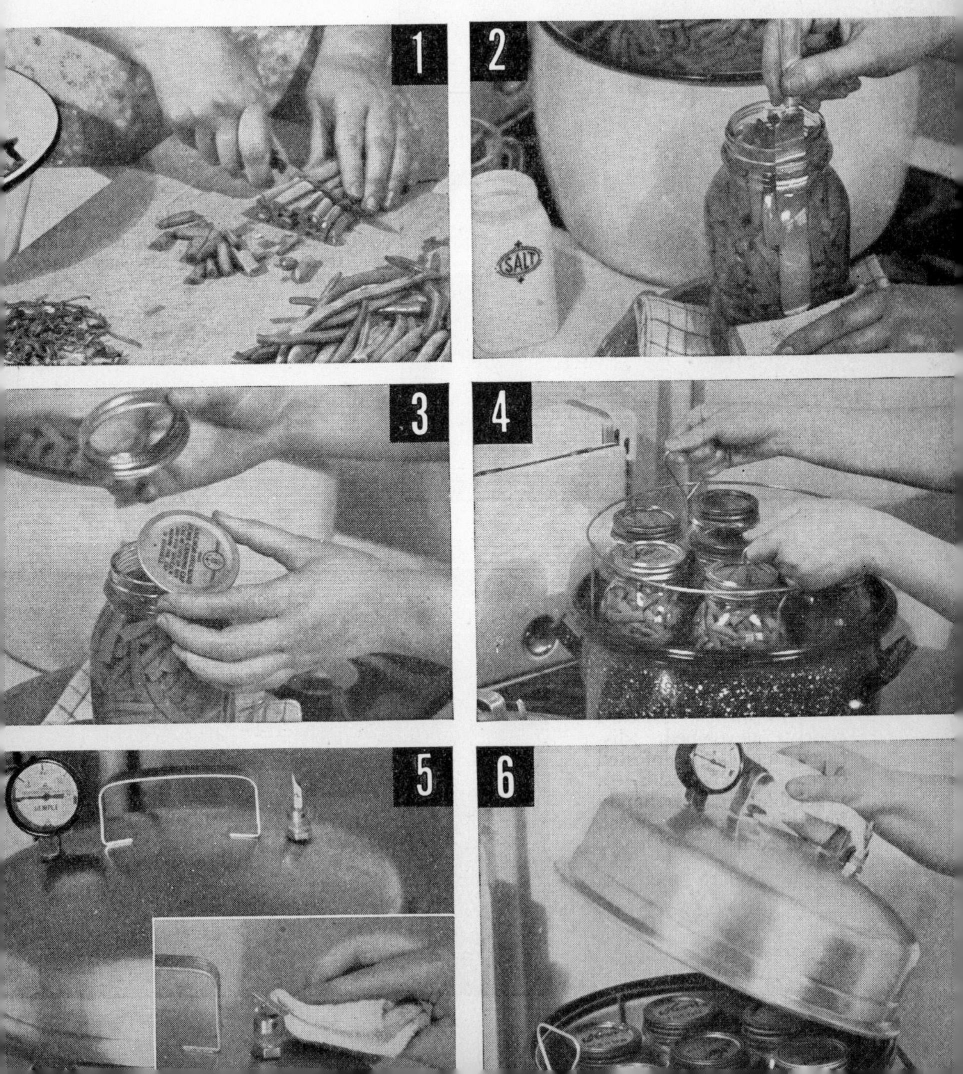

FIG. 160. CANNING CORN: IN TIN

Special kinds of cans must be used for some vegetables — see Tables A and B, pages 536 and 545. Use C-enamel tin can for corn. Check tin cans and lids, discarding all defective ones before starting to can. See that the sealer is in good working order. Be sure that the pressure gauge on the canner is correct. Have this checked before starting to can.

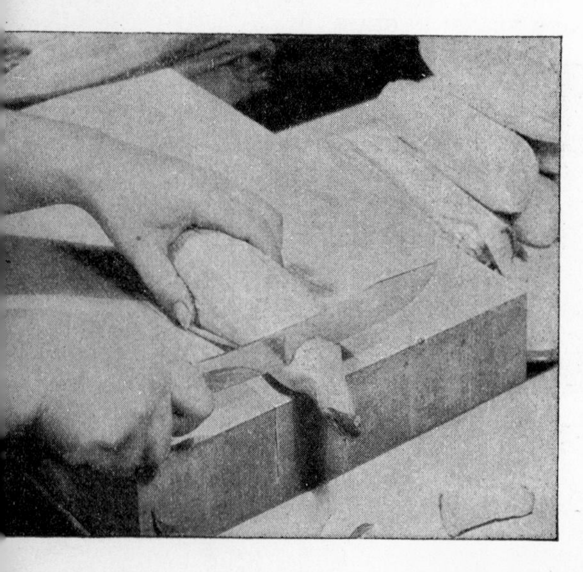

1. Choose corn at just the right stage for eating. Cut both ends from ears of corn for easy husking.

2. Remove husks. Discard poorly developed, diseased, and badly infested corn. Remove silk — a vegetable brush is handy for this purpose. Wash ears of corn.

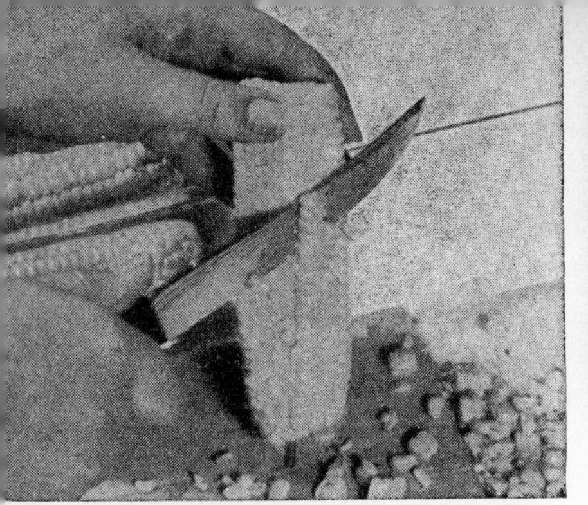

3. For whole-kernel corn, cut with a smooth stroke at about two-thirds the depth of kernels. Use a sharp knife. A nail through cutting board at an angle will hold the cob steady.

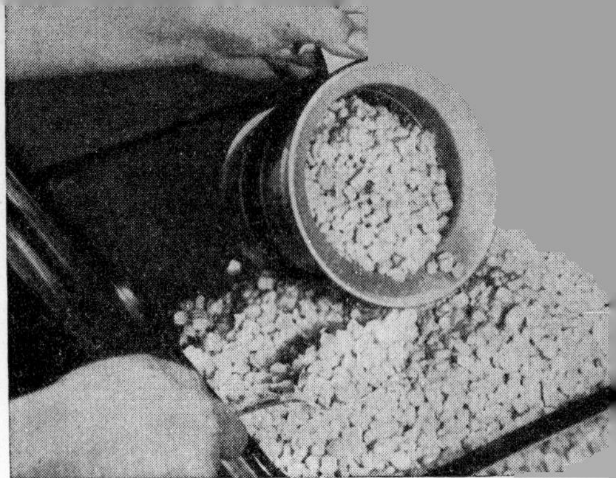

4. Measure corn into cooking pan. Cook 2 or 3 quarts at a time. Add one half as much boiling water as corn. Cover pan and let mixture come to a rolling boil.

5. Fill clean cans with hot corn, leaving ½-inch space at top. Add ½ t. salt to a No. 2 can; 1 t. to a No. 2½ can.

6. Fill cans to top with hot cooking liquid.

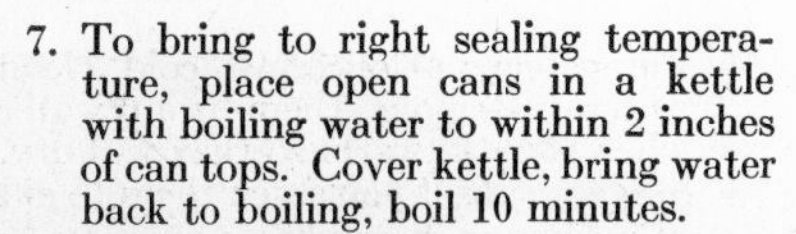

7. To bring to right sealing temperature, place open cans in a kettle with boiling water to within 2 inches of can tops. Cover kettle, bring water back to boiling, boil 10 minutes.

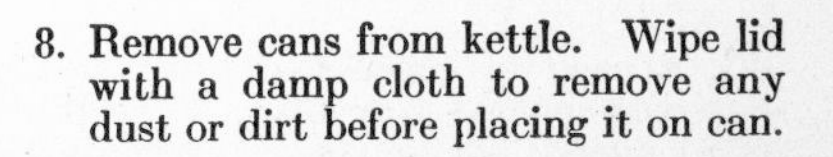

8. Remove cans from kettle. Wipe lid with a damp cloth to remove any dust or dirt before placing it on can.

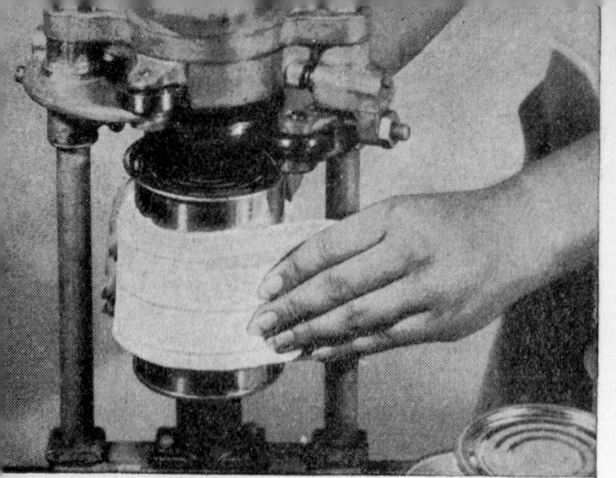

9. Seal cans at once. A folded towel protects the hands while cans are lifted to platform of sealer. While sealing one lot of filled cans, heat another lot.

10. Lower rack of sealed cans into pressure canner which has 2 or 3 inches of boiling water in the bottom. Stagger cans if a second layer is placed on the first.

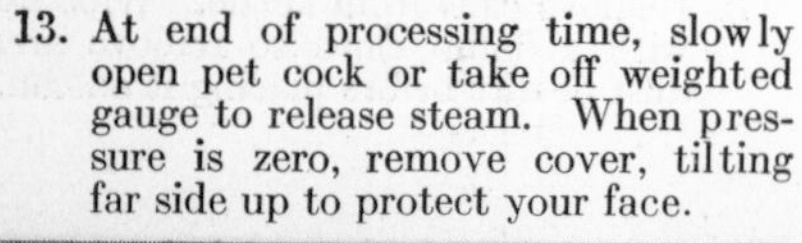

11. Fasten cover. Be certain pet cock is open or weighted gauge is left off. Use full heat. Let steam escape at least 10 minutes. Close pet cock or put on weighted gauge.

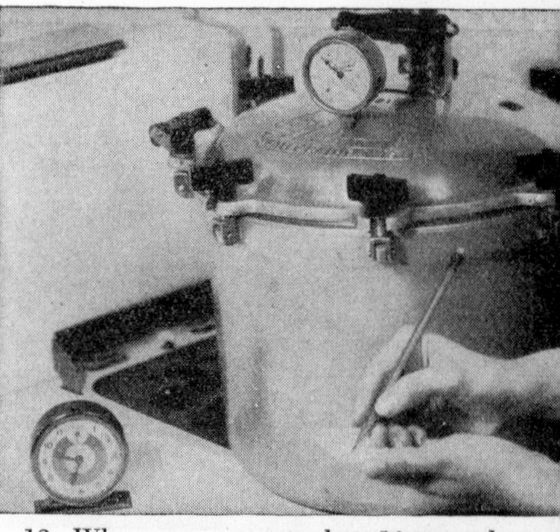

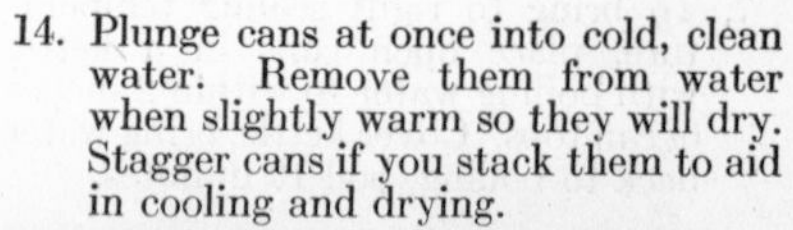

12. When pressure reaches 10 pounds, count time — 60 minutes for No. 2 and No. 2½ cans, at sea level. (For higher altitudes, see p. 545). Regulate heat to keep pressure even.

13. At end of processing time, slowly open pet cock or take off weighted gauge to release steam. When pressure is zero, remove cover, tilting far side up to protect your face.

14. Plunge cans at once into cold, clean water. Remove them from water when slightly warm so they will dry. Stagger cans if you stack them to aid in cooling and drying.

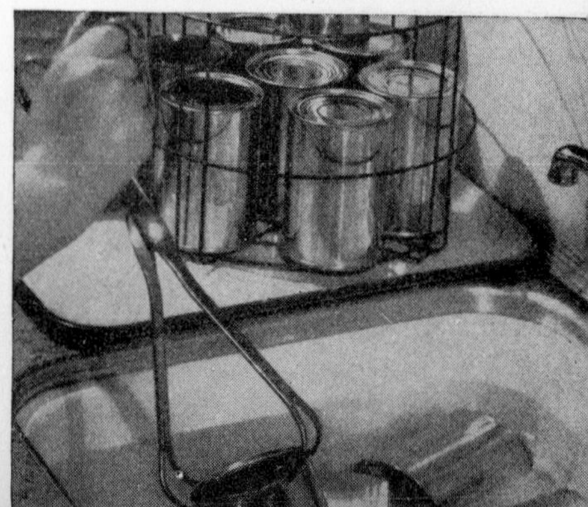

TABLE B

TIMETABLE FOR PROCESSING NON-ACID VEGETABLES IN THE STEAM PRESSURE CANNER (10 LB. OR 240° F.) [1]

(*See also Chapter 33*)

The processing times given here apply to places with altitudes of 2000 feet or less. At altitudes over 2000 feet, add one pound pressure for each additional 2000 feet. Cool tin cans in cold water immediately after processing. For directions for operating pressure canner, see Chapter 33.

PRODUCT	IN GLASS		IN TIN		
Preparation and Packing	*Pints*	*Quarts*	*Type of Can*	*No. 2*	*No. 2½*
ASPARAGUS Wash asparagus; trim off scales and tough ends and wash again. Cut into 1-inch pieces. Cover with boiling water. Boil 2 or 3 minutes. Pack hot and cover with hot cooking liquid, or if liquid contains grit use boiling water. Leave ½-inch space in glass; ¼-inch in tin. Add ½ t. salt per pint.	**25 min.**	**55 min.**	Plain tin	**20 min.**	**20 min.**
BEANS, FRESH LIMA Can only young, tender beans. Shell; wash. Cover beans with boiling water and bring to boil. Pack hot and cover with boiling water. Leave 1-inch space in glass; ½-inch in tin. Add ½ t. salt per pint.	**35 min.**	**60 min.**	C-enamel	**40 min.**	**40 min.**
BEANS, SNAP Wash beans. Trim ends; cut into 1-inch pieces. Cover with boiling water; boil 5 minutes. Pack hot and cover with hot cooking liquid. Leave ½-inch space in glass; ¼-inch in tin. Add ½ t. salt per pint.	**20 min.**	**25 min.**	Plain tin	**25 min.**	**30 min.**

[1] *Home Canning of Fruits and Vegetables* — AWI–93 and AIS–64. Courtesy of the Bureau of Human Nutrition and Home Economics.

TABLE B (*continued*)

PRODUCT *Preparation and Packing*	IN GLASS *Pints*	*Quarts*	IN TIN *Type of Can*	*No. 2*	*No. 2½*
BEETS Sort for size. Cut off beet tops, leaving an inch of stem. Also leave root. Wash beets. Cover with boiling water and boil until skins slip easily — 15 to 25 minutes, depending on size. Skin and trim. Leave baby beets whole. Cut medium or large beets in ½-inch slices; halve or quarter very large slices. Pack hot and cover with boiling water. Leave ½-inch space in glass; ¼-inch in tin. Add ½ t. salt per pint.	**25 min.**	**55 min.**	R-enamel	**30 min.**	**30 min.**
CARROTS Wash and scrape carrots. Slice or dice. Cover with boiling water and bring to boil. Pack hot and cover with hot cooking liquid. Leave ½-inch space in glass; ½-inch in tin. Add ½ t. salt per pint.	**20 min.**	**25 min.**	C-enamel	**20 min.**	**25 min.**
CORN, CREAM-STYLE Husk corn and remove silk. Wash. Cut corn from cob at about center of kernel and scrape cobs. To each quart of corn add 1 pint boiling water. Heat to boiling. Pack hot, using pint jars or No. 2 cans only. Leave 1-inch space in glass; ½-inch in tin. Add ½ t. salt per pint.	**85 min.**		C-enamel	**105 min.**	
CORN, WHOLE-KERNEL Husk corn and remove silk. Wash. Cut from cob at about two-thirds the depth of kernel. To each quart of corn add 1 pint boiling water. Heat to boiling. Pack hot and cover with hot cooking liquid. Leave 1-inch space in glass; ½-inch in tin.	**55 min.**	**85 min.**	C-enamel	**60 min.**	**60 min.**

TABLE B (*continued*)

PRODUCT	IN GLASS		IN TIN		
Preparation and Packing	*Pints*	*Quarts*	*Type of Can*	*No. 2*	*No. 2½*
OKRA Can only tender pods. Wash; trim. Cook for 1 minute in boiling water. Cut into 1-inch lengths or leave pods whole. Pack hot and cover with boiling water. Leave ½-inch space in glass; ¼-inch in tin. Add ½ t. salt per pint.	**25 min.**	**40 min.**	Plain tin	**25 min.**	**35 min.**
PEAS, GREEN Shell and wash peas. Cover with boiling water. Bring to boil. Pack hot and cover with boiling water. Leave 1-inch space in glass; ¼-inch in tin. Add ½ t. salt per pint.	**40 min.**	**40 min.**	Plain tin	**30 min.**	**30 min.**
PUMPKIN, STRAINED Wash, remove seeds, and peel pumpkin. Cut into inch cubes. Steam until tender, about 25 minutes. Put through food mill or strainer. Simmer until heated through, stirring to keep from sticking to pan. Pack hot; add no liquid or salt. Leave ½-inch space in glass; ⅛-inch in tin.	**60 min.**	**80 min.**	R-enamel	**75 min.**	**90 min.**
SPINACH Can only freshly picked, tender spinach. Pick over and wash thoroughly. Cut out tough stems and midribs. Place about 2½ pounds of spinach in a cheesecloth bag and steam about 10 minutes or until well wilted. Pack hot and cover with boiling water. Leave ½-inch space in glass; ¼-inch in tin. Add ¼ t. salt per pint.	**45 min.**	**70 min.**	Plain tin	**60 min.**	**75 min.**

TABLE B *(continued)*

PRODUCT	IN GLASS		IN TIN		
Preparation and Packing	*Pints*	*Quarts*	*Type of Can*	*No. 2*	*No. 2½*
SQUASH, SUMMER Wash; do not peel. Trim ends. Cut squash into ½-inch slices; halve or quarter to make pieces of uniform size. Add just enough water to cover. Bring to boil. Pack hot and cover with hot cooking liquid. Leave ½-inch space in glass; ¼-inch in tin. Add ½ t. salt per pint.	30 min.	40 min.	R-enamel	20 min.	20 min.
SQUASH, WINTER Prepare, pack, and process like pumpkin.	60 min.	80 min.	R-enamel	75 min.	90 min.
SWEET POTATOES *Dry Pack.* Wash sweet potatoes. Sort for size. Boil or steam until partially soft (20 to 30 minutes). Cut in pieces if large. Pack hot sweet potatoes tightly, leaving 1-inch space in glass; ½-inch in tin. Add no salt or liquid.	65 min.	95 min.	R-enamel	80 min.	95 min.
Wet Pack. Wash sweet potatoes. Sort for size. Boil or steam just until skins slip easily. Skin and cut in pieces. Pack hot and cover with boiling water. Leave 1-inch space in glass; ¼-inch in tin. Add ½ t. salt per pint.	55 min.	90 min.	R-enamel	70 min.	90 min.

TABLE C

TIMETABLE FOR PROCESSING MEATS AND CHICKEN IN THE STEAM PRESSURE CANNER [1]

At altitudes over 2000 feet, add one pound of pressure for each additional 2000 feet. Cool tin cans in cold water.

250° F., OR 15 POUNDS PRESSURE

Product	*No. 2 Can*	*No. 2½ Can*	*Pint Glass Jar*	*Quart Glass Jar*
Beef:	*(Minutes)*	*(Min.)*	*(Min.)*	*(Min.)*
Fresh	85	110	85	120
Ground (hamburger)	90	115	90	120
Hash	90	115	90	120
Heart and tongue	85	110	85	120
Stew meat	85	110	85	120
Stew with vegetables	85	110	85	120
Corned	85	110	85	120
Chicken and other poultry:				
With bone	55	65	65	75
Boned	85	110	85	120
Giblets	85	....	85	....
Sandwich spread	No. 1, 55 No. 2, 90	....	½-pint, 65 Pint, 90	....
Liver paste	No. 1, 55 No. 2, 90		½-pint, 65 Pint, 90	....
Lamb and mutton	85	110	85	120
Liver paste	90	....	90	....
Pork:				
Fresh	85	110	85	120
Headcheese	90	....	90	....
Sausage	90	115	90	120
Rabbit, domestic	85	110	85	120
Soups:				
Broth, clear	25	30	25	30
Broth with rice or barley	35	40	35	40
Chicken gumbo	65	75	65	80
Soup stock	40	45	40	45
Veal	85	110	85	120

240° F., OR 10 POUNDS PRESSURE

Product	*No. 2 Can*	*No. 2½ Can*	*Pint Glass Jar*	*Quart Glass Jar*
Chili con carne	120	135	120	150
Pork and beans	70	80	80	90

[1] *Home Canning of Fruits, Vegetables, and Meats.* Farmers' Bulletin 1762, United States Department of Agriculture.

Jellies, Preserves, and Relishes

See Chapter 34

To Prepare Glasses for Jelly

Wash glasses; put in a kettle of cold water and heat water gradually to the boiling point. Boil 15 minutes. Remove and drain the glasses; place on a wet cloth to be filled.

Apple Jelly

Wash fruit and remove blossom and stem ends. Cut into quarters; nearly cover with water. Cook slowly until soft. Mash and strain through a wire strainer, then through a jelly bag. Return pulp to kettle, cover with water, heat to boiling point. Remove and heat over hot water 20 to 25 minutes. Strain juice as in making first extract. The pulp may be used for a third extraction, or may be used for making fruit butter (page 553).

Test juice for pectin (page 375). If a good test is obtained, measure ¾ cup of sugar for each cup of juice. Boil 3 or 4 cups of juice 3 to 5 minutes, add sugar, and boil until the mixture "sheets" from the side of the spoon (see page 375), or until the temperature reaches 222 to 224 degrees F. Fill prepared jelly glasses to within one-fourth inch of the top; cool. When cool, cover with melted paraffin and tin covers. Label and store in a cool, dark place.

Plum, Grape, or Currant Jelly

Wash fruit. Place in a pan set in hot water and heat until fruit is softened and juice comes out freely. Strain, as for apple jelly, and obtain a second extraction of juice, as for apple jelly.

For proportions of sugar and juice, see table, page 374. Fill glasses, cover, cool, label, and store as for apple jelly.

Cranberry Jelly

Proceed as for cranberry sauce (see page 391). Strain before adding sugar. Use equal quantities of sugar and juice.

Apple Pectin Extract

4 lb. apples　　4½ pt. water for first extraction

Select tart, sound apples, just under ripe. Scrub clean and remove stems, blossom ends, and all spots, but do not peel or core.

Slice apples thin; cover slices with water and let boil rapidly in covered enamel saucepan for 20 minutes. Strain through four thicknesses of cheesecloth without squeezing.

Remove pulp and add an equal quantity of water for a second extraction. Boil 20 minutes and strain. Add to the first extraction. The total quantity should be about 3 quarts.

Boil this extract until it is reduced to one fourth of its original volume or about 1½ pints. If pectin extract of unusual strength is desired, reduce to 1 pint.

Cherry Jelly with Added Pectin and Acid [1]

1 c. cherry juice
1 to 1¼ c. sugar
4 T. apple or lemon pectin extract, or 6 T. orange pectin extract

To prepare juice, thoroughly wash cherries and put in saucepan, adding one-fourth cup of water for each pound of fruit. Heat to boiling, and boil 10 minutes. Strain through colander and then strain the juice through jelly bag. Mix the juice with the remaining ingredients in the proportions indicated and cook until the jelly test is tried with success.

Raspberry, grape, or loganberry juice may be used.

Mint Orange Jelly

1½ c. water
1½ c. orange pectin juice
2 c. (1 lb.) sugar
2 drops of oil of peppermint
Green coloring

Heat pectin juice and water to boiling, add sugar and boil until jelly test succeeds. Add green coloring and oil of peppermint. Fill glasses and proceed as with apple jelly.

Grapefruit and Orange Marmalade

1 grapefruit
1 orange
1 lemon
Sugar

Cut each fruit into quarters and slice the quarters very thin through pulp and rind, discarding all the seeds. Weigh the prepared fruit, and to each pound add three pints of cold water. Set aside for 24 hours.

The second day let the fruit boil gently for about 2 hours or until the rind is perfectly tender; set it aside until the next day.

[1] For recipe for pectin extract from citrus fruit and for recipes for the use of both apple and citrus pectin see *Homemade Jellies, Jams, and Preserves*, United States Department of Agriculture, Farmers' Bulletin 1800.

Weigh the material, and to each pound add one pound of sugar. Cook, with occasional stirring to avoid burning, to a temperature of 222° to 224° F. Store in glasses according to directions for apple jelly. Cool slightly before filling glasses to prevent the fruit rising to top.

Short Method. Chop fruit and measure. Add water in proportion of 3 parts of water to 1 of fruit. Boil 15 minutes and let stand overnight. Next morning boil for 15 minutes or until the peel is tender, and let stand again for several hours. When cold, measure and add sugar in the proportion of a pint for each pint of fruit. Cook over a rapid fire until jelly stage is reached (222° F.).

Preserved Peaches, Apricots, Pears, or Crab Apples

Prepare fruit for preserving. Small pears and apricots may be peeled but left whole. Crab apples may be peeled or not, as desired. Peaches and large pears should be peeled, cut in halves, and the stones or cores removed.

For each pound of prepared fruit use 1½ c. sugar and ¾ c. water.

Make a sirup of half the sugar and all the water. When this boils drop into it the prepared fruit. Cook fruit in this thin sirup to make the preserves tender, plump, and light in color. When half cooked, remove from the stove, pour off most of the sirup, add the remaining sugar, and bring to a boil. Return the fruit to this thick sirup and finish cooking. Finishing the cooking in a heavier sirup will help the fruit to hold its shape (see page 377).

Fig Preserves

6 qt. sound, firm figs	2 qt. cold water
1 c. soda	2 lb. sugar
1 gal. boiling water	

Make a sirup of cold water and sugar, using a little brown sugar if desired, and bring sirup to a boil. Sprinkle soda over figs, add boiling water, and let stand 5 minutes. Drain and rinse figs well. Peel if desired. Add to sirup and boil one hour. Remove fruit, pack in hot containers, fill with boiling sirup and process immediately for 5 minutes in boiling water or for 10 minutes in the oven at 250° F.

Small recipe: 1 qt. figs, 2½ T. soda, 1½ c. cold water, ⅔ c. sugar, 2⅔ c. boiling water.

Jam

General Proportions: 1 lb. prepared fruit to ¾ lb. sugar (1½ c.). Make any desired combination of fruit. Wash fruit and put in a kettle, adding just enough water barely to cover the bottom of the pan. Heat slowly, to avoid burning, for about 15 minutes. Add sugar and cook about 1½ hours, or until thick. Pour into jars or jelly glasses according to directions for apple jelly.

Apple: Use ¾ lb. apples and ¼ lb. some other desired fruit, such as peaches, apricots, raisins.

Peach or Apricot: Combine in equal quantities with shredded pineapple, or use peach or apricot alone, adding 1 sliced lemon to each pound.

Raspberry and Strawberry: Add ½ sliced lemon or orange to each pound of fruit.

Fruit Butter

2 lb. fruit pulp
3 T. vinegar or fruit jelly
½ lb. (1 c.) sugar
1 t. cinnamon (if desired)
2 T. lemon juice
3 T. grated lemon rind
¼ t. cloves (if desired)
Few grains ginger (if desired)

Use fruit pulp left from jelly-making or fresh-fruit sauce. Cook with the other ingredients until smooth and thick. Fill jelly glasses according to directions for apple jelly.

Grape Conserve

10 lb. grapes
1 lb. seeded raisins
8 c. (4 lb.) sugar
2 c. (½ lb.) walnut meats

Pick over, stem, wash, and drain the grapes. Separate the pulp from the skins (use Concord type grapes). Cook pulp slowly until the seeds separate from the pulp. Rub through a colander or sieve. Combine this pulp with the skins, add raisins and sugar, and cook 20 minutes, or until thick. Add broken nut meats 2 or 3 minutes before removing the conserve from the fire. Store in jelly glasses according to directions for apple jelly.

Small recipe: 1⅛ lb. grapes, ⅛ lb. raisins, ½ lb. sugar, ¼ c. nuts.

Prune or Apricot Conserve

1 lb. dried prunes or apricots
1½ qt. (6 c.) water
2 cans pineapple, cut fine
1 c. seeded raisins
½ c. cranberries
Juice and rind of 2 lemons
2 c. walnut meats (if desired)

Wash dried fruit and soak overnight; cook in the same water until soft. Remove stones from dried fruit. Mash to a pulp and add other fruit. Weigh fruit and add half its weight in sugar. Add 1 c. water and cook until thick and jelly-like (about 10 to 20 minutes). Store in jelly glasses according to directions for apple jelly, leaving one-fourth-inch at the top of each glass for paraffin.

Small recipe: ¼ lb. dried prunes or apricots, 1½ c. water, ½ c. shredded pineapple, ¼ c. seeded raisins, 2 T. cranberries, juice and rind of ½ lemon, ½ c. walnut meats (if desired).

Chili Sauce

4 lb. ripe tomatoes (peeled)	2 c. mild vinegar
1 pepper, finely chopped	4 T. sugar (1 T. brown if desired)
1 onion, finely chopped	1 T. salt
1 T. ground cinnamon	2 t. ground cloves

2 t. ground allspice

Cook together to the desired thickness. Store in glass jars.

Sweet Pickled Peaches, Pears, or Crab Apples

8 lb. fruit	1 qt. white vinegar
3½ lb. light brown sugar	1 oz. whole cloves

1 oz. stick cinnamon

Make a sirup of the brown sugar and vinegar, put in it spices tied in cheesecloth.

Method 1. Cook fruit in sirup until tender and clear. Remove it from sirup; boil down sirup and pour over fruit in jars.

Method 2. Heat fruit in sirup to boiling point. Let stand overnight. Then heat until fruit is tender and clear. Remove fruit; boil down sirup and pour over fruit in glass jars. This method gives a plump and well-flavored fruit.

Small recipe: 1 lb. fruit, ½ lb. light brown sugar, ½ c. white vinegar, 8 cloves, 1 two-inch stick cinnamon.

Spiced or Pickled Cherries

1. Seed the cherries. Weigh. Cover with spiced vinegar and let stand 12 hours. Drain well. Cover with sugar pound for pound. Stir each morning. Leave for 10 days or until all the sugar is dissolved. Pack in jars and seal. Do not process.

2. Select large firm cherries, either red or black, leaving the stems on. Wash, dry, prick with needle and pack in jars with

stems up. Make a sirup, using for each quart of fruit 1 cup of spiced vinegar and ⅔ cup sugar, boiled together for 5 minutes.

Cool the sirup about 5 minutes, pour over the fruit, and let stand 2 or 3 hours. Then process 15 minutes below boiling (188° F. simmering).

Spiced Vinegar

½ ounce mixed pickle spice (about 3 T.) 1 gallon vinegar

Enclose spice in cheesecloth bag, drop into the vinegar and heat to nearly boiling for not more than one-half hour. Then remove the spice bag.

Spiced vinegar may be used in making both cooked and uncooked pickles.

Freezing Foods

See Chapter 34

Vegetables

On page 558 you will find a table telling how to prepare the vegetables that are most commonly frozen. Other vegetables such as beets, Brussels sprouts, cabbage, carrots, mushrooms, okra, and sweet potatoes have been frozen successfully and directions have been developed by some of the state agricultural experiment stations.

Whole tomatoes, lettuce, celery, cucumbers, and onions have not been frozen satisfactorily.

When you pack your vegetables, leave head space as follows:

In carton or bag —

When packed without liquid, leave ½ inch head space for vegetables that pack tightly, such as peas and corn. No head space is needed for vegetables that pack loosely, such as broccoli and cauliflower.

For vegetables packed with brine or for vegetable purees, leave 1 inch head space.

In glass jars or tin cans, leave 1½ inches head space.

FIG. 161. FREEZING PEAS

1. Shell freshly picked, sweet, tender peas. Sort out immature and tough ones, unsuitable for freezing.

2. Wash peas and pour into wire basket to drain.

3. Dip about 1 pound of peas into rapidly boiling water for about 1 minute. Note wire lid that holds peas under water. Cover kettle and begin to count time.

4. Chill scalded peas at once in iced water or running cold water until a broken pea feels cold to tongue. Drain.

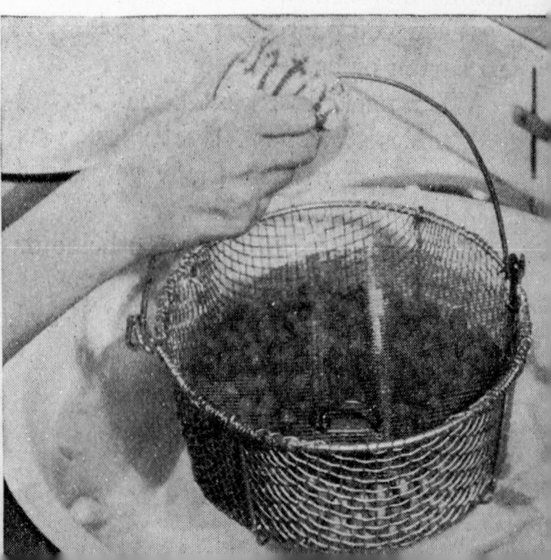

5. Pour peas into freezing package, leaving ½-inch head space at top. Wipe moisture from inside edges of bag. Press out air.

6. Heat-seal bag, using a warm iron or a curling iron. A wooden box or platform is convenient for this job.

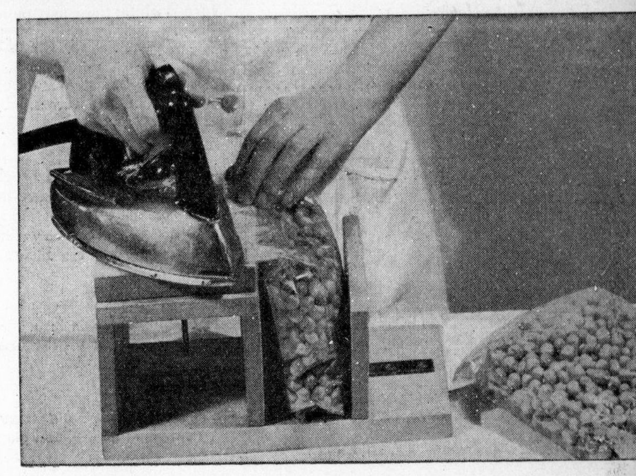

7. Put filled containers in freezing compartment. When frozen, store at 0° F. or lower.

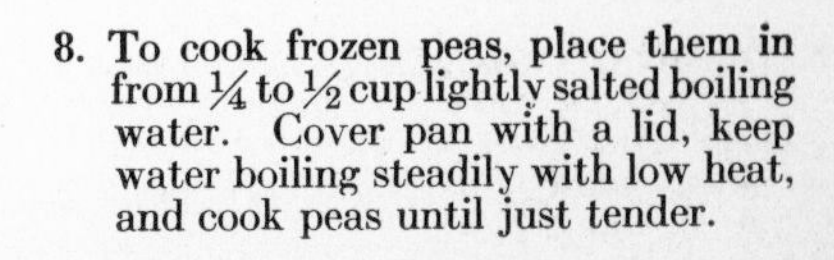

8. To cook frozen peas, place them in from ¼ to ½ cup lightly salted boiling water. Cover pan with a lid, keep water boiling steadily with low heat, and cook peas until just tender.

TABLE D

HOW TO PREPARE VEGETABLES FOR FREEZING [1]

Vegetable	*How to Prepare*	*Time to Scald* [2]
Asparagus	Wash well and cut into desired lengths. Sort into 3 groups, according to thickness of stalk. Scald, chill, and pack.	2 to 4 minutes in boiling water, according to size of stalk.
Beans, Lima	Shell, wash, and sort according to size. Scald and chill. Then sort out any beans that have turned white; these may be cooked or canned. Pack.	2 to 3 minutes in boiling water, according to size.
Beans, snap	Wash well, cut off stem and tips. Leave whole, slice, or cut into pieces. Scald, chill, and pack.	2 to 3 minutes in boiling water.
Broccoli	Cut off large leaves and tough stalks. Wash well and soak, heads down in salted water (4 teaspoons salt to 1 gallon cold water), for about ½ hour. Split lengthwise so heads are not more than 1½ inches across. Scald, chill, and pack.	5 minutes in steam, or 4 minutes in boiling water.
Cauliflower	Select white, compact heads. Break flowerlets into pieces about 1 inch across. Wash, scald, chill, and pack.	3 minutes in boiling water.
Corn, on cob	Husk, remove silk and trim off bad spots. Wash. Scald, chill, and pack.	7 minutes in boiling water for slender ears; 9 minutes for medium; 11 minutes for large, thick ears.
Corn, whole-grain	Husk, remove silk, and trim off bad spots. Wash and sort according to thickness of ear. Scald, then chill. Cut kernels off cob. Pack.	5 to 7 minutes in boiling water.
Greens	Wash well, remove imperfect leaves and large, tough stems. Scald, chill, and pack.	1 to 2 minutes in boiling water.
Peas	Shell, sort out immature and tough peas, wash, scald, chill, and pack.	1 minute in boiling water.
Peppers, green, and pimiento	Wash. Remove seeds and slice or cut as desired. Scald and chill. Pack in brine of 1 teaspoon salt to 1 cup cold water.	2 minutes in boiling water.
Soybeans	Boil in pods for 5 minutes. Chill. Squeeze beans out of pods. Wash, drain, and pack.	No additional scalding required.

[1] *Home Freezing of Fruits and Vegetables* — AIS–48. Courtesy of the Bureau of Human Nutrition and Home Economics.

[2] If you live 5000 or more feet above sea level, scald the vegetables 1 minute longer.

1. Carefully sort and cap strawberries. Do not use green, crushed, or overripe berries. Wash berries a few at a time and lift them into a colander to drain.

2. Mix whole or sliced berries with sugar, using 1 cup sugar with 5 to 8 cups of berries. Turn over and over until all sugar is dissolved.

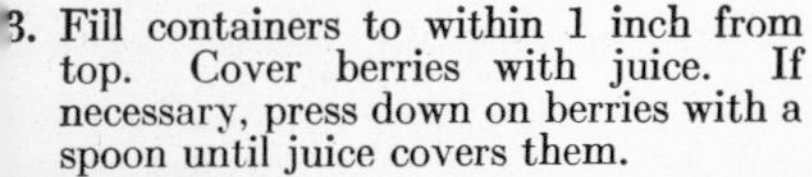

3. Fill containers to within 1 inch from top. Cover berries with juice. If necessary, press down on berries with a spoon until juice covers them.

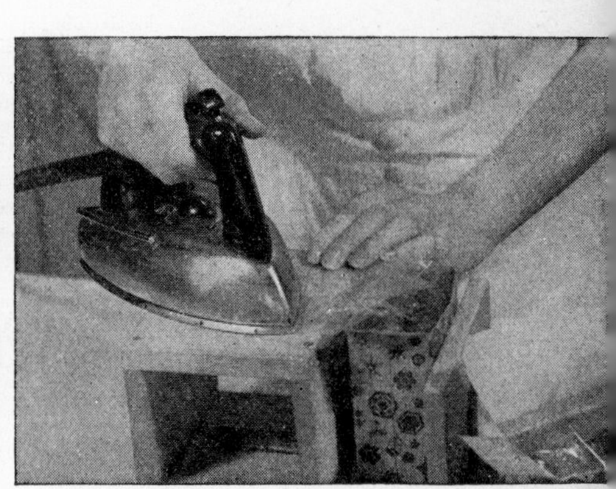

4. Wipe the inside edges of liner clean and dry. Press out air, and seal edges together with a warm iron. Label.

FIG. 162. FREEZING STRAWBERRIES

FRUITS

Special directions for preparing fruits for freezing are given in the table on pages 560 and 561. When packing fruit, leave head space as follows:

In carton or bag, leave ½ inch head space if packed without liquid. Leave 1 inch head space if packed with sirup, or for purees or crushed fruits.

In glass jars or tin cans leave 1½ inches head space.

When packing fruit in dry sugar, be sure to mix thoroughly until all sugar is dissolved and sufficient sirup is formed to cover the fruit when packed. If necessary, press fruit down in package until sirup covers the fruit.

TABLE E

FREEZING FRUITS — PREPARATION AND PACKAGING [1]

Fruit	*How to Prepare*	*How to Pack*
Apples	Peel, core, and cut into sections of uniform thickness (about 12 sections for medium-sized, more for larger apples to insure sufficient scalding). Scald apples in steam or boiling water 1½ to 2 minutes to prevent darkening. Or if sirup is used for packing you can slice apples directly into it.	Pack in 1 part by weight of sugar to 3 or 4 parts by weight of fruit (1 cup sugar to 5 cups fruit); or in sirup to cover (3 to 4 cups sugar to 4 cups water).
Apricots	Sort for ripeness. Wash, halve, pit, and cut in sections. To keep from darkening, dip for 1 to 2 minutes in a solution of ¼ teaspoon citric acid dissolved in 1 quart water or use ascorbic acid (see *How to Pack*).	*With citric acid.* Pack in 1 part by weight of sugar to 3 or 4 parts by weight of fruit (1 cup sugar to 4½ to 6 cups fruit); or in sirup to cover (3 to 4 cups sugar to 4 cups water). *With ascorbic acid.* Put apricots directly into sugar sirup to which has been added ¼ teaspoon ascorbic acid to each 1 to 1½ cups sirup.
Berries (except blueberries and strawberries)	Pick over, wash, drain well. Do not wash raspberries unless necessary.	Pack without sugar; or pack in 1 part by weight of sugar to 4 parts by weight of fruit (1 cup sugar to 6 cups fruit); or in sirup to cover (3 cups sugar to 4 cups water).
Blueberries	Pick over, wash, drain well.	Pack in 1 part by weight of sugar to 4 parts by weight of fruit (1 cup sugar to 6 cups fruit); or in sirup to cover (3 cups sugar to 4 cups water); or pack without sugar.
Cherries, sour	Wash, drain, and pit.	Pack in 1 part by weight of sugar to 3 or 4 parts by weight of fruit (1 cup sugar to 4 to 5 cups fruit).
Cherries, sweet	Wash and drain. Pit or not, as desired.	*Pitted cherries.* Pack in 1 part by weight of sugar to 4 parts by weight of fruit (1 cup sugar to 5 cups fruit). *Whole cherries.* Pack in sirup to cover (3 cups sugar to 4 cups water with ¼ teaspoon ascorbic acid added to each 1 to 1½ cups sirup).

[1] *Home Freezing of Fruits and Vegetables* — AIS–48. Courtesy of the Bureau of Human Nutrition and Home Economics.

TABLE E (*continued*)

FREEZING FRUITS — PREPARATION AND PACKAGING

Fruit	*How to Prepare*	*How to Pack*
Cranberries.........	Pick over and wash.	Pack without sugar; or pack in 1 part by weight of sugar to 3 or 4 parts by weight of berries; (1 cup sugar to 6 to 8 cups berries); or pack in sirup to cover (4 cups sugar to 4 cups water).
Figs...............	Sort, wash, remove stems. Leave whole, halve, or slice.	Pack without sugar; or pack in 1 part by weight of sugar to 4 parts by weight of fruit (1 cup sugar to 6 cups fruit); or pack in sirup to cover (3 cups sugar to 4 cups water).
Peaches (free stone) and nectarines....	Sort, pit, peel (skins may be loosened by scalding whole peaches 15 to 30 seconds in boiling water). Cut in sections. To keep from darkening, dip sections for 1 to 2 minutes in a solution of ¼ teaspoon citric acid dissolved in 1 quart water or use ascorbic acid (see *How to Pack*).	*With citric acid.* Pack in 1 part by weight of sugar to 3 or 4 parts by weight of fruit (1 cup sugar to 4½ to 6 cups fruit); or in sirup to cover (3 cups sugar to 4 cups water). *With ascorbic acid.* Put peaches directly into sugar sirup to which has been added ¼ teaspoon ascorbic acid for each 1 to 1½ cups sirup.
Plums and prunes...	Sort, wash, halve, and pit.	Pack in 1 part by weight of sugar to 3 to 5 parts by weight of fruit (1 cup sugar to 4½ to 10 cups fruit); or in sirup to cover (3 to 5 cups sugar to 4 cups water, with ¼ teaspoon ascorbic acid added to each 1 to 1½ cups sirup).
Rhubarb..........	Wash, trim, and cut stalks into 1-inch pieces.	Pack without sugar; or pack in 1 part by weight of sugar to 4 or 5 parts by weight of rhubarb (1 cup sugar to 5 to 6 cups fruit); or in sirup to cover (3 cups sugar to 4 cups water).
Strawberries.......	Cap and sort, wash, and drain well. Leave berries whole, or slice.	Pack in 1 part by weight of sugar to 3 or 4 parts by weight of fruit (1 cup sugar to 5 to 8 cups fruit). Pack tightly so juice covers berries.

Meats

The first step in preparing meat for freezing is to determine the size of the cuts your family will use, and then have the meat cut to that size. It is a long, hard job to cut frozen meat, and smaller pieces are more easily wrapped and stored than larger pieces.

Beef cuts are used here to illustrate the steps in preparing fresh meat for freezing, but the same principles apply to pork, veal, lamb, and some game. These are general instructions.[1] Be sure to maintain sanitary conditions. If you are inexperienced in handling meat, let your butcher or locker plant operator prepare your meat for you.

Wrap all meat cuts firmly in moisture- and vapor-resistant freezer paper. Avoid air pockets which lead to dehydration. Fold ends at least once and seal tightly to make airtight. Special wrapping material is essential. Do not use ordinary wax paper. To assist you in locating meats in your freezer, label all packages clearly, giving kind and cut of meat, number of pieces in each package, and weight. The date frozen should also be given so that oldest packages may be used first for proper turnover.

Special directions for steaks and chops: Cut into the thickness preferred. Wrap together only the number required for one meal. Place cellophane sheets between pieces so they will not freeze together. Keep pieces flat while wrapping and freezing. This will conserve space. (See Figure 163, No. 1.)

Special directions for hamburger: Grind first. Form into patties. Pack, with cellophane squares separating patties. Seal tightly in freezer wrapping paper or pack in cartons. Remove patties as needed. (See Figure 163, No. 2.)

[1] Courtesy of Sears Roebuck and Company.

Fig. 163. FREEZING MEATS

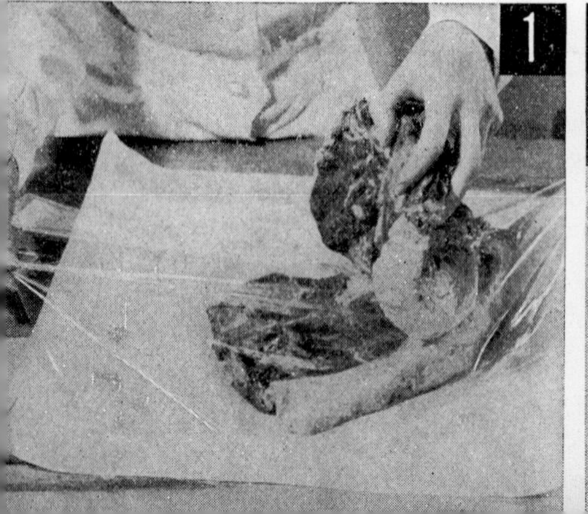

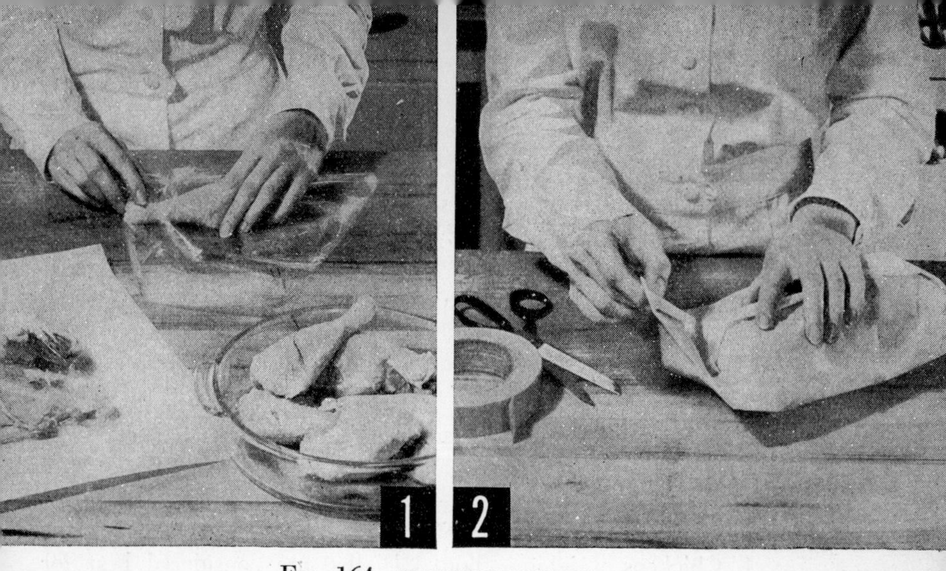

FIG. 164. FREEZING FRYERS

POULTRY [1]

Poultry may be frozen in several ways. Chickens, ducks, and turkeys of high quality, well fattened, give excellent results when frozen if properly prepared. Poultry may be stored for as long as one year. When dressing, you will save time by preparing several at one time. Starve the birds for 24 hours. This empties the crop. All poultry should be thoroughly cleaned and drawn, and chilled for 12 to 18 hours before freezing. Prompt cleaning and chilling prevents bacterial action.

Preparing Fryers for Freezing

1. Disjoint fryers. Wrap each piece, also the giblets, separately in cellophane paper to prevent freezing together. Chickens weighing up to 3½ lbs. are suitable for frying. Prepare and package, in this same manner, chickens for fricassee and stews for later ease of handling.

2. Wrap all pieces together in a generous piece of freezer paper, folding ends at least once and sealing tightly. If preferred, freeze only the choice pieces, using the others at once. Wrap no more than two chickens together. Label with weight and date. This assures proper turnover.

[1] Courtesy of Sears Roebuck and Company.

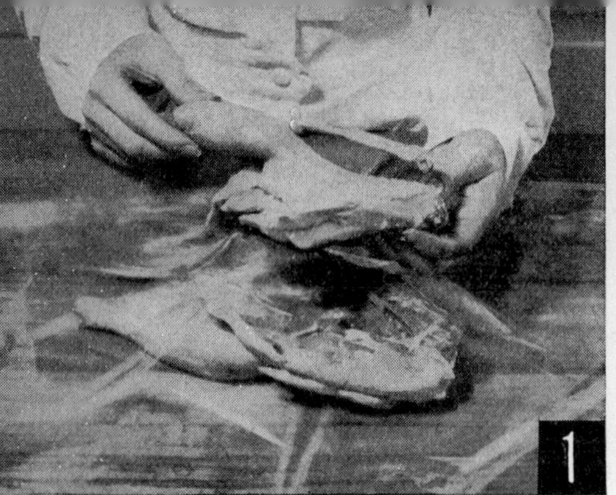

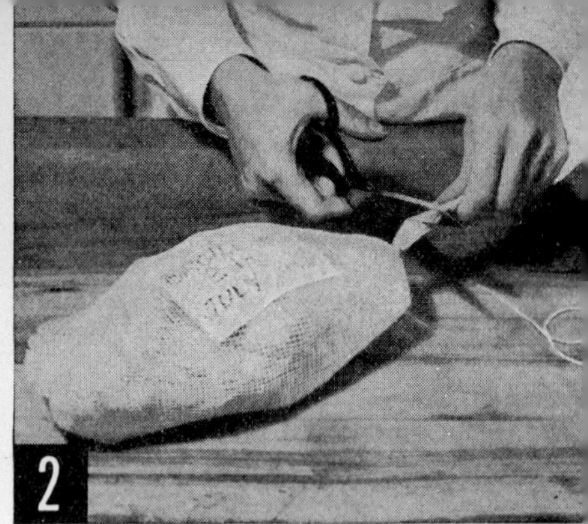

Fig. 165. FREEZING BROILERS

Preparing Broilers for Freezing

1. Chickens weighing about 2½ lbs. are considered best for broiling. Split them in half, lengthwise. If desired, you may cut them into quarters. Separate each piece from the others by a sheet of cellophane. This prevents freezing together.

2. Wrap pieces together in cellophane. Fold edges and ends and seal tightly. Draw on stockinette tightly, insert label, tie securely, and freeze at once.

Preparing Roasters for Freezing

1. Chickens weighing 3½ to 5 lbs. and averaging 24 to 28 weeks of age are suitable for roasting. Capons are generally superior for freezing. These may weigh from 6 to 9 lbs. Prepare for roasting. Wrap giblets in cellophane and place in cavity.

2. Draw legs tightly against body and tie. Wrap in cellophane, using confectioner's fold. Fold ends once or twice; seal tightly. Insert in stockinette, insert label, and tie ends. Cellophane-lined parchment bags also make fine poultry packages.

Fig. 166. FREEZING ROASTERS

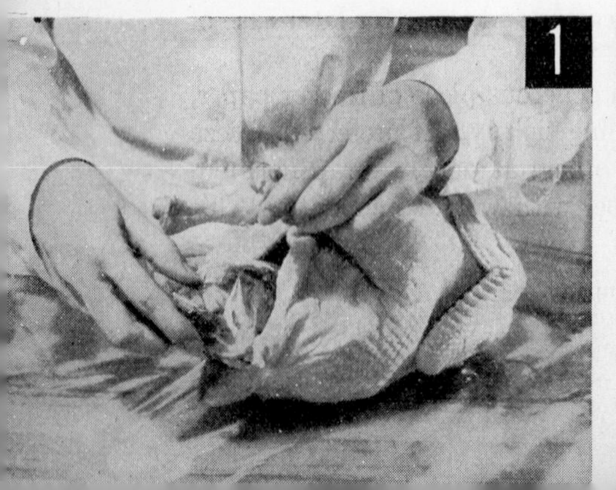

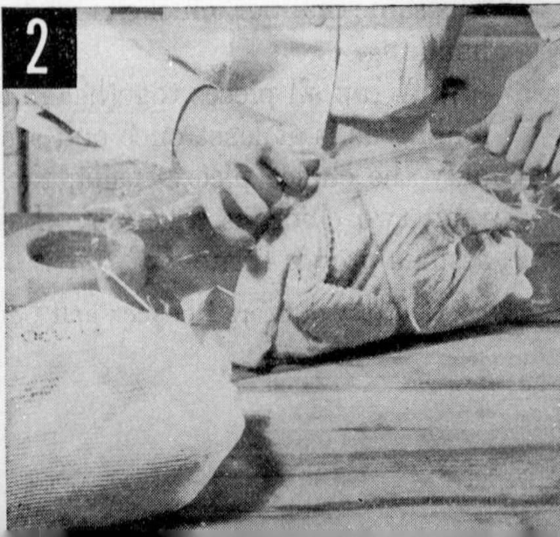

Cooking Frozen Foods

Vegetables

Vegetables will retain color and flavor better if cooked without thawing. However, the vegetables may need partial thawing so they can be broken up in small pieces in order to insure even cooking. Corn on the cob is an exception. It must be completely thawed. Also, such vegetables as greens, asparagus, and broccoli, cook more evenly if thawed just enough to separate the leaves or stalks. Vegetables packed in brine should be thawed before cooking — use part of the brine for cooking instead of water.

Frozen vegetables cook more quickly than fresh vegetables because they are already partially cooked when blanched or scalded.

Use only a little water and cook vegetables quickly until *just tender* — ¼ to ½ cup of water is enough for 4 or 5 servings. The amount of water will vary with the cooking time required.

Never refreeze thawed vegetables. Cook only enough vegetables for one meal at a time.

In cooking, bring lightly salted water to a boil, add the frozen vegetable, use a tightly covered pan so the steam will be retained, and cook the vegetable. The pressure cooker is good for cooking frozen vegetables, but no pressure is needed. Leave vent hole open.

Cook only until tender — overcooking destroys flavor, texture, and vitamins.

Approximate Cooking Times for Frozen Vegetables [1]

Cooking times for frozen vegetables will vary with the variety and maturity of the vegetable. You can use the times given below as a guide for cooking vegetables of your own pack. Be sure to bring the vegetables back to boiling before you start counting time.

	MINUTES		MINUTES		MINUTES
Asparagus	7	Cauliflower	5	Peas	7
Beans, Lima	7–15	Corn, cut	5	Soybeans	10–15
Beans, snap	12–15	Corn, on cob	5	Spinach	5
Broccoli	7				

[1] *Home Freezing of Fruits and Vegetables* — AIS–48. Courtesy of the Bureau of Human Nutrition and Home Economics.

Fruits

Thawed frozen fruits are good desserts with no further preparation. Thaw only what is to be served at one time because frozen fruits very quickly lose their freshness when thawed. Serve frozen fruits before completely thawed.

For thawing, leave the fruit in the sealed original package. Turn the package several times during the thawing. This will keep the fruit coated with sirup and prevent discoloration.

Thawing may be best done in the refrigerator. It will require about 6 to 8 hours to thaw a 1 pound package of fruit in the refrigerator or 2 to 3 hours at room temperature.

Never refreeze fruits. If the fruit is to be kept after thawing, cook it and then store it in the refrigerator. In using frozen fruits in recipes, make allowances for the sugar used in freezing.

Meats and Poultry

Meat and poultry is best thawed before cooking. To thaw meat remove from the freezer 24 to 28 hours before it is to be cooked. It is best to keep it on a shelf in the refrigerator, thawing it slowly. For more rapid thawing, leave meat out of the refrigerator at room temperature. Do not use water to thaw meat or poultry. A good estimate of thawing time is 5 hours per pound in the refrigerator, or 2½ hours per pound at room temperature.

Cook meat or poultry just as soon as thawing is completed. This will prevent deterioration of the meat, and loss of valuable juices.

If unthawed meat is cooked, it will require a longer time, usually half again as long, and a lower temperature. Cook thawed poultry as you would fresh dressed poultry. See pages 476–480.

Approximate Cooking Times

CUT	IF THAWED BEFORE COOKING	IF COOKED FROM FROZEN STATE	METHOD OF COOKING
Standing Rib Roast	22 minutes per lb.	47 minutes per lb.	Roast at 300°–325° F.
Rolled Rib Roast	32 minutes per lb.	57 minutes per lb.	Roast (medium) at 300°–325° F.
Steak:			
Porterhouse 1 inch thick	8–10 minutes total	21–33 minutes per lb.	Broiling (raw to medium)
Round Steak ½ inch thick	7 minutes total	11 minutes total	Pan broiling
Meat Patties	8 minutes total	16 minutes total	Pan broiling

Pressure Cooking

The pressure cooker is a modern cooking utensil that makes "live steam" available in the home kitchen. It may be used on any kind of stove, but, for good results and for safety, it must be used according to specific rules. "Live steam" is steam under pressure. This is the kind of steam that, when intelligently handled, has the power to drive machinery safely, pull trains, and drive boats; but it is also the kind of steam that causes explosions when carelessly handled.

The pressure cooker is designed with safety devices, but it is not foolproof. The person who is using the pressure cooker should understand it and should give it her undivided attention when using it.

There are a number of good pressure cookers available. Each manufacturer provides a booklet of instructions which should be read carefully and understood before the utensil is used. The principles in using steam for cooking are the same for all pressure cookers; therefore, the same general rules for the use of a pressure cooker apply to all such utensils.

What the Pressure Cooker Does — if Directions Are Followed

1. Saves time. The most spectacular thing about a pressure cooker is its speed. Foods cook in one third to one fourth the time or less required by the more ordinary cooking methods. This means that whole potatoes may be cooked in from 12 to 15 minutes instead of 25 to 35 minutes; fresh peas in 1 to 3 minutes instead of 10 to 12 minutes; vegetable and meat soups in 20 minutes instead of two hours.

2. Saves fuel — an important item in the family budget. Pressure cooking saves fuel in proportion to the reduction in time — that is, ⅔ to ¾ of the cost of fuel for cooking the same items.

3. Saves food values. This is most important of all. Many of the valuable vitamins and minerals in vegetables may be lost through overcooking or by being dissolved in the water in which the vegetables are cooked. The pressure cooker, properly used, can save these valuable protective nutrients, for which we include vegetables in our diets.

4. Saves color, flavor, texture, and appearance. The beautiful color of fresh vegetables has an eye appeal which is closely associated with taste appeal. The art of cookery is dependent upon preserving the color, appearance, texture, and flavor of natural foods. The pressure cooker, if properly used, will help retain the natural characteristics of foods.

5. Converts tough meat and poultry into tender, tasty dishes. Thus with a pressure cooker you can make use of the less expensive cuts of meat without the expenditure of a large amount of time and energy — and without over-heating the kitchen, an important item in hot weather.

Parts of a Pressure Cooker and Their Function

Each pressure cooker consists of a pan, called the body, a tightly fitted cover, and a rack. The cover and pan are so designed that they fit tightly together, being held in place by the design of the cooker and the top. Often the handles serve to "lock" the cover and the body for use. The rack fits inside the cooker and is used when cooking certain foods.

Gasket. Between the cover and the pan is a band of rubber or other material called a gasket, which seals the cooker when in use so that no steam can escape around the cover. After much use, this gasket may need replacing. All types of cookers have an inexpensive, replaceable gasket.

Vent Hole. The vent hole is an important safety device in the top of each pressure cooker. At the beginning of the cooking process, the air in the cooker must escape through the vent hole before the pressure rises. This vent hole is closed when the steam comes out in a steady stream, indicating that the air has been driven out. The vent hole remains closed through the cooking process unless the pressure, through the carelessness of the cook becomes too high, in which case the vent hole serves as a safety valve to release steam and lower the pressure. It can only function as a safety valve if kept clean and open.

The vent hole is equally important at the end of the cooking. *After* the pressure has gone down to *zero*, when the cooking is completed, the vent hole again serves an important purpose. It must be opened to let some remaining steam out before the top is removed from the cooker.

Pressure Gauge. The pressure gauge may be one of two kinds

(1) A dial gauge on which a pointer clearly indicates the number of pounds of pressure in the cooker. Most cookers are gauged from 0 to 15 pounds. (2) A weight type of gauge where the number of pounds of pressure is indicated by the weight that can be lifted by the steam. Usually there are three positions marked on this weight, indicating 5, 10, and 15 pounds.

The pressure gauge is located over the vent hole and serves as a means of closing it, and is the safety valve that opens the vent hole if the steam pressure in the pan goes too high.

Over-Pressure Plug. The safest cookers also have this additional safety valve. It may look like a screw or plug in the top of the cooker. If the vent hole is stopped up, as it might be from careless cleaning or from filling the cooker too full, this plug will blow out, releasing the steam and avoiding an explosion. When this "over-pressure plug" blows out, it must be replaced by a new one before the pressure cooker can be used.

These are the essential parts of a pressure cooker. You should understand the function of each one. Read the directions supplied by the manufacturer very carefully. Be sure you understand the utensil and how to handle it before you use it.

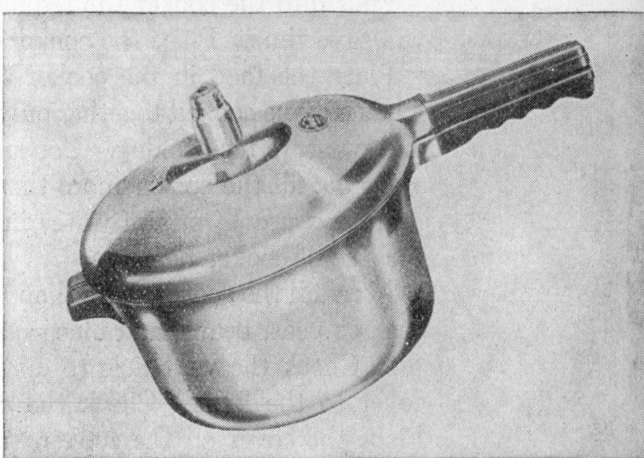

FIG. 167. ALL PRESSURE COOKERS VARY

Study and understand the parts of a pressure cooker before you use it.

General Directions for Cooking Most Foods in a Pressure Cooker

1. Prepare food for cooking according to the recipe. If the rack is to be used, place it in the bottom of the cooker. The rack will be needed for large pieces of meat, whole potatoes, and other large pieces of food. It will not be needed for soups, stews, or vegetables cut in small pieces.

Pour into the cooker the required amount of water. Hot water will save time. Place the cooker over high heat.

Place the food in the cooker and season as desired. Different foods may be cooked together only when they require the same time and pressure for cooking. Consult timetables.

Do not fill the cooker more than two thirds full.

Always use ½ cup of water in cooking vegetables regardless of the size of cooker being used.

Never fill the cooker more than half full when cooking dried foods, such as peas, beans, and macaroni.

2. Check the vent hole to make sure it is clean by holding the cover to the light. Check the gasket to see that it is in place. Place the cover on the cooker, making sure it is correctly placed and fastened according to the directions for the utensil used.

3. With the cooker on high heat, leave the vent hole open until all the air has been exhausted. After the steam has flowed freely for about one minute, close the vent hole.

4. Watch the pressure gauge closely. Count the cooking time accurately, beginning the moment the pressure gauge shows the number of pounds called for in the recipe or timetable used.

After the desired pressure is reached, the cook must so manage the heat that the pressure gauge remains at the required pressure for the correct number of minutes. With experience, she learns how to do this. If she has a gas or oil stove, she lowers the flame; if she has a coal, wood, or electric stove, she moves the cooker from the area of high heat; if she has an electric stove, she may switch to a lower heat just before the desired pressure is reached.

5. When the cooking time is up, remove the cooker from the heat at once. In cooking certain foods, the timetables indicate that it is necessary to cool the cooker immediately to avoid overcooking. Do this by running cold water on the outside of the cooker, or by setting the cooker in cold water. Do not open the vent hole until the pressure returns to zero.

FIG. 168. GENERAL STEPS IN USING A PRESSURE COOKER

Foods not indicated for immediate cooling in the time tables should be allowed to cool in the cooker with the vent hole tightly closed by the gauge.

6. After the pressure returns to zero, open the vent hole by lifting the pressure gauge or weight, allowing steam to flow out of the cooker and air to go in.

Never lift the gauge opening the vent hole until the pressure returns to zero.

Never open the cooker until the vent hole has been opened for a minute.

If the cover of the cooker is difficult to remove, *do not force it.* There may still be some steam pressure in the cooker. If this occurs, run cold water over the cooker (again if necessary).

A true story that could happen to you if you are careless: One home economics student, who did not pay close attention to the instructions for using a pressure cooker, disregarded instruction 6 above. She opened a cooker, in which she had cooked soybeans, before the pressure had returned to zero and without opening the vent. The result was soybeans all over a freshly painted kitchen, and some bad burns for herself and some of her classmates.

Moral: The pressure cooker is a modern utensil that is very useful in the hands of an intelligent cook, but it is not foolproof.

Special Instructions for Cooking Meats and Poultry

1. Place the cooker, without the cover, over high heat. When the cooker is heated, add shortening or fat as called for in the recipe.

2. Sear the meat, turning it until it has a crisp, brown exterior all over to keep the juices in while cooking.

3. Season according to taste. Lift the meat up and put the rack under the meat. Add the water called for in the recipe, and cook according to the foregoing directions for the use of the pressure cooker.

4. Vegetables may be cooked with meat. If they require the same time and pressure, they may be put into the cooker after the meat is seared. If the vegetables require less cooking than the meat, the meat should be partly cooked with the correct meat pressure. When the meat lacks the time required for cooking the vegetables, remove the cooker, cool with cold water to reduce the pressure to zero, follow the directions under 6, above, for open-

ing the cooker. Add the vegetables, and finish the cooking according to the time required for cooking the vegetables.

5. For making gravy, after the cooking is completed, use the cooker as you would any other utensil.

Recipes for Pressure Cookery

Special recipes for pressure cookery are not required *except* for time and pressure. You may use recipes elsewhere in this Cook Book, but you should consult the booklet which accompanies your pressure cooker for the amount of water, time, and pressure.

Books on pressure cookery, such as the following, would be a valuable aid in every home economics department:

Name	*Author*	*Publisher*
Pressure Cooking	Ida Bailey Allen	Garden City Publishing Co.
Pressure Cookery	Leone Rutledge Carroll	Barrows and Co., New York

Feeding Many

In planning for many, fifty is a convenient number to consider because the quantity can be easily halved for twenty-five or increased for seventy-five. Let us consider playing hostess to fifty.

The menu may not seem very different from the one planned for a similar occasion for six or eight, but the market orders, and perhaps the recipes, may be very different. Instead of teaspoons, tablespoons, and cups, our measures for fifty are usually in quarts, gallons, and pounds.

Whether the refreshments are wieners and rolls, ice cream and cake, or a full dinner, some important questions are: (1) How shall the work be organized? (2) What shall the menu be? (3) How much of each food will be needed? (4) How much will the refreshments cost? (5) What recipes will be needed and for what quantities?

Planning for Many

There are enough problems in planning for twenty-five to fifty guests to challenge the organizing ability of any home economics group. There must be committees. What could be more democratic? But there must be a general manager to mobilize all resources and co-ordinate all efforts.

Planning Committee

The chairman of the Planning Committee should be the general manager, and it would be well to select for the chairman of each committee a member of the Planning Committee, thus making for co-ordination of the work of all committees. The decisions which the Planning Committee must make before other committees can function are: Number to be planned for; budget; menu and recipes; place and type of service; decorations, dishes, linens, etc.; hostess duties and entertainment; appointment of working committees; and co-ordinating of the work of all committees. A file of written reports of all the committees should be kept for the benefit of future committees.

Working Committees

Publicity or Invitation Committee. The procedure this committee will follow depends upon the type of affair planned.

Marketing Committee. The Marketing Committee should be responsible for securing all the food and other supplies purchased or donated. (See tables for estimating quantities for fifty, pages 576–580.)

Hostess Committee. The Hostess Committee should be responsible for carrying out the decisions of the Planning Committee regarding space, invitations, decorations, reception of guests, and plans for entertaining guests so that all will have a good time. This is not an easy job, but is one on which the success of the affair depends. Inviting the guests for refreshments and seating them is also a function of the Hostess Committee.

Serving Committee. This committee should plan for adequate space for seating the guests comfortably. If it is a dinner or banquet, it is important that both the guests and the waitresses have sufficient space for each cover for convenience in serving. Twenty inches per person is the least cover space permissible, but twenty-five to thirty inches is better spacing. Small tables seating four to eight persons are preferable to the long banquet table, and are to-day more in favor even for formal banquets. The linen, silver, glassware, dishes, serving equipment, tables, and chairs to be used are all important.

One waitress can serve eight to ten people. All the rules that apply to home table service also apply when a larger group is being served. In fact, the Committee's aim should be to keep the food, the table service, and the appointments as homelike as possible.

Food Preparation Committee. The first responsibility is to provide good food. So far as method of preparation is concerned, new recipes may not be needed, but the quantity must be increased. For example, for pies, cakes, salads, and vegetables, home-size recipes may be used, making as many times the recipe as will be needed.

In multiplying recipes it is very easy to make a mistake; too much or too little of even one ingredient may "spoil the pudding." Therefore, the best plan is to select the recipe and write down on a card the exact quantities and the method of making to be used for each dish on the menu. (On pages 581–584 a few quantity recipes are given. Consult a quantity cook book for others.) Perhaps the school cafeteria director will lend the committee large-size utensils; she may also have suitable recipes.

Finance Committee. Whatever the financial problem, it calls for planning and either a small committee or an individual must be delegated to manage the finances.

The Follow-up Committee. Last but not least, there must be a follow-up committee whose responsibility it is to see that "all's well that ends well." If the home economics laboratory, the school cafeteria, or any other parts of the school building are used for the "party," this committee must see that each part is left in a clean and orderly condition. Even a picnic needs the clean-up squad. The dishwashing, general cleaning-up, checking equipment and supplies, returning borrowed property, and all the other duties that follow in the wake of "throwing a party" are carried out most cheerfully and most effectively when it is some group's special job.

Menus

Menus should be appropriate. Gingerbread, baked apples, and popcorn balls are appropriate for a Halloween party, but one would not expect these refreshments at a tea. Menus should be simple in order that all may have a good time, including those who do the work of preparing and serving. Expensive foods are out of place for a school or community gathering. If the menu is expensive, some must forego the pleasure of attending. The same food may be served for a dinner as for a banquet, but the service should be simpler and the food combined into two or three courses. For tea, refreshments may be dressed up a bit and still be few in number. Decorated cookies, open sandwiches, and table decorations give opportunity for using both ingenuity and artistic ability, and make a tea festive.

On all occasions and for all menus good nutrition and good cooking have priority. The occasion will be remembered best by good food, well planned and well prepared.

No new rules of etiquette are called for when there are many people. Good manners are always in style. "The more, the merrier" makes for a festive occasion, but never make the mistake of interpreting this to mean "the more the rougher."

QUANTITIES OF FOOD FOR FIFTY

Weights and Measures

Canned goods	*Number of cups*
No. 2	2½
No. 2½	3½
No. 10	13
Scoops or dishers	
No. 8	½ c. or 8 T.
No. 10	6 ⅔ T.

Food	Amount to Serve per Person	Amount for Serving Fifty
Butter		
For table	1 square (1 lb. cuts 48 squares)	1 or 1½ lb. (allows for 2 servings to some)
For seasoning vegetables		½ lb.
Bread and Rolls		
Bread		
Sliced for table	1 to 2 slices	2 to 3 Pullman loaves (30 medium slices per loaf) 6 short loaves (1 lb.)
Rolls for wieners or hamburgers	2 per person (average)	8⅓ dozen
For sandwiches	2 sandwiches per person	6 loaves thin-sliced bread (35–40 slices)
Saltines or soda crackers	2 crackers per serving	1 lb. (saltines) to 1½ lb. (soda crackers)
Beverages		
Cocoa	1 c. (½ measuring c.)	2 c. dry cocoa will make 2½ gal. of beverage
Coffee	1 c. (½ measuring c.)	1¼ lb. of coffee (to 2½ gal. of water)
Fruit juice (see tomato juice)		
Lemonade (for juice)	1 glass (¾ measuring c.)	1¼ qt. juice — 3 doz. lemons (approximate) to 2½ gal. of water
Milk	1 glass (¾ c.)	10 qt.
Oranges (for juice)	1 fruit juice glass (⅓ measuring c.)	5 or 6 doz. (medium)
Punch	1 to 2 punch c. servings	2½ gal.

Food	Amount to Serve per Person	Amount for Serving Fifty
Tea	1 c. per person	50 individual tea bags or 2½ to 3 oz. bulk tea (use larger amount for iced tea)
Tomato juice or fruit juice	½ cup	6½ qt. (2 No. 10 cans)
Cake and Cookies		
Layer cake (10″) (2 layers)	1 slice	4 cakes (cut in 12 to 14 pieces per cake)
Gingerbread or loaf cake (pans 2″×12″×18″)	1 piece (3″×2½″)	2 pans (2″×12″×18″) or equivalent in smaller pans
Cup cakes	One (plus) per person	5 doz. (allow a few extras)
Cookies	2 to 3	12 doz.
Cereals		
Oatmeal and other dry cereals for cooking	½ to ⅔ c. (cooked)	2 to 3 lb. (dry)
Prepared, as puffed wheat, etc.	⅔ to 1 c.	6 pkg. (large size)
Cheese		
American	one slice or cube	3½ lb. sliced for sandwiches 2½ lb. sliced for pie or dessert
Cottage	¼ to ⅓ c.	6 to 8½ lb.
Cream		
Single (thin) (coffee)	1½ T. per serving	1¼ qt. or 5 half-pt. bottles
Double (thick) (whipping)	1 T. of whipped cream (rounded)	1 qt. or 4 half-pt. bottles Cream doubles in bulk when whipped
Eggs	1 per person	4½ doz. or 2½ qt. liquid eggs
Whole		5 whole eggs = 1 c.
Yolks		12 egg yolks = 1 c.
Whites		8 egg whites = 1 c.
Fruit Cup	⅓ to ½ c.	4½ to 6 qt.
Fruit Juice	½ c. (4 oz. glass)	6½ qt., or 2 No. 10 cans
Fruits		
Apples		
For sauce	2 T. apple sauce	15–20 lb.
For pie	1 slice (6 per pie)	15–20 lb. (8-inch pie)
Berries or cherries (for pie) canned	1 slice (6 per pie)	6 to 8 qt. (1½ No. 10 cans) for 8 pies (8-in. pie tins)
Cherries, frozen (for pie)	1 slice (6 per pie)	10 lb.
Cranberries, fresh	¼ c. cranberry sauce	4 lb.
Grapes		1 lb. will make 2¾ c. of grapes cut and seeded

Food	Amount to Serve per Person	Amount for Serving Fifty
Grapefruit	½ grapefruit	½ crate or 25 grapefruit for salad or fruit cup. Medium sized (54 to 64 per crate)
Lemons		5 to 6 lemons (medium sized) will make 1 c. juice
Oranges	1 orange (medium)	4½ doz. Large, 80–126 per crate Medium, 150–216 per crate Small, 250–392 per crate
Orange juice (see beverages)	½ orange (large)	
Peaches		
Fresh	½ c. peeled and sliced	12½ lb. (one pk. or ½ bu.)
Canned	2 halves	2½ or 3 cans (No. 10)
Pears, canned	2 halves	3 cans (No. 10)
Pineapple, canned	2 slices	2 No. 10 cans or 13 No. 2½ cans
Strawberries, fresh	½ c. for berries ⅓ c. for shortcake	12 or 13 qt. 9 or 10 qt.
Ice Cream		
Bulk	1 serving (No. 10 scoop)	2 gal. (one gal. equals 25 or more servings)
Brick	1 slice (qt. brick cut in 6 or 7 slices)	7 or 8 qt. in brick shape
Marshmallows	For campfire toasting 4–6 per person	(1 lb. contains 50 to 60 marshmallows) 4 to 6 lb.
Meats, Poultry, Fish		
Beef		
Rolled rib boned	3 oz. per serving	16 to 20 lb.
Hamburger		
Ground round steak	3 oz. each pattie	16 to 20 lb.
Steaks		
Country fried (round)	4½ oz. per serving	16 to 20 lb. (amount needed varies with the cut)
Broiled-sirloin	5 to 6 oz. per serving (besides bone)	20 to 24 lb.
Broiled-T-Bone	5 to 6 oz. (besides bone)	22 to 25 lb.
Chicken		
Roast	2 to 3 oz. of meat	7 to 10 chickens of 4 to 5 lb. each dressed weight 35 to 50 lb. dressed weight or 25–35 lb. drawn weight
Broiler	½ broiler	25 broilers (1½ to 2½ lb. each)
Turkey	2 to 3 oz. of meat	30 to 35 lb. dressed weight 2 turkeys 15 lb. dressed weight

Food	Amount to Serve per Person	Amount for Serving Fifty
Pork		
Ham-cured	2 oz. sliced	16 to 20 lb.
Roast	3 oz. sliced	16 to 20 lb.
Sausage (cakes)	1 large or 2 small (4 oz.)	12½ lb.
Wieners	2 wieners	12½ to 14 lb. (7 or 8 wieners per lb.)
Fish — fresh fillets	4 to 5 oz.	14 to 17 lb. (3 to 4 per lb.)
Oysters		
Frying	4 to 6 large (30 to 36 per qt.)	7 or 8 qt.
Stew or scalloped	4 to 6 medium oysters (60 to 72 per qt.)	3 to 4 qt.
Macaroni or Spaghetti	¾ c. (cooked)	3½ lb. (and 2½ lb. of cheese for macaroni)
Nuts — shelled and salted	1 T. per serving	1½ to 2 lb.
Peanut Butter	One sandwich	4 lb. (1 lb. = 1¾ c.)
Pie	One slice (6 to 7 cuts per pie)	8 pies (8 in.) cut in 6 or 7 pieces
Potato Chips	¾ oz. (approximate) per serving	2 lb. approximately or 10 qt.
Relishes		
Carrot strips raw	2 to 3 pieces	2 to 2½ lb.
Olives	3 to 4	2 qt.
Pickles, mixed	2 to 3 pieces	2½ qt.
Radishes	2 or 3	10 to 12 bunches
Salad Mixtures	½ c. per serving	7 to 8 qt.
Salad Dressing		
Mayonnaise or cooked	Allows for mixing and for garnish	2 to 2½ qt. (1 qt. for garnish)
French	¾ to 1 T.	¾ to 1 qt.
Sandwiches		
Bread	2 slices — thin cut	3 loaves of sandwich or Pullman bread thin-sliced (30 to 35 slices per loaf)
Butter	Spread on one slice of bread for each sandwich	¾ to 1 lb.
Filling	2 T. per sandwich	2 qt. (approximate) for 50 sandwiches
Sauce for vegetables (white sauce or tomato sauce)	2 to 3 T.	2 to 3 qt.
Soup	¾ to 1 c.	3 gal.

Food	Amount to Serve per Person	Amount for Serving Fifty
Sugar and Sweets		
Loaf	1 to 2 cubes	1 to 2 lb.
Granulated	1 to 2 t.	½ to 1 lb.
Jelly	2 T.	3 pt.
Mints		1½ to 2 lb.
Vegetables		
Beans		
Green—fresh	½ c.	10 to 12 lb. fresh or 3 pkg. Frozen (3½ lb. each)
Lima—frosted	⅓ c.	3 pkg. (3½ lb. each)
Cabbage		
Raw	1 to 2 oz.	8 to 10 lb.
Cooked	½ c.	12 to 15 lb.
Carrots		
Cooked	½ c.	14 to 16 lb. (raw) (4–6 carrots per lb.)
Raw — strips (see relishes)		
Celery		
Raw	¼ celery heart bunch	12 bunches (1 medium bunch weighs about 1 lb.)
Cooked	½ c. (diced-buttered)	15 bunches (1 lb. each)
Greens — cooked	½ c.	15 to 18 lb. — garden fresh
Lettuce		
head	⅙ to ⅛ of a head	8 to 10 heads (approximate weight 1 lb. as purchased)
Peas		
Fresh	½ c. (cooked)	25 lb. unshelled (1 lb. = 1 c. shelled) 6¼ qt. shelled
Canned	½ c.	10 to 12 cans (No. 2½) or 2 cans (No. 10)
Frosted	½ c. (cooked)	4 pkg. (2½ lb. each)
Potatoes		
White	½ c. mashed or 1 potato baked	15 to 20 lb. (3 medium potatoes per lb.)
Sweet	3½ oz. or 1 potato—medium	18 to 20 lb.
Tomatoes		
Fresh	½ to 1 tomato sliced	10 to 12 lb. (3 to 4 medium tomatoes to lb.)

QUANTITY RECIPES

A quantity cook book should be in every Home Economics Department. Some good ones are as follows:

Name	*Author*	*Publisher*
Meals for Many	Katharine W. Harris and Marion A. Wood	Cornell University Ithaca, New York
Food for Fifty	Sina Faye West and Bessie Brooks West	John Wiley & Sons, Inc.
Recipes at Moderate Cost	Constance C. Hart	F. S. Crofts & Co.

Beverages

Cocoa (for 50)

2 qt. water
2 c. cocoa
2½ c. sugar
½ t. salt
8 qt. milk, or (2 lb. dry milk solids and 7½ qt. water)

Mix cocoa, salt, and sugar (and cinnamon if spiced cocoa desired). Add 1 pint of cold water. Mix well. Add 1½ quarts hot water. Boil to make a cocoa sirup (10 minutes). Add the hot cocoa sirup (which can be made ahead of time) to hot milk. Beat well and serve at once.

Variations

1. Add 1 t. of vanilla.
2. Add 1 marshmallow to each cup or top each cup with 1 t. of whipped cream.
3. For spiced cocoa add 1 t. cinnamon to sugar. Add 2 t. each of vanilla and almond extract to beverage before serving.

Coffee (for 50)

1¼ lb. coffee
10 qt. water

Coffee must be freshly ground and water must be freshly drawn.

Make one or two cheesecloth bags large enough to hold the ground coffee. Tie bag with a clean string.

Bring water to boil. Add coffee-filled bags and boil 5 minutes. Remove bags. Serve coffee hot.

If stronger coffee desired, increase coffee.

If weaker coffee desired, either decrease coffee or serve with hot water.

Serve with thin cream (also called coffee cream).

Spiced Punch (Hot) (for 50)

Make 3 times the recipe for Oriental Punch, page 397, *Everyday Foods*.

Fruit Punch (Cold) (for 50)

Make twice the recipe, page 396, *Everyday Foods*.

Main Dishes

Roast Turkey [1]

A 10- to 12-pound young turkey (will serve 15 to 18 people).

Draw and singe the turkey. Remove oil sac and pinfeathers. Cleanse thoroughly and wipe dry. Sprinkle inside the turkey with salt and fill with hot stuffing, but do not pack. Fold wings back on the neck (see Figure 110, p. 327). Tuck the legs into a slit in the skin and flesh below the tail and tie down. After stuffing the neck, draw the skin back and sew, or fasten in place with a skewer (see Figure 141, p. 477). Then rub the surface with fat creamed with flour, seasoned with salt and pepper. Lay a piece of bacon or salt pork over the breast bone and place on a rack in the roaster, uncovered (Figure 110, p. 327). Place in a hot oven (450°) for about 30 minutes to brown lightly. Turn breast down first on one side and then on the other (see Figures 111 and 112, p. 327) and baste frequently to insure even browning. Reduce oven heat to 350° F. and continue to roast for 2½ hours or longer. Baste occasionally with drippings. If the turkey is older, when brown cover and cook 4 hours. The turkey is done when the thigh, near the breast, is pierced and the juice shows no red tinge.

Stuffing for Turkey (10-12 lb.)

3 qt. bread crumbs (soft) — may be part cornbread if desired
1 c. butter, or half butter and half turkey fat
¼ c. minced onion
¼ c. chopped parsley
1½ c. chopped celery (include tops)
2 t. salt
¼ t. pepper
1 t. savory seasoning
Hot stock, water, or milk to moisten

Melt butter in skillet and cook onion, celery, and parsley in melted fat for a few minutes. Combine bread crumbs, salt, pepper, and savory seasoning. Add the butter with the other seasonings. Combine well with the bread crumbs. Moisten if necessary.

Chestnut stuffing. Cook one pound of large chestnuts by boiling in water to cover for 20 minutes. Shell, remove brown skins, chop, and mix with the bread crumbs.

Giblet Gravy

Simmer giblets (liver and gizzard) and the neck in 1 qt. of water until tender. Remove giblets and chop fine. Discard the neck.

[1] Courtesy of Bureau of Human Nutrition and Home Economics.

Use ½ c. drippings from the roaster, add 6 T. flour, blend well. Add liquid in which giblets were cooked and cook a few minutes until thick. If necessary add water to thin. Add the chopped giblets and one or two chopped hard-cooked eggs. Season to taste with salt and pepper and serve with turkey and dressing.

Baked Ham (for 50)

(1) 22–24 pounds of home cured or non-tenderized ham. For preparation see page 466, *Everyday Foods.*

(2) 18–20 pounds tenderized ham (a newer type of commercially prepared ham). Tenderized hams do not require soaking or precooking. Place tenderized ham in baking pan. Add 1 c. of water and bake in slow oven (250–300° F.) 1½ hours (or until tender). Skin the ham. Put in pan with fatty side up. Cut the fat crisscross, stick in cloves, and cover fat with brown sugar (1½ c.). Pour over the ham 2 c. of apple cider, pineapple juice, mild vinegar, or the liquid from sweet pickled peaches. Bake in moderate oven (350° F.) for 30 minutes. Baste occasionally during the cooking. If a meat thermometer is available, cook until the internal temperature of the ham registers 170° F.

Macaroni and Cheese (for 50)

3½ lb. macaroni
3½ gal. of hot water
½ c. salt
1 gal. medium white sauce
2½ lb. cheese

Cook macaroni in boiling salted water. Drain in a colander. Place in buttered pan in which it is to be baked.

Make a well-seasoned white sauce (add to the usual seasoning ½ t. paprika). Melt most of the cheese in the sauce and pour over the macaroni. Cut thin slices of cheese and distribute well over the surface of the macaroni. Bake in moderate oven (375° F.) until brown (30 minutes).

Soups

Vegetable Soup (for 50)

Make 4 times recipe, page 424, *Everyday Foods.*

Oyster Stew (for 50)

3½ qt. oysters	2 T. salt
1 c. butter	1 t. white pepper
9 qt. milk	½ t. paprika

1 T. Worcestershire sauce (if desired)

Remove all pieces of shell and other materials (as oyster crabs) from the oysters. Heat oysters in half the butter until the edges "ruffle." Heat milk and add seasonings. Add oysters and remaining butter. Taste for seasoning. Serve immediately.

Sauces

White Sauce

	Thin I (Cream soup)	Medium II (For vegetables and Escalloped dishes)	Thick III (For Croquettes)
Milk	2 qt.	2 qt.	2 qt.
Fat	¼ c.	½ c.	1 c.
Flour	½ c.	¾ to 1 c.	1½ c.
Salt	1 T.	1 T.	1 T.

Heat milk in top of double boiler. Melt fat and add flour. Add some of milk to flour and fat mixture and combine with hot milk, beating all the time with a wire whip. Add salt. Cook until thick, stirring all the time.

Variations

For tomato sauce. Use canned tomatoes or tomato juice instead of milk. Season with bay leaves, pepper corns (1 t.), cloves (1 t.) 1 garlic clove or a few slices of onion. Heat and strain. Combine with fat and flour. Add salt.

For cheese sauce. Add ¾ lb. chopped American cheese to sauce. Stir until melted.

For egg sauce. Add six chopped hard-cooked eggs before serving.

Cranberry Sauce (4 qt.) (50 servings)

4 qt. (or 4 lb.) fresh cranberries
6 c. sugar
4 c. water

Wash and pick over cranberries. Cook water, cranberries, and sugar in covered saucepan until the skins burst (10 to 15 minutes). Skim if necessary. Pour into containers and cool.

Appendix

TABLE I[1]

BALDWIN-WOOD WEIGHT-HEIGHT-AGE TABLE FOR BOYS

Height (inches)	5 Yr. (lb.)	6 Yr. (lb.)	7 Yr. (lb.)	8 Yr. (lb.)	9 Yr. (lb.)	10 Yr. (lb.)	11 Yr. (lb.)	12 Yr. (lb.)	13 Yr. (lb.)	14 Yr. (lb.)	15 Yr. (lb.)	16 Yr. (lb.)	17 Yr. (lb.)	18 Yr. (lb.)	19 Yr. (lb.)
38	34	34													
39	35	35													
40	36	36													
41	38	38	38												
42	39	39	39	39											
43	41	41	41	41											
44	44	44	44	44											
45	46	46	46	46	46										
46	47	48	48	48	48										
47	49	50	50	50	50	50									
48		52	53	53	53	53									
49		55	55	55	55	55	55								
50		57	58	58	58	58	58	58							
51			61	61	61	61	61	61							
52			63	64	64	64	64	64	64						
53			66	67	67	67	67	68	68						
54				70	70	70	70	71	71	72					
55				72	72	73	73	74	74	74					
56				75	76	77	77	77	78	78	80				
57					79	80	81	81	82	83	83				
58					83	84	84	85	85	86	87				
59						87	88	89	89	90	90	90			
60						91	92	92	93	94	95	96			
61							95	96	97	99	100	103	106		
62							100	101	102	103	104	107	111	116	
63							105	106	107	108	110	113	118	123	127
64								109	111	113	115	117	121	126	130
65								114	117	118	120	122	127	131	134
66									119	122	125	128	132	136	139
67									124	128	130	134	136	139	142
68										134	134	137	141	143	147
69										137	139	143	146	149	152
70										143	144	145	148	151	155
71										148	150	151	152	154	159
72											153	155	156	158	163
73											157	160	162	164	167
74											160	164	168	170	171

[1] Prepared by Bird T. Baldwin, Ph.D., and Thomas D. Wood, M.D. Reproduced by permission of the Child Health Association, New York. See also Table II.

TABLE II

BALDWIN-WOOD WEIGHT-HEIGHT-AGE TABLE FOR GIRLS

Height (inches)	5 Yr. (lb.)	6 Yr. (lb.)	7 Yr. (lb.)	8 Yr. (lb.)	9 Yr. (lb.)	10 Yr. (lb.)	11 Yr. (lb.)	12 Yr. (lb.)	13 Yr. (lb.)	14 Yr. (lb.)	15 Yr. (lb.)	16 Yr. (lb.)	17 Yr. (lb.)	18 Yr. (lb.)
38	33	33												
39	34	34												
40	36	36	36											
41	37	37	37											
42	39	39	39											
43	41	41	41	41										
44	42	42	42	42										
45	45	45	45	45	45									
46	47	47	47	48	48									
47	49	50	50	50	50	50								
48		52	52	52	52	53	53							
49		54	54	55	55	56	56							
50		56	56	57	58	59	61	62						
51			59	60	61	61	63	65						
52			63	64	64	64	65	67						
53			66	67	67	68	68	69	71					
54				69	70	70	71	71	73					
55				72	74	74	74	75	77	78				
56					76	78	78	79	81	83				
57					80	82	82	84	88	92				
58						84	86	86	88	93	96	101		
59						87	90	90	92	96	100	103	104	
60						91	95	95	97	101	105	108	109	111
61							99	100	101	105	108	112	113	116
62							104	105	106	109	113	115	117	118
63								110	110	112	116	117	119	120
64								114	115	117	119	120	122	123
65								118	120	121	122	123	125	126
66									124	124	125	128	129	130
67									128	130	131	133	133	135
68									131	133	135	136	138	138
69										135	137	138	140	142
70										136	138	140	142	144
71										138	140	142	144	145

When taking measurements, remove the child's outdoor clothing, shoes, and coat. Take heights with a square, consisting of two flat pieces of wood joined at right angles (a chalk box will serve). The child is placed in a good erect position, with heels and shoulders against the wall or wide board, upon which has been marked or pasted an accurate measure. Age is taken to the nearest birthday.

TABLE III

AVERAGE HEIGHTS AND WEIGHTS — MEN [1]

AGE	5 ft. 0 in.	5 ft. 1 in.	5 ft. 2 in.	5 ft. 3 in.	5 ft. 4 in.	5 ft. 5 in.	5 ft. 6 in.	5 ft. 7 in.	5 ft. 8 in.	5 ft. 9 in.	5 ft. 10 in.	5 ft. 11 in.	6 ft. 0 in.	6 ft. 1 in.	6 ft. 2 in.	6 ft. 3 in.	6 ft. 4 in.	6 ft. 5 in.
15	107	109	112	115	118	122	126	130	134	138	142	147	152	157	162	167	172	177
20	117	119	122	125	128	132	136	140	144	148	152	156	161	166	171	176	181	188
25	122	124	126	129	133	137	141	145	149	153	157	162	167	173	179	184	189	194
30	126	128	130	133	136	140	144	148	152	156	161	166	172	178	184	190	196	201
35	128	130	132	135	138	142	146	150	155	160	165	170	176	182	189	195	201	207
40	131	133	135	138	141	145	149	153	158	163	168	174	180	186	193	200	206	212
45	133	135	137	140	143	147	151	155	160	165	170	176	182	188	195	202	209	215
50	134	136	138	141	144	148	152	156	161	166	171	177	183	190	197	204	211	217
55	135	137	139	142	145	149	153	158	163	168	173	178	184	191	198	205	212	219

TABLE IV

AVERAGE HEIGHTS AND WEIGHTS — WOMEN [1]

AGE	4 ft. 8 in.	4 ft. 9 in.	4 ft. 10 in.	4 ft. 11 in.	5 ft. 0 in.	5 ft. 1 in.	5 ft. 2 in.	5 ft. 3 in.	5 ft. 4 in.	5 ft. 5 in.	5 ft. 6 in.	5 ft. 7 in.	5 ft. 8 in.	5 ft. 9 in.	5 ft. 10 in.	5 ft. 11 in.	6 ft. 0 in.
15	101	103	105	106	107	109	112	115	118	122	126	130	134	138	142	147	152
20	106	108	110	112	114	116	119	122	125	128	132	136	140	143	147	151	156
25	109	111	113	115	117	119	121	124	128	131	135	139	143	147	151	154	158
30	112	114	116	118	120	122	124	127	131	134	138	142	146	150	154	157	161
35	115	117	119	121	123	125	127	130	134	138	142	146	150	154	157	160	163
40	119	121	123	125	127	129	132	135	138	142	146	150	154	158	161	164	167
45	122	124	126	128	130	132	135	138	141	145	149	153	157	161	164	168	171
50	125	127	129	131	133	135	138	141	144	148	152	156	161	165	169	173	176
55	125	127	129	131	133	135	138	141	144	148	153	158	163	167	171	174	177

Height and weight taken with shoes on and coat and vest or dress off.

[1] Courtesy of the Life Extension Institute and Funk & Wagnalls. From *How to Live*, by Fisher & Fisk. Copyright by Funk & Wagnalls Company, New York and London.

TABLE V

RECOMMENDED DAILY DIETARY ALLOWANCES

Revised 1948 (Adapted with permission)

Food and Nutrition Board, National Research Council

	Calories	Protein gm.[1]	Calcium gm.[1]	Iron mg.[2]	Vitamin A I.U.[3]	Thiamin mg.[2]	Riboflavin mg.[2]	Niacin (Nicotinic Acid) mg.[2]	Ascorbic Acid mg.[2]	Vitamin D I.U.[3]
Men (154 lb.)										
Sedentary	2400	70	1.0	12	5000	1.2	1.8	12	75	[4]
Physically active	3000	70	1.0	12	5000	1.5	1.8	15	75	[4]
With heavy work	4500	70	1.0	12	5000	1.8	1.8	18	75	[4]
Women (123 lb.)										
Sedentary	2000	60	1.0	12	5000	1.0	1.5	10	70	[4]
Moderately active	2400	60	1.0	12	5000	1.2	1.5	12	70	[4]
Very active	3000	60	1.0	12	5000	1.5	1.5	15	70	[4]
Sedentary, pregnant (latter half)	2400	85	1.5	15	6000	1.5	2.5	15	100	400
Nursing mothers	3000	100	2.0	15	8000	1.5	3.0	15	150	400
Children up to 12 yrs.[5]										
Under 1 yr.[6]	50 per lb.	1.6 per lb.	1.0	6	1500	0.4	0.6	4	30	400
1–3 yrs. (27 lb.)	1200	40	1.0	7	2000	0.6	0.9	6	35	400
4–6 yrs. (42 lb.)	1600	50	1.0	8	2500	0.8	1.2	8	50	400
7–9 yrs. (58 lb.)	2000	60	1.0	10	3500	1.0	1.5	10	60	400
10–12 yrs. (78 lb.)	2500	70	1.2	12	4500	1.2	1.8	12	75	400
Children over 12 yrs.[5]										
Girls, 13–15 yrs. (108 lb.)	2600	80	1.3	15	5000	1.3	2.0	13	80	400
16–20 yrs. (122 lb.)	2400	75	1.0	15	5000	1.2	1.8	12	80	400
Boys, 13–15 yrs. (108 lb.)	3200	85	1.4	15	5000	1.5	2.0	15	90	400
16–20 yrs. (141 lb.)	3800	100	1.4	15	6000	1.7	2.5	17	100	400

[1] The abbreviation "gm." stands for *gram*. One gram is about the same weight as $\frac{1}{25}$ ounce. A five-cent piece weighs 5 grams.

[2] The abbreviation "mg." means *milligram*. One milligram is $\frac{1}{1000}$ gram.

[3] The abbreviation "I.U." means *international unit*, a special measure used for Vitamins A and D.

[4] Adults who get plenty of outdoor sunshine probably do not need to supplement their food with Vitamin D. But elderly people and adults who seldom get in the sunshine should take some Vitamin D.

[5] Allowances for children are based on the needs for the middle year in each group (as 2, 5, 8, etc.) and are for moderate activity and for average weight at the middle year of the age group.

[6] Needs for infants increase from month to month with size and activity. The amounts given are for approximately 6 to 8 months. The dietary requirements for some of the nutrients such as protein and calcium are less if derived largely from human milk.

TABLE VI

NUTRITIVE VALUE OF FOODS *

Food	Wt.	Measure	Calories	Protein	Fat	Carbohydrate	Ca	P	Fe	Vitamin A	Thiamin	Riboflavin	Niacin	Ascorbic Acid	Fiber
	gm.			gm.	gm.	gm.	gm.	gm.	mg.	I.U.	μ†	μ	mg.	mg.	gm.
Apples, fresh	100	1, 2″ diam.	60	.3	.4	13.9	.01	.01	.4	75	35	10	.5	6	1.0
Apple sauce	100	⅜ c.	124	.4	.5	30.1	.01	.02	.4						.6
Apricots, fresh	100	2, 1⅝″ diam.	54	1.0	.1	12.3	.01	.03	.6	4000	45	105		7	.6
Apricots, dried	100	½ c. packed	268	4.7	1.0	60.1	.07	.12	7.6	6000	90	100		2	3.2
Apricots, dried, cooked	100	⅓ c.	128	1.3		30.7	.02	.03	2.0						
Asparagus, fresh	50	6, 5-inch stalks	12	1.1	.1	1.6	.02	.02	.5	bleached 0–25 green 450	90	60		bleached 15 green 20	.4
Bacon, cooked	15	4 strips, 3¼″ long	77	2.5	7.5	—	0	.03	.3			105			
Bananas	100	1, 6½″ long, or ¾ c. sliced	96	1.2	.2	22.4	.01	.03	.6	350	50	75	.61	10	.6
Beans, fresh, lima	100	½ c.	125	7.5	.8	22.0	.03	.13	2.4	300	300	175	.29	30	1.5
Beans, fresh, snap, green	100	⅔ c.	37	2.4	.2	6.3	.05	.05	1.0	1000	75	110	.64	25	1.4
Beans, fresh, snap, wax	100	⅔ c.	37	2.4	.2	6.3	.05	.05	1.0	300	75	100	.76	25	1.4
Beans, fresh, soy	100	+ ½ c.	155	12.4	6.3	12.2	.08	.22	.3	200	500	300		40	1.5
Beans, dried, kidney	100	½ c.	350	22.0	1.5	62.1	.16	.47	7.9		480	324	2.82	0	3.9
Beans, dried, lima	100	⅔ c.	349	18.1	1.5	65.9	.07	.34	8.6	100	525	750	1.83	0	4.3
Beans, dried, navy	100	½ c.	327	22.5	1.8	55.2	.16	.47	7.9		480	324		0	3.9
Beans, dried, soy	100	½ c.	417	36.7	18.2	26.6	.21	.58	.8	100	1200	750	4.32	0	5.0
Beans, canned, baked	100	½ c.	118	6.9	2.5	17.1	.04	.34	2.1	55	132	102		—	1.0
Beef, round, lean	100	4″×4″×½″	151	19.7	8.0		.01	.21	4.1	50	230	260	7.5	0	
Beef, roast, fat	100	1 slice, 5″×2½″ × ¼″	347	22.3	28.6		.01	.24	4.9						
Beet greens	100	½ c. cooked	27	2.0	.3	4.2	.04	.09	3.1	21000	42	625		50	1.4
Beets	100	½ c. diced	41	1.6	.1	8.7	.03	.04	.9	0	30	50	.64	15	.9
Biscuit, baking powder	35	2 small biscuits	94	2.5	2.9	14.4	.02	.03	.2						
Blackberries, fresh	100	1⅙ c.	46	1.2	1.1	7.8	.02	.03	.9	150	45			7	4.1
Blueberries	100	⅔ c.	63	.6	.6	13.9	.02	.01	.8	100	45	15		6	1.2
Bran	100	2 c.	169	16.4	6.1	12.2	.12	1.22	8.5	138	600		4.2	0	8.4

* Adapted from *Nutrition*, by Margaret S. Chaney and Margaret Ahlborn, Houghton Mifflin Company.

† μ is the symbol for micrograms.

TABLE VI (*continued*)

Food	*Wt.*	*Measure*	*Calories*	*Protein*	*Fat*	*Carbohydrate*	*Ca*	*P*	*Fe*	*Vitamin A*	*Thiamin*	*Riboflavin*	*Niacin*	*Ascorbic Acid*	*Fiber*
	gm.			gm.	gm.	gm.	gm.	gm.	mg.	I.U.	μ	μ	mg.	mg.	gm.
Bread, rye	30	1 slice	76	2.7	.2	15.8	.01	.04	.5		63	10		0	.2
Bread, white, enriched	30	1 slice	76	2.9	.4	15.3	.02–.05[a]	.03	.53–.83[a]		73–119[a]	46 106[a]	6.6–9.9[a]		.1
Bread, white (milk)	30	1 slice	76	2.9	.4	15.3	.02	.03	.2		20	39	.28	0	.1
Bread, white (water)	30	1 slice	77	2.8	.4	15.7	.01	.03	.3			12–30	.20		.2
Bread, whole wheat	30	1 slice	72	2.9	.3	14.6	.02	.05	.5		63	54	.86	0	.4
Butter	10	1 square, 1¼"×1¼"×¼"	77	.1	8.5					270				0	
Butter	14	1 T.	108	.1	11.9					378				0	
Butter	226	1 c.	1738	2.3	192.1		.05	.05	.5	6102				0	
Buttermilk	100	½ c.	36	3.0	.5	4.8	.11	.10	.3	0	42	80		1	
Cabbage, mature, white	100	⅔ c. cooked; 1½ c. raw	25	1.4	.2	4.3	.05	.03	.4	0	30	25	.29	60	1.0
Cabbage, young, green	100	⅔ c. cooked; 1½ c. raw	25	1.4	.2	4.3	.05	.03	1.2	150	30	50		60	1.0
Cake, chocolate	50	2½"×2½"×1¾"	191	3.0	9.3	24.0	.02	.05	.4						
Cake, plain	56	1¾"×1¾"×1¼"	199	3.7	7.4	29.3	.03	.05	.4						
Cantaloupes	100	½ c. pulp; ⅓ of 4½" melon	25	.6	.2	5.1	.02	.02	.4	1000	150	60		30	.5
Carrots	100	⅝ c. cooked	40	1.2	.3	8.2	.06	.05	.6	10000	60	60	1.47	10	1.1
Cauliflower	100	⅔ c. cooked	27	2.4	.2	4.0	.12	.06	.9	50	150	105	.57	75	.9
Celery, bleached	100	4 med. stalks or ¾ c. cut	19	1.3	.2	3.0	.08	.04	.6	10	30	35		5	.7
Celery, green	100	4 med. stalks or ¾ c. cut	19	1.3	.2	3.0	.08	.04	.6	1000	30	100		5	.7
Chard (leaves only)	100	⅓ c. cooked	28	2.6	.4	4.0	.20	.04	3.1	9000	450	138		38	.8
Cheese, cheddar	100	3"×2"×1" or ⅞ c. grated	458	27.7	36.8	4.1	.93	.68	1.4	1500	24	550	.2	0	
Cheese, cottage, skim	100	½ c.	110	20.9	1.0	4.3	.12	.18	.3	500	18	297		0	

a. Proposed standards set by the Food and Drug Administration, August, 1943.

TABLE VI (continued)

Food	Wt.	Measure	Calories	Protein	Fat	Carbohydrate	Ca	P	Fe	Vitamin A	Thiamin	Riboflavin	Niacin	Ascorbic Acid	Fiber
	gm.			gm.	gm.	gm.	gm.	gm.	mg.	I.U.	μ	μ	mg.	mg.	gm.
Cheese, cream	100	6 T.	367	7.1	36.9	1.7	.36	.27	.5	2100	176	100–120		0	
Cherries, sweet	100	15 large	78	1.1	.5	17.4	.02	.03	.8						.4
Chicken, broilers	100	½ med. size	108	21.5	2.5	0	.01	.20	2.8	0	96		11.2	0	
Chicken, fowl, uncooked (dark meat)	100	one thigh	125	21.1	4.5	0	.01	.23	3.2	0	240	260	6.5	0	
Chicken, fowl, uncooked (light meat)	100	½ breast	194	20.2	12.6	0	.02	.29	4.1	0	160	80	7.2	0	
Chicken, fowl, stewed	70	½ breast or one thigh	206	19.3	14.3										
Chocolate, bitter	28	1 square	171	3.6	13.6	8.5	.03	.13	.9	0	8			0	.7
Chocolate, milk	60	bar, 6½″×3″×3/16″	331	4.8	21.0	30.7									
Cocoa, dry	2.5	1 t.	12	.5	.7	.9		.02	.1	0	1			0	.1
Cocoa, dry	7.5	1 T.	37	1.6	2.2	2.8	.01	.05	.2	0	6			0	.3
Cod, fresh	100	4″ × 1½″ × 1″	70	16.5	.4		.02	.19	.3	0	90	80	2.3	0	
Cod liver oil	14	1 T.	126		14.0					85000[b]	0			0	
Cola drinks	100	½ c.	48			12.0									
Cookies, chocolate drop	16	1, 2¼″ diam.	65	1.2	3.7	6.5	.01	.02	.2						
Cookies, sugar (plain)	12	1, 2¼″ diam.	47	.7	1.8	7.0		.01	.01						
Corn, sweet, white	100	⅜ c. cooked	102	3.7	1.1	21.9	.01	.10	.5	0–50	135			10	.8
Corn, sweet, yellow	100	⅜ c. cooked	102	3.7	1.1	21.9	.01	.10	.5	600	135	60	1.56–2.60	10	.8
Corn, canned	100	½ c.	97	2.5	.9	19.6	.01	.10	.5	0–500	135			6	.4
Cornflakes	20	⅔ c.	77	1.6	.1	17.3		.04	.5					0	.1
Cornmeal, yellow	100	⅔ c.	356	8.3	1.2	78.0	.02	.19	.1	420	234	80	1.03	0	.7
Cornmeal, white	100	⅔ c.	355	7.5	1.1	78.8				0–42	300	80	1.76	0	.8
Cornstarch	6	1 T.	22			5.4	0	0	0	0	0	0		0	
Corn sirup (Karo)	40	2 T.	120			30.0			.6	0	0	0		0	
Crabmeat, canned	100	⅔ c. flaked	79	15.8	1.5	.7	.02	.18	.9		230	150			

b. Minimum set by U.S.P.

TABLE VI (continued)

Food	Wt.	Measure	Calories	Protein	Fat	Carbohydrate	Ca	P	Fe	Vitamin A	Thiamin	Riboflavin	Niacin	Ascorbic Acid	Fiber
	gm.			gm.	gm.	gm.	gm.	gm.	mg.	I.U.	μ	μ	mg.	mg.	gm.
Crackers, graham	10	1 cracker	41	1.0	.9	7.2		.02	.2		7			0	.1
Crackers, saltines	8	1 double cracker, 4" × 2"	34	.9	1.0	5.4		.01		0	0	0		0	
Crackers, soda	3	1 cracker, 2" × 2"	12	.3	.3	2.2				0	0	0		0	
Cranberries	100	1 c.	47	.4	.7	9.9	.02	.01	.4	50	0	0	.13	12	1.4
Cream, 20%	15	1 T.	31	.4	3.0	.6	.01	.01		90	5	(23–30)[d]			
Cream, 20%	226	1 c.	470	6.5	45.2	9.0	.22	.19	6.0	1356	68	(339–452)[d]		2	
Cream, 40%	15	1 T.	57	.3	6.0	.4	.01	.01		180	—	(18–27)[d]		—	
Cream, 40%, whipped	10	1 T.	38	.2	4.0	.3	.01	.01							
Cucumber	100	3" × 1¾" diam.	12	.7	.1	2.2	.02	.03	.3	20	30	25	.32	9	.5
Custard	134	½ c.	147	6.3	6.3	16.3	.14	.13	.8						
Dandelion greens	100	½ c. cooked	44	2.7	.07	7.0	.11	.07	3.0	12000	150–225			100 0	1.8
Dates	100	14 dates	347	2.1	2.8	78.4	.07	.06	3.6	300	75	45	2.18	0	2.4
Eggs, whole	50	1 medium	74	6.7	5.2		.04	.09	1.6	500	75	125	.038	0	
Egg, white	34	1 white	17	4.2	.1		.01	.01		0	0	78		0	
Egg, yolk	16	1 yolk	58	2.5	5.3		.02	.08	1.5	448	67	46	.006	0	
Eggplant	100	slice, 4½" × ½" or 1 c. diced	25	1.1	.2	4.6	.01	.03	.5	100	45	30	.6	10	.9
Endive, French	100	2 to 4 stalks or ½ hd.	21	1.6	.2	3.2	.10	.04	1.2	970	78	235	.72	13	.4
Farina, cooked	100	½ c.	59	1.8	.3	12.4		.02	.1						.1
Filberts	100	½ c.	702	15.6	65.3	13.0	.29	.35	4.5	100	400			15	3.4
Flour, buckwheat	100	¾ c.	346	6.4	1.2	77.5	.01	.18	3.2	—	450	—		0	.4

d. Data enclosed in parentheses are based on evidence less direct than in the majority of cases. These figures are taken from Sherman and Lanford, *Essentials of Nutrition.*

TABLE VI (*continued*)

Food	Wt.	Measure	Calories	Protein	Fat	Carbohydrate	Ca	P	Fe	Vitamin A	Thiamin	Riboflavin	Niacin	Ascorbic Acid	Fiber
	gm.			gm.	gm.	gm.	gm.	gm.	mg.	I.U.	μ	μ	mg.	mg.	gm.
Flour, rye, medium	100	⅚ c.	368	11.0	1.2	75.8	.02	.29	1.3	0	171	60	dark 1.22 light .71	0	.4
Flour, white, unsifted	8	1 T.	28	.9	.1	6.0		.01		0	6	3	.06	0	
Flour, white, sifted	110	1 c.	388	12.3	1.1	82.2	.02	.10	1.0	0				0	.2
Flour, white, unsifted	125	1 c.	441	14.0	1.2	93.4	.03	.12	1.1	0	94	50	.075	0	.2
Flour, white, enriched	100	– ¾ c.	353	11.2	1.0	74.7	.02	.09	2.87–3.64[e]	0 0	441–551[e]	265–331[e]	3.53–4.41[e]	0	.2
Flour, white, enriched	30	⅓ c.	106	3.4	.3	22.4	.01	.03	.86–1.09[e]	0	132–165[e]	80–99[e]	1.06–1.32[e]	0	
Flour, whole wheat	100	¾ c.	356	13.8	1.9	71.0	.03	.24	3.5	14	480	100–200		0	.9
Flour, whole wheat	30	⅓ c.	107	4.1	.6	21.3	.01	.07	1.1	4	144	30–60		0	
Frankfurters	100	2, 5¼″×1″ diam.	250	19.6	18.6	1.1	.01	.22	2.5						
Fudge, chocolate	25	1″ cube	93	.5	1.9	18.5	.01	.02	.1						
Gelatin	3	1 t.	11	2.7						0	0	0		0	
Ginger ale	100	– ½ c.	32			8.0									
Gingerbread	34	2″×2″×1″	92	1.7	2.4	15.9	.04	.02	1.0						.1
Grapefruit	100	½, 4″ diam. or ½ c.	43	.5	.2	9.8	.02	.02	.3	0	40	20–100		43	.3
Grapefruit juice, canned sweetened	100	½ c.	66	.4		16.1	.03	.02	.2	0	60	20–100		30	
Grapefruit juice, canned, unsweetened	100	½ c.	46	.4		11.1	.03	.02	.2	0	60			30	
Grapes, American types	100	½ c. or 24 grapes	76	1.4	1.4	14.4	.02	.03	.7	50	45	30–60	.84	3–5	.5
Grape juice	100	– ½ c.	70	.3		17.3	.01	.01	.3		45			2	
Gravy, meat stock	100	⅜ c.	102	.7	9.0	4.5		.01	.1						
Halibut	100	4″×1¾″×¾″	121	18.6	5.2		.02	.21	.9		90	(200)[d]	6.08	—	

e. Minimum and maximum standards set by the Food and Drug Administration. July 1943.

d. Data enclosed in parentheses are based on evidence less direct than in the majority of cases. These figures are taken from Sherman and Lanford, *Essentials of Nutrition.*

TABLE VI (continued)

Food	Wt.	Measure	Calories	Protein	Fat	Carbohydrate	Ca	P	Fe	Vitamin A	Thiamin	Riboflavin	Niacin	Ascorbic Acid	Fiber
	gm.			gm.	gm.	gm.	gm.	gm.	mg.	I.U.	μ	μ	mg.	mg.	gm.
Ham, boiled, medium fat.	100	2 sl., 4½″×4½″ ×⅛″	282	20.2	22.4		.01	.22	1.7		660	280	6.3		
Heart, beef	100	2″×3″×1″	248	16.0	20.4		.01	.17	4.8		680	860	7.0	.1	
Hermits	10	1 cookie, 2″ diam.	41	.6	1.5	6.3		.01	.1						
Hickory nuts	100	½ c. chopped	714	15.4	67.4	11.4			2.4					0	2.2
Hominy, cooked	100	½ c.	82	2.2	.2	17.8			.1						.1
Honey	20	1 T.	65	.1		16.3	0	.01	.2	0	0	0		0	
Ice Cream, vanilla	100	⅝ c.	237	2.5	17.1	18.2	.08	.08	.2						
Jelly	20	1 T.	62	.2		15.4		0	.1						
Kale	100	1 c. cooked	45	3.9	.6	6.0	.20	.06	2.5	16000	150	400		100	1.2
Kidney, beef	100	½ c. diced	142	15.0	8.0		.01	.16	5.5	1000	270	2050	10.0	11	
Kidney, veal	100	½ c. diced	125	16.9	6.4		.01	.18	4.0	1000	270	2050	10.0	11	
Kohlrabi	100	½ c. diced	32	2.1	.1	5.6	.08	.07	.6		50		.27	60	1.1
Lamb chops, A.P.	100	2 med. sized chops	281	16.0	24.1		.01	.17	1.4	0	300	320	8.0	0	
Lamb, roast	100	slice, 4½″×5″ ×¼″	193	19.7	12.7		.01	.21	1.7	0	300	320	8.0	0	
Lard	14	1 T.	126		14.0		0	0	0	4	0	0		0	
Lemons, A.P.	100	1 lemon, 2¾″ long	25	.6	.4	4.8	.02	.03	.4	0	20	4		30	.6
Lemon juice	100	½ c.	9			2.3	.02	.01	.2	0	30	0	.08[f]	45	
Lemon juice	15	1 T.	1			.3				0	5	0		7	
Lettuce, bleached	100	16 leaves of leaf, or 8 of head, or ¼, 4″ head +1 leaf	16	1.2	.2	2.3	.04	.04	head .4	100	75	45		15	.6
Lettuce, green	100	16 leaves of leaf, or 8 of head, or ¼, 4″ head+1 leaf	16	1.2	.2	2.3	.04	.04	leaf 1.9	5000	75	150	.5	15	.6
Liver, beef	100	3″×6″×½″	132	19.7	3.2	6.0	.01	.22	8.3	30000	380	3000	17.5	37	
Liver, calf	100	3″×6″×½″	136	19.0	4.9	4.0	.01	.21	5.4	27000	520	3300	16.5	32	
Liver, lamb	100	3″×6″×½″	131	21.0	3.9	2.9				27000	410	2660	15.0	37	

f. Per 100 cc.

TABLE VI (*continued*)

Food	Wt.	Measure	Calories	Protein	Fat	Carbohydrate	Ca	P	Fe	Vitamin A	Thiamin	Riboflavin	Niacin	Ascorbic Acid	Fiber
	gm.			gm.	gm.	gm.	gm.	gm.	mg.	I.U.	μ	μ	mg.	mg.	gm.
Liver, pork	100	3″×6″×½″	129	19.7	4.8	1.7				27000	520	2700	19.0	27	
Loganberries	100	1⅙ c.	64	1.0	.6	13.6	.04	.02	1.4		33			35	1.4
Macaroni, cooked	100	+½ c.	89	3.0	1.5	15.8	.01	.03	.3						.1
Mackerel	100	2″×3″×1″	139	18.7	7.1		.02	.22	.8	175	90	(200)[d]	5.5		
Marmalade, orange	30	1⅓ T.	102	.2		25.3									
Marshmallows	25	3	82	.5		20.									
Mayonnaise	100	½ c.	687	1.1	74.8	2.5	.01	.04	.5						
Milk, fresh, whole	200	¾ c. or 1 glass	138	6.6	8.0	10.0	.24	.19	.5	240	84	390	.2	past. 2.6 fresh 4.4	
Milk, fresh, whole	240	1 c.	166	7.9	9.6	12.0	.29	.22	.6	288	101	468	.2	past. 3.1 fresh 5.3	
Milk, fresh, skim	100	½ c.	37	3.4	.3	5.1	.12	.10	.3	10	45	200	.06–.09	0	
Milk, dry, whole	100	1 c. scant	496	25.8	26.7	38.0	.9	.7	1.7	875	360	1500	1.1	0	
Milk, dry, skim	100	1 c. scant	359	35.6	1.0	52.0	1.2	1.0	3.0	20	360	1800	.88	0	
Milk, condensed	100	⅓ c.	326	8.8	8.3	54.1	.30	.24	.6	280	96		.18	2	
Milk, evaporated	100	⅓ c.	167	9.6	9.3	11.2	.35	.27	.7	460	57	330	.18	2	
Milk, malted, dry	12	1 T.	48	1.7	.8	8.6	.04	.04	.3	37	41	60			
Molasses	100	5½ T.	287	2.4		69.3	.21	.04	8.0	0	0	0	0	0	
Muffins (1 egg)	47	1 muffin	134	3.9	4.1	20.2	.04	.05	.4						.1
Mushrooms, fresh	100	1½ c.			.3		.02	.11	.7	0	60	5		1	.9
Mustard greens	100	½ c. cooked	25	2.3	.3	3.2	.22	.06	5.0	12000	135	375		125	.8
Oats, rolled, cooked	100	½ c. scant	66	2.7	1.2	11.1	.01	.07	.5						.2
Oil, olive or salad	14	1 T.	126		14.0		0	0	0	0	0	0		0	
Okra	100	½ c. canned	35	1.8	.2	6.4	.07	.02	.6	400	120	455		20	1.0
Oleomargarine	14	1 T.	105	.1	11.6					8	0	0		0	
Oleomargarine, fortified	14	1 T.	105	.1	11.6					278	0	0		0	
Olives, green, plain, A.P.	8	1 olive 1¼″×¾″	17	.1	1.6	.7	.01	0	.2	15	1	0		0	.1

d. Data enclosed in parentheses are based on evidence less direct than in the majority of cases. These figures are taken from Sherman and Lanford, *Essentials of Nutrition.*

TABLE VI (*continued*)

Food	*Wt.*	*Measure*	*Calories*	*Protein*	*Fat*	*Carbohydrate*	*Ca*	*P*	*Fe*	*Vitamin A*	*Thiamin*	*Riboflavin*	*Niacin*	*Ascorbic Acid*	*Fiber*
	gm.			gm.	gm.	gm.	gm.	gm.	mg.	I.U.	μ	μ	mg.	mg.	gm.
Olives, ripe, A.P.	5	1 med. size	10	.1	1	.2	.01	0	.1	6	0	0		0	.1
Onions, mature	100	½ c. or 3, 1½″ diam.	45	1.4	.2	9.5	.03	.05	.5	0	30	50	.77	15	.8
Onions, young, green	100	20, 5″ long	41	1.0	.2	8.8	.03	.05	.5	5000			.10	30	1.8
Oranges	100	pulp of orange, 2½″ diam.	48	.9	.2	10.6	.05	.02	.5	90–700	78	28–90		45	.6
Orange juice	100	½ c.	39	.6		9.1	.03	.02	.2	150	70	28–90	.22*f*	45	
Oysters	100	4 large	50	6.2	1.2	3.7	.05	.16	5.8	140	150		1.3	5	
Parsley	20	bunch, 1″ diam.	10.6	7.4	.2	1.44	.04	.01	.86	3600				20	.35
Parsnips	100	½ c. diced	74	1.5	.5	16.0	.06	.08	.8	0	80	60–90		22	2.2
Pastry, plain	80	1, 9″ crust	396	5.3	26.4	34.1	.01	.04	.4						.1
Peaches, fresh	100	1 medium	48	.5	.1	11.4	.02	.02	.3	yel. 2000 wh. 100	40	60	.95	10	.6
Peaches, canned in sirup	100	2 halves	79	.4	0	18.2	0	.01	.2					4	.4
Peanuts, roasted	100	¾ c.	538	25.8	38.6	21.9	.07	.40	2.3	360	270	100–200	13.0	—	2.6
Peanut butter	16	1 T.	97	4.7	7.4	2.7	.01	.07	.4		53		3.0		.3
Pears, fresh	100	1 medium	64	.7	.4	14.4	.02	.03	.3	30	40	20	.14	7	1.4
Pears, canned in sirup	100	1½ halves	74	.2		18.4	.01	.01	.2		30			2	.8
Peas, fresh	100	¾ c.	92	6.7	.4	15.5	.03	.13	2.1	1000	420	200	.7	25	2.2
Peas, dried	100	½ c.	337	24.6	1.0	57.5	.08	.40	5.7	750	525	300	1.8	0	1.2
Peas, canned, incl. liquor	150	¾ c.	77	5.2	.5	12.9	.03	.12	2.1	1000	276	200		4–12	1.3
Pecans	100	⅞ c.	738	11.0	71.2	13.3	.09	.34	2.6	300	500	300		0	2.2
Peppers, green	100	1, 3⅝″ long	24	1.2	.2	4.3	.01	.03	.4	3000	30	138	.2	125	1.4
Pie, apple	134	⅙ of pie, 9″ diam.	262	2.1	9.2	42.8	.01	.03	.5						1.0
Pie, cream	122	⅙ of pie, 9″ diam.	239	6.5	9.4	32.2	.11	.12	.8						
Pineapple, fresh	100	½ c. diced or 2 slices 3½″×⅜″	57	.4	.2	13.3	.02	.03	.4	150	50	5		20	.4
Pineapple, canned in sirup	100	2 slices	86	.4		21.1	.01	.01	.2	25	63	20–30		10	.3

f. Per 100 cc.

TABLE VI (*continued*)

Food	Wt.	Measure	Calories	Protein	Fat	Carbohydrate	Ca	P	Fe	Vitamin A	Thiamin	Riboflavin	Niacin	Ascorbic Acid	Fiber
	gm.			gm.	gm.	gm.	gm.	gm.	mg.	I.U.	μ	μ	mg.	mg.	gm.
Pineapple juice, canned	100	½ c.	53	.3		13.0	.02	.01	.1	50	75	20–30		15	
Pistachio nuts	100	⅔ c.	640	22.3	54.0	16.3			7.9	200				0	2.2
Plums, fresh	100	3, 1½" diam.	54	.7	.2	12.4	.02	.03	.6	350	50	45	.56	7	.5
Pomegranates	100	1 medium	86	1.5	1.2	17.3	.01	.11	.8					6	3.6
Popcorn, popped	100	9 c.	397	10.7	5.0	77.3				350				0	1.7
Pork chops, lean, A.P.	100	1 med. chop, ½" thick	252	20.3	19.0		.01	.22	1.5		1520	240	8.0	2	
Pork chops, med. fat, A.P.	100	1 med. chop, ½" thick	337	16.6	30.1		.01	.18	1.3						
Potato, white, raw, or steamed	100	1, 2½" diam. or ⅝ c. diced	84	2.0	.1	18.7	.01	.06	.9	30	100	40	1.18	10	.4
Potato, white, baked	67	1, 2½" diam.	84	2.0	.1	18.7	.01	.06	.9					10	.4
Potato, white, mashed	100	½ c.	129	2.0	6.4	15.7	.03	.06	.7						.3
Potato chips	20	10 to 12 large chips	115	1.4	8.0	9.3									
Potato, sweet, raw	100	½ med. size	121	1.8	.7	26.9	.02	.05	.8	3500	90	75	1.29	20	1.0
Potato, sweet, baked	85	½ med. size	121	1.8	.7	26.9	.02	.05	.8						1.3
Prunes, dried, cooked, A.P.	100	3 prunes + 3 T. juice	139	.6		34.2	.02	.03	.8						
Puffed rice	10	½ c.	35	.8		7.9		.01	.1		d				.3
Puffed wheat	10	½ c.	35	1.3	.2	7.0		.04	.4		d				1.8
Pumpkin	100	½ c. cooked	31	1.2	.2	6.0	.02	.06	.9	2000	45	45	.7	5	1.3
Radishes	100	10, 1" diam.	18	1.2	.1	3.5	.02	.03	.8	25	60	30		25	.7
Raisins	100	¾ c.	344	2.6	3.3	76.1	.06	1.3	seeded 5.69 seedless 2.99	50	90	125	.63	0	seeded .65 seedless 1.5
Raspberries, red, fresh	100	1 c.	56	1.1	.6	11.6	.05	.05	1.0	150	30			25	2.8
Rhubarb, fresh	100	–½ c. cooked	15	.5	.1	3.1	.04	.03	.6	100	15			20	.7

d. Data enclosed in parentheses are based on evidence less direct than in the majority of cases. These figures are taken from Sherman and Lanford, *Essentials of Nutrition*.

TABLE VI (*continued*)

Food	*Wt.*	*Measure*	*Calories*	*Protein*	*Fat*	*Carbohydrate*	*Ca*	*P*	*Fe*	*Vitamin A*	*Thiamin*	*Riboflavin*	*Niacin*	*Ascorbic Acid*	*Fiber*
	gm.			gm.	gm.	gm.	gm.	gm.	mg.	I.U.	μ	μ	mg.	mg.	gm.
Rice, polished, uncooked	100	½ c.	350	8.0	.3	78.8	.01	.10	1.1	0	30		.90	0	.2
Rice, polished, cooked	100	½ c.	93	1.8	.1	21.3		.03							.1
Rice, brown, uncooked	100	½ c.	354	8.0	2.0	76.0	.07	.34	2.0	75	225		6.90	0	.6
Rutabagas	100	½ c. mashed	36	1.1	.1	7.6	.07	.06	.4	25	70	50–70		45	1.3
Salad dressing, boiled	100	⅜ c. or 5 T.	157	3.6	10.9	11.2	.08	.10	.9						
French dressing	13	1 T.	60		7.3										
Mayonnaise, see Mayonnaise dressing															
Salmon, canned	100	½ c. flaked	196	21.8	12.1		.02	.25	1.3	325	30	225	6.0	0	
Sardines, canned	100	4, 3½″ long	269	23.0	19.7		.03	.26	1.8	400	90	(200)[d]	2.9	0	
Sauerkraut	100	⅔ c.	27	1.7	.5	3.8	.04	.03	.4	20	0			25	1.4
Scallops, fresh	100	6 small	74	14.8	.1	3.4	.02	.17	3.0	0				3	
Shredded wheat	28	1 biscuit	101	2.9	.4	21.3	.01	.09	1.3						.6
Shrimp, canned	100	½ c.	111	25.4	1.0	.2	.03	.30	2.9		90	159	.78	3	
Spaghetti, cooked	100	½ c.	80	2.7	.1	16.9	.01	.03	.3						.1
Spinach	100	½ c. cooked	22	2.3	.3	2.6	.07	.07	2.6	18000	100	400	.72	50	.6
Squash, summer	100	½ c. cooked	17	.6	.1	3.4	.02	.02	.4	750	45	50			.5
Squash, winter	100	½ c. mashed	38	1.5	.3	7.4	.02	.02	.6	4000	45	50		5	1.4
Strawberries, fresh	100	⅔ c.	36	.8	.6	6.9	.04	.03	.7	50	25	180		50	1.2
Sugar, granulated	13	1 T.	52			13.0	0	0	0	0	0	0		0	
Sugar, granulated	210	1 c.	840			10.0	0	0	0	0	0	0		0	
Sugar, powdered	12	1 T.	48			212.0	0	0	0	0	0	0		0	
Sugar, powdered	170	1 c.	680			170.0	0	0	0	0	0	0		0	
Sugar, brown	165	1 c.	627			156.7	.15	.02	4.3	0	0	0		0	
Sweetbreads	100	2½″×3″×¾″	176	16.8	12.1						320	550	5.84		
Tangerines	100	2, 2″ diam.	45	.8	.3	9.9	.04	.02	.3	350	70	20		35	1.0
Tapioca, cooked	100	⅓ c.	55	.1		13.7		.01	.3						

d. Data enclosed in parentheses are based on evidence less direct than in the majority of cases. These figures are taken from Sherman and Lanford, *Essentials of Nutrition.*

TABLE VI (*continued*)

Food	Wt.	Measure	Calories	Protein	Fat	Carbohydrate	Ca	P	Fe	Vitamin A	Thiamin	Riboflavin	Niacin	Ascorbic Acid	Fiber
	gm.			gm.	gm.	gm.	gm.	gm.	mg.	I.U.	μ	μ	mg.	mg.	gm.
Tomato, raw	100	1, 2½″ diam.	20	1.0	.3	3.4	.01	.03	.4	1000	75	45	.58	22	.6
Tomato juice, canned	100	½ c.	23	1.0	.2	4.3				900				19	.2
Tomato soup, canned	100	⅓ c.	50	1.5	.7	9.5			2.2						
Trout	100	2″×3″×1″	164	17.8	10.3		.02	.20	.8		87	(200)[d]		0	
Tuna fish in oil	100	½ c. flaked	275	23.8	20.0		.03	.26	1.3	200		(200)[d]			
Turkey, dark meat, cooked	100	4 slices, 1¾″×1½″×⅛″	195	39.2	4.3		.02	.42	5.9						
Turkey, light meat, cooked	100	2 slices, 3½″×3″×¼″	182	34.6	4.9		.02	.37	5.2						
Turnips	100	½ c. cooked	30	1.1	.2	6.0	.06	.05	.5	0	30	30		30	1.1
Turnip greens	100	½ c. cooked	32	2.9	.4	4.2	.35	.05	3.5	18000	100	350		100	1.2
Veal chop, med. fat, A.P.	100	1 med. size, ⅜″ thick	177	19.9	10.8		.01	.22	2.7		350	290	8.0		
Veal roast	100	3″×2¾″×⅛″	150	26.6	4.8		.02	.29	3.6		350	290	8.0		
Walnuts, black	100	1 c. chopped	657	27.6	56.3	10.0			6.0	70	330			0	1.9
Walnuts, English	100	1 c.	700	18.4	64.4	11.6	.09	.36	2.1	50	450			0	2.1
Watercress	13	5 sprigs	6	.2	.1	.4	.02	0	.4	500	13	35		4	.1
Watermelon	100	2½″×2½″×1″	29	.5	.2	6.3	.01	0	.2	50	30	15		7	.6
Wheat germ	100	¾ c.	389	25.2	10.0	49.5	.07	1.05	7.5	100	1200–6600	600–800	4.2	0	2.5
Whey	100	⅜ c.	27	1.0	.3	5.0	.04	.04							
Whitefish	100	2″×3″×1″	150	22.9	6.5		.15	.26	.4						
White sauce, medium	100	± ⅓ c.	156	3.6	12.0	8.6	.11	.12	2.8						
White sauce, medium	285	1⅙ c. (using 1 c. milk)	438	10.0	33.6	24.0	.29	.34	.8						
Yeast, dried, brewers'	100	¾ c.	348	46.1	1.6	37.4	.08	1.89	5.2	0	5000–7000	2500–4700	40.0	0	.8

d. Data enclosed in parentheses are based on evidence less direct than in the majority of cases. These figures are taken from Sherman and Lanford, *Essentials of Nutrition.*

TABLE VII

SHARES OF ENERGY, PROTEIN, CALCIUM, PHOSPHORUS, IRON, AND VITAMINS YIELDED BY COMMON MEASURES OF FOOD MATERIALS [1]

1 Energy Share	=	100 calories
1 Protein Share	=	2.5 grams or 10 calories
1 Calcium Share	=	0.023 gram
1 Phosphorus Share	=	0.044 gram
1 Iron Share	=	0.0005 gram
*1 Vitamin A Share	=	100 Sherman Munsell Units
1 Vitamin B_1 Share	=	10 Sherman Chase Units
1 Vitamin C Share	=	2 Sherman LaMer Units
1 Vitamin G Share	=	20 Sherman Boruquin Units

* Vitamins have been stated in shares wherever possible. Otherwise, signs have been used.

+, vitamin is present
++, the food is a good source of vitamin
+++, the food is an excellent source of the vitamin
−, the food contains no appreciable source of the vitamin
Blank, no definite information is available
R, raw
CK, cooked
AP, as purchased

[1] Adapted from *Foundations of Nutrition*, by Rose, M. S. The Macmillan Company, New York.

TABLE VIII. NUTRITIVE VALUES EXPRESSED IN SHARES[1]

Material	Approximate Measure	Weight		Shares Contributed to the Diet								
		Ounces	*Grams*	*Calories*	*Protein*	*Calcium*	*Phosphorus*	*Iron*	*Vitamin A*	*Vitamin B_1*	*Vitamin C*	*Vitamin G*
Almonds, shelled	⅞ cup	3.5		6.39	8.4	11.0	10.3	7.8		8.0		
Almonds, shelled	12–15 nuts	0.6	16	1.00	1.3	1.7	1.6	1.2		1.3		
Apples	1 medium	4.5	127	0.80	0.2	0.4	0.3	0.9	1.0	3.2	6	1.3
Apricots, dried	9 halves	1.3	36	1.00	0.7	1.0	1.0	5.5	25.2	+	7	1.7
Banana	1 medium	3.5	100	1.00	0.5	0.4	0.7	1.3	2.4	2.9	9	1.5
Beans, Lima, dried	1 cup	5.5	156	5.46	11.3	5.0	13.7	30.3	+	35.6(CK)	—	24.6
Beans, navy, dried	1 cup	7.0	200	6.84	17.9	12.9	21.0	40.0	1.1	48.5	—	+
Beans, string, fresh	¾ cup	3.5		0.42	0.9	2.4	1.2	2.3	10.0	3.2	5(CK)	1.3
Beef, lean, round	1 piece, 2½′ × 2½″ × ¾″	3.5		1.56	8.5	0.5	4.6	6.0	0.7	5.0	—	5.0
Bread, white with water	2 slices, 3″ × 3½″ × ½″	1.4	39	1.00	1.4	0.5	0.8	0.7	—	—	—	—
Bread, whole-wheat with water	1 slice, 3″ × 3¾″ × ½″	1.0		0.70	1.1	0.6	1.0	0.9	—	4.4	—	+
Butter	1 Tbsp.	0.5	13	1.00	0.1	0.1	0.1	0.1	5.1	—	—	—
Butter	1 cup	8.0	227	17.44	0.9	1.6	0.9	1.0	82.0	—	—	—
Buttermilk	1 cup	8.5	241	.088	3.5	11.3	5.4	1.2	—	2.7	4(R)	3.9
Cabbage, shredded	¾ cup	2.3	64	0.20	0.4	1.2	0.4	0.5	0.4	3.2	18(R)	1.6
Carrots, diced	¾ cup	3.5		0.45	0.4	2.0	0.8	1.2	31.0	5.0	4(R)	2.5
Cauliflower	1 small head	11.6	328	1.00	2.8	17.4	4.5	6.2	1.6	17.0	161	9.9
Celery, bleached stems	¾ cup, ¼″ pieces	3.5		0.20	0.5	3.4	1.1	1.2	0.2	++	5(R)	
Cheese, American	1⅛″ cube	0.8	23	1.00	2.6	9.2	3.6	0.6	5.8	+	—	2.3
Cheese, American, dry	1 Tbsp. grated	0.2	4	0.20	0.5	1.8	0.7	0.1	1.2	+	—	0.5
Cheese, American, fresh	1 Tbsp. grated	0.3	8	0.35	0.9	3.1	1.2	0.2	2.0	+	—	0.8
Cheese, cottage, skim	5 Tbsp.	3.2	91	1.00	7.6	3.3	5.4		0.7	+	—	+
Chicken, broiler	½ medium	3.5		1.09	8.6	0.6	5.3	6.4		15.0	—	+
Chocolate, unsweetened	1 square	1.0		1.73	1.5	1.1	2.9	1.5				
Chocolate, unsweetened	1 Tbsp. grated	0.2	5	0.29	0.2	0.2	0.5	0.3				
Cod liver oil	1 Tbsp.	0.4	11	1.00	—	—	—	—	47.8	—	—	—
Corn, canned	1 cup	9.0	255	2.60	3.1	0.7	5.9	2.3				
Cornflakes	¾ cup	0.9	26	1.00	0.9	0.2	0.7	1.4			—	
Cornmeal, yellow, uncooked	1 cup	5.0	142	5.04	5.0	1.0	4.9	3.0	8.5	17.7	—	2.3
Cottonseed oil	1 Tbsp.	0.4	11	1.00	—	—	—	—	—	—	—	—

[1] From *Foundations of Nutrition*, by M. S. Rose. Reprinted by permission of The Macmillan Company, publishers.

TABLE VIII (*continued*)

Material	Approximate Measure	Weight		Shares Contributed to the Diet								
		Ounces	*Grams*	*Calories*	*Protein*	*Calcium*	*Phosphorus*	*Iron*	*Vitamin A*	*Vitamin B_1*	*Vitamin C*	*Vitamin G*
Crackers, graham	1 cracker	0.4	11	0.40	0.4	0.1	0.5	0.4			—	
Crackers, soda	1 cracker	0.2	6	0.25	0.3	0.1	0.2	0.2			—	
Cranberries, fresh	1 cup	3.5		0.47	0.2	0.5	0.2	0.9	0.2	—	13	
Cream, 185% fat	1 Tbsp.	0.6	16	.030	0.1	0.7	0.3	0.1	1.2			
Cream, 145% fat	1 cup	8.0	227	4.40	2.2	9.6	4.4	0.9	16.8			
Cream, 40% fat	1 Tbsp. or 1¾ T. whipped	0.6	16	0.60	0.1	0.5	0.3	0.1	2.5			
Cream, 40% fat	1 cup	7.8	221	8.42	1.9	7.3	3.8	0.8	34.7			
Dates, dried, stoned	4 dates	1.0	29	1.00	0.2	0.9	0.4	2.1	0.3	1.2	—	
Egg plant	2 slices, 4″ diameter	3.5		0.28	0.5	0.5	0.7	1.0	0.5	4.0	4	
Eggs, A.P.	⅜″ thick, 1 egg	1.9	53	0.70	2.5	1.3	2.4	2.7	9.4	2.7	—	3.4
Egg, white	1 white	1.0	28	0.14	1.4	0.2	0.1	0.1	—	—	—	1.4
Egg, yolk	1 yolk	0.6	16	0.56	1.0	0.9	2.2	2.6	5.7	2.8	—	1.8
Farina, dark, cooked	¾ cup	6.0	170	1.00	1.2	0.6	2.7	2.8	—	3.6	—	1.1
Farina, light, uncooked	3 Tbsp.	1.0	28	1.00	1.2	0.3	0.8	0.4	—	0.1	—	—
Figs, dried	2 medium	1.1	32	1.00	0.5	2.2	0.8	1.8	0.2	1.1	—	0.7
Flour, rye	1 Tbsp.	0.3	9	0.33	0.3	0.1	0.6	0.3		1.0	—	
Flour, rye	1 cup	5.0	142	4.96	3.9	1.1	9.2	4.3		15.6	—	
Flour, wheat, white	1 Tbsp. sifted	0.3	7	0.25	0.3	0.1	0.2	0.1	—	—	—	—
Flour, wheat, white	1 cup, sifted	3.9	112	3.95	5.1	0.8	2.7	2.2	—	0.6	—	—
Flour, whole-wheat	1 Tbsp.	0.3	9	0.34	0.5	0.1	0.6	0.7	—	1.4	—	0.4
Flour, whole-wheat	1 cup	5.0	142	5.10	7.5	2.2	9.8	10.2	0.2	21.3	—	5.7
Gelatin	1 Tbsp.	0.3	9	0.33	3.3	—	—	—	—	—	—	—
Grapefruit	½ medium	7.5	213	1.00	0.5	1.7	0.8	1.2	—	4.3	69	4.3
Grapes, malaga	20 grapes	3.5		0.77	0.5	0.8	0.7	0.6	0.3	2.0	2	—
Grapejuice	½ cup, scant	3.5		0.70	0.1	0.4	0.2	0.7	—	—	—	—
Ham, boiled, lean	1 slice, 5″ × 5″ × 8″	1.7	47	1.00	4.3	0.3	2.6	2.4	+	++	—	++
Hominy grits, cooked	⅘ cup	6.8	193	1.00	0.9	0.2	0.5	0.5			—	
Ice cream, commercial, vanilla	½ cup	3.5		2.19	1.0	3.3	1.5	0.4	6.4	0.4	1	1.1
Lamb, leg, roasted	1 slice, 3½″ × 4½″ × ⅛″	1.8	52	1.00	4.1	0.3	2.5	1.7	—	+	—	+
Lard	1 Tbsp., scant	0.4	11	1.00	—	—	—	—	—	—	—	—
Lard	1 cup	8.0	227	20.42	—	—	—	—	—	—	—	—

TABLE VIII (*continued*)

Material	Approximate Measure	Weight		Shares Contributed to the Diet								
		Ounces	*Grams*	*Calories*	*Protein*	*Calcium*	*Phosphorus*	*Iron*	*Vitamin A*	*Vitamin B_1*	*Vitamin C*	*Vitamin G*
Lemon juice	1 Tbsp.	0.5	13	0.05	—	0.2	—	0.2	—	+	4	+
Lettuce	3 large leaves or ⅕ head	2.0	57	0.10	0.3	0.4	0.5	0.6	0.7	2.2	2	0.7
Liver, beef	1 piece, 3″ × 3″ × ¾″	4.0	117	1.50	10.1	0.6	9.5	18.6	114.7	11.7	+	52.7
Macaroni, cooked	¾ cup	5.8	163	1.00	1.5	0.3	0.9	0.7	—	—	—	—
Mayonnaise dressing	1 Tbsp.	0.5	14	1.00	0.1	0.1	0.1	0.1	0.5	0.1		0.2
Milk, condensed, sweetened	1 Tbsp.	0.7	20	0.66	0.6	2.8	1.1	0.3	+	+	+	+
Milk, condensed-sweetened	1 cup	11.0	312	10.35	9.9	42.5	16.7	4.1	+	+	+	+
Milk, evaporated, unsweetened	1 cup	8.0	227	3.20	6.2	31.1	12.5	3.0	10.0	5.9	+	15.2
Milk, skimmed	1 Tbsp.	0.7	20	0.07	0.3	1.0	0.4	0.1	—	0.2	—	0.3
Milk, skimmed	1 cup	8.5	241	0.88	3.3	12.7	5.2	1.2	—	2.7	4(R)	3.8
Milk, whole, fresh	1 Tbsp.	0.7	20	0.14	0.3	1.0	0.4	0.1	0.4	0.2	—	0.3
Milk, whole, fresh	1 cup	8.6	244	1.70	3.2	12.6	5.2	1.2	5.1	2.7	4(R)	3.9
Milk, whole, fresh	1 quart	34.4	975	6.75	12.8	50.0	20.6	4.7	20.2	10.8	15(R)	15.6
Molasses, cane	1 Tbsp.	0.8	23	0.65	0.2	2.5	0.2	3.3	—	—	—	—
Molasses, cane	1 cup	10.0	284	8.15	2.7	31.8	1.9	41.4	—	—	—	—
Mustard greens, steamed	¾ cup	3.5		0.31	1.0	9.6	1.5	11.2	3.0	++	++	7.5
Oats, rolled, cooked	¾ cup	4.8	136	1.00	1.7	0.7	2.2	2.4	—	3.0	—	+
Okra	10–12 pods	3.5		0.38	0.6	3.1	1.4	1.2	6.0	++	—	+
Onions	1 medium	2.2	62	0.30	0.4	1.1	0.7	0.6	—	0.6	5(R)	0.4
Orange juice	½ cup (scant)	3.5		0.56	0.2	0.8	0.3	0.5	0.7	8.0	33	1.8
Oranges	1 medium	5.5	156	0.80	0.6	1.8	0.7	1.6	0.9	11.1	45	2.5
Peaches, canned	1 large half, plus 1½ T. juice	3.5		0.47	0.3	0.4	0.3	0.4			3	
Peaches, fresh, yellow	1 medium	3.5		0.53	0.2	0.4	0.4	0.6	20.0	+	5	
Peanut butter	1 Tbsp., scant	0.6	17	1.00	1.9	0.5	1.5	0.6	+	4.0	—	1.8
Peanuts, roasted	1 Tbsp., chopped	0.3	9	0.50	1.0	0.3	0.9	0.4	+	2.0	—	0.9
Pears, canned	2 halves, 2 Tbsp. juice	3.5		0.62	0.2	0.4	0.4	0.4				
Pears, fresh	1 large	3.5		0.63	0.2	0.7	0.4	0.6	0.1	3.5	4	2.5
Peas, canned, drained	½ cup	5.2	148	1.00	2.7	1.0	2.8	3.8	+	+	—	+

TABLE VIII (*continued*)

Material	Approximate Measure	Weight		Shares Contributed to the Diet								
		Ounces	*Grams*	*Calories*	*Protein*	*Calcium*	*Phosphorus*	*Iron*	*Vitamin A*	*Vitamin B_1*	*Vitamin C*	*Vitamin G*
Peas, canned, including liquor	½ cup	3.5		0.55	1.4	0.6	1.6	2.2	+	+	+	+
Peas, dried, whole	½ cup	3.5		3.55	9.8	3.4	9.3	11.4	12.5	60.0	—	18.5
Pecans, shelled	12 meats	0.5	14	1.00	0.5	0.5	1.0	0.7	0.3	1.4	—	
Pineapple, canned	2 slices, 3 Tbsp. juice	3.7	104	1.00	0.1	0.2	0.2	0.4	0.3	2.6	11	0.5
Pineapple, fresh	1 cup, ½″ pieces	5.7	162	0 92	0.2	0.6	0.4	1 2	1.0	8.1	20	2.0
Pork, roast, lean	1 piece, 3″ × 2½″ × ¼″	2.1	59	1.00	7.0	0.4	4.3	6.5	+	++	—	++
Potatoes, sweet	½ medium	2.9	8	1.00	0.6	0.7	0.8	1.3	20.8	5.7	6	1.4
Potatoes, white	¾ cup, riced	3.5		0.83	0.8	0.5	1.2	1.8	0.3	4.0	6(CK)	1.3
Potatoes, white	1 medium, baked	3.0		1.00	1.1	0.6	1.5	2.2	0.3	4.8	7(CK)	1.5
Prunes, dried, stewed	4 medium	1.2	33	1.00	0.3	0.8	0.6	1.9	6.7	2.5	2	4 8
Raisins	¼ cup seeded or 2 T. seedless	1.0	29	1.00	0.3	0.7	0.9	1.7	0.3	1.7	—	0.7
Rhubarb	⅞ cup, cut, 1″ pieces	3.5		0.18	0.2	1.9	0.4	1.1			18(R)	
Rice, brown, uncooked	½ cup	3.5		3.51	3.2	2.8	7.6	4.0	—	11.0	—	—
Rice, white	¾ cup, steamed	4.0	113	1.00	0.9	0.1	0.6	0.5	—	—	—	—
Salmon, red canned	⅜ cup	2.7	75	1.00	5.9	2.2	4.9	2.0	2.3	2.3		3.0
Spinach	1 cup chopped, steamed	5 9	167	0.40	1.5	(1)	1.8	8.5	247.2	12.9	74(R)	8.4
Squash, Hubbard	½ cup, steamed	3.5		0.42	0.6	0.8	0.6	1.1	50.0			
Strawberries	½ cup	3.5		0.39	0.4	1.5	0.6	1.4	0.9	+	25	
Sugar, granulated	1 Tbsp.	0.5	13	0.50	—	—	—	—	—	—	—	—
Sugar, grauulated	1 cup	7.4	210	8.40	—	—	—	—	—	—	—	—
Tapioca	2 Tbsp.	1.0	28	1.00	—	0.2	—	0.9	—	—	—	—
Tapioca	1 cup	6.5	184	6.53	0.3	1.3	0.3	5.8	—	—	—	—
Tomato juice	½ cup, scant	3.5		0.24	0.4	0.3	0.3	1.2	6.0	3.0	15	1.0
Tomatoes, canned	2 cups	17.1	485	1.00	2.3	2.1	3.2	4.3	38.1	17.0	85	4.9
Tomatoes, fresh	2–3 large	17.1	485	1.00	2.3	2.1	3.2	4.3	38.1	17.0	85	4.9
Turnip greens	⅝ cup, steamed	3.5		0.35	1.2	15.0	1.1	6.9	70.0	3.0(CK)	12(CK)	15.0
Turnips, white	¾ cup cubed	3.5		0.35	0.5	2.4	1.1	1.0	—	3.0	20	2.0
Walnuts, English	8–16 meats	0.5	14	1.00	1.0	0.6	1.2	0.6	+	4.3	—	
Wheat, puffed	1 cup	0.5	14	0.50	0.8	0.25	1.25	1.1	+	—	—	+
Wheat, shredded	1 biscuit	1.0	27	1.00	1.3	0.5	2.0	2.5	—	2.8	—	1.1

(1) Calcium in spinach not available.

TABLE IX

VITAMINS — FUNCTIONS AND SOURCES

Name	*Normal Functions in Body*	*Some Deficiency Symptoms*	*Excellent Sources*	*Good Sources*
Vitamin A	Promotes growth Essential for health of lining tissues of body Essential to the normal adaptation of the eye to light and dark Essential for pregnancy and lactation	Retarded growth Poor appetite Poor tooth enamel Night blindness	Spinach Turnip greens Kale Collards Broccoli Carrots Sweet potatoes Squash, yellow Apricots Butter Fortified oleomargarine Cheese Eggs Liver Cod-liver oil	Asparagus Bananas Beans, green Cantaloupe Corn, yellow Cream Ice cream Kidney Lettuce Milk, whole Peaches Peas, green Tomatoes
Thiamin (Vitamin B_1)	Promotes growth Related to the use of carbohydrates and fat in the body Essential for health of nerve tissue Essential for pregnancy and lactation	Retarded growth Slow heart beat Poor appetite Digestive disturbances Loss of motor control Beri-beri	Bran Grains, whole or enriched bread and cereals Legumes, dried Nuts Peas, green Pork, lean Ham Soybeans Liver	Meat Fish Milk Eggs Oysters Potatoes Sweet potatoes Tomatoes Greens Beans, green Lettuce Oranges
Riboflavin	Promotes growth Essential to function of normal cells Part of mechanism of cell respiration	Digestive disturbances Impaired growth Extreme sensitiveness to light Very sore mouth and tongue	Liver Heart Kidney Milk Cheese Meat Eggs Cream Legumes Enriched grain or bread Whey, dried Greens	Chicken Nuts Oatmeal Spinach Tomatoes Potatoes Lettuce Fish Grains, whole Corn, yellow Raisins Strawberries
Niacin	Promotes growth Part of mechanism of cell respiration Maintains normal functions of the skin and digestive tract	Soreness of mouth Lack of appetite Pellagra	Liver Kidney Heart Meat, lean Wheat germ Enriched bread and cereals Whey, dried	Peanuts Fish Eggs Milk Potatoes Greens

TABLE IX (*continued*)

Name	*Normal Functions in Body*	*Some Deficiency Symptoms*	*Excellent Sources*	*Good Sources*
Ascorbic Acid (Vitamin C)	Favors development of good teeth Essential part of connective tissues Protects system of blood vessels Essential to healthy normal cells Involved in body defense against bacterial infection	Defective teeth Poor bone knitting Poor resistance to infections Weakened blood capillaries Poor appetite Swollen gums Scurvy	Orange juice Grapefruit Lemon juice Tomatoes Cabbage Cauliflower Greens Strawberries Peppers Liver	Potatoes Beans, green Cantaloupe Lettuce Peaches Sweet potatoes Pineapples Raspberries Rhubarb Turnips Parsnips
Vitamin D (antirachitic)	Essential to normal bone growth and tooth development Favors good form of body Aids in maintaining normal calcium in blood Valuable during pregnancy and lactation	Poor bone formation Rickets	Cod-liver oil Halibut-liver oil Vitamin D milk Egg yolk Salmon Herring Sardines	Butter Fortified oleomargarine

TABLE X

MINERALS — FUNCTIONS AND SOURCES [1]

Name	Functions in Body		Distribution in Foods	
	Normal Functions in Body	*Some Deficiency Symptoms*	*Excellent Sources*	*Good Sources*
Calcium	Building of bones and teeth Coagulation of blood Functions of heart, nerve and muscle Essential for lactation Necessary for chemical functions (enzymes of the body	Poor development of bones and teeth Brittle bones and teeth Rickets Dental caries (decayed teeth) Excessive bleeding Flabby condition of heart muscle Nervousness	Beans Broccoli Cauliflower Cheese Cream Kale Milk Sardines Turnip greens	Almonds Bran Bread Cabbage Carrots Egg yolk Figs Filberts Lettuce Oranges Peas Prunes Raspberries Salmon Shellfish Strawberries Turnips
Copper	Essential for the use of iron in building red coloring matter of blood Stimulates growth of red blood cells	Anemia Restricted growth Impaired respiration Poor use of iron Weakness	Bran Liver Mushrooms Nuts Shellfish	Bacon Bread Duck Egg yolk Fish Grains, whole or embryo Leafy vegetables Legumes Oatmeal Prunes Sea foods Yeast
Iodine	Functioning and size of thyroid gland Regulation of basal metabolism Protection from goiter Necessary for growth processes	Subnormal basal metabolism Goiter Overweight Lowered mental activity Lowered body activity Nervous disturbances Weakness Deformed body	Iodized salt Cod liver oil Sea foods Fish	Vegetables, cereals, dairy products, and fruits produced on soils which are good in iodine content

[1] Adapted from *Nutritional Charts*, ninth edition, September, 1940, Research Department, H. J. Heinz Company, Pittsburgh. Used by permission.

TABLE X (*continued*)

Name	Functions in Body		Distribution in Foods	
	Normal Functions in Body	*Some Deficiency Symptoms*	*Excellent Sources*	*Good Sources*
Iron	Formation of hemoglobin (red coloring matter of blood) Carries oxygen to cells Respiration of tissues Blood cell development Normal complexion	Anemia Low vitality Decreased hemoglobin Decreased number of red blood cells Pallid complexion Retarded growth	Apricots (95) * Beans (80) Beet greens Bran Chard Clams Egg yolk (100) Heart (80) Kidney (66) Liver (89) Molasses (100) Oatmeal (77) Oysters (25) Peas (100) Soybeans (80) Turnip greens	Asparagus Bananas (100) Beets (94) Bread Broccoli Brusselssprouts (75) Dates (82) Figs (96) Fish Meat Mushrooms (99) Parsnips (95) Potatoes (98) Prunes (72) Raisins (96) Shrimp Spinach (45) Tomatoes (64) Whole grains
Phosphorus	Building of bone and teeth Necessary for function of enzymes (chemical processes in body) Aids use of carbohydrates and fats by body Essential constituent of all cells Aids in maintaining normal functions of blood and muscle	Poor development of bones and teeth Retarded growth Perverted appetite in cattle Loss in weight Weakness Rickets	Beans, dried Bran Cheese Eggs Fish Grains, whole or embryo Liver Meat Milk Oatmeal Shellfish Peas Yeast	Beans, green Bread Cauliflower Corn Cream Kale Peanuts Potatoes Prunes Turnip greens

* The figures given in parentheses in these columns indicate the respective percentages available in those foods.

Many other minerals are needed by the body, but since they occur widely in nature and are needed in very small amounts in the body a deficiency is little likely to occur under normal conditions.

Index